AFRICA IN ANTIQUITY

The Arts of Ancient Nubia and the Sudan

AFRICA IN ANTIQUITY II.

The Arts of Ancient Nubia and the Sudan

The Catalogue

Steffen Wenig

The Brooklyn Museum

Cover:
Details from a two-sided votive tablet of King Tanyidamani (Cat. 121), Meroitic Period, about 100 B.C.
(Baltimore 22.258).

Frontispiece:
Criosphinx on a column (Cat. 94), Napatan Period, late eighth century B.C.
(Boston 24.972).

Translators: Diana S. Peters, Charles M. Stern.
Editors: Sylvia Hochfield, Elizabeth Riefstahl.
Design: Graphicon, Ltd.
Typesetting: Foto-Spectrum Inc.
Printed in the U.S.A. by the Falcon Press.

Published in two volumes by the Division of Publications and Marketing Services,
The Brooklyn Museum, Eastern Parkway, Brooklyn, New York 11238.

Library of Congress Cataloging in Publication Data
Africa in antiquity.
Catalog of the exhibition held at the Brooklyn Museum, September 30-December 31, 1978 and other places.
Includes bibliographies and index.
1. Nubia—Antiquities—Addresses, essays, lectures.
2. Sudan—Antiquities—Addresses, essays, lectures.
3. Egypt—Antiquities—Addresses, essays, lectures.
4. Art—Nubia—Addresses, essays, lectures. 5. Art—Sudan—Addresses, essays, lectures. 6. Art—Nubia—Catalogs. 7. Art—Sudan—Catalogs. I. Brooklyn Institute of Arts and Sciences. Museum.
DT159.6.N83A34 709'.32 78-10925

ISBN 0-87273-065-4 (Volume I, paperback)
ISBN 0-87273-063-8 (Volume I, clothbound)
ISBN 0-87273-066-2 (Volume II, paperback)
ISBN 0-87273-064-6 (Volume II, clothbound)

This catalogue, in two volumes,
is published in conjunction with the exhibition
Africa in Antiquity:
The Arts of Ancient Nubia and the Sudan.

This exhibition was organized by The Brooklyn Museum with the scholarly participation of the Staatliche Museen zu Berlin/DDR and has the patronage of the International Council of Museums. It was made possible with the aid of grants from the National Endowment for the Arts and the National Endowment for the Humanities in Washington, D.C., Federal agencies, the New York State Council on the Arts, and the Jerome Foundation. The preparation of the exhibition was funded with gifts from the Bankers Trust Company, Mrs. Jean de Menil, Jack A. Josephson, Mathias Komor, the L.A.W. Fund, the Robert Lehman Foundation, the late Mme Paul Mallon, the Maya Corporation, the Menil Foundation, Mrs. Henry L. Moses, Mrs. Ashton Sanborn, Carl L. Selden, Miss Alice Tully, and Mrs. Lila Acheson Wallace. The exhibition is supported by a Federal indemnity from the Federal Council on the Arts and Humanities.

AFRICA IN ANTIQUITY
The Arts of Ancient Nubia and the Sudan

The Brooklyn Museum, New York, New York
September 30-December 31, 1978

Seattle Art Museum, Seattle, Washington
February 15-April 15, 1979

New Orleans Museum of Art, New Orleans, Louisiana
May 19-August 12, 1979

Haags Gemeentemuseum, The Hague, The Netherlands
September 15-November 11, 1979

Contents

Lenders to the Exhibition

National Archaeological Museum	Athens
The Walters Art Gallery	Baltimore
Staatliche Museen zu Berlin, Ägyptisches Museum	Berlin/DDR
Humboldt-Universität	Berlin/DDR
Bolton Museum and Art Gallery (Lady Lever Art Gallery)	Bolton
Museum of Fine Arts	Boston
The Brooklyn Museum	Brooklyn
Musées Royaux d'Art et d'Histoire	Brussels
Museum of Egyptian Antiquities	Cairo
Fitzwilliam Museum	Cambridge
The Oriental Institute Museum, The University of Chicago	Chicago
Khartoum University, Department of Archaeology	Khartoum
Sudan National Museum	Khartoum
Karl-Marx-Universität, Ägyptisches Museum	Leipzig
Merseyside County Museums	Liverpool
The University of Liverpool, School of Archaeology and Oriental Studies	Liverpool
The British Museum	London
UCLA Museum of Cultural History	Los Angeles
Staatliche Sammlung Ägyptischer Kunst	Munich
Christos G. Bastis Collection	New York
Mr. and Mrs. Carl L. Selden	New York
Ashmolean Museum of Art and Archaeology	Oxford
The University Museum, University of Pennsylvania	Philadelphia
Muzeum Narodowe	Warsaw
National Museum of Natural History, Smithsonian Institution	Washington, D.C.
Worcester Art Museum	Worcester

Abbreviations

Bar. — Barkal
Beg. N. — Begrawiya North
Beg. S. — Begrawiya South
Beg. W. — Begrawiya West
Copenhagen NCG — Ny Carlesberg Glyptotek
Gen. — Generation
K — Kerma
Ku. — Kurru
Liverpool MCM — Merseyside County Museums
Liverpool SAOS — School of Archaeology and Oriental Studies
N — Nuri
S — Sudan

Abbreviations used by G.A. Reisner:

B.P. — Black polished ware
Bkt. — Black-topped red polished ware
Blk.W. — Black of local origin, brown on black surface
R.P. — Red polished ware
WSR — Ordinary red ware with white slip or wash

Preface

Scholars—chiefly Egyptologists—have been engaged in studying the ancient history and cultures of Nubia and the northern Sudan for the past century. Their research, however, has been directed mainly toward tracing the influence of Egypt upon its southern neighbors rather than upon the indigenous elements in the cultures and civilizations south of Aswan.

The main phases of Nubian development have been known since the beginning of the twentieth century, when, during the first Archaeological Survey of 1907-11, the Nile Valley in Lower Nubia was carefully investigated. It is only very recently, however, that scholars have begun to study the cultures of Nubia and the northern Sudan in detail with an eye toward their connections to the interior of Africa. The past few decades have brought an increasing recognition of the fact that Africa is not a continent without a history, as it was commonly believed to be during the age of colonialism. Nubia and the northern Sudan indeed once formed a region of great importance that functioned like a conduit for the dissemination of ideas, providing a corridor between Egypt and the African interior.

Egypt's recent decision to erect the High Dam (Sadd el Ali) at the First Cataract near Aswan stimulated intensive investigation of Nubia. In 1959, UNESCO launched an appeal to save the monuments of Lower Nubia. Since that time, more than thirty expeditions from many countries have investigated the Nile Valley between Aswan and the region beyond the Second Cataract, an area of about three hundred and fifty kilometers. These excavations have brought to light an unexpected wealth of material from all periods of Nubian history. Our picture of Nubia's past has been altered and revised in many details. One of the results of the increased research has been the creation of two new scholarly disciplines: Meroitics, which deals with the Kingdom of Kush (Napata and Meroe, ca. 760 B.C.—A.D. 320), and Nubiology, which is concerned mainly with the Christian Era.

Only a few expeditions have published their results in final form. Many of the recent discoveries are still unpublished or have only been recorded in brief preliminary reports. When more results become available, the opinions presented here will certainly have to be revised, supplemented, and made more precise. The organizers of this exhibition are aware that much of the information contained in the catalogue can possess only a temporary validity, for the study of the arts of Nubia and the northern Sudan was long neglected and is still in its infancy.

It seems appropriate, nevertheless, to trace for the first time the artistic developments of this area over four millennia, from their origins down to the Christian Era, to show by striking examples that, at least since the latter part of the fourth millennium B.C., cultures have existed in Nubia and the northern Sudan, which, despite their proximity to Egypt, were largely independent of Egypt or influenced by that country only during restricted periods of their history. It is hoped that the present exhibition will stimulate scholarly research and at the same time satisfy to some extent the legitimate curiosity of the public concerning the ancient civilizations of the Upper Nile Valley — a curiosity aroused and stimulated not merely by the recent rescue operations but chiefly by the awakening of the new African states to a national consciousness.

The present exhibition covers only a small part of the cultural heritage of the great African continent; it is, moreover, largely limited to such objects as we of the present day consider to be works of art. These objects were not, however, so considered by their makers. Most of them were made for everyday use; only a few had an exclusively non-utilitarian religious or magical significance. But all of them express in some way man's aspiration to embellish and make significant his environment — to put beauty and order into an uncertain and perilous existence.

An effort has been made to exclude from the exhibition works of Egyptian art made in Nubia or imports. Exceptions have been made principally for works from Dynasty XXV and the Ballana Period. Objects of Egyptian or foreign manufacture from these periods have been included because they express Nubian and Sudanese artistic ideals.

Many of the objects included in this exhibition have never before been shown or published. In the course of several trips abroad, B. V. Bothmer and his assistants visited numerous museums and collections, examined their Nubian and Sudanese material, and collected the data from which this catalogue was written.

The administrations of The Brooklyn Museum and the Staatliche Museen zu Berlin made it possible for the present writer to visit the Sudan and Egypt as well as various museums in Europe in order to see at first hand objects selected for the exhibition. I wish to express warm thanks to the directors and curators in Bolton, Brussels, Cairo, Cambridge, Edinburgh, Khartoum, Leipzig, Liverpool, London, Oxford, and Warsaw, who not only provided me with access to their collections and storerooms but made my task easier in many ways. Among them special acknowledgment is due to A. Badawy, Los Angeles; T. G. H. James, London; E. R. Russmann, Boston; and A. J. Spencer, London; as well as to B. Brentjes, Berlin; A. J. Mills, Toronto; H. Å. Nordström, Stockholm; P. L. Shinnie, Calgary; E. Strouhal and M. Verner, Prague; A. Vila, Paris; and L. V. Žabkar, Waltham, Massachusetts; all of whom provided me with information and helpful suggestions. At University College, London, I was permitted to examine unpublished objects from J. Garstang's excavation at Meroe. A. F. Shore most kindly gave me access to Garstang's unpublished records of that excavation preserved in the School of Archaeology and Oriental Studies at Liverpool. In the Sudan, Negm e-Din Sherif, Commissioner for Archaeology, was particularly helpful in organizing a trip to Naqa, Musawwarat es-Sufra, and Begrawiya, in which I was accompanied by my New York friends P. and C. Cardon.

I am particularly indebted to my Berlin colleagues U. and P. Hintze and K.-H. Priese, who read my manuscript, gave advice, and made valuable suggestions, as well as making available to me data from the excavation at Musawwarat es-Sufra. I wish also to thank my colleagues in the Department of Egyptian and Classical Art at The Brooklyn Museum, who provided material otherwise inaccessible to me and checked my references and quotations.

To all of them I wish to express my sincerest thanks, but especially to B. V. Bothmer, to whom I am indebted for providing me with his critical and stimulating suggestions, and to E. Riefstahl, S. Hochfield, and F. Lattin, who were extremely helpful in correcting and editing the English translation of this catalogue.

The Chronology of Nubia and the Northern Sudan

Several terms used in this catalogue will be unfamiliar to the non-specialist. The terms A-group and C-group were invented by the American archaeologist George Andrew Reisner, who conducted the first large-scale investigation of sites in Lower Nubia and used the designations A-, B-, C-, D-, and X-group to describe the peoples who had settled in that region and to indicate the chronological order of their occupation of the various sites.

The A-group can now be dated to a period late in the fourth millennium B.C. Recent investigations have shown that a B-group never existed and that the burials formerly assigned to that group belong either to an impoverished A-group or to a C-group that migrated to Lower Nubia at around 2300 to 2200 B.C., the period of the Egyptian Dynasty VI, and remained there until the fifteenth or fourteenth century B.C. Reisner designated the partly Egyptianized Nubians of the New Kingdom as the D-group. This term, however, is no longer used. The X-group, denoting a stage of transition between the Meroitic Period of the Kingdom of Kush and the beginning of the Christian Period (fourth to sixth century A.D.), is a term still used, but B. G. Trigger has recently suggested that the designation "Ballana culture" more accurately emphasizes the culture's independent character.

The name "Kush" was first used by the Egyptians of Dynasty XII (around 2000 B.C.) who occupied Lower Nubia. At that time, Kush designated a small area south of the Second Cataract, but the word soon became a synonym for Upper Nubia, and from Dynasty XVIII onward it was used to describe the entire territory from Aswan to the area beyond the Fourth Cataract that was administered by the Egyptians. The "Kingdom of Kush", however, is a separate political entity, which arose sometime before 760 B.C. with its center at Gebel Barkal. The Kushite kings conquered Egypt and ruled there as Dynasty XXV (716-556 B.C.). From that time until about 270 B.C., the site of the royal necropolis was at Napata, near Gebel Barkal, and the epoch is accordingly called the Napatan Period of the Kingdom of Kush. This period was followed by the Meroitic Period of the Kingdom of Kush, which began with the transfer of the royal cemetery to Meroe (around 270 B.C.) and lasted until the end of the Kushite Kingdom in about A.D. 350.

In 1923, Reisner (1923d) formulated a list of rulers and a relative chronology for the Napatan and Meroitic Periods. Working from the known dates for Dynasty XXV, Reisner established a list of generations of the rulers of Kush based upon the comparative analysis of the archaeological record. In excavating the royal cemeteries (El Kurru, Nuri, Gebel Barkal, Meroe), he had observed variations in tomb design, methods, and burial arrangements and assigned each pyramid a relative position in time. This position he called a generation, numbering them numerically from Kashta, who began the conquest of Egypt and the subsequent formation of Dynasty XXV, down to the fall of Meroe. Reisner arrived at A.D. 350 as the date for the fall of the Kingdom of Kush based upon the victory inscription of the Axumite King Ezana. The royal burials that antedated Kashta were designated Generations A through E. Within the period of nearly one thousand years, only a few kings can be dated with absolute certainty. Ergamenes I is known to be a contemporary of Ptolemy II (283-246 B.C.; see Diodorus Siculus *Bibliotheca Historica* 3.6), and Natakamani's coronation occurred shortly after the Roman invasion of Kush in 23 B.C.

Reisner's chronology for this period has proved to be substantially accurate, and in the half century since it was published, only minor refinements have been made. Dunham—Macadam (1949), Arkell (1955b; 1961), Hintze (1959; 1962a; 1973), and Wenig (1967; 1973b) have verified Reisner and in certain cases modified his chronology. Reisner listed sixty-eight generations of the rulers of Kush. The following list has added eight generations and represents the present state of our knowledge, imperfect though it remains. Akinidad (Gen. 51) has been retained, though it is uncertain that he ever reigned independently. Thanks to the work of K.-H. Priese (1977), we are here able to add the name of Aktisanes (Gen. 28) to the list of the rulers of Kush.

Dates given in this catalogue are based upon the following relative chronology. For Nubia and the northern Sudan we possess several radiocarbon dates and a few absolute dates which fall in the Napatan and Meroitic Periods. Fortunately, it is possible in many cases to correlate the history of Nubia and the northern Sudan with the relatively well established chronology of Egypt. The list of periods and rulers also includes a short chronology of Egyptian history. The Egyptian chronology is based upon the dates given by J. von Beckerath (1971) with the exception of Dynasty XXV, which is based upon the dates proposed by K. A. Kitchen (1973). Dates given for the Middle Kingdom and those from the year 664 B.C. onward in Egypt are absolute, based upon the observation of astronomical phenomena recorded in ancient times. Old Kingdom dates are believed to be accurate to within thirty years. Those suggested for the prehistoric periods may vary by as much as a century.

The pre-Islamic history of Nubia and the northern Sudan may be divided into three eras: the pre-Kushite, the Kushite (including Ballana), and the Christian. In the chronology of the pre-Kushite era, Nordström's (1972) dates and divisions for the A-group, Bietak's (1968) chronology and nomenclature for the C-group, and Gratien's (1975) work on the Kerma culture have been adopted.

Griffith (1925; 1926) attempted to establish a rough Meroitic chronology based upon the cemetery at Faras. It must be remembered, however, that his divisions into Period A (first century B.C. to first century A.D.), Period B (first to second century A.D.), and Period C (second to third century or, more precisely, fourth century A.D.) are only approximate.

Great problems remain in establishing reliable dates for the Ballana culture. No correlation has yet been worked out between the history of the Ballana culture and that of contemporary Egypt.

The dates for the Christian Period can be verified by the relative wealth of literary sources (principally Arab and Christian ecclesiastical) which mention events in Nubia from the time of the official conversion of the rulers of Nobatia (A.D. 543-45) to the fall of the Kingdom of Alwa to the Funj in 1504.

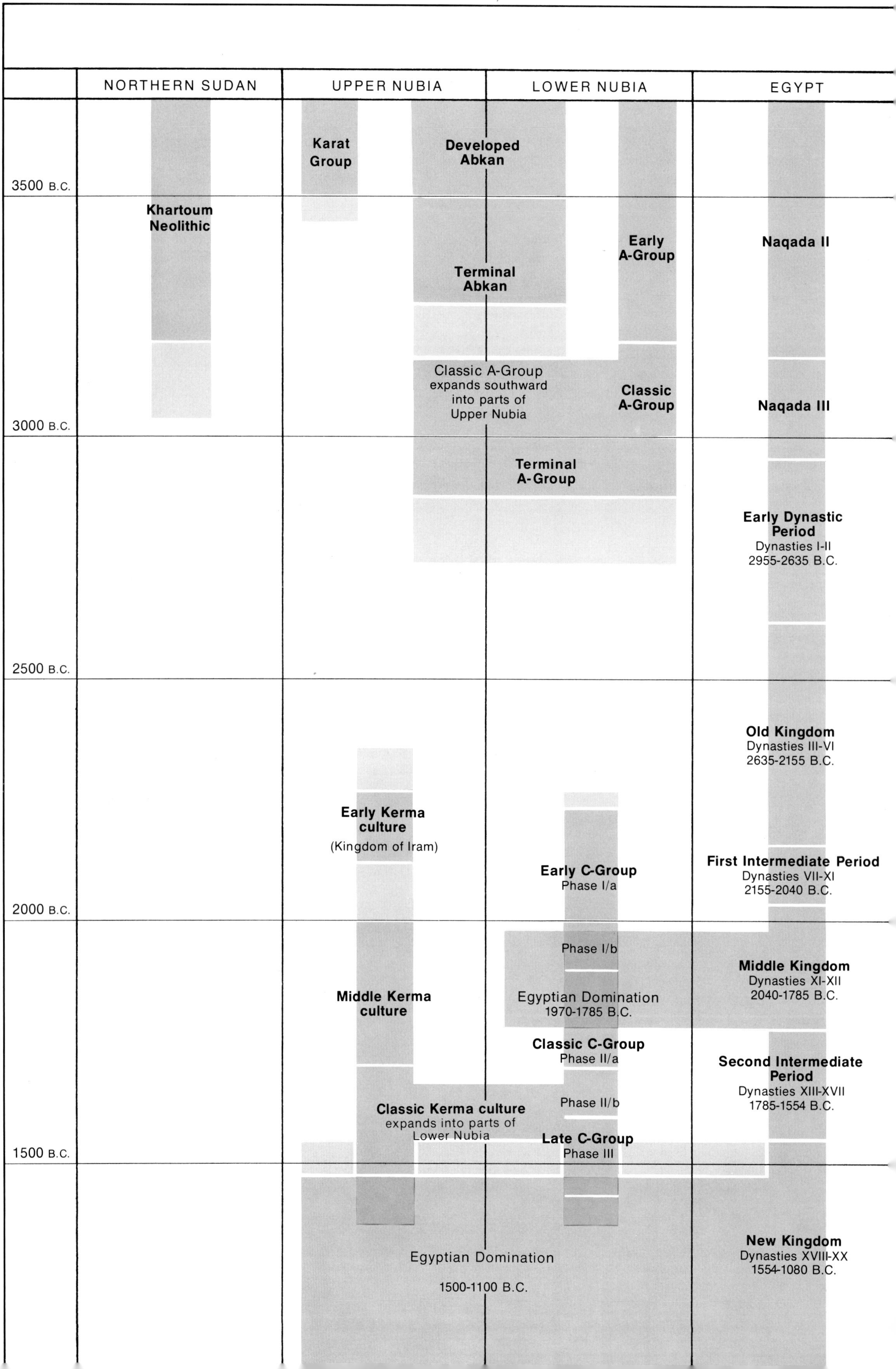
NORTHERN SUDAN
UPPER NUBIA
LOWER NUBIA
EGYPT
3500 B.C.
3000 B.C.
2500 B.C.
2000 B.C.
1500 B.C.
Khartoum Neolithic
Karat Group
Developed Abkan
Terminal Abkan
Early A-Group
Classic A-Group expands southward into parts of Upper Nubia
Classic A-Group
Terminal A-Group
Naqada II
Naqada III
Early Dynastic Period
Dynasties I-II
2955-2635 B.C.
Old Kingdom
Dynasties III-VI
2635-2155 B.C.
Early Kerma culture
(Kingdom of Iram)
Early C-Group
Phase I/a
First Intermediate Period
Dynasties VII-XI
2155-2040 B.C.
Phase I/b
Middle Kerma culture
Egyptian Domination
1970-1785 B.C.
Middle Kingdom
Dynasties XI-XII
2040-1785 B.C.
Classic C-Group
Phase II/a
Second Intermediate Period
Dynasties XIII-XVII
1785-1554 B.C.
Classic Kerma culture
expands into parts of Lower Nubia
Phase II/b
Late C-Group
Phase III
Egyptian Domination
1500-1100 B.C.
New Kingdom
Dynasties XVIII-XX
1554-1080 B.C.

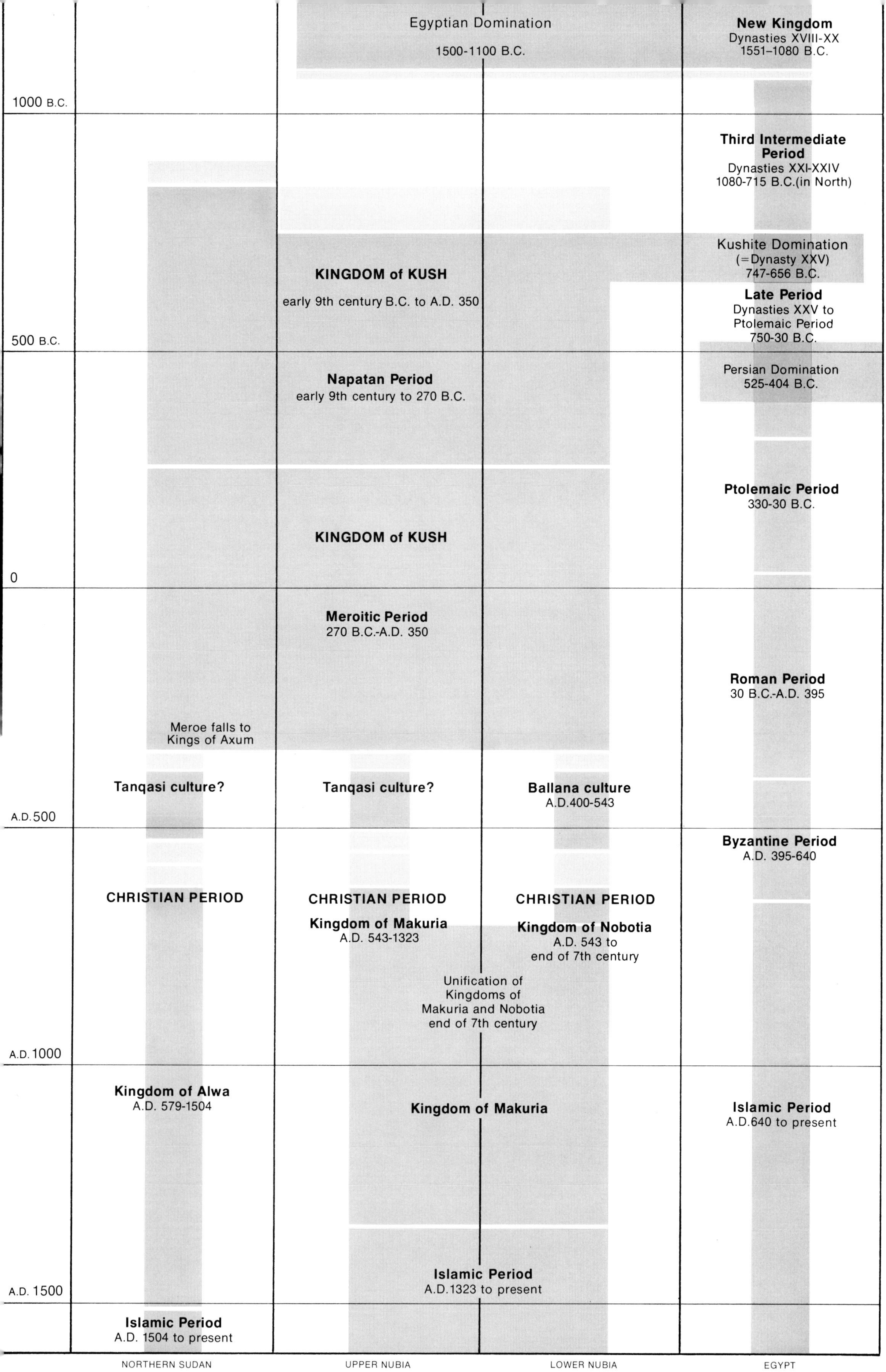
Egyptian Domination
1500-1100 B.C.
New Kingdom
Dynasties XVIII-XX
1551–1080 B.C.
1000 B.C.
Third Intermediate Period
Dynasties XXI-XXIV
1080-715 B.C.(in North)
Kushite Domination
(=Dynasty XXV)
747-656 B.C.
KINGDOM of KUSH
early 9th century B.C. to A.D. 350
Late Period
Dynasties XXV to Ptolemaic Period
750-30 B.C.
500 B.C.
Napatan Period
early 9th century to 270 B.C.
Persian Domination
525-404 B.C.
Ptolemaic Period
330-30 B.C.
KINGDOM of KUSH
0
Meroitic Period
270 B.C.-A.D. 350
Roman Period
30 B.C.-A.D. 395
Meroe falls to Kings of Axum
Tanqasi culture?
Tanqasi culture?
Ballana culture
A.D.400-543
A.D.500
Byzantine Period
A.D. 395-640
CHRISTIAN PERIOD
CHRISTIAN PERIOD
Kingdom of Makuria
A.D. 543-1323
CHRISTIAN PERIOD
Kingdom of Nobotia
A.D. 543 to end of 7th century
Unification of Kingdoms of Makuria and Nobotia end of 7th century
A.D.1000
Kingdom of Alwa
A.D. 579-1504
Kingdom of Makuria
Islamic Period
A.D.640 to present
Islamic Period
A.D.1323 to present
A.D. 1500
Islamic Period
A.D. 1504 to present
NORTHERN SUDAN
UPPER NUBIA
LOWER NUBIA
EGYPT

Reigning Kings and Queens of the Kingdom of Kush

Generation	Name	Pyramid	Date
A through E			900–760 B.C.
	Alara		before 760 B.C.
1	Kashta	Ku. 8	760–747 B.C.
2	Piye	Ku. 17	747–716 B.C.
3	Shabaqo	Ku. 15	716–702 B.C.
4	Shebitqo	Ku. 18	702–690 B.C.
5	Taharqo	Nu. 1	690–664 B.C.
6	Tanwetamani	Ku. 16	664–653 B.C.
7	Atlanersa	Nu. 20	653–643 B.C.
8	Senkamanisken	Nu. 3	643–623 B.C.
9	Anlamani	Nu. 6	623–593 B.C.
10	Aspelta	Nu. 8	593–568 B.C.
11	Aramatelqo	Nu. 9	568–555 B.C.
12	Malonaqen	Nu. 5	555–542 B.C.
13	Analmaaye	Nu. 18	542–538 B.C.
14	Amani-natake-lebte	Nu. 10	538–519 B.C.
15	Karkamani	Nu. 7	519–510 B.C.
16	Amaniastabarqo	Nu. 2	510–487 B.C.
17	Siaspiqa	Nu. 4	487–468 B.C.
18	Nasakhma	Nu. 19	468–463 B.C.
19	Malowiebamani	Nu. 11	463–435 B.C.
20	Talakhamani	Nu. 16	435–431 B.C.
21	Irike-Amanote	Nu. 12	431–405 B.C.
22	Baskakeren	Nu. 17	405–404 B.C.
23	Harsiyotef	Nu. 13	404–369 B.C.
24	*Unknown king*	Nu. 1	369–353 B.C.
25	Akhratan	Nu. 14	353–340 B.C.
26	Amanibakhi	Nu. ?	340–335 B.C.
27	Nastasen	Nu. 15	335–315 B.C.
28	(Aktisanes)	Bar. 11	
29	(Aryamani)	Bar. 14	
30	(Kash . . . merj Imen)	Bar. 15	315–270 B.C.
31	Irike-Piye-qo	?	
32	Sabrakamani	?	
33	Arkamani-qo (Ergamenes I)	Beg. S. 6	270–260 B.C.
34	Amanislo	Beg. S. 5	260–250 B.C.
35	Aman . . . tekha	Beg. N. 4	250–235 B.C.
36	Arnekhamani	Beg. N. 53	235–218 B.C.
37	Arqamani (Ergamenes II)	Beg. N. 7	218–200 B.C.
38	Tabirqo (=Adikhalamani?)	Beg. N. 9	200–190 B.C.
39	*Unknown king*	Beg. N. 10	190–185 B.C.

Succession uncertain

Generation	Name	Pyramid	Date
40	*Unknown king*	Beg. N. 8	185–170 B.C.
41	(Shanakdakhete)	Beg. N. 11	170–150 B.C.
42	*Unknown king*	Beg. N. 12	150–130 B.C.
43	(Naqyrinsan)	Beg. N. 13	130–110 B.C.
44	(Tanyidamani)	Beg. N. 20	110–90 B.C.
45	*Unknown king*	Bar. 2	
46	*Unknown queen*	Bar. 4	90–50 B.C. (45–47)
47	Nawidemak	Bar. 6	
48	(Amanikhabale)	Beg. N. 2	50–40 B.C.
49	(Teriteqas)	Beg. N. 14	
50	(Amanirenas)	Beg. N. 21	40–10 B.C. (49–51)
51	Akinidad	?	
52	Amanishakheto	Beg. N. 6	10 B.C.–0
53	Natakamani	Beg. N. 22	0–A.D. 20
53,1	Amanitore	Beg. N. 1	
53,2	Arikhankharer	Beg. N. 5	
53,3	Arikakahtani	Beg. N. 56	
54	Shorkaror	?	A.D. 20–30
55	(Pisakar)	Beg. N. 15	A.D. 30–40
56	Amanitaraqide	Beg. N. 16	A.D. 40–50
57	Amanitenmemide	Beg. N. 17	A.D. 60–62
58	Amanikhatashan	Beg. N. 18	A.D. 62–85
59	(Teritnide)	Beg. N. 40	A.D. 85–90
60	Teqerideamani	Beg. N. 28	A.D. 90–114
61	(Tamelerdeamani)	Beg. N. 34	A.D. 114–134
62	(Adeqetali)	Beg. N. 41	A.D. 134–140
63	Takideamani	Beg. N. 29	A.D. 140–155
64	Tarekeniwal	Beg. N. 19	A.D. 155–170
65	(Amanikhalika)	Beg. N. 32	A.D. 170–175
66	(Aritenyesbokhe)	Beg. N. 30	A.D. 175–190
67	(Amanikhareqerem)	Beg. N. 37	A.D. 190–200
68	(Teritedakhatey)	Beg. N. 38	A.D. 200–215
69	Aryesbokhe	Beg. N. 36	A.D. 215–225
70	*Unknown king*	Beg. N. 51	A.D. 225–246
71	*Unknown king*	Beg. N. 35	A.D. 246
72	Teqerideamani II	?	A.D. 246–266
73	(Maleqorobar)	Beg. N. 27	A.D. 266–283
74	(Yesbokheamani)	Beg. N. 24	A.D. 283–300
75	*Unknown queen*	Beg. N. 26	A.D. 300–308
76	*Unknown queen*	Beg. N. 25	A.D. 308–320

A History
of the Art, Architecture, and Minor Arts
# of Nubia and the Northern Sudan

1

From Prehistoric Times to the Ninth Century B.C.

At the end of the Old Stone Age (Paleolithic), various cultures in which the fashioning of stone tools achieved a high level of competence developed separately and independently on the great continent of Africa. The people of these earliest known cultures were not yet familiar with the manufacture of clay vessels that could be shaped by hand and made durable through firing. When men of the Middle Stone Age (Mesolithic) did learn how to work with clay, they made a great leap forward in their cultural development. Around eight or nine thousand years ago, early Africans discovered how to fashion clay pots in which to store and cook their food. This discovery accompanied a change in their habits of everyday life. They established temporary settlements, and they found in clay a way in which to express themselves artistically; almost from the beginning, they decorated their pots with designs scratched or impressed into the wet clay. Archaeologists have used the variations in pottery to describe the successive cultures of the past, and recently discovered settlements and cemeteries can now be assigned their proper place in history on the basis of earlier findings.

The beginning of artistic creativity in Nubia and the northern Sudan reaches back to the seventh and sixth millennia B.C. Of this awakening to a consciousness of beauty in form and decoration, ceramics provide the only visible evidence. During this very early period, however, began the process that led to the development of art in the regions directly south of Egypt — an art that has hitherto received little attention but which, especially in ceramics and small objects, deserves a permanent place in art history.

From the earliest times down to the Christian Era, the production of clay vessels was of such major importance in the Sudan and Lower Nubia that its development is described here at great length. This catalogue may thus appear to be overloaded with ceramics, especially for the period up to the middle of the second millennium B.C. The preponderance of pots, however, reflects an actual situation: pottery was for long the chief medium for self-expression possessed by early Nubians. Long shaped by hand, evidently by women, and later, from the first millennium B.C. onward, turned on a primitive wheel by men (Adams 1973,181ff.,194), pottery has not only provided the scholar with important clues for the dating and sequential ordering of archaeological sites but in its decoration has given glimpses of the cultural peculiarities of peoples of the past and of their age-old desire for artistic self-expression.

THE EARLIEST CULTURES

The knowledge of pottery making in northeastern Africa seems to have originated in the central Sudan in the seventh and sixth millennia B.C. (Arkell 1977) and to have spread northward from there to southern Upper Nubia and gradually to all of Lower Nubia. The knowledge also traveled southeast to the vicinity of Kassala and the Red Sea region, and west to northern Chad, Tibesti, the Borkou-Wanyanga area, and the Ennedi region (Nordström 1972,11,80). While it has been accepted by some scholars that pottery making was invented independently at different times and places, similarities in technique and form make it seem likely that the craft originated at a single point, from which it was gradually disseminated; this problem, however, demands further research.

The oldest ceramic culture of northeastern Africa known to us is Khartoum Mesolithic or Early Khartoum (Arkell 1949a; 1977), named for the largest site at which it has been identified and the only one that has been systematically excavated. Other known settlements of this culture are distributed over a wide area, in the region of Atbara, Kassala, Wadi Howar in northern Darfur, and along the upper course of the White Nile (Hofmann 1967,18-19).

The people of Khartoum Mesolithic congregated in settlements, but we know nothing of their domestic architecture (Hofmann 1967,13). Since the dead were buried within the settlements and thus "shared" the food and shelter of the living, there are no cemeteries with grave offerings to give an idea of daily life. Only stone implements, pots, and potsherds survive to provide a glimpse of these early people and their manner of living.

The ceramics of Khartoum Mesolithic were hand shaped, rough, and unpolished. They show, however, an attempt at artistic expression, for they were decorated in a very characteristic manner with what are commonly termed "wavy line patterns," achieved by drawing the backbone of a fish across the soft clay (Fig. 1). In a later phase of Khartoum Mesolithic, vessels were decorated with "dotted wavy lines," which consisted, as the name implies, of closely set impressed dots, probably made with a pointed bone or stick.

This "improvement" of an older and simpler decorative technique certainly signified an advance in artistic awareness. It also marked the transition to the New Stone Age. The Khartoum Neolithic was the most important cultural phase of the prehistory of central and northern Sudan. The principal site of this civilization was at Esh-Shaheinab, north of Khartoum (Arkell 1953). From there, between the fifth and the end of the fourth millennium B.C., it spread along the Nile to Gebel Aulia and the Sixth Cataract and beyond (Hofmann 1967, 34-35). It also reached into the great wadis (dry desert watercourses), along which it left settlements and cemeteries as far distant as fifty kilometers from the Nile.[1]

Although our knowledge of the people of Khartoum Neolithic is incomplete, it is evident that they lived in settlements and began gradually to bury their dead in cemeteries (Hofmann 1967,20). We have as yet no knowledge of the type of houses and graves they built. No sculpture is known, although the art of ceramic decoration became considerably more sophisticated.

The ceramics of Khartoum Neolithic, consisting

chiefly of brown cooking pots, are more varied in shape than those of Khartoum Mesolithic from which they are derived. They are now polished to a smooth surface and in some cases are blackened on the inside and around the outside of the rim. Pottery decoration shows an advance in technique and a greater variety of motifs. Mussel shells, fingernails, and stamps made of fishbones are now used to produce "impressed wares," vessels with designs impressed into the soft clay. These designs include round or oval dots, semicircles, triangles, rectangles, squares, and herringbone patterns, as well as straight, cross-hatched, zigzag, and wavy lines. "Incised wares" were produced with an edged tool, made probably of bone. Impressed and incised designs are sometimes combined on a single pot, at times covering the entire exterior surface.

More important, however, the patterns on pottery begin to show a sense of order and symmetry; a simple design may, for example, emphasize a vessel's rim (Fig. 2). This indicates a new attitude on the part of the Neolithic people who lived on the Upper Nile during the fifth and fourth millennia B.C.

In the southern part of Upper Nubia, between Korti and Ed-Debba, several sites have been located in which were found ceramics decorated with both wavy lines and dotted wavy lines. Since these finds indicate a connection with Khartoum Mesolithic, the sites have been identified as belonging to the Early Khartoum Related Group (Nordström 1972,11).

Two roughly contemporaneous cultures of the early fourth millennium B.C. in southern Lower Nubia between Faras and the Second Cataract region are now known as Khartoum Variant and Abkan. Khartoum Variant, closely associated with both Khartoum Mesolithic and Khartoum Neolithic (Nordström 1972,8-12), is distinguished, however, by certain innovations. Its pottery includes large, unpolished hemispherical bowls, light red to pale gray in color, with decorative patterns on the rim and the body. These patterns were impressed into the clay with fingernails, sticks, or a "rocker-stamp," one of man's earliest mechanical devices. This was a rocker-shaped piece of stone or pottery with projections on one side, which stamped a design into the wet clay. The traditional and more tedious method of incision continued to be used. The important contribution of Khartoum Variant, however, lies in the realm of stone technology rather than ceramics.

The Abkan culture is named for its type-site, Abka, situated slightly south of Wadi Halfa. This culture is distinguishable from Khartoum Variant in both its tools and its ceramics. Three stages have been recognized (Nordstrom 1972,12ff.), the final one contemporary with the early A-group culture. In general, the surfaces of earlier Nubian vessels were smoothed by hand. Some Abkan pots were polished by rubbing with a pebble, a method that gave rise to what are known as "rippled wares."[2] Aside from these and an occasional pot with

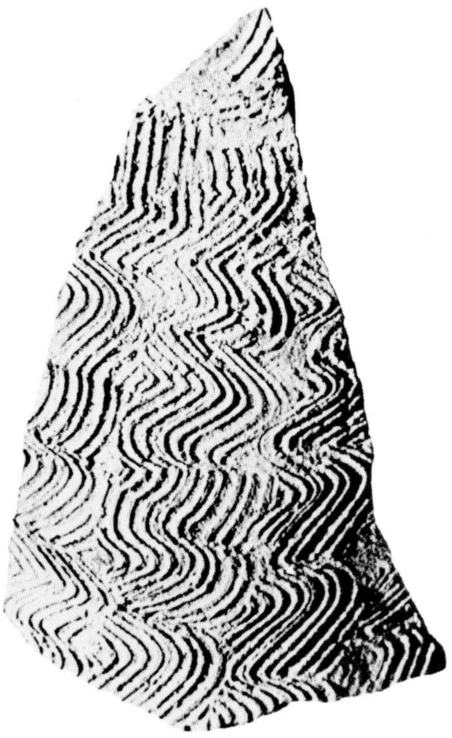

Fig. 1. Fragment of a Khartoum Mesolithic jar showing the "wavy line pattern" commonly used for ceramic decoration, sixth millennium B.C.

Fig. 2. Rim fragment of a Khartoum Neolithic vessel decorated with "dotted wavy line" patterns, fifth to fourth millennium B.C.

impressed pattern, Abkan pottery is generally undecorated, but the variety of forms has increased, distinguishing it from the other early cultures.

THE A-GROUP CULTURE

In the course of the late fourth millennium B.C., there appeared in Lower Nubia a culture that still belonged to the Neolithic but showed a significantly higher level of development. This culture was discovered and named "A-group" by George A. Reisner.

The A-group culture embodied many traditions of the Nubian past. Its artifacts, particularly its pottery, reveal connections with the cultures of neighboring lands. The A-group expanded to cover a large area from Kubanieh, slightly north of Aswan, to the Second Cataract and beyond. Numerous settlements and cemeteries in this area have been excavated, yielding a wealth of material that has given us a relatively clear picture of A-group culture and its development, since the graves of the A-group people were richly supplied with goods for the use of the deceased in the afterlife.

The A-group culture developed in several phases, of which three — Early, Classic, and Terminal — have now been established (Nordström 1972,28-32). The cultural peak was reached about 3000 B.C., at approximately the time of transition in Egypt from the Naqada III culture to the establishment of a centralized state.

The earliest evidence of domestic architecture in northeastern Africa dates from the A-group, whose people constructed hemispherical huts consisting of simple frames made of saplings or strong reeds covered with straw or grasses and very occasionally floored with stone, sometimes cemented with tamped earth. Caves and rock shelters were used for habitation as well as for storage of supplies. No traces survive of a more advanced form of domestic architecture.

The people of the A-group made mats and baskets of grasses and wove linen cloth from flax fibers. They cured and dyed animal skins for both domestic purposes and clothing. A belt, simple loincloth, or penis sheath was the only garment. An occasional leather cap has been found, though headgear usually consisted of one or two feathers stuck into the hair. Jewelry became more abundant and varied than it had been in earlier times, consisting mainly of necklaces and bracelets of seeds or of beads made of shell, ivory, bone, and stone; sometimes bracelets, armbands, and anklets were fashioned from ostrich shell or ivory; oftener, they were of bone or stone. Amulets hung around the neck were common. Finger rings, combs, and hairpins were rare, and there is no evidence for ear, lip, or nose plugs.

There seems to be ample proof that the A-group people painted their bodies and faces. Excavators have found many palettes, which were used for the grinding of colors. They are very simple in form, usually rhomboid, oval, or occasionally round. Most of them are made of quartz, but some are of limestone imported from Egypt. These simple palettes reveal a dawning aesthetic sensitivity on the part of their makers.

The artistic aspirations of the A-group people found expression chiefly in their pottery, and it was at this time that the first sculptures appeared on Nubian soil. Such works as the fired clay hippopotamus head, Cat. 3, and the relief-decorated limestone vessel, Cat. 4, both found in the 1960s, indicate that the A-group people must be credited with a higher level of artistic achievement than had been assumed in the past.

The A-group people used the old techniques for the decoration of pottery. Patterns, as in earlier times, were generally impressed or incised into the soft clay by the potter's fingernails or with the aid of simple tools such as bones, sticks, or rocker-stamps; sometimes a woven band was used to leave an impression in the clay. Of particular beauty is a group of vessels burnished with pebbles that left vertical ripples on their surfaces (Vol. I, Fig. 94).

Nordström's (1972,81ff.) catalogue of ten indigenous Nubian ceramic types shows that several pottery types were found earlier and others persisted into later periods. It was in the Classic A-group that painted ceramics first appeared. Painting most commonly occurs on "eggshell ware," which marks the zenith of A-group ceramic development. This ware, so called because of its thinness (three to five millimeters), is remarkable not only in form but also in decoration. The vessels of one eggshell-ware group are light to pale brown in color, highly polished and embellished with painted decoration both inside and out. A very beautiful bowl in the present catalogue (Cat. 10) is decorated inside and out with a geometric pattern. The vessels of another, related group of eggshell ware have painted geometric patterns on the buff or yellow-brown polished outer surface, while the inside surface is black (Cats. 6-8).

The painting on A-group ceramics is, as a rule, confined to the eggshell ware. The only color used is red, and the patterns, drawn with the finger or a thin, brushlike implement, are usually linear. They include horizontal stripes encircling the body of the vessel, hatched patterns (Cat. 8), spirals (Cat. 10), and imitations of basketwork designs (Cat. 7). Triangles of solid red (Cat. 6) are exceptions to the linear rule, as are the broad areas of solid red that sometimes entirely cover the lower parts of vessels and their undersides.

Nordström (1972,22) asserts that these painted, thin-walled pots "from the modern aesthetic point of view ... represent the first peak of ceramic art in Nubia, and only the potters in Kerma and in Meroë reached this high standard in later times." It should be added that nothing comparable to the Nubian eggshell ware existed in contemporary or later Egypt.

Figural decoration such as appeared on the vessels of the contemporaneous Naqada I and Naqada II cultures of Egypt is almost completely lacking in Nubian pottery from this period. An animal frieze reminiscent of Nubian rock drawings and perhaps painted by a Nubian artist occurs on a vessel from Dakka, which was apparently imported from Egypt (Fig. 3).[3]

The A-group culture is distinguished from older Nubian cultures not only by its superiority in the manufacture of pottery vessels but also by its introduction of sculpture in the round. For the first time in Nubian history, there now appear in burials small figures modeled in Nile mud, fired and unfired. Similar figures, fashioned of mud, clay, stone, ivory, or bone, some of them exhibiting considerable artistic merit, had long existed in Egypt, but the A-group statuettes seem to mark the first appearance of sculpture in the round on Nubian soil.

Nubian figurines were noted by modern scholars as early as the beginning of this century,[4] but they were largely ignored until the Scandinavian Joint Expedition near Halfa Degheim brought to light two small figures in a burial containing the bodies of a woman and a girl (Cat. 1; Fig. 4). These sculptures surpass in quality any previously found and require that the artistic accomplishments of the A-group people be reappraised.

Many of the figurines represent seated women leaning far backward. Their heads, as in many early Egyptian figurines, are without detail save for beaked, birdlike noses. The arms are either entirely lacking or reduced to stumps; the legs are joined together and taper to a rounded point, an incised line sometimes indicating their separation. The breasts are usually not emphasized, but hips and buttocks are exaggerated. Although this type of sculpture also occurs in Egypt, it has been suggested (Ucko 1968,405) that it originated in Nubia.

The two figures from Halfa Degheim correspond to this general type but are somewhat more developed in form. In one figure (Cat. 1), the breasts are clearly shown, as are the arms crossed beneath them. In the other (Fig. 4), which may represent a very young girl since the breasts are not indicated, the arms were modeled separately and attached to the torso. Similar figures found by Reisner and Firth during the first Archaeological Survey usually show traces of red paint, which perhaps imitated the painting of the body customary for the A-group, but the Halfa Degheim sculptures are not painted. The abdomen of the woman (Cat. 1), however, is covered with incised lines that may indicate fatty folds, tattooing, or painting.

So far, only Ucko (1968,428) has discussed the artistic significance of the Nubian figurines, but he was not yet acquainted with the Halfa Degheim sculptures presented here. He was, moreover, interested primarily in the connections between the Nubian figures and similar ones found in Egypt, Crete, Greece, and the Near East, where comparable sculptures had appeared in abundance and in greater variety of form. With the discovery of the Halfa Degheim figurines, however, the theory that the A-group statuettes are incomplete or artistically imperfect can be dismissed. These small figures certainly reproduce what the artist considered to be the essential characteristics of the female form.

Although we cannot know for certain the precise significance of these figurines, the context in which they were discovered may give some clue to their meaning. The two or three dozen such sculptures that have survived all come from graves, particularly from those of women and children. Ucko (1968,409ff.) has shown that the figurines do not represent a mother goddess, as has sometimes been assumed. It has been convincingly suggested that they were intended to secure the continued existence of the person represented (Säve-Söderbergh 1973,228). Such an interpretation seems very plausible, although most such figurines come from children's graves, and in one instance a child's grave contained several examples.[5] These figures may well have been "dolls," as Firth suggested,[6] but they might also have been intended as surrogate mothers. Ucko (1968,420ff.) has suggested several possibilities, among them that the figurines must have been important to the deceased during his lifetime, perhaps being used in initiation rites. He further surmised that the statuettes may have been "twin figures" or, more precisely, representations of a deceased brother or sister.

Whatever their function may have been, it was probably a magical one, whether to serve as a toy in the world to come or to assure survival after death. Since most of the figurines assigned to the A-group were found in children's graves, and since they often lacked secondary sexual characteristics, we can assume that they did not represent wives or concubines given to the dead, as similar figurines did in Egypt. Although stylistic differences clearly exist (as may be seen by comparing Cats. 1 and 2), we should be wary of concluding that they are the result of differences in meaning, and indeed Ucko (1968,423-24) has warned against this conclusion. The stylistic differences may signify only artistic variations or development.

Many finds, among them the Egyptian vessel, Cat. 11, and objects of imported limestone, show that the A-group people had close connections with Egypt. In Qustul, Seele found a fine limestone cylindrical vessel, probably a mortar or an incense burner, decorated with an elaborate scene of boats and animals carved in sunk relief (Cat. 4).[7] To date, this is the only example of sunk relief found in an A-group grave. It is especially remarkable because sunk relief was apparently not known in Egypt before Dynasty IV, although stonecutting on cylinder seals was common, and the question arises whether the vessel was carved out of the raw material in Nubia or in Egypt. It is unlikely that the vessel was made in Egypt, since it would be highly improbable that this novel technique of sunk relief decoration would appear for the first time in a single example found outside of Egypt and not be seen again for several hundred years. The possibility of an isolated example would be more likely in Nubia. Indeed, the stonecutter may have learned his craft in Egypt and brought back his skills to apply them in his homeland in a unique example. It is possible that future research will uncover parallels for this object in Nubia, though it cannot be regarded as typical of the A-group. It is a unique artistic achievement.

The same seems true of the Qustul hippopotamus head (Cat. 3). While the context in which it was found clearly indicates that it belongs to the A-group, the sculpture remains an isolated example. The modeling is not naturalistic, nor does it suggest the style of the hippopotamus sculptures so frequently found in contemporary Egypt. Nevertheless, the essential features of the animal have been captured by the artist and rendered in simplified form. Here again, because Egyptian representations of the hippopotamus reflect such different aesthetic principles, we must assume that the sculptor who created this head was a Nubian. This unique piece, however, like the stone vessel decorated in sunk relief (Cat. 4), cannot be used to make general deductions about the artistic productivity of the A-group. The head does prove that some A-group artists were capable of considerable sophistication; it does not greatly matter whether or not the inspiration came from Egypt.

Fig. 3. Pot from Dakka decorated with painted animal frieze reminiscent of Nubian rock drawings, about 3000 B.C. *(Munich ÄS 2728).*

Fig. 4. Fired clay figure of a young girl, found near Halfa Degheim, A-group culture, about 3000 B.C. *(Khartoum, Sudan National Museum).*

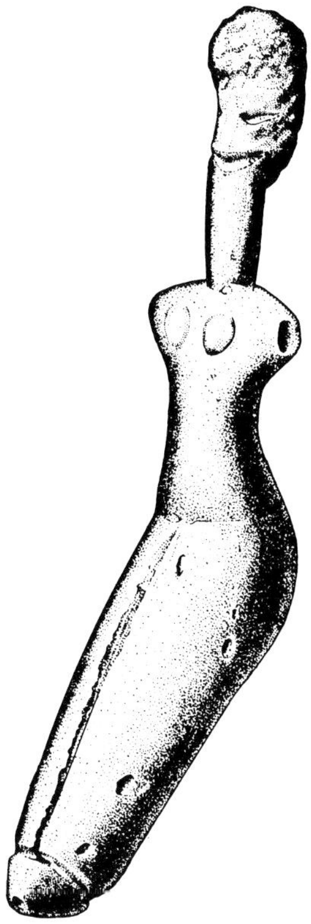

THE C-GROUP CULTURE

G. A. Reisner applied the term "C-group" to a people who migrated to Lower Nubia in the late third millennium B.C., at about the time of the Egyptian Dynasty VI (2290-2135 B.C.). They probably came from the region between Ennedi and Darfur, and settled in the territory previously occupied by the A-group. The C-group people belonged to the same cultural horizon as did the earlier cultures of Nubia and the northern Sudan, including the A-group, and the Kerma culture of Upper Nubia (Hofmann 1967,289ff.). According to Steindorff (1935,6), the C-group represents a "peak of specifically Nubian life."

Although the A-group produced works of great merit in small sculpture and in ceramics, especially the fine painted eggshell ware, the C-group reached a much higher stage of material development. As may be seen in its burial customs, grave construction, and ceramic decoration, this group was initially, like all other early Nubian cultures, a closed and unified civilization. The C-group stood on the threshold of the Copper-Stone Age (Chalcolithic) and hence at the beginning of a revolution in lifestyle brought about by the introduction of tools and utensils made of copper. Toward the end, the C-group culture also began to be infiltrated by foreign influences.

Until a comparatively late date in their history, however, the customs of the C-group people differed little from those of their A-group predecessors. Like them, the C-group people wore feathers in their hair, and their dress was limited to long or short loincloths made of cloth or dyed leather or sometimes only belts, which were beaded in geometric patterns. Their jewelry consisted of rings, armbands, and hair rings usually made of bone, stone (Cat. 24), or, rarely, copper. Pincer-shaped hair ornaments made of mother-of-pearl (Cats. 25, 26) appear (some archaeologists believe they were earrings); and necklaces composed of flat, rectangular pieces of bone or ostrich or mussel shell (Cat. 23) were adopted from the people of the Pan-grave culture in the later phases of the C-group.

Most of these objects come from graves. A very small number were discovered in C-group settlements, few of which have been excavated. Those that have been explored are poorly preserved, but they show that the C-group people had made considerable advances in domestic architecture. The earliest C-group people, like their A-group predecessors, lived in round huts made of bundled reeds or grasses attached to a post placed asymmetrically in the ground. These tentlike structures, which reflect a nomadic past, were superseded in the later C-group period by more permanent dwellings. These were still round, but their walls were constructed of upright rectangular stone slabs bonded with mud.

Additional rooms could be added to these houses, and sometimes several dwellings were joined to form compounds that were set within oval or round enclosures. As time passed, sun-dried mud-bricks came into use and were employed to construct square or rectangular rooms, which were at first rather haphazard but later became more regular in shape. At Areika was discovered a large complex of rectangular rooms that had been built in many successive stages and may have been the residence of a C-group chieftain. While such a construction certainly implies Egyptian influence, the building technique is wholly Nubian.

Although remains of domestic architecture are scanty, C-group cemeteries now reveal more sophisticated construction. Funerary offerings to the dead consist mainly of vessels. In the beginning, these were placed outside the eastern wall of the superstructure and not within the tomb itself, as was the usual Nubian practice. To this custom we owe the preservation intact of so many vessels, which, buried as they were outside the tombs and covered by the wind-blown sands of centuries, escaped destruction at the hands of plunderers who ransacked the graves for treasure. Some vessels were always placed in the grave pits, and by the time the C-group entered its final phase, this had become the general custom — a change that can probably be ascribed to closer contact with Egypt and with the Kerma culture.

After Egyptian sovereignty over Lower Nubia came to an end (in the seventeenth century B.C.), innovations appeared in many phases of the C-group culture. Some of the changes are traceable to contact with the Kerma culture and with the nomads of the Eastern Desert, the bearers of the Pan-grave culture. From the latter group came burials containing gazelle horns and certain forms

Fig. 5. Detail of a pot decorated with incised figures of women, C-group culture, 1900-1550 B.C. (Khartoum, Sudan National Museum).

Fig. 6. Rock drawing of a woman reminiscent of C-group figures, Gebel Sahaba, near Argin, Lower Nubia.

of jewelry. The Kerma culture, advancing slowly northward after the Egyptian withdrawal, brought the custom of animal burials, the placing of cattle skulls outside tomb superstructures, and the inclusion of fans among the grave gifts. These influences began the process of weakening the cultural identity of the C-group, which was completed when the Egyptians reconquered Nubia in Dynasty XVIII.

Observation of the C-group's cultural development has enabled modern scholars to form a fairly exact idea of its chronology, although the transitional periods leading from one phase of development to another are necessarily somewhat fluid. The arrangement and dating of C-group material are founded on the work of Bietak (1968), who has identified and established the following phases:

Phase I/a: Dynasty VI to the First Intermediate Period (between 2200 and 2000 B.C.). There are few graves. The dead were buried in round or oval pits, over each of which was erected a circular or oval stone-walled superstructure about two meters in diameter and surmounted by a stone stela. The stelae are usually undecorated and only occasionally show roughly incised figures of cattle. Ceramic offerings were placed outside along the eastern wall of the superstructure.

Phase I/b: First Intermediate Period to beginning of Dynasty XII (between 2000 and 1900 B.C.). The graves have the same kind of superstructure as in phase I/a, but it is less carefully built. There are no stelae.

Phase II/a: Second half of Dynasty XII to the beginning of the Hyksos Period (between 1900 and 1650 B.C.). The graves continue to have superstructures as before. The burial pits are rectangula and are lined with stone (so-called stone chests; Vol. I, Fig. 30). The funerary offerings are placed to the north on the outside of the superstructure. Crude decorated ceramics and clay figures appear for the first time. The end of phase II/a coexisted with phase II/b until the beginning of the Hyksos Period, and shows the dawning influence of the Pan-grave culture.

Phase II/b: End of Dynasty XIII to early Dynasty XVIII (between 1700 and 1550 B.C.). This was the golden age of C-group culture. Graves are surmounted by large, massively built tumuli, mostly with chapels at the northern side of the superstructure (Vol. I, Fig. 31). Grave pits are lined with mud-brick and sometimes brick vaulting, but there are still burials in simple stone chests. There is an increasing tendency to place funerary offerings inside the pit. Cattle skulls appear among the funerary gifts along with clay sculptures, a sign of the increasing influence of the Kerma culture.

Phase III: Hyksos Period to Dynasty XVIII (between 1600 and fifteenth century B.C.). Phase III is partly contemporary with phase II/b. There are signs of increasing decline. Burial customs are extraordinarily heterogeneous, due to widely varying influences. After the Egyptian conquest of Nubia, phase III gradually merges with Egyptian culture.

The material remains of the C-group people testify to considerable prosperity at various stages of their history. However, the main evidence for C-group artistic creativity lies in the decoration of pottery and, in later phases, the creation of small sculptures.

The number of C-group ceramic types is smaller than that of the A-group. A large number of polished red-ware vessels with blackened rims and interiors (Cat. 42) are similar to those produced by the A-group but often less fine in quality. This deterioration led Heidenreich (in Steindorff 1935, 86, n. 2) to the assumption that the style was not derived from the A-group but created anew by the C-group. But these black-topped red wares, usually hemispherical and ovoid bowls (Steindorff 1935, pls. 51, 5-7, 52), are distributed through all phases of the C-group culture and hence cannot be chronologically placed.

A second, more important type of C-group pottery consists of spherical or ovoid jars with short cylindrical or concave necks. These jars are made of coarse red-brown clay and sometimes have geometric or figural designs incised on the body or shoulder (Steindorff 1935, pls. 54-57; Bietak 1968, 103, II/a/23). While most of the motifs are geometric — zigzags, triangles, rhomboids, or squares in varying combinations, sometimes covering the entire surface of the vessel — figural representations do occur and include birds, perhaps ostriches, occasionally shown in flight, cattle (usually cows), and goats or ibexes. Human figures, which are very rarely represented, usually show little artistic imagination. However, a pot (Fig. 5) found in 1960 by the Scandinavian Joint Expedition at Faras West (Site 24/E/3; now Khartoum) is decorated with the figures of four women, each differentiated from the others, although they all have the typical prominent buttocks. The style of the figures is clearly reminiscent of C-group rock drawings (Fig. 6), and it is possible that investigation will cast new light on both the C-group culture and the dating of the rock drawings.

Related to this second group is a dish with a stand (Cat. 41). The designs are incised, a technique commonly used for the decoration of Khartoum Neolithic pottery, though as used by the C-group it is sometimes crude or even clumsy.

The most important type of C-group ceramics is the polished white-filled incised ware, which consists chiefly of shallow dishes and deep hemispherical bowls with recurved rims. The C-group potters displayed a rich imaginative faculty in the decoration of vessels of this type. The pottery is almost always black or grayish black; the occasional reddish vessel is probably the result of insufficient firing. The outside of the vessel is polished and almost always decorated with incised geometric motifs, into which a white pigment has been rubbed to emphasize the design; in phase II/b, the pigment may be colored, usually red and yellow. Figural designs have so far been found only in the recent excavations at Adindan (Cats. 31, 32) and Tomas. In phase I/a, these bowls are of

28

flattened form (Cats. 7, 8). They are still decorated with undulating lines, halfmoon patterns (Cat. 28), and pretzel or snake designs (Bietak 1968, I/a/9 and 11), which are later abandoned. In addition to the basketwork pattern (Cat. 29), found already in phase I/a, phase I/b adds a lozenge motif (Cat. 30), zigzags (Cat. 33), herringbone designs (Cat. 34), and diamonds (Cat. 36). Checkered and star patterns are increasingly used; sometimes two different patterns are combined on a single vessel (Cat. 35). Horizontal lozenges appear only in phase II/b (Cat. 38); they also decorate the rare footed bowls (Cat. 37). Cat. 39, an unpolished bowl decorated with several asymmetrical motifs filled with cross-hatching, is unique and may represent a transitional form. Cat. 40 is also exceptional. This bowl is closely related to the usual incised ware in form, but its impressed decoration recalls the pottery of early Nubian and Sudanese cultures, including the A-group, in which similar patterns were common.

The most recent finds of vessels with incised figural representations have not yet been evaluated. Among them are the two bowls from Adindan (Cats. 31, 32) decorated with three rows of cattle, which can be definitely dated to phase II/a by their small bases. In contrast to the cattle depicted on rock drawings, which often display real elegance (Fig. 7), the animals on these two bowls (perhaps made by the same potter) are somewhat crude and awkward. This is all the more surprising since small clay figures of animals attributable to phase II/a generally show, apart from their legs, considerable elegance of form. These two bowls are not isolated examples, as is indicated by the bowl from Tomas, which is decorated with a row of women facing right and rendered in an abstract manner (Lal 1967, pl. XXXVII). Such representations support the view that the coarse-ware vessels with figural decorations (Fig. 5) should also be dated to phase II/a, for they are clearly related to the small sculptures produced by the C-group in that period.

In comparison with the sculpture of the A-group, that of the C-group is truly remarkable (Steindorff 1935, pls. 71-74). As in the past, only clay was used as a medium, and the small sculptures, generally of women or girls, come primarily from burials; only a few have been found in settlements (e.g., Aniba, Areika, Faras). Male figures are extremely rare. The statuettes are always naked, with breasts and pubic mounds barely suggested, and the posture is usually the same as that of the A-group figurines (Cat. 13). A few new forms appear. Some sculptures show only a torso with head and arms (Cat. 18); others represent the full figure of a standing woman (Cats. 15, 16), and, in one case (Cat. 12; Fig. 8), the figure has an animal's head. A single example (Fig. 9) shows a seated woman. Heads with holes in the underside (Cats. 14, 17; Vol. I, Fig. 29) may have been attached to bodies or bases. Finally, numerous clay figures of animals have been found; while most

Fig. 7. Rock drawing of a bovine animal similar in style to Cats. 20-22, Shirgon-dinarti, north of Gemai, Lower Nubia.

Facing page:
Fig. 8. Female figure with sheep's head and protruding abdomen (Cat. 12), C-group culture, 1900-1550 B.C. *(Los Angeles 400-1541).*

Fig. 9. Fragments of a female figure, C-group culture, 1900-1550 B.C. *(Aswan 611, 612).*

represent cattle (Cats. 21, 22), some depict sheep (Cat. 19) and other quadrupeds (Cat. 20).

Bietak (1968,28,104,112) has established that all these sculptures originated in phases II/a and II/b, the golden age of C-group culture. Their significance is the same as that of the A-group sculptures. The animals were clearly magical substitutes for flocks or herds intended to supply the dead with meat and milk in the future life. Some of the female figurines may have been dolls, as were perhaps those of the A-group, but since some of them were found in settlements, it is unlikely that they served as wives or concubines of the dead.

However, a female figure (Cat. 12; Fig. 8), found in a settlement near the fortress of Askut, in a room that was possibly a chapel, may shed new light on the significance of these small sculptures. This figurine of a pregnant woman with the head of a sheep may represent a fertility deity. It cannot, however, be assumed on the basis of a single figure that all statuettes of women portrayed fertility goddesses or even mother goddesses.

Stylistically, C-group sculptures are astonishingly varied and many are very expressive. Figurines of cattle with sweeping horns (Cat. 22) are striking examples of the skill of the craftsmen in rendering essential forms. As with the A-group figures, it is impossible to determine whether variations reflect local traditions, stylistic development, or simply the idiosyncrasies of individual craftsmen. C-group sculptures show greater variety of subject matter and form than those of the A-group. With the possible exception of the seated woman shown in Fig. 9, which may have been inspired by similar Egyptian figurines, the small clay sculptures produced by the C-group are truly Nubian products.

THE KERMA CULTURE

When G. A. Reisner began in 1913 to excavate the gigantic ruins and cemeteries near the village of Kerma, in Upper Nubia, he observed that they belonged to a culture completely different from those previously known in the Nile Valley. Accordingly, he designated it the Kerma culture, and so we call it today, although we now know that it was not limited to the Kerma region but extended over all of Upper Nubia, reaching from the Second Cataract in the north to the Island of Argo in the south (Maystre 1973,194).

The bearers of the Kerma culture came to Upper Nubia in the late third millennium B.C. (Edel 1955; 1967; Hofmann 1967,159). Its origin, however, remains uncertain. Since the Kerma culture shares certain characteristics possessed by both the A-group and the C-group, we can assume that all of these Nubian peoples belonged to a single broad cultural horizon which spread over central and northern Sudan. Several years ago, the internal chronology of the Kerma culture was first made the subject of scholarly investigation when B. Gratien posited four phases of the Kerma culture in a still unpublished dissertation (Gratien 1974) and summarized her results in an article dealing with the Kerma graves of the Island of Sai (Gratien 1975,45ff.). Her study revealed that Kerma cultural development proceeded very differently than had previously been assumed. Those characteristics which had been regarded as early were shown to date to the end of the Kerma period and vice-versa.

The first Kerma phase (Early Kerma), which followed the A-group culture at the end of the Old Kingdom, has been identified in the area between Aniba in Lower Nubia and Kerma in Upper Nubia. In Lower Nubia, Early Kerma designates a transitional period between the A-group and the C-group. In Upper Nubia, however, the first Kerma phase forms a link between the A-group and the second phase of the Kerma culture (Middle Kerma).

In the first phase of the Kerma culture, the dead were buried in an east-west position facing north; they lay on their right sides, with flexed limbs, in round or oval pits covered with mounds of earth. A simple stela, undecorated and uninscribed, was set on each mound to mark the burial, and within the pit were placed food offerings in pottery vessels for the sustenance of the dead in the future world. While these burial customs clearly have affinities with the early C-group, the pottery is related to that of the A-group (Gratien 1975,46, fig.2).

After a period of interruption, the second phase (Middle Kerma) continued from the beginning of the Egyptian Middle Kingdom into Dynasty XIII. The border between the Kerma culture and the C-group lay somewhat to the south of the Second Cataract. We do not know how far to the south Middle Kerma extended (Gratien 1975,49). In this second phase of the Kerma culture, burials become more elaborate. The burial pits are large and round. Offerings of animals are frequent, and animal skulls are often buried under a layer of earth to the south of the mound. The pottery found in these burials is reminiscent of that discovered in C-group graves (Gratien 1975,49, fig. 3 on 48); black-topped vessels now make an appearance.

The third phase (Classic Kerma) began in Dynasty XIII and reached its peak in Dynasty XVII. It is in this phase that the typical Kerma pottery becomes abundant. Graves of this phase are fundamentally rectangular. Animal offerings, except in royal burials, are rare, and articles imported from Egypt provide evidence of increasing trade with the north (Gratien 1975,52). The great tumuli of the royal residence at Kerma originated during this phase. Although the bulk of the population was at this time settled in Upper Nubia, the southernmost find-site being Bugdumbush, about eighty kilometers south of Dongola, many graves of this period have been found also in Lower Nubia, and isolated burials have been discovered even in Egypt (Gratien 1975,50). The last phase of the Kerma culture was characterized by a rapid process of Egyptianization; its own cultural development ended at the beginning of Dynasty XVIII with the

Egyptian occupation of Upper Nubia (Gratien 1975,53).

The Egyptians were familiar with the territory around Kerma as early as the Old Kingdom, and they called the region *Yam* (later *Irm*). This name became *Irame* in the Meroitic Period, and may well survive in the modern name *Kerma* (Priese 1974). The northernmost part of Upper Nubia, the territory immediately to the south of the Second Cataract, was called *Kush* by the Egyptians from the time of Dynasty XII. Inscriptions on two stelae found at Buhen and dated to late Dynasty XVII refer to the "rulers of Kush" (Khartoum 18 and Philadelphia E 10984: Säve-Söderbergh 1949,50ff.). These inscriptions suggest that the Kerma culture had by that time expanded to Lower Nubia and that a large kingdom had arisen which was known as Kush.

Reisner thought that Kerma was an Egyptian trading post and that the Western Deffufa, a prominent mud-brick ruin, was a fortress, because he discovered in the great tumuli of the cemetery numerous Egyptian objects such as statues and statuettes, stelae, vessels, and other articles inscribed with Egyptian hieroglyphs. Among the Egyptian sculptures were statues of an Egyptian provincial prince, Hepzefa, or Hapdjefai, who lived at the beginning of Dynasty XII, and of his wife, Sennuwy, or Sennui (Boston 14.720; Vol. I, Fig. 36). Reisner concluded on the basis of these finds that Egyptian governors had lived at Kerma since early Dynasty XII but that they had been buried in a totally un-Egyptian fashion. He regarded the other works of art he discovered mainly as products of Egyptian craftsmen who had come to Kerma in the wake of Egyptian officials. In his view, such artists adopted little from local craftsmen. Reisner's opinion, however, was long ago opposed by Junker (1920a,20ff.; 1920b,11; 1921,95ff.) and Scharff (1926), and more recently by Säve-Söderbergh (1941). Nevertheless, his assumption that Kerma was an Egyptian trading post and that the persons buried in the great tumuli were Egyptians was for long accepted (Smith 1965a,98,102,121-22).

It was not until 1964 that Hintze first put forth the view that Kerma was the residence of the "rulers of Kush" and that it was these rulers who were buried beneath the great tumuli (Hintze 1964). The Egyptian objects found in the burials were either booty brought in triumph to the royal residence after the conquest of Lower Nubia or gifts from the Hyksos kings who ruled Egypt at that time. Hintze's hypothesis has been supported by Gratien's recent investigation of the chronology of the Kerma culture, and there is no longer any doubt that, apart from Egyptian imports, almost all the objects found at Kerma were made by local artists and craftsmen. This fact is of the utmost importance in the evaluation of the Kerma culture and its art.

In its Classic phase, the Kerma culture represents the peak of Nubian development. Its achievements far surpassed those of the contemporaneous C-group culture in Lower Nubia, although, like the latter, it remained without a written language. Admittedly, many Egyptian elements were adopted by the local artisans; this is evident in painting, in greatly expanded faience production, and in many other highly skilled crafts. Remarkably, Egyptian influence was stronger in the Kerma culture than in the contemporaneous C-group culture. Nevertheless, it was the bearers of the Kerma culture and not the Egyptians who created the works of art presented in this catalogue. Although the artists of Kerma skillfully adapted Egyptian elements, they also drew upon their own storehouse of forms and motifs to produce works that reflected their perceptions and ideals.

As is so often the case in exploring the past, our principal source of information for the Kerma culture is found in burials, and Kerma burials provide the earliest evidence of a custom unique to the Nile Valley. The princes and high officials of Kerma were laid to rest not in coffins but on beds. They were accompanied to their tombs by retinues of followers, who were buried alive with their lords to serve them in eternity. The attendants who accompanied their masters to the hereafter generally lay on mats, hides, or on the bare floor.

Reisner called the Kerma burials "sati-burials" — a name derived from the Indian custom of sati, the immolation of widows on the funeral pyres of their deceased husbands, which persisted in India almost to our own time. We need not go so far afield as India, however, to search for the origin of the mass immolations of Kerma. There is evidence of burials of living victims in both Mesopotamia and Egypt on the verge of historic times, but there the custom had already been abandoned, and it is all the more surprising to find it persisting at a later period in Kush.

Few cultures have matched Kerma in providing for the continuing service of their dead. In graves attributable to minor officials, only one or two sacrificed retainers were found; in rare instances, the number increased to twelve. The retinues who followed great princes into eternity reached into the hundreds. In Tumulus K X at Kerma, for example, 322 skeletons were found; since the tumulus has been ravaged by plunderers, who doubtless destroyed many remains, there may have been in that single burial as many as four hundred persons. It is clear from the unnatural positions of their skeletons that the victims were buried alive and suffocated to death.

The beds on which the deceased were placed are similar in form to those still used in Nubia and the Sudan today, but of finer construction. They consist of a simple rectangular wooden frame, criss-crossed by leather strips or cords that serve as "springs," resting on four legs that are often carved to resemble the legs of cattle. The beds had no headboards but were provided with footboards that were often decorated with inlays (Cats. 45-52; Vol. I, Fig. 35), and the deceased was sometimes furnished with a headrest similar to those long used in Egypt. The funerary beds of princes were occasionally constructed of slate or blue-glazed quartz (often erroneously called quartzite; Lucas—Harris 1962, 168), and some were enclosed in canopies stretched over rectangular frames.

Possessions the deceased required for use in his future life were usually piled at the foot of his bed. Although much of this equipment was long ago scattered or stolen by plunderers, enough remains to give an idea of the rich material culture. Objects made of precious metals or even of copper have usually been carried off by robbers, but sufficient clothing has survived to disclose that Nubians were now more elaborately dressed than ever before. They often wore long or short kilts of beaded cloth or leather with stamped or beaded patterns, and skullcaps with applied mica ornaments (Cats. 53-57) were worn by both masters and servants.

In princely graves, token representatives of the wealth of the dead in flocks and herds were sometimes interred with their owners (Gratien 1975,49). Rams, sheep, and goats, up to six in number, were buried alive, always facing east. The tips of the rams' horns were frequently encased in cylindrical "protectors" (as Reisner called them) made of wood, bone, or ivory and often inlaid with shell or ivory in geometric patterns. This type of geometric ornament is again seen at a much later date in a handsome cylindrical cosmetic container of the Meroitic Period (Cat. 203), which shows the persistence of traditional Nubian motifs over many centuries.

The architectural accomplishments of the Kerma people can be best judged from the remains of a few constructions in the vicinity of the village of Kerma and from the burial chambers and funerary chapels in the neighboring cemetery. The so-called Western or Lower Deffufa of Kerma (Reisner's K I) is a large and impressive structure built of sun-dried mud-brick, its massive walls rising today to a height of nearly twenty meters and covering an area of fifty by twenty-six meters. Reisner, who first excavated this imposing edifice, thought that it must have been a fortified administrative center. Hintze (1964), however, believes it to have been the palace of the rulers of Kerma; similarly, the installation at Areika (see p. 26) is considered to have been the seat of a C-group chieftain.

Although the Kerma edifice has a decidedly defensive character, it must have contained living rooms reached by a staircase from the ground floor. That the building was used for a considerable time is indicated by later additions, including two rectangular rooms on the ground floor (perhaps for guards), and two rubbish pits about four meters deep, which suggest a long habitation. Found in them were fragments of hundreds of clay figurines of humans and animals, model boats, stone dice, and clay jar-stoppers bearing seal impressions.

The construction of this palace, for which millions of bricks must have been required, and the evidence of long occupancy presuppose the existence of a stable and well-functioning administration that endured for many years. Such an assumption is supported by the settlement that lies to the west of the palace. The houses here, apparently belonging to officials, were repeatedly rebuilt and enlarged. While most of the Kerma people lived in round thatched huts similar to those of the A-group and C-group peoples, a few houses in the larger settlements were built of stone on a more or less rectangular plan, with one or two or even, in rare instances, three or four rooms. Generally speaking, however, the architectural efforts of the Kerma people were directed toward their tombs. It is the size, construction, and contents of the grave that clearly reflect the social status of its owner (Gratien 1975,50).

Funerary architecture is best represented at Kerma itself, where we find the first great tumuli. There, the simple pits in which humble Nubians were customarily buried were enlarged and covered by mounds of earth, some of which reached great size. Tumulus K III (Fig. 10), which covered the elaborate burial of a prince, is the largest of all the funerary monuments of the Kerma culture. Circular in form, the mound has a diameter of 90 meters and covers an area of 6,358 square meters. It is 2.11 meters high and is surrounded by a brick enclosure approximately 10 centimeters high.

The interior of the tumulus is bisected by a central corridor about two meters wide and running in an east-west direction. At right angles to the central corridor are numerous brick-walled passages in which were found burials of a somewhat later period than that of the main burial, which was placed on the south side of the central corridor and approximately in the center of the mound. While the princes of Kush usually had only a single burial chamber, the prince for whom K III was erected had his interment area divided into two vaulted chambers sealed with wooden doors. The walls of these chambers were of mud-brick, plastered, whitewashed, and painted, probably with religious scenes or devices; of these paintings only a winged sun disk (a motif borrowed from Egypt) survives.

Forty-five sacrificial victims were found in the long corridor leading to the royal burial chamber, but since this corridor, like the rest of the tomb, had been sacked and destroyed by plunderers, there may have been many more. On the basis of the fragments remaining in the prince's burial and of the objects found in better-preserved burials of the period, its contents can be reconstructed with reasonable accuracy.

The deceased lay in a flexed position on his right side, his head resting on his right hand, on a bed of blue-glazed quartz, at the foot of which were piled numerous funerary offerings. These included many stone and faience vessels, chiefly Egyptian in type, and many pots of typical Kerma manufacture — a fine, thin-walled ware characteristic of the region. Numerous Egyptian statuettes were found; among them were at least two model boats in blue-glazed faience with crews modeled in the round. There were also faience and quartz

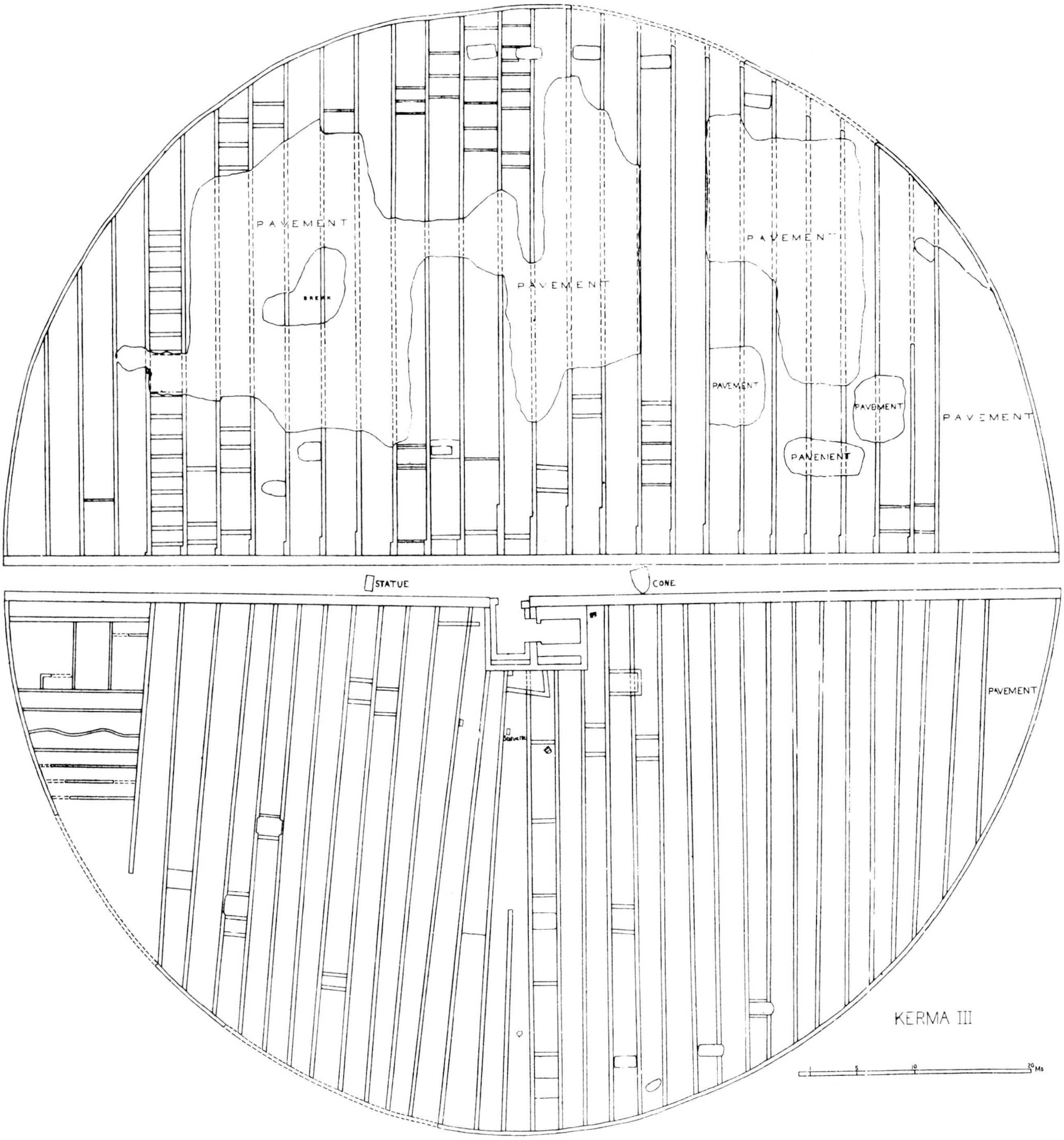

Fig. 10. Ground plan of Tumulus K III at Kerma, Kerma culture, 1750-1550 B.C.

figures of animals, including lions and rams (Cat. 44).

After the burial mound was completed by layers of sand and pebbles, contained within the circular mud-brick retaining walls, it was used for later burials, some of which were also provided with sacrificial victims, human and animal. It is impossible to determine whether these subsidiary burials were those of members of the royal family or of persons of high rank who were accorded the honor of proximity to their former ruler. Thirty-eight of these later burials were discovered in Tumulus K III, most of them found where the long subterranean passages of the mound were intersected by cross-walls to form small compartments. These one-room tombs must have been marked in some way at the time when the mound was first erected over the principal burial.

On the southern slope of Kerma mounds, cattle skulls were found. From a thousand to fourteen hundred such skulls marked the burial of a single prince; they must represent the sacrifices on the occasion of the royal funeral. It is interesting to note that the largest of these tumuli had immense burial chambers. In one instance, the corridor and burial chamber of a prince totaled 490 square meters.

Aside from the great tumuli, the royal cemetery at Kerma contained a few buildings that may have functioned as mortuary chapels. In addition to eleven one-room edifices, the cemetery contained two massive brick constructions that in size rank second only to the palace described above; these buildings were designated by Reisner K II and K XI.

K II (Fig. 11; Vol. I, Fig. 34), the Upper or Eastern Deffufa, is a solid brick structure, in the heart of which are two rectangular chambers. A door in the south wall leads by way of a short corridor into the first chamber, which is connected to the second chamber by another short corridor; the ceilings of both chambers were supported by four central columns, of which only the bases are preserved. The walls were covered with stucco, whitewashed, and painted with designs in red, yellow, blue, and black. Of these designs only crumbling fragments remain, but Reisner could still distinguish in the first room ships and giraffes. Faience was also used in decoration; and fragments of two large blue-glazed lions in relief indicate that parts of the interior walls were faced in this material.

The exceptional ratio of wall thickness to surface area, 85:15, may support the theory that this strange structure was the mortuary chapel belonging to Tumulus K III and was used for the temporary housing of a body awaiting burial. Such a massively built structure may have served to keep out the heat and thus to delay the disintegration of the body pending the final ceremonies and completion of the mound. Such portions of the wall decoration as have survived, however, lend no support to this theory, nor do the fragments of objects found within the chambers, which include such Egyptian artifacts as stelae, stone and faience vessels, statues, and statuettes.

A second chapel similar to K II is the third largest building surviving at Kerma. This structure, known as K XI, has the distinction of being the only stone-walled building discovered at Kerma (Fig. 12).

Fig. 11. Groundplan of the Upper or Eastern Deffufa (K II) at Kerma, perhaps a mortuary chapel, Kerma culture, 1750-1550 B.C.

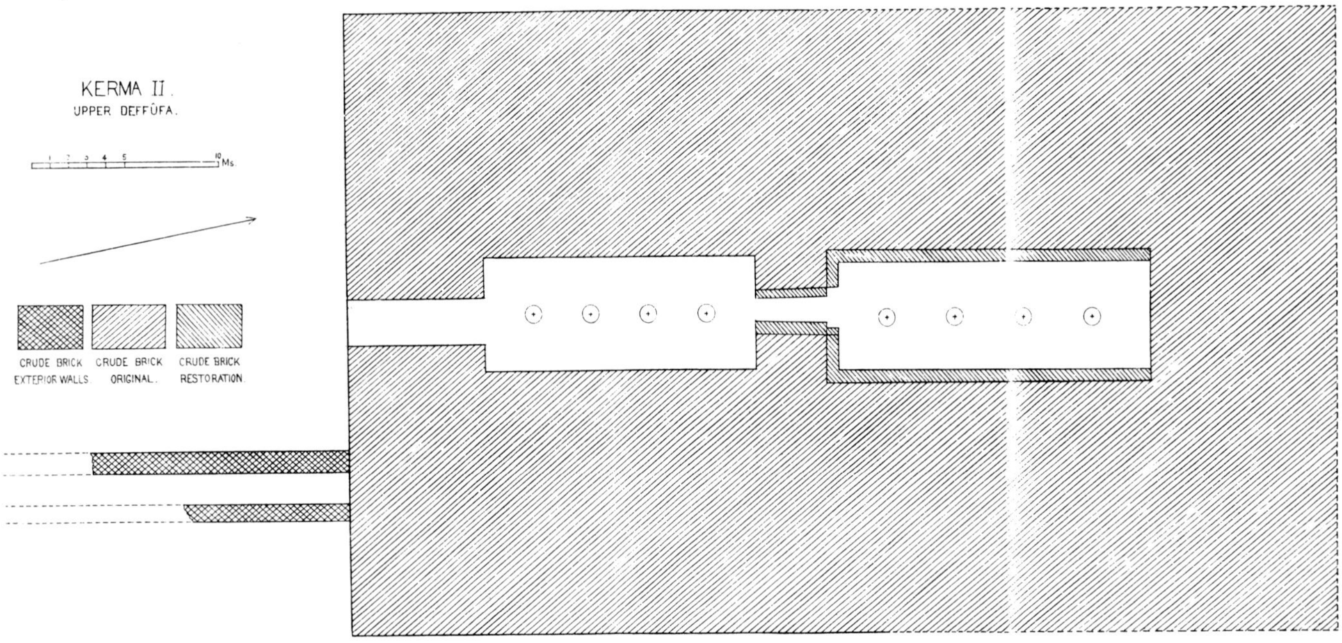

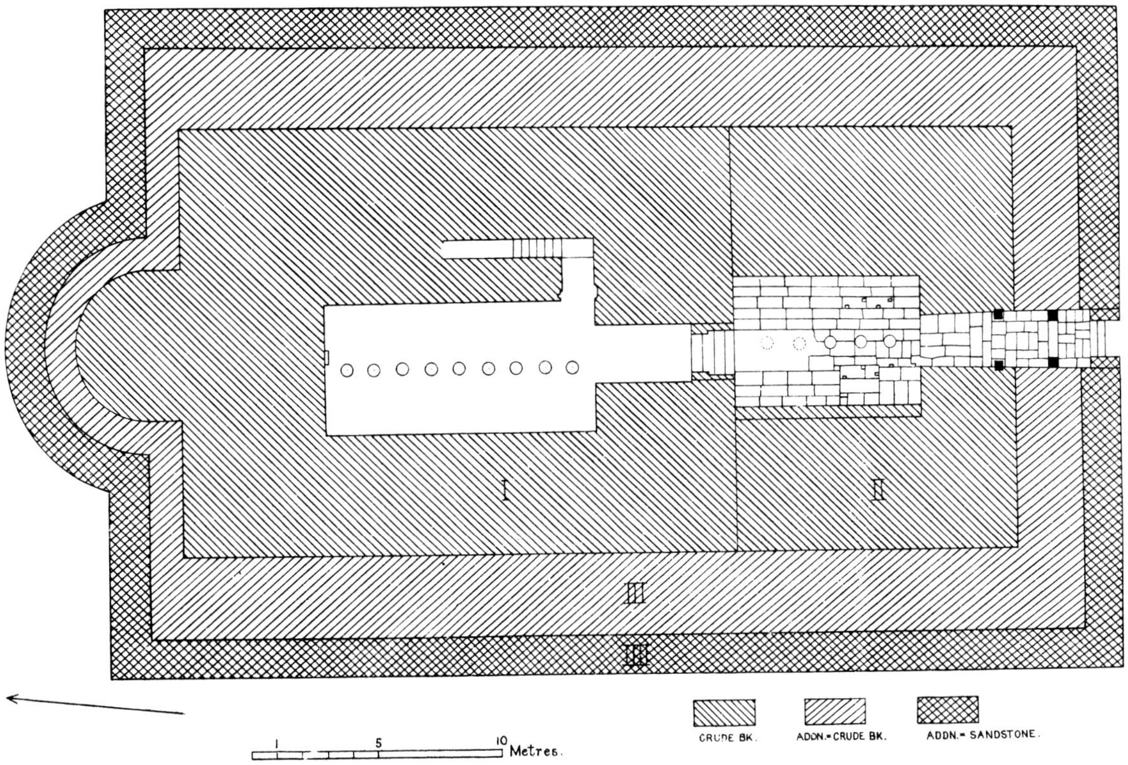

Fig. 12. Groundplan of the only stone-walled building (K XI) discovered at Kerma, perhaps a mortuary chapel, Kerma culture, 1750-1550 B.C.

It reached its final size after several stages of construction, but even its original plan shows unusual features. The massive walls enclosing a rectangular cella with nine central columns have an apselike extension at the rear, and the cella itself is joined by a flight of steps to what may have been an upper chamber or perhaps to the now missing roof. In the second stage of construction, an entrance hall with five columns was added, and in the fourth stage, the entire mud-brick surface of the exterior was faced with sandstone. The plan in Fig. 12 shows that the ratio of wall thickness to surface area in this building is 91.5:8.5.

As with K II, the function of K XI is unknown. Nothing remotely similar to these chapels has survived either in Egypt or Nubia. The fragmentary paintings in K XI, like those in K II, are Egyptian in style, but they may have been painted by Nubian artists. They show men and what appears to be a house, manned boats, red cows, bulls, a donkey, more typical southern animals such as giraffes (also pictured in K II), and at least eight rows of hippopotami (Vol. I, Fig. 37). Among the debris found in the rooms were several flat sandstone blocks inlaid with faience rosettes, comparable to the faience plaques used for wall decoration at Amarna and perhaps used here for the same purpose.

The architecture of Kerma shows that the Kushite princes presided over a well-organized administration under which the arts and crafts flourished. Although surviving paintings and sculptures are few, and most of those that have come down to us are strongly marked by Egyptian influence, the same is not true of the skilled crafts. Reisner assumed that the carpenters, potters, leather and metal workers of Kerma were all Egyptians, but it is now almost certain that the majority of craftsmen were Nubians of the Kerma region who were able to absorb foreign elements and rework them into something entirely new and recognizably Nubian in character, as Nubian artisans were able to do throughout history.

The craftsmen of Kerma, like their ancestors, were especially skilled in minor arts and pottery. The inlaid footboards of funerary beds provide a striking example of their inventiveness (Fig. 13). The inlays, usually confined to the inner surface of the footboard, were arranged in regular patterns. In only two instances were the outsides of the footboard decorated, once with ivory and once with copper inlays. These last, the only examples of metal inlay that have survived, are in the form of highly stylized lions (Cat. 52).

Some of the decorative motifs employed, such as representations of the hippopotamus-goddess Taweret (Cats. 45, 46), can be definitely traced to Egyptian sources. The vulture with outspread wings, a symbol of sovereignty, originated in Egypt. On the other hand, the many animal motifs used at Kerma bespeak an African

Fig. 13. Reconstruction of a burial bed with ivory inlays from Kerma, Kerma culture, 1750-1550 B.C. *(Boston, 40.469).*

origin, even though some of them were influenced by Egyptian style. Among the animals represented are giraffes, with and without wings, rhinoceroses (very rarely depicted anywhere in the Nile Valley), elephants, gazelles or antelopes, ibexes (Cat. 47), hyenas (Cat. 48; Vol. I, Fig. 35), foxes, ostriches and their chicks (Cat. 50), bustards (Cat. 49), falcons and other birds, bees, crocodiles, and turtles. All of these animals were represented on the footboards of Nubian beds, inlaid in two or three rows, sometimes interspersed with rosettes or triangles. The curving supports that joined the footboards to the beds were decorated with stylized plants or even more stylized animal skins (Cat. 51). This unusual animal-skin motif, which Reisner interpreted as plantlike, reappears in late Meroitic times on a black bowl.[8] Here we have a typically Nubian motif that was used at various periods of history and speaks strongly for the cultural continuity of the region.

The artistic independence of Kerma is even more clearly seen in the variety of forms displayed in the mica ornaments that decorate the typically Nubian skullcaps made of leather or cloth. Such caps were often adorned at the crown with a six-petaled rosette and around the edge with a frieze of animals or plant motifs, all cut from fragile sheets of mica. These friezes show more variety than is displayed on the footboards of the funerary beds. On both beds and caps we find rosettes, figures of Taweret, giraffes with and without wings (Cat. 55), gazelle heads, ostrich chicks, and bustards; but heads of cattle and ibexes, *rekhyt*-birds (Cat. 54), pelicans, and hoopoes appear only on caps. Other cap motifs are double-headed birds, heraldic lion's heads, sometimes double, sometimes with three or four heads springing from a single neck (Cat. 56), and double eagles (Cat. 57). Such motifs do not occur either in Egypt or later in Nubia. Other motifs, however, such as the stylized plant forms of Cat. 53, suggest the so-called *Stabstrauss*, or formal bouquet, so familiar in the later art of both Nubia and Egypt. These caps with their mica ornaments are a unique contribution of the Kerma culture, without parallel in the Nile Valley.

The high point of Kerma craftsmanship was reached in the manufacture of faience. Objects made in this material included beads of many shapes (Cat. 59), often with painted designs; small human and animal figures, of which only fragments survive; amulets of various forms, including figures of scorpions (Cat. 60); maceheads; model boats; tiles and inlays; and above all vessels. Among these vessels Reisner distinguished no less than twenty-three types. Many of them were painted; some were inlaid. The technique of cutting designs into the surface of a faience vessel and filling them with contrasting color was practiced only sporadically in Egypt, but in Nubia it seems to have been fairly common. Only fragments of these vessels survive; one of the most beautiful is illustrated in Fig. 14. Since the forms and style of decoration of these faience vessels are Egyptian, it is difficult to determine whether they were made by Nubian craftsmen or by Egyptians employed by the princes of Kerma. In any event, a great deal of faience was produced at Kerma; Reisner stated that he had encountered no other site in the Nile Valley that yielded the quantity of faience fragments recovered by his excavations here.

Other artifacts reveal that many crafts besides that

Fig. 14. Fragment of a faience vessel from Kerma decorated with birds and leaves, Kerma culture, 1750-1550 B.C. *(Boston 20.1235).*

of the potter were practiced. A few small objects show that stone was used for small articles such as bracelets, earplugs, and maceheads; copper and bronze articles are almost as rare. Copper knives, axes, tweezers, needles, mirrors, and the so-called Kerma daggers are known to scholars for their typical and unmistakably Nubian form, but such objects were usually carried off by grave robbers, along with the more valuable jewelry wrought in precious metals. A beautiful necklace of gold and carnelian beads (Cat. 58) was an unexpected find, showing that the goldsmith's art flourished in the once rich and prosperous capital.

The evaluation of Kerma sculpture in the round depends mainly on the broken discards found in great abundance in the rubbish pits of the fortified palace (K I) and in a few Kerma graves. The publication of these fragments is inadequate, providing only cursory descriptions and poor illustrations of a few of the hundreds of fragments uncovered. Most of these small sculptures modeled in unfired clay represent human beings, but among them are figurines of dogs, bulls, and recumbent cows. A few small red-painted boats suggest the riverine life of the Kerma people.

In addition to these fragments in unfired clay, important works in blue-glazed quartz were created at Kerma. This was a process demanding great skill. Small objects in glazed stone had been made in Egypt as early as Predynastic times, but no previous epoch has yielded anything approaching the Kerma products in size and skill of execution. It is unfortunate that most of the sculptures in this technique have survived only in fragments, but these fragments provide some insight into the lives of the people and the skill of the many craftsmen who served the princes of Kerma.

In addition to countless small objects such as beads and amulets, the Kerma craftsmen engaged in more ambitious efforts. In at least one instance, an entire funerary bed was constructed of blue-glazed stone, fragments of which were found in Tumulus K III. From that burial came a ram's head, approximately half life size, in the same technique (Cat. 44), and fragments of many other animals have come to light in the Kerma cemetery.

It has been suggested that these animal figurines were magical substitutes for real beasts destined for the use of the deceased in the afterlife. While in some cases, for instance figures of cattle, this would seem possible, in others, such as figures of lions and hippopotami, it is improbable. It is likely that all of the animal figures found at Kerma were objects of worship in the region — even perhaps the giraffes, rhinoceroses, and cattle that were represented in the funerary chapels K II and K XI. If this hypothesis is correct, the ram must have enjoyed a prominent role, since even living rams were buried with the princes of Kerma.

Wildung (1973) believes that the identification of the ram with the god Amun, which had developed in Egypt by Dynasty XVIII, originated in Nubia, where a ram cult had existed. Such a cult would explain the small C-group figure of a woman with a sheep's head (Cat. 12; Fig. 8; see p. 29). Since both the Kerma and the C-group peoples belonged to the same Sudanese cultural horizon, one can expect to find some continuity in their religious concepts.

The most common product of Upper Nubian craftsmen and the one least influenced by Egypt was pottery. The high point of ceramic production was reached in the third or Classic phase of the Kerma culture. As examples of imaginative form and decoration, the Kerma wares and those of Meroe represent the summit of ceramic production in the entire Nile Valley, including Egypt. When compared with previous achievements in Nubia and the northern Sudan, Kerma pottery shows a substantially greater variety of forms. Its thin-walled vessels were technically surpassed only by the so-called eggshell wares of the Meroitic Period. The most typical ceramic product, the black-topped red polished wares, increasingly thin-walled and varied in form, achieved an ideal union of utility and elegance.

Reisner divided Kerma pottery into eighteen groups comprising three hundred different forms. The black-topped red polished ware is the most important of these groups. A new technical development occurs with the appearance of a mottled gray zone between the black rim and the rich red of the body of the vessel.
That Nubian potters carried their skills far afield from Kerma may be inferred from similar vessels found in Nubian burials in Egypt. The most common form of this ware is a tulip-shaped beaker with a slightly projecting rim (Cat. 61), but it occurs in many other shapes: round bowls, spherical vessels with narrow necks and flaring lips, and vessels with long spouts (Cat. 62; Fig. 15). The potters of Kerma also produced zoomorphic shapes in this ware, as is shown by a pot in the form of an ostrich (Cat. 63), one of two surviving examples. The exterior and often the inner rim of these vessels are polished while the interior is usually not, although it is always black. A small group of Kerma vessels are entirely black with thick or thin walls and always highly polished. These vessels occur in a great variety of forms: flasks, beakers (Cat. 67), and cylindrical jars. Tall beakers with lids are rare, and we do not know their function.

Red polished wares are frequent. These are mainly medium-sized flasks (Cat. 66), but included in the group are vessels with handles, small pots with long spouts (Cat. 64), and spherical containers. A unique feature of this group is a vessel that Reisner dubbed a "teapot" because of its short spout and its handle arching over a wide opening in the top. The spouts of vessels of this group are sometimes modeled in animal forms. There is, for example, a hippopotamus head (Reisner 1923b,406, fig. 284), the head of a cow, or a ram (Cat. 65); in one example, a small monkey squats on the

Fig. 15. *Vessel with long spout and handles in the form of falcons (Cat. 62), Kerma culture, 1750-1550* B.C. *(Boston 13.4102).*

Fig. 16. Vessel with spout in the form of an animal head and raised relief figure of a striding man carrying a staff, Kerma culture, 1750-1550 B.C. (Khartoum 1123).

Fig. 17. Vessel with painted scene of a man in combat with two lions, Kerma culture, 1750-1550 B.C. (Boston 20.1694a-d).

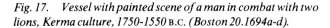

head of an ox (ibid.407, fig. 285). It is interesting to note that vessels of this type also provide the only examples of relief work found at Kerma; a few pots that Reisner thought may have been containers for beer or wine have scenes in relief on their bodies. In one instance, the figure of a man with a staff in his outstretched hand has been preserved (Fig. 16).

Among the numerous other types of Kerma pottery should be mentioned a group of unpolished red ware and a group of white ware, polished and unpolished. Drab wares, such as the three-legged bowl, Cat. 69, were abundant, and in the second phase of the Kerma culture appear vessels with white-filled incised decoration derived from the ceramics of the C-group.

Also slightly reminiscent of C-group pottery are the designs on a small group of vessels painted in black, white, red, and yellow. Most of these pots take the form of a lidded basket (Cat. 68), but among them were found a few "keel" vases with narrow, projecting tubelike rims. One of the pots in this group bears a unique scene of a man in combat with two lions (Fig. 17).

In this short summary, it is impossible to describe the variety of form and decoration of Kerma pottery or to express the beauty of the mostly fragmentary works that have survived. It is also idle to speculate about how the art of Kerma might have developed if the civilization had not been abruptly ended by the Egyptian advance shortly after 1550 B.C. As a result of the conquest of the New Kingdom pharaohs, the two great Nubian cultures south of Aswan, the C-group and Kerma, were so completely assimilated into Egyptian culture that hardly a trace of them survived. Egyptian sources reveal, however, that the Nubian people did survive and that they clung tenaciously to their native customs and practices; their clothing, jewelry, and dwellings, for example, continued to exist unchanged, and it is clear that many of the unique elements of their society were preserved in traditions that reemerged in later times. How and where these traditions were preserved and shielded against total Egyptianization is unknown. Perhaps many Nubians of the C-group or the Kerma culture migrated southward, where they could live undisturbed by the Egyptian conquerors.

Around 1100 B.C., a depopulation of Nubia occurred, probably as a result of climatic changes. It is not until the ninth century B.C. that we again have evidence of the indigenous cultures south of Aswan. By then, Kushites were settled in the vicinity of the Fourth Cataract, and a powerful population had clustered near the ancient city of Napata. With the growth of this population, the northern Sudan and Nubia embarked on a new golden age. Even though Lower Nubia remained largely uninhabited until the third or second century B.C., a Nubian renaissance began with the Napatan Period of the Kingdom of Kush.

1. Among these may be mentioned Gebel Shaqadud (Otto 1963; 1964).
2. Rare pebble-polished examples occur in Khartoum Neolithic.
3. Munich ÄS 2728 (Firth 1915,65f.; Eggebrecht 1975, fig.399a).
4. The first Archaeological Survey of Nubia (1907-11) turned up small sculptures that were classified as late prehistoric or Early Dynastic or were categorically assigned to the A-group.
5. Grave 152, Cemetery 87, near Koshtamna (Firth 1912,185).
6. Firth 1912,170 (Grave 87:66), 185 (Graves 87:147, 87:152).
7. Some similar but narrow stone vessels have a smoke-blackened interior, which suggests that they were used as incense burners (Reisner 1910,277). Nordström (1972,119ff.) suggests that they may have been lamps or mortars because they have traces of color on the interior. A few have incised patterns on the outer surface (Reisner 1910,277, pl.64h, from Bugga near Khor Dehmit, Cemetery 47, Grave 1).
8. Philadelphia E 8734, from Grave 292, Karanog (Woolley—Randall-MacIver 1910, pl. 102).

2

In the first half of the ninth century B.C., chiefs probably from the Island of Meroe led their people to the region of Napata and there laid the foundations of a capital for the emerging Kingdom of Kush (see Vol. I, Chap. 6). From this beginning there evolved the first high culture in Africa beyond the borders of Egypt. Although Egyptian civilization exerted a great and lasting influence on the lands to the south, the art of Kush, despite imitations and borrowings, retained a character of its own. In its later phase — the Meroitic Period, beginning around 300 B.C.— it achieved a truly independent status. It was a long road from the first flowering of Kushite art to its full bloom of independence.

BURIAL CUSTOMS AND FUNERARY ARCHITECTURE

The chieftains who made their capital at Napata were buried in a cemetery near El Kurru. The oldest graves here span five generations, which Reisner, who excavated the cemetery, designated by the letters A through E. The earliest burials (Gen. A) were very simple. A short vertical shaft led to a pit in which the body rested on its left side, facing east with head to the north. The burial pit was usually somewhat to one side of the shaft. The grave was marked by a flattened tumulus of earth, covered with pebbles. Similar superstructures had been typical of the Kerma culture, more than a thousand years earlier (see p. 30).

Two tombs assigned to Generation B (Tum. Ku. 6 and Ku. 19) show interesting additions. Ku. 6 was provided with a simple, stone-built cult chapel placed on the east side of the mound, which was surrounded by a roughly horseshoe-shaped stone wall (Fig. 18). Ku. 19 had a similar structure, but it is less well preserved.

Tombs Ku. 14 and Ku. 13 were dated to Generation C. Ku. 14 was originally a simple tumulus with a chapel on the east, but at some time after its erection the mound was surrounded by a rectangular wall and set within a stone-walled enclosure roughly rectangular in shape. Ku. 13, however, was initially provided with a rectangular superstructure, and thus closely resembles an Egyptian mastaba. Not until Generations D (Ku. 9-11) and E (Ku. 21, 23) did "pure" mastaba forms with eastern outer chapels and regular rectangular enclosures evolve, but these installations are so badly damaged that little can be learned from them.

At latest by Generation B, the bodies of the deceased were placed on beds. This custom, which was followed by queens certainly until the period of Shebitqo (702-690 B.C., Gen. 4), had been characteristic of the Kerma culture, and its reappearance speaks strongly for the continuity of Kushite civilization. In Ku. 19 and Ku. 14 are two troughlike depressions that indicate where the legs of a bed once stood, and four postholes appear in many later tombs of the cemetery. Tomb Ku. 3, for example, in which a queen (king's sister and king's wife) was buried (Gen. 5), contains alabaster-lined holes or sockets into which the legs of now vanished beds were fitted; two very beautiful bronze bed legs ornamented with a squatting goose (Cat. 91; Fig. 19) were found in Ku. 72 (Gen. 4).

It is clear that in the form of their tombs and manner of burial, the people of Napata followed types that were characteristic of and native to the Sudan. This is evident also in the objects buried with them for their use and enjoyment in the hereafter.

Among the treasures that have slipped through the fingers of tomb robbers at El Kurru are biconical gold beads such as were common during the Kerma culture (Cat. 58). The very few typically Egyptian objects found in El Kurru tombs are insignificant and were probably dropped there by later generations of grave robbers; they cannot be used as evidence to support the Egyptian origin of the people buried here.

The picture changes, however, with the Kushite advance northward toward Upper Egypt under Kashta (ca. 760 B.C., Gen. 1). The Kushites of Napata then began to adopt Egyptian burial customs. From the time of Kashta on, for example, the alignment of the bodies of the dead shifted from north-south to east-west and, as may be inferred by jars containing viscera, these bodies were mummified. Coffins of Egyptian type gradually began to replace the customary Nubian funeral beds, and *shawabtis* and amulets of Egyptian style appear among the offerings to the dead.

Although Kashta and his wife, Pabatma, apparently had mastaba tombs (probably Ku. 8 and Ku. 9), their burials were largely destroyed and thoroughly plundered; all that has been determined is that the burial chamber of Ku. 8 was a simple rectangular pit cut into the rock. Kashta's son Piye (747-716 B.C., Gen. 2) had a new type of tomb (Ku. 17; Fig. 20). A long staircase on the east side of the superstructure gave access to the burial chamber, which was roofed with a masonry vault and entered by an arched doorway carefully sealed with rectangular masonry blocks. In the center of the chamber was a rock bench on which the royal coffin rested. Although Piye introduced coffin burial, alongside the bench were four depressions in the floor to receive the legs of a funerary bed.

Like all the other tomb superstructures at El Kurru, that of Piye is today leveled to the ground. It may be assumed, however, that it was a pyramid built of well-cut stone, imitating on a smaller scale the great pyramids of Egypt. The pyramids of El Kurru, like the earlier Sudanese tumuli (Gens. B-E), had cult chapels attached to their eastern sides. Although these have been destroyed along with the pyramids, later Sudanese pyramids permit the inference that the interiors of the chapels were decorated with reliefs representing the deceased enthroned. Perhaps a niche in the rear wall of the chapel contained a stela showing the deceased in the company of a god, and there may have been an offering table in front of it to receive the food and drink required in eternity.

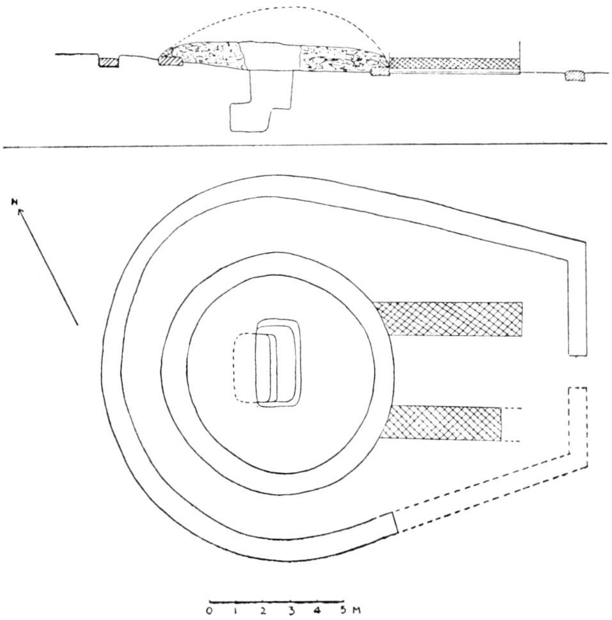

Fig. 18. Ground plan of the tumulus (Ku. 6) of an early Napatan chieftain at El Kurru, about 840-820 B.C.

Illustrated in color on page 46:
Fig. 19. Bronze bed leg in the form of a squatting goose (Cat. 91), from a royal burial of the Napatan Period, 730-715 B.C. *(Boston 21.2815).*

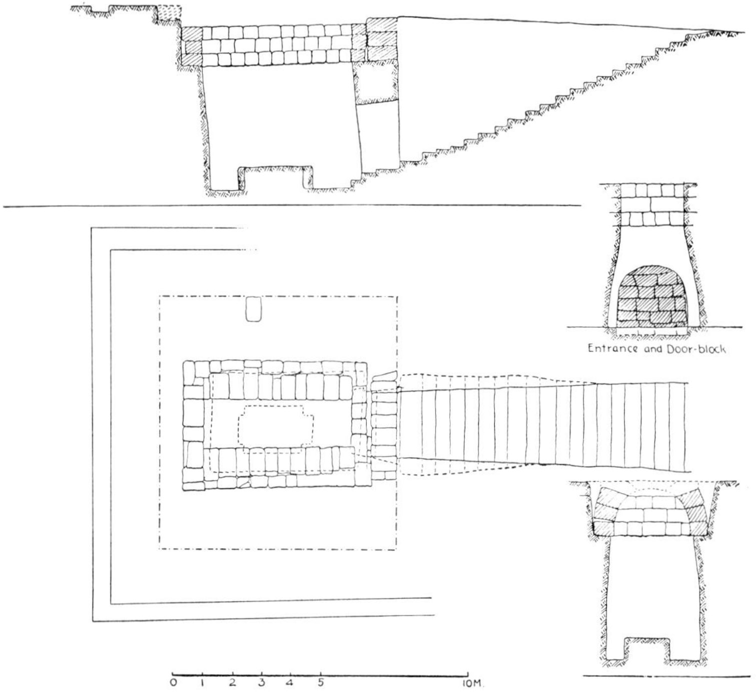

Fig. 20. Ground plan of the pyramid (Ku. 17) of King Piye at El Kurru, Napatan Period, 747-716 B.C.

Shabaqo, Piye's successor, expanded his burial chamber at El Kurru (Ku. 15) into two carefully constructed rooms, the walls of which were adorned with scenes and magical texts taken from Egyptian sources. In contrast to the king's burial, however, the royal wives were laid to rest on beds, according to the custom of their ancestors.

Taharqo (690-664 B.C., Gen. 5) introduced many innovations in tomb construction. He was buried not at El Kurru but at Nuri, where he caused a small pyramid to be erected for his interment (Nu. 1). This structure originally had smooth surfaces, but the king later had it heightened and converted into a kind o stepped pyramid. Similar superstructures had probably appeared on the tombs of Egyptians buried in Nubia during the New Kingdom. It remained a feature of tomb construction for Sudanese kings until the end of the Meroitic Period in the fourth century A.D.

Taharqo's tomb presents numerous other innovations. Like the tombs of his two predecessors, it enclosed two rooms, a small antechamber and a large rectangular burial chamber with a vaulted ceiling. The latter chamber, however, contained six pillars hewn from the rock, and in both of its long walls were niches that doubtless once held figures of deities.

Tanwetamani (664-653 B.C., Gen. 6) returned for burial to El Kurru, where he built a pyramid (Ku. 16) of the same type as Shabaqo's, containing a small antechamber and a large burial chamber. The paintings on the walls of the latter room, representing the royal experience in the afterworld, are in an excellent state of preservation (Fig. 21). They are Egyptian in style and may have been painted by Egyptians or by Kushites trained under northern artists.

Atlanersa (653-643 B.C., Gen. 7) was buried at Nuri, which remained the site of the royal cemetery for approximately three hundred years, until the end of the Napatan Period. Atlanersa's tomb, like Taharqo's, was a stepped pyramid, but the interior design of the divided burial chamber continued the tradition begun by Piye and followed by all his successors except Taharqo. F. Hintze, in an unpublished study, has pointed out that kings' pyramids, while generally larger, were in a few instances the same size as those of their queens. There is nothing to explain why Atlanersa and later Napatan rulers — Analmaaye (542-538 B.C., Gen. 13), Nasakhma (468-463 B.C., Gen. 18), Talakhamani (435-431 B.C., Gen. 20), and Baskakeren (405-404 B.C., Gen. 22) — had funerary monuments no larger than those of their consorts.

Atlanersa's successor, Senkamanisken (643-623 B.C., Gen. 8), had a three-room tomb built for himself, setting an example that was followed by all later Kushite kings. This feature never occurs, however, in the pyramids erected for queens, which contained only the customary two chambers, even in the cases of sovereign queens. Moreover, while the size of the royal pyramids

Illustrated in color on page 47:
Fig. 21. Painting of King Tanwetamani in the burial chamber of his pyramid (Ku. 16) at El Kurru, Napatan Period, 664-653 B.C.

Fig. 22. Groundplan of the Great Temple of Amun (B 500) at Gebel Barkal, showing the various stages of construction. The temple was begun by Egyptians during the New Kingdom and enlarged several times during the Napatan Period.

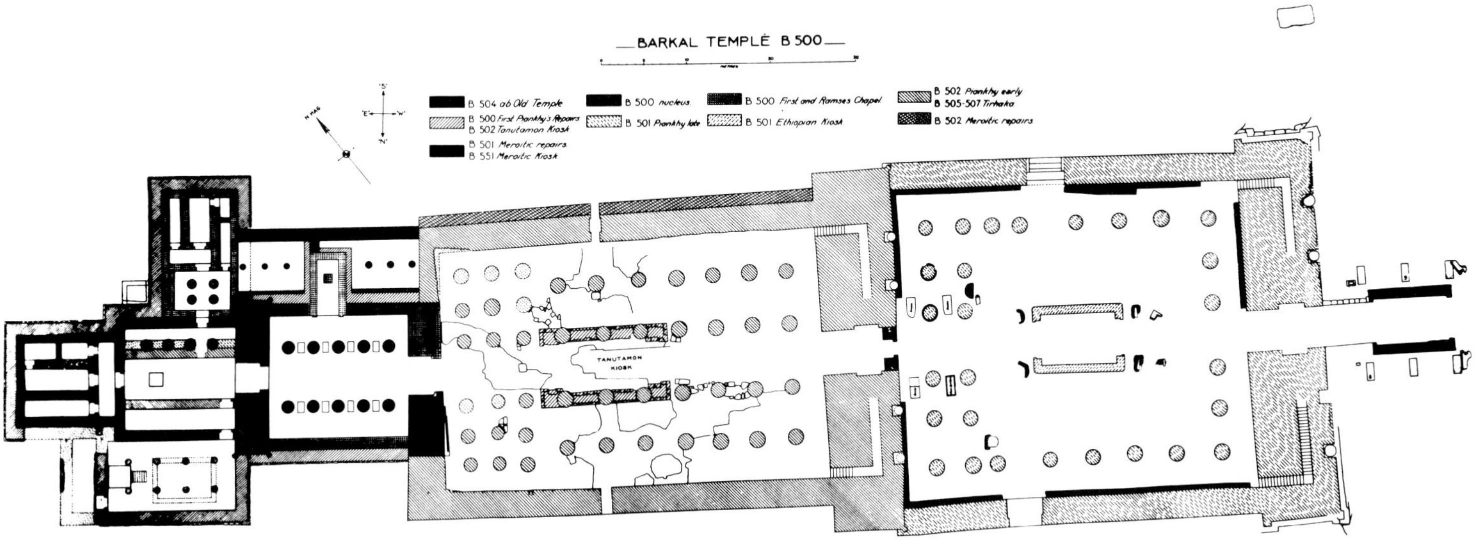

changed somewhat over the years, all of the structures built for kings or queens were generally similar in size. There must have existed, as Hintze has noted, rigid guidelines regulating size and form, but precisely what these were and why they were modified from time to time remains unknown.

After Piye's time, many Kushite rulers and members of their families were buried in coffins of Egyptian type. These wooden coffins have fallen victim to termites so that hardly a trace of them has survived. Two royal brothers, however, were buried in imperishable granite sarcophagi (Khartoum 1868 and Boston 23.729; Vol. I, Fig. 56). These brothers, the sons and successors of King Senkamanisken, were King Anlamani (623-593 B.C., Gen. 9) and King Aspelta (593-568 B.C., Gen. 10). Their massive sarcophagi are covered inside and out with texts written in Egyptian hieroglyphs and accompanied by appropriate representations in Egyptian style. The texts include passages taken from the Old Kingdom Pyramid Texts, from the New Kingdom Book of the Dead, from Egyptian royal coffins of Dynasty XVIII and private coffins of Dynasties XXV and XXVI (Allen 1950, 12-13,14-15 and passim). The granite for these sarcophagi came from the great quarries near the Third Cataract, and the copy for the texts and models for the representations with which they are covered could have been provided by Egyptian scribes working in the service of the Kushite kings. The sarcophagi testify to the increasing preoccupation of Kushite rulers with Egypt's past — a past they claimed as their own.

TEMPLE ARCHITECTURE

No temple constructions datable to the time of Kashta have been discovered, but Piye, who completed the Kushite conquest of Egypt, carried on Egyptian tradition in many areas, including temple architecture. The gods of Egypt were now worshipped by the Kushites. Even as far back as the New Kingdom, the cult of Amun had spread from the Great Temple dedicated to him by the Egyptians at Gebel Barkal (Reisner's B 500; Fig. 22). This temple, which had fallen into ruins, was restored by Piye, who built in front of it a hypostyle hall, entered through a monumental gateway flanked by massive pylons. After his conquest of Egypt, he added a colonnaded court, preceded by even greater pylons.

Piye's successors, Shabaqo and Shebitqo (702-690 B.C., Gen. 4) left many constructions in Egypt, especially in the Theban region, where they renovated and enlarged existing temples and built new structures of smaller size. Thus, after a period of stagnation, Egyptian architecture was given a fresh impetus; the revival has been compared to the rejuvenation of Egyptian art in Dynasties XI and XVIII following periods of decline (Bothmer 1960, xxxiii). Apart from some minor repairs at Kawa undertaken by Shabaqo, neither king built in his own homeland.

Bronze bed leg in the form of a squatting goose (Fig. 19).

Painting of King Tanwetamani (Fig. 21).

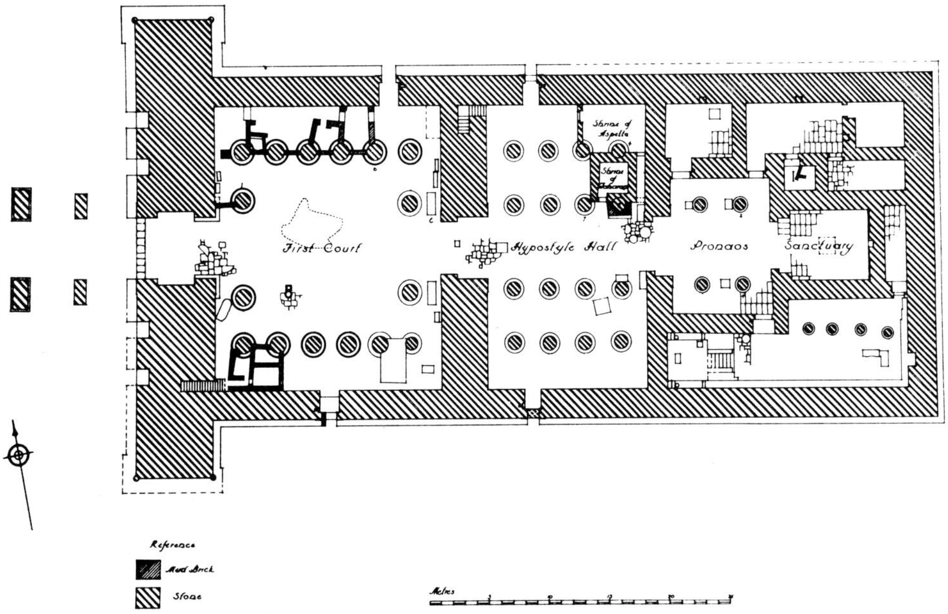

Fig. 23. Groundplan of the Amun Temple at Kawa, built by King Taharqo, Napatan Period, 690-664 B.C.

Taharqo, however, was a great personality and a great builder, approaching the scale of Ramesses II. Like his predecessors, he was deeply concerned with Egypt's past and expressed his concern in temple construction and repair in Egypt as well as in the south. Among his Egyptian building projects are the colossal columns in the first court of the Great Temple of Amun at Karnak. It was in Nubia, however, that he concentrated his efforts.

Remains of a temple built by Taharqo, recently uncovered at Qasr Ibrim, have yielded fragments of wall paintings (Plumley 1975, 19f., pl. XII). These in themselves are unusual, for temples were usually decorated with reliefs rather than paintings. Moreover, the king depicted in the scenes that have survived is shown, not with red-brown skin, as was customary in Egypt, but with the dark brown flesh tone characteristic of Kushites. This suggests that the Kushite rulers were proud of their southern origin and, however Egyptianized they became, they remained so throughout their history.

Taharqo built in Semna and Buhen.[9] He made additions to the Great Temple of Amun at Gebel Barkal (B 500), and erected there a large pedestal of polished granite for the sacred bark. Also at Gebel Barkal he ordered the construction of a rock temple dedicated to Amun (B 200) and another sanctuary in honor of Amun's consort, Mut (B 300).

In Sanam, Tebo (on the Island of Argo), and Kawa (Fig. 23), Taharqo built temples for the worship of Amun, which, with almost identical ground plans, adhered strictly to Egyptian prototypes in layout (Arnold 1962). A pylon led into a columned festival court, which led in turn to a hall of appearances (hypostyle hall), opening into the dwelling of the god — the offering room (pronaos), containing an offering table; the bark room (sanctuary), with the sacred bark on its pedestal; and finally the statue room, in which reposed the image of the god. In addition, an open court was provided for adoration of the sun. At Kawa, the processional way leading to the temple was bordered by figures of rams (the sacred animals of Amun), each of which protected a statuette of the ruler. Taharqo later added a relief-covered shrine to the pronaoi of the temples at Kawa, Sanam, and probably also at Tebo. These shrines may have had some function in a cult unknown to us. They may be forerunners of the one-room temples dedicated to local gods in later Meroitic times (see p. 74).

Little can be said of Kushite temple architecture between the end of Taharqo's rule and the end of the Napatan Period. Tanwetamani added a single shrine to the columned hall of the Great Temple of Amun at Gebel Barkal (B 500), and a small temple there (B 900) is also credited to him.

Atlanersa constructed a beautiful little two-room temple (B 700) at the foot of the "Holy Mountain" (Gebel Barkal) and endowed it with a large pedestal decorated with fine reliefs (see p. xx) for the sacred bark (Boston 23.728). Senkamanisken completed the wall decoration of this structure and also added reliefs in Taharqo's temple at Sanam.

Aspelta, the last king of the Napatan Period to build significantly, erected shrines in the temples at Sanam and Kawa. A few repairs to the latter temple have been attributed to the much later King Harsiyotef (404-369 B.C., Gen. 23).

Not much is known about the secular architecture of the Napatan Period. Although numerous palaces were uncovered by Garstang in the city of Meroe, they all date from the Meroitic Period. Blocks bearing the names of Napatan kings found in their foundations were few and generally small. There is hardly a trace of the palaces of the Napatan rulers. These structures were of sandstone, which is subject to rapid disintegration. They were, moreover, handy sources of cut stone that could be reused in later structures. Ruins found by S. Donadoni a few years ago near Gebel Barkal could date from the Napatan era and may yield information concerning the palace architecture of that period.

SCULPTURE IN THE ROUND

As has already been said, the Kushite kings after Kashta turned to Egypt for inspiration. They had themselves represented as pharaohs and used Egyptian as their official written language. Their titulary was the same as that of the pharaohs; their robes, crowns, and much of their jewelry were modeled on those of Egyptian rulers; the attitudes in which they had themselves represented in relief and sculpture were taken over from their Egyptian predecessors. Such borrowings are surely traceable to practical political motives. It was by appearing, so to speak, in Egyptian "disguise" that these foreigners legitimized their rule in Egypt.

In fact, the Kushite sovereigns never denied their southern origin. They all bore Meroitic names and maintained close ties with the land in which they had been born and to which they returned for burial. With the Egyptian attributes of kingship, they mingled insignia brought with them from the south. Chief among these is the skullcap, a Nubian symbol of sovereignty. Russmann (1974,29ff.) traces this cap, probably incorrectly, to an Egyptian origin, but by Napatan times it had become a distinctive emblem of Sudanese kingship. A sandstone stela found at Gebel Barkal (Khartoum 1851) depicts the god Amun presenting King Piye with such a cap as well as with the Red Crown of Lower Egypt.

As with Egyptian crowns, the Nubian cap was often encircled by a diadem, and a pair of streamers hung from the back. The diadem was sometimes Egyptianized by uraei (Cat. 75). Two large uraei, rather than a single one, marked the forehead; to this rule, Cat. 71 is among the few exceptions. This practice makes it certain that every king's head with the double uraeus must be identified as Kushite and thus attributed either to Dynasty XXV or to the later Napatan Period. These two uraei are less symbols of the dual kingdoms of Upper and Lower Egypt than of the united sovereignty over Kush and Egypt, now joined under a single king.

Another feature of Napatan royal dress is the ram's-head pendant. One or three such pendants, showing the head in frontal view with a sun disk between its horns, were hung by a cord around the necks of Napatan kings. Royal earrings and other ornaments show the same motif (Cats. 98, 99), which had already developed in Napata as early as Dynasty XVIII. Probably it is to be connected with the age-old veneration of the ram in Nubia (Wildung 1973), which is also to be assumed for the Kerma culture. Small wonder that the Kushite kings, descended from long lines of pastoralists, retained this emblem, especially as it also symbolized the state god of Egypt. Unlike earlier Egyptian rulers, the Kushite kings wore the wide armbands, bracelets, and anklets (Cat. 75) typical of the Sudan, and they had their southern features naturalistically portrayed (Cats. 70, 75-77, 80-82; Fig. 24).

Kushite royal sculptures also have stylistic characteristics which, even in the absence of inscriptions, place them definitely in the Napatan era. On this basis, Russmann has been able to assign a number of heads to a definite period. Cats. 80 and 81 show features that are unmistakably Kushite and can therefore be dated definitely to the Napatan Period. In relief as well as in sculpture in the round, heads are round rather than ovoid. The faces have high cheekbones and pronounced folds, the so-called Kushite fold, on the cheeks at the sides of the nose; the lips are frequently thick and swollen (Cats. 75, 77, 82; Fig. 24).

Although foreigners had often sat on the Egyptian throne, it was only in the Napatan Period that kings caused themselves to be represented in a way that made their foreignness manifest. Egyptian sculptors were suddenly confronted with a new problem (Russmann 1968-69,87-88); they were obliged to represent the pharaoh in the traditional Egyptian manner, but they were also required to show his foreign features. The new Kushite style, which is sometimes very harsh, has been termed "brutal realism" (Bothmer 1960, xxxviii; Smith 1965a,239), but "brutal realism" exists along with two other styles. One represents the historical evolution of the Ramesside and Third Intermediate Periods; the other reflects an archaizing tendency.

Given this mixture of influences, the lack of stylistic unity in the sculpture of Dynasty XXV is understandable. Both the statuette of King Shabaqo, Cat. 75, and the head of a sphinx, Cat. 81, have the long cylindrical neck characteristic of Kushite art. The head of Taharqo, Cat. 76, and that of an unidentified Kushite ruler, Cat. 80, on the other hand, have necks that are short, compressed, and bull-like.

Many additional factors entered into the composition of Kushite art. Traditional features, local variations, and, perhaps most of all, the "signatures" of individual artists all played a role in the stylistic evolution of Kushite sculpture. We possess inadequate information, however, to trace the origins and development of the art of this period.

The oldest securely dated royal sculptures of Dynasty XXV are those of Shabaqo. That nothing hitherto found can be ascribed with certainty to Kashta or Piye may be due to the fact that neither of these kings

Fig. 24. Granite sphinx of King Taharqo (Cat. 77), from the Amun Temple at Kawa, Napatan Period, 690-664 B.C. (London BM 1770).

resided in Egypt. Shabaqo, however, transferred the royal residence to Egypt, and it is in Egypt that all royal Kushite sculpture (with a single exception) was made until the reign of Taharqo. Several sculptures representing Shabaqo have survived. The most impressive is a bronze statuette (Cat. 75), which expresses Kushite characteristics with particular clarity.[10]

No likeness clearly attributable to Shebitqo has been preserved, but Russmann (1968-69,95; 1974,16) gives cogent reasons for attributing to this king a granite head in Cairo (CG 1291; Fig. 25). In contrast, a number of works definitely representing Taharqo are known. The most important of these is a head, over life size, purchased in Luxor (Cat. 76). B. V. Bothmer believes that it was created in the Sudan. The head presents a problem. While it clearly possesses Kushite characteristics, the king's features have been refined and idealized — one might almost say they have been tamed — to conform to the canons of Egyptian royal portraiture. In contrast, a head in Copenhagen (NCG 1538; Fig. 26), probably also representing Taharqo, reveals the individualism introduced by the Kushites.

The earliest of a series of fragmentary colossal sculptures found at Gebel Barkal (Temples B 500 and B 800) is also attributed to Taharqo. Here, for the first time, a Kushite ruler is shown wearing the four-feathered crown adopted from the Egyptian god Onuris (Khartoum 1841; Fig. 27). Since this sculpture served as a model for a series of similar statues made during the Napatan Period, it deserves detailed description.

The stocky figure of the king strides, left leg forward, on a high rectangular base with rounded front. His arms are held at his sides, and in his clenched fists he grasps the so-called *Schattenstäbe*. The musculature of the legs is emphasized, indicating power and vitality. The king's head is set on a short neck; his face is round and full-cheeked; two uraei rest on his forehead, a feature occurring elsewhere in royal relief and sculpture but not in his *shawabtis* (Cats. 78, 79). His elongated eyebrows are indicated in relief, and the eyes are lengthened by cosmetic lines. The mouth is narrow and compressed, and a line following the contour of the upper lip suggests a mustache. The roughening of the stone at the wrists, on the crown, and on the sandals suggests that these parts were once gilded.

Smith (1965a,241) and Russmann (1974,17) have established a stylistic relationship between this statue and the Cairo head, Cat. 76. Both, however, regard the Gebel Barkal figure as the less subtle of the two. Russmann sees in it a "considerable diminution both in skill and in vigor," and Smith finds the statue "more smoothly and conventionally worked" than the Cairo head. There are, of course, differences between these two works of art, and certainly the Gebel Barkal statue is based on more formalistic principles. Such differences, however, are usually apparent if one compares Kushite with Egyptian works, and in my opinion the Gebel Barkal colossus has a

Fig. 25. Granite head of King Shebitqo (?), Napatan Period, 702-690 B.C. *(Cairo CG 1291).*

Fig. 26. Gray granite head of King Taharqo, Napatan Period, 690-664 B.C. *(Copenhagen NCG 1538).*

Fig. 27. Detail of a colossal granite statue of King Taharqo, from Gebel Barkal, Napatan Period, 690-664 B.C. *(Khartoum 1841).*

true stylistic personality. Statues of later kings from Gebel Barkal show the same style as Khartoum 1841. This similarity is, however, to my way of thinking, not the result of slavish imitation but simply a Napatan reflection of a characteristic Kushite style.

The granite sphinx of Taharqo from Kawa (Cat. 77; Fig. 24) shows neither the idealization of the Cairo head nor the formalism of the Gebel Barkal statue. The face of the sphinx, with its wide mouth and swollen lips, is almost brutal. Its features, however, are not to be regarded as portrait-like. The sculpture must be viewed as a provincial expression of kingship as embodied in the person of a particular ruler.

The same elements are evident in the small statues of Taharqo placed under the heads of four ram sculptures found at Kawa.[11] Although they are stylistically related to neither the Cairo head (Cat. 76) nor the Gebel Barkal statue, they are somewhat similar to the granite sphinx from Kawa. One may conclude, therefore, that three concurrent variants of the Kushite style existed during the reign of Taharqo.

The colossi that Taharqo caused to be carved into the face of the rock massif of Gebel Barkal itself (Vol. I, Fig. 50), at the foot of which the Kushite temples lie, are today so badly decayed that some scholars doubt their existence. Traces of inscriptions bearing Taharqo's name have, however, been discovered in the face of the cliff between their remnants (Arkell 1947,214f.; 1961,131; Chittick 1957a,42ff.).

Numerous small bronze statuettes of Kushite kings are known, among which are several inscribed with the name of Taharqo and others that are tentatively dated to his period (Cat.82). These figures frequently lack the customary second uraeus and the necklace with ram's-head pendant, both having been erased. Terrace (1959,48ff.) has suggested that such statuettes formed part of the equipment of the divine barks, which are also represented in reliefs of Piye and Taharqo. Similar barks were used at Thebes to carry the image of Amun from one shrine to another on certain feast days, and there is evidence that this practice was adopted by the Kushite kings.

We have already indicated that the earliest Kushite pharaohs brought a fresh impulse to art and stimulated the emergence of a new and sometimes individualistic style. While this style generally appears only in a restrained and modified form in royal sculpture, some private statues of late Dynasty XXV and early Dynasty XXVI approach true portraiture. It is noteworthy that all the personages so realistically portrayed in sculpture of this period were in some way connected with the Kushite court.

Harwa, Great Steward of the Divine Consort Amenirdas I and hence an official of considerable importance, is frankly portrayed (Cairo JE 37386; Fig.28) as a potbellied man with pronounced breasts, squatting on the ground with one leg under him. He has a deeply seamed face and a bald head.

Fig. 28. Asymmetric squatting statue of Harwa, Great Steward of the Divine Consort Amenirdas I, from Karnak, Dynasty XXV, about 700 B.C. (Cairo JE37386).

Mentuemhat, Count of Thebes and Fourth Priest of Amun, married a Kushite and played an important role in Upper Egypt at the end of Kushite rule, during the brief Assyrian occupation, and at the beginning of Dynasty XXVI. His statue (Cairo CG 647; Fig.29) is within the tradition of Kushite stylistic realism. He is represented as an old, balding man, with tufts of hair standing out at the sides of his forehead and narrow eyes peering from under heavy eyelids and bushy brows. There are deep wrinkles under his eyes and furrows in his fleshy cheeks. This far-from-flattering portrait gives the impression of an aged but still energetic and influential functionary. A third example of the "brutal realism" of Kushite art is seen in a statue of the official Iriketakana (Cat. 83).

It is rather surprising that, with the exception of a number of divine consorts, no statues of women exist in Dynasty XXV (Bothmer 1960,xxxvii), although many queens are represented in relief on temple walls.[12]

Sphinxes are rare in Dynasty XXV. In addition to the sphinx of Taharqo from Kawa (Cat. 77; Fig. 24) and a head from the sphinx of an unknown king (Cat. 81), only one other example is known (Turin 1413). This uninscribed statue resembles the Kawa sphinx. Russmann (1974,55, app. I, no. 33) believes that it may represent Taharqo.[13]

A number of other works can be attributed to Kushite rulers. Tanwetamani, the last Kushite king to rule in Egypt (Gen. 6), left three sculptures inscribed with his name.[14] One of these, the head from a statue of Amun (Cat. 84), is of very high quality, but it tells us little about Kushite portraiture. Since the artists of Dynasty XXV were unwilling to endow the gods with the likenesses of reigning kings, as was customary in Egypt, they simply idealized their representations of deities in vague conformity with prevailing Egyptian fashion. Consequently, this head of Amun, although inscribed with the name of Tanwetamani, does not help us to trace the stylistic evolution of Kushite portraiture during his reign. Two larger-than-life statues representing Tanwetamani were found in the Great Temple of Amun (B 500) at Gebel Barkal (Khartoum 1846; Toledo 49.105), but they tell us nothing about royal portraiture since the heads are missing. In type, however, and in details of dress, the statues correspond to the Gebel Barkal colossus of Taharqo, which probably served as their model.

A statue of Tanwetamani's second successor, Senkamanisken (Gen.8), from Gebel Barkal, shows the ruler in the usual Kushite royal costume (Cat. 85), but two companion figures represent him as a priest cloaked in a panther skin (Khartoum 1842; Richmond 53-30-2). These sculptures give a somewhat more brutal impression than does the statue of Taharqo, but on the whole the sculptors have adhered very closely to an already established model.

Two colossi of Senkamanisken's successor, Anlamani (Gen.9), found at Gebel Barkal, show no

Fig. 29. Detail of black granite bust of Mentuemhat, Count of Thebes and Fourth Priest of Amun under Tanwetamani, from Karnak, Dynasty XXV, about 665-650 B.C. (Cairo CG 647).

Fig. 30. Head of a colossal statue in light gray granite of an unknown Napatan king, from Gebel Barkal, fifth to fourth century B.C. *(Khartoum 5209).*

typological variations. Nevertheless, they are not identical. One (Boston 23.732) wears the four-feathered crown of Taharqo, and the somewhat idealized face resembles that king's. The neck cord with ram's-head pendants has been replaced by a broad collar, and the musculature of knees and calves is markedly stylized. The head of the second statue (Khartoum 1845) has an entirely different shape and resembles Senkamanisken more than Taharqo.

The series of royal colossi that formerly stood in the Great Temple of Amun at Gebel Barkal (B 500) ends with a figure of Aspelta (Boston 23.730), the successor of King Anlamani. It differs little in style from the Kushite sculptures already described. Only a slight variation in the treatment of the eyes tells us that this sculpture is from a different period.

In addition to the nine colossal statues of kings, Gebel Barkal has also yielded the headless statue of a queen (Khartoum 1843). It represents Queen Amanimalol of the court of Senkamanisken. She is clothed in a long robe. Her left arm lies across her body, beneath her breasts; her right arm is held at her side, and in her right hand she holds an object decorated with the head of Mut, the consort of Amun. It can perhaps be inferred that this sculpture of a queen, unique for the era following Dynasty XXV, represents the royal lady in her role as priestess of Mut.

From the later Napatan Period only two statues of kings are known, both from Gebel Barkal. The first (Boston 23.735) is of black granite and headless; the back pillar bears an inscription naming King Akhratan (353-340 B.C., Gen. 25). He wears a pleated kilt with a carefully worked, patterned belt. Neither the clavicles nor the median line of the torso is emphasized, but the navel is deeply indented and the breasts are somewhat pointed. The fine workmanship of this figure suggests an upsurge of creative activity in the late Napatan Period.

This suggestion is supported by a second royal statue of the same period found at Gebel Barkal (Khartoum 5209; Fig. 30). This figure, about 5.50 meters tall, is the largest of all Napatan statues. Moreover, in contrast to the dark granite usually employed, a light gray granite has been used. Although it does not differ typologically from other contemporary royal figures, it presents a number of stylistic variations. The king wears the Double Crown with two uraei at the forehead, a headdress seldom found in the Napatan Period. He wears a long skirt reaching to the ankles under the usual short kilt, above which his fleshy breasts are indicated by a transverse bulge. His face is full, with very large eyes and ears and a fleshy nose; the mouth is wide and full-lipped, with deep depressions at the corners. Since there are no stylistic parallels for this sculpture in Napatan or Meroitic times, it very probably dates to the fifth or fourth century B.C., a period for which no securely dated sculptures are known (Wenig 1975a,409-10, pl.411).

Only two sphinxes from the time after Taharqo are

preserved. One of these is the beautifully worked sphinx of Senkamanisken from the Great Temple of Amun (B 500) at Gebel Barkal (Cat. 86). The other, less fine, was found near Khartoum and bears the name of Aspelta (Khartoum 11777: Vercoutter 1961).

A final reference should be made to a unique statue of the god Amun with ram's head and inlaid eyes, which was found in Atlanersa's temple (B 700) at Gebel Barkal (Cat. 89). Reisner found fragments of other sculptures with inlaid eyes in the vicinity, but this practice seems to have been rare during the Napatan Period.

Very few examples of Kushite sculpture can be firmly dated after Dynasty XXV. Only the colossal statues of Kushite kings and the figure of a queen from Gebel Barkal have survived to give an idea of stylistic development during the latter part of the Napatan Period. All these statues adhere typologically to Egyptian tradition, but they show only those indigenous iconographic elements that had already found expression in royal Kushite statues at the beginning of Dynasty XXV. Only minor differences in style and execution mark the development of Napatan sculpture.

RELIEF SCULPTURE

What is true of sculpture in the round is true also of Napatan relief: artists took over the formal principles of Egyptian art to depict Kushite rulers and their subjects. The earliest royal relief is found on fragments of a stela from Elephantine (Cairo JE 41013) representing Kashta as an Egyptian pharaoh. Reliefs of Piye are more abundant. He appears on the round-topped victory stela from the Great Temple of Amun at Gebel Barkal (Cairo JE 48862) as well as on temple walls there. At the top of the stela was a large central figure of the king, now erased, standing before Amun. In two registers on each side of them are representations of vanquished Egyptian kinglets groveling in token of submission; one figure leads a captured horse cantering along on thin, elongated, muscular legs. Smith (1965a,239) thought that this scene represented an independent Kushite contribution that lent new vigor to the languishing art of Egypt.

The Piye reliefs from the Great Temple of Amun (B 500), still not fully published, show similar features. They depict rows of gods, the king and his entourage confronting priests bearing the sacred bark, groveling Egyptian princes, and men leading horses. In contrast to the horses of the stela, these animals are much larger than the men who lead them, though they are rendered in the same capricious style, with exaggeratedly long, thin legs. The legs of the men are also thin, and their round heads are set on long, cylindrical necks, so often seen in Kushite sculpture in the round. Although the horses in the relief overlap somewhat, they look as if they had been designed separately and then combined. This characteristic, particularly evident in the Piye reliefs, reappears later in the Sun Temple of Meroe (see p. 59). The scene of the bark-bearing priests, on the other hand, goes back to much earlier sources; many of its elements reflect Theban relief art of the late Ramesside Period.[15]

Iconographic innovations are also evident in representations of the royal women, who frequently appear in reliefs. They wear the long Kushite robe that tapers to a point at the back, a garb first observed on the stela from Pyramid Ku. 53 of Tabiri (Khartoum 1901). Tabiri, represented with an unusually long, cylindrical neck, was a daughter of Alara (Gen. E) and the wife of Piye (Gen. 2).

After Shabaqo, Kushite reliefs place added emphasis on the musculature of arms and legs, which are stylized in a manner resembling that of Assyrian reliefs. Since a similar stylization is evident on Egyptian monuments, especially those of the Old Kingdom, it does not seem necessary to see in this detail anything more than evidence of the antiquarian interests of the Kushite kings (Russmann 1974,23). Certain details may be the result of Assyrian influence; they may equally well be derived from Egyptian sources; or they may be independent developments.

Reliefs show certain details that seem new. The double uraei on the royal foreheads, for example, are depicted in a manner peculiar to the Kushites, previously unknown in Egypt and never appearing there after Dynasty XXV. The body of each serpent extends over the top of the head in the form of a large bow resembling a figure eight and reaches down to the nape of the neck. This detail would be very puzzling in relief work, but sculpture in the round supplies the answer (Fig. 31).

The large number of reliefs dating from Taharqo's reign includes many scenes derived from the Egyptian repertoire of traditional subjects connected with the divine kingship. Among such scenes are representations of the pharaoh in the company of the gods or making offerings to them; scenes depicting the *sed*-festival, the thirty-year jubilee of the royal accession to the throne; processions of provincial and fertility deities, offering bearers, and musicians (Griffith 1922, pls. XXIVff.; Macadam 1955, pls. 10ff.). In Kushite reliefs, special preference is given to a scene showing the king being suckled or "mothered" by a goddess (Cat. 71), a motif found not only on reliefs but on cult objects such as a bronze aegis of the time of Kashta (Leclant 1963,77ff.). The divine wet-nurses include Mut, Bastet, and Isis, and in a single notable exception (Cat. 95), even a Kushite queen is shown at the breast of a goddess.

A relief in Temple T at Kawa reproduces a scene borrowed from Egypt but long since out of use there. It represents the king as sphinx trampling upon his enemies (Vol. I, Fig. 58). Craftsmen brought by Taharqo from Memphis to Kawa were familiar with the monumental buildings of their homeland and with the scenes on the walls of the funerary temples of Sahura and Pepy II, from which they drew inspiration. Thus, the representation of a Libyan prince conquered by Sahura, already used as a model by Pepy II for his funerary temple, again reappears

Fig. 31. Detail of a bronze statuette of King Shabaqo (Cat. 75), Napatan Period, 716-702 B.C. *(Athens 632).*

Fig. 32. Relief from Kawa with three men and a horse wearing a wide-brimmed sun-hat, Napatan Period, 690-664 B.C. *(Oxford 1931.551).*

after nearly two thousand years in a place far up the Nile from Memphis.

Kushite artists and artisans had a vast store of themes at their disposal for the decoration of the temples at Kawa and Sanam. Nevertheless, new elements crept into their work. Blocks from Sanam depict horsemen and soldiers in two-wheeled chariots drawn by horses. A frieze from the same temple shows carts with one, two, and even three wheels, pulled by donkeys or oxen. A horse depicted on a block from Kawa wears a wide-brimmed sun-hat (Oxford 1931.551; Fig. 32). This is an exceptional thematic variation, for the Memphite artists employed at Kawa usually leaned heavily on traditions of the ancient Egyptian capital. Their workmanship was technically superior to that of the Sanam artisans, who created several less traditional scenes.

Five stelae of Taharqo were found at Kawa (Kawa III-VII), all decorated differently. On one (Kawa V), the king is twice shown presenting offerings, once to a human-headed Amun and a second time to a ram-headed Amun. In each case, the ruler is accompanied by his mother, Abara. These scenes were taken over in the stelae of later kings (see p.60 and Cat.72).

Aside from stelae, little remains of the decoration of the pyramid chapels. Although the walls of most of them were originally adorned with reliefs, only a few blocks have been preserved, and it is thus impossible to trace a developmental sequence. The principal motif of every long wall was a representation of the enthroned king facing the entrance of the chapel. Before him a priest presents an offering; behind him are members of the royal family or inscribed funerary texts. Other chapel reliefs depict artisans (Pyramid Nu. 6 of King Anlamani, Gen. 9, for example) or offering bearers (Pyramid Nu. 15 of King Nastasen, 335-315 B.C., Gen. 27). A block from the chapel of King Akhratan (Nu. 14, Gen. 25) shows a carefully executed sun disk flanked by uraei in raised relief. This elaborate detail may indicate a continuous development or it may indicate a rejuvenation of art in the late Napatan Period, though from Aspelta to Akhratan there is little evidence to support the latter theory.

Temple reliefs later than Dynasty XXV have almost totally disappeared. From Temple B 700 at Gebel Barkal, begun by Atlanersa and completed by Senkamanisken, we have only drawings, made by nineteenth-century travelers, of reliefs that have since been destroyed (Griffith 1929). These drawings are of interest chiefly because they reproduce portraits of queens, who all wear a headdress consisting of one or more topknots (Fig. 33), a coiffure that also occurs on a Kushite stela of Dynasty XXV (Habachi 1977) and reappears in somewhat different form in the Meroitic Period (Cats. 125, 128).

A pedestal for the sacred bark that Atlanersa (Gen. 7) presented to Temple B 700 is one of the outstanding works of art of the Napatan Period (Boston 23.728; Fig. 34). Beautifully cut reliefs representing

Fig. 33. Nineteenth-century drawing of a now destroyed relief scene on the inner face of the pylon of Temple B 700 begun by King Atlanersa, Napatan Period, 653-643 B.C., *at Gebel Barkal (by Major Orlando Felix, from a manuscript of Lord Prudhoe, 1829).*

Fig. 34. Pedestal for the sacred bark of Amun installed by King Atlanersa in Temple B 700 at Gebel Barkal, Napatan Period, 653-643 B.C. *(Boston 23.728).*

the unification of Egypt through the gods Horus and Seth appear on the front, and the heraldic plants of the Two Lands, the lotus and the papyrus, are entwined around the hieroglyphic sign for "unification." By using these symbolic motifs, Atlanersa still laid claim to sovereignty over Egypt. Stylistically, these reliefs belong entirely within a Napatan tradition reaching back to Dynasty XXV. This is evident in the figure of the king above the symbol for "unification," which represents the ruler supporting the sky itself. The stylistic features typical of Kushite art are present here: the round head of the king, his long, cylindrical neck and level shoulders, and the prominent muscles of his arms and legs, all bespeak his origin. The king wears, in addition to the kilt, a long coat reaching almost to his calves. This garment appears in a Nubian sculpture of later date (Khartoum 5209), but the prototype is Egyptian.

The reliefs of the so-called Sun Temple at Meroe, which Garstang excavated (1909-10) and connected with a tale told by Herodotus (3.17) are of quite a different sort. According to Herodotus, there was a meadow on the outskirts of Meroe where cooked meat was placed by officials for anyone who wished to partake of it. This meadow was called the Table of the Sun, and thus a temple erected here was called by Garstang the Sun Temple, an inaccurate name for a temple consisting of a single room or cella (Fig. 35). We have no idea who was worshipped in this modest structure surrounded by a row of columns, but a stela of King Aspelta (Gen. 10), now lost, which was discovered there, provides a clue for dating the temple. Representations on its outer walls depart strikingly from the subjects long familiar in Kush. They consist mainly of scenes of triumph, which are found neither in the few extant reliefs of the Napatan Period nor in those of the Meroitic Period. On the south wall is a row of Kushite soldiers slaughtering unnamed enemies, who are represented in much smaller scale. On the north wall is a long procession of cattle, horse-drawn carts, women with children, men walking and dancing, and musicians. The scenes on the outside of the back wall (Fig. 36) never occur in Egyptian temples. They show a seated king with a smaller man standing before him. Behind the king, however, stands a person much larger than the ruler himself. The facade of a kiosk with four columns forms a background for this scene; perhaps it represents a structure, now vanished, which stood in front of the Sun Temple. Two additional registers hint at some long-forgotten war. In the top register are running soldiers; the lower register shows horsemen, lances in hand, the ends of ample cloths wrapped around their shoulders.

This small temple displays a mingling of old and new motifs, some of them difficult to interpret, indicating that during the reign of Aspelta the Kingdom of Kush reached a height of artistic production. The style of the reliefs on the south wall is strongly reminiscent of that of the Piye reliefs in the Great Temple of Amun at Gebel Barkal (B 500). In both temples, the groups of figures seem

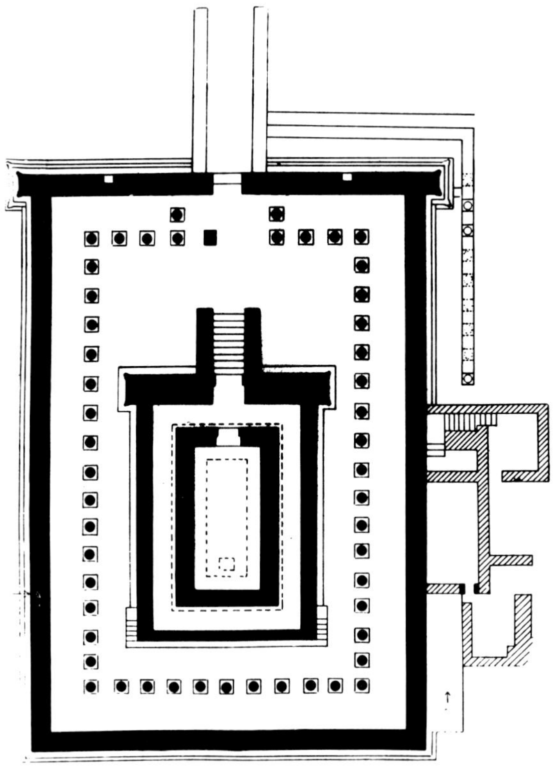

Fig. 35. Ground plan of the Sun Temple at Meroe, Napatan Period, probably early sixth century B.C.

to have been executed as individual scenes, with no organic connection between them.

The reliefs are undoubtedly Napatan, presumably dating from the reign of Aspelta.[16] That there are certain stylistic differences between the Sun Temple reliefs and other reliefs of Aspelta's time does not preclude this opinion; a similar stylistic dichotomy has already been observed in sculpture in the round. One stylistic tendency derived from the Piye reliefs of Gebel Barkal remained operative in the reliefs of the Sun Temple. A second tendency adhered to a style that emerged in Egypt under Shabaqo and Shebitqo and was continued under Taharqo and Atlanersa; examples of this tradition are found at Gebel Barkal.

The still unpublished reliefs excavated by Garstang in the later palaces at Meroe, which can certainly be assigned on the basis of their partly preserved names to the Napatan Period, bear witness to the stylistic excellence of that era (Fig. 37). There were many themes to draw upon, and the Kushite artists interpreted them in a very lively manner.

In the period following Dynasty XXV, two groups of royal stelae were erected. The first group consists of the official records of kings set up in temples. The second consists of the stelae placed at the rear of the funerary chapels of their pyramids. The representations on the stelae of these two groups naturally differ according to their use. Most of the temple stelae follow the pattern established by Taharqo. They present scenes that are almost identical: a king approaches, from the left and from the right, a central figure of Amun, who is represented in one instance with a ram's head and in the other with a human head; the king is accompanied in one instance by his wife and in the other by his mother. This pattern occurs on the stelae of Tanwetamani (Cairo JE 48863; Vol. I, Fig. 53), Anlamani (Copenhagen NCG 1709), Harsiyotef (Cairo JE 48864; Vol. I, Fig. 54), and Nastasen (Cat. 72). The decoration of the two temple stelae of Aspelta (Cairo JE 48865-6) departs completely from this model.

The royal stelae from the cemetery at Nuri can be divided into three successive groups. To the first and earliest group belongs the monumental granite stela of King Anlamani (Gen. 9), on which the king is represented in bold raised relief standing before the enthroned Osiris (Boston, not registered "G"). Under Aspelta (Gen. 10) appears a new type of decoration, in which the king approaches from the right with hands raised in worship of

Fig. 36. Scene on the outside back wall of the Sun Temple at Meroe, Napatan Period, probably early sixth century B.C.

Osiris, who is accompanied by Isis and Anubis. This pattern is followed in sunk relief on the stelae of King Amaniastabarqo (510-487 B.C., Gen. 16) and King Siaspiqa (487-468 B.C., Gen. 17). All these stelae are approximately the same height (1.35 meters).

King Talakhamani (Gen. 20) built a very small pyramid (Nu. 16) with a correspondingly small stela only about fifty-five centimeters high. This stela shows a condensed version of the scene described above, omitting the figure of Anubis and showing the deceased ruler before Osiris and Isis. The stelae of King Baskakeren from Nu. 17 (Gen. 22), Queen Batahaliye from Nu. 44 (Cat. 74), and King Amanibakhi (340-335 B.C., Gen. 26) all show this scene in bold raised relief. It is only in the stela of Queen Sakhmakh, the wife of Nastasen (Cat. 73), that a return is made to sunk relief — more precisely, to incised pictures.

MINOR ARTS

The royal burials of the cemetery of El Kurru yielded a wide variety of objects. Though the most valuable had been carried off by tomb robbers, enough remains to give an idea of the wealth and taste of the Napatan aristocracy. A few of the queens' burials, overlooked by plunderers, yielded objects of gold and bronze that rank among the most beautiful works created in the entire Nile Valley and give an idea of the artistic taste of the Kushite artisans and the royal patrons for whom they labored.

A queen's collar made of thin gold sheets (Cat. 96) and a crystal ball surmounted by a golden Hathor head (Cat. 93; Vol. I, Frontis.) come from these burials. There is also the figurine of a ram-headed sphinx seated on a column inlaid in colored glass (Cat. 94; Frontis.), a technique that reached high perfection in Meroitic times. A unique amulet in silver gilt (Cat. 95) shows the goddess Isis suckling a queen — a privilege usually enjoyed only by kings. A bronze object of amazing size and perfection is a bed leg in the form of a squatting goose (Cat. 91; Fig. 19); this is a purely Egyptian motif applied to the uniquely Kushite funerary bed. Several bronze mirrors have been found. A unique example (Boston 21.318) with a handle shaped like a palm trunk encircled by four goddesses comes from the burial of King Shabaqo (Gen. 3). It evidently established a precedent, for two more mirrors of the same type but from a later period have been found. One of them (Cat. 115) dates from the time of Amani-natake-lebte (538-519 B.C., Gen. 14) and the other from the time of Nastasen (Gen. 27) in the late

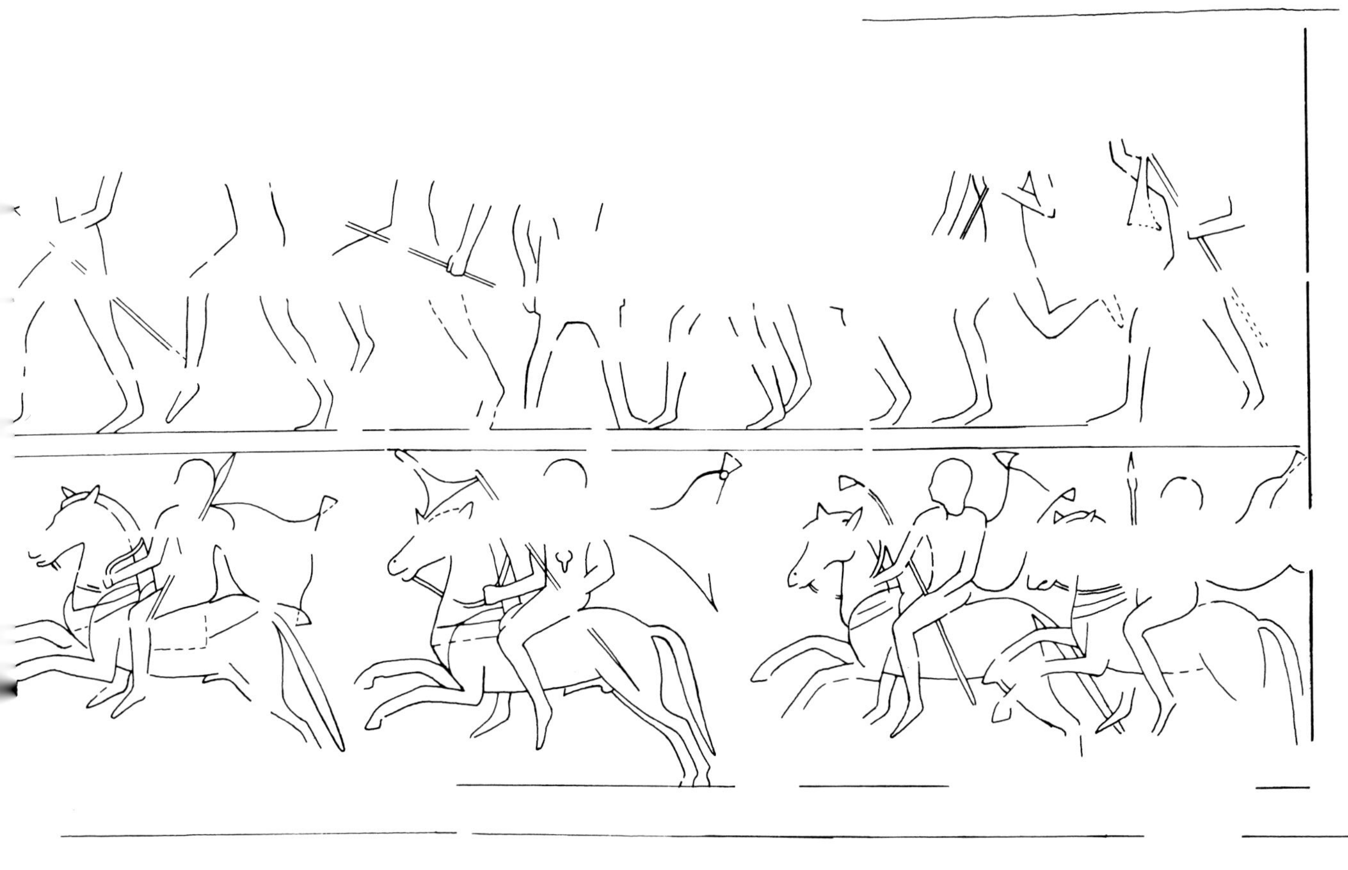

Fig. 37. Block decorated with men's heads, from a palace at Meroe, Napatan Period, sixth to fourth century B.C.

fourth century B.C. Although Egyptian deities stand around the column-shaped handles of these mirrors, there appear to be no Egyptian parallels for them; they bespeak a truly Sudanese concept.

All these objects are outstanding not only because of their technical perfection but also, and chiefly, because they present forms and motifs that are characteristically Sudanese. Although some of their elements are Egyptian in origin, the manner in which they are used and combined is Sudanese. No Egyptian parallels have been found for any of these objects. A tall bronze object (Cat. 92) from the burial of Piye is also unique. Although it has been described as a libation stand, it may be a lamp.

Conventional works were also produced in Kushite workshops. These include countless amulets (Cats. 103-108) and scarabs and scaraboids (Cat. 117), but, strangely enough, not a single *shawabti* was found in the fifteen hundred graves excavated in the popular cemetery of Sanam, although many were discovered in royal burials (Cats. 78, 79, 87). This seems to indicate that the servant figurines known as *shawabtis* were restricted to the use of the royal dead; and indeed it is clear from the funerary equipment in general that there was a great distinction between the Kushite ruling classes and the common people of Napatan times.

In summary, there is no doubt that Kushite art, although based on Egyptian models, had a unique character of its own. It originated with the Kushite advance into Egypt and flourished well into the reign of Aspelta. After a brief period of decline, an artistic rejuvenation is observable in the late Napatan Period, coupled with the increased affluence of the kingdom, until finally, the center of Kushite art shifted south to the new royal residence at Meroe. There, in the early third century B.C., Kushite art underwent fundamental changes.

9. At Old Dongola was discovered an altar block bearing his name (Jakobielski 1973, pl. 32).
10. A small faience head, probably of the same king, in the Louvre (A.F. 6639) and a quartzite head in Munich (ÄS 4859) are, in contrast, somewhat idealized and hence show more Egyptian influence.
11. Khartoum 1581 and 2682; London 1770; Oxford 1931.553.
12. Among the sculptures in the round representing a divine consort, only two may be mentioned: the beautiful alabaster figure of Amenirdas I (Cairo CG 565) and the granite sphinx of Shepenwepet II (Berlin/DDR 7972).
13. In this connection, we might cite a small bronze sphinx of that ruler now in Paris (Louvre E. 3916: Russmann 1974, 19, 58, app.II, no. 3, fig. 14).
14. Although Russmann (1968-69, 101ff.) has attributed the uninscribed sphinx head (Cat. 81) to Tanwetamani, it is still not certain whether it actually represents that ruler or is simply the more or less stereotyped portrait of a king as sphinx.
15. Particularly strong parallels may be found in the famous relief at Karnak which shows the High Priest Amenhotep standing before a statue of Ramesses IX (Smith 1965a, pl. 161). The bark-bearers in the Gebel Barkal relief, however, have the elongated cylindrical necks that are characteristic of Kushite style.
16. Hofmann (1975b, 513ff.) assumed that the reliefs of the Sun Temple originated in the first century A.D. and were therefore Meroitic. I find this view impossible on stylistic grounds.

the Meroitic Period

An event of great political significance is reflected in the transfer of the royal cemetery from Napata to Meroe at about 270 B.C. It is possible that there occurred at this time a great dynastic shift (see Vol. I, pp. 94-95). Whatever the reasons, the transfer of the royal cemetery coincided with important cultural and artistic developments that marked the beginning of the Meroitic Period of the Kingdom of Kush. In contrast to the Napatan Period, the Meroitic Period was characterized by its growing independence of Egyptian models. Southern influence became more apparent, and a new, indigenous script gradually supplanted Egyptian hieroglyphs as the official written language.

The process of change, which resulted in a profound transformation in art, may have begun in the southern Butana region. Meroitic art was produced throughout the kingdom, from Lower Nubia in the north to the vicinity of the Sixth Cataract in the south, from the third century B.C. to the fourth century A.D.[17] Meroitic objects have also been found in graves near Sennar, hundreds of kilometers south of Khartoum on the Blue Nile. Until it has been established that the city of Sennar belonged to the Kushite kingdom, it is impossible to tell if these objects were made locally or came here by trade.[18]

The new style in art appeared much earlier in the south than at Napata. The earliest known example dates from the fourth to the early third century B.C. and was found in Room 108 of the Great Enclosure at Musawwarat es-Sufra. It is an unfinished column base in the form of an elephant and a lion (Fig. 38).[19]

The Temple of Apedemak at Musawwarat es-Sufra, built by King Arnekhamani about 225 B.C., is the earliest Meroitic work that can be dated with certainty, on the basis of its inscriptions, which are still written in Egyptian.

An important circumstance that has necessarily affected research is the relatime scarcity of objects dating from the Meroitic Period, which covers six hundred years. Meroitic palaces and temples were generally built of very soft sandstone, a material that succumbs relatively quickly to wind and weather. Moreover, buildings were torn down even in ancient times to supply material for new structures. While Lower Nubia has been thoroughly investigated, excavations in the area south of the Second Cataract have been generally restricted to the temples at Gebel Barkal, the pyramids at Napata and Meroe, the city of Meroe, and the ruins at Musawwarat es-Sufra.

Meroitic art has seldom been treated scientifically. It was not until the expeditions that followed the Archaeological Survey of Nubia (1907-11) that a relatively clear picture of the cultural development of the territories south of Aswan emerged (for a history of early research, see Vol. I, Chapter 3). The art of this area, however, remained largely ignored. Remarkable though this may seem, this lack of interest in art was probably, at least in part, the result of an exaggerated predilection for what was regarded as the superior culture and art of Egypt. A change of perspective became possible only when investigators finally began to observe Nubia and the northern Sudan as unique entities that had developed independently of Egypt. This transformation of perspective brought with it an increased interest in Meroitic art. Our knowledge of this art has been greatly increased by recent publications, though it is still in its infancy.

Given the present state of our knowledge, Meroitic art can be said to have the following features. Its primary characteristic is its lack of stylistic unity. So far, five styles can be distinguished, which may have coexisted to some extent or may have succeeded one another or may reflect regional variations. The absence of a fixed canon of style makes it difficult to group and to date material. Iconography is presently the sole tool we have for the identification and attribution of works of art.

The five stylistic groups may be described as follows:

Group I: Works belonging to this group continue the traditions of Napatan art and reveal few specifically Meroitic features. This style occurs only in official art and belongs to the early Meroitic Period; no works in this style can be dated later than the first century A.D.

Group II: In contrast to the works of Group I, some monuments of Group II are decidedly Egyptian in style. They consist only of reliefs from buildings erected about A.D. 20 by King Natakamani on behalf of the Egyptian gods Amun and Isis.[20] Temple reliefs found by P. L. Shinnie in 1974 and 1975 in the city of Meroe, (Fig. 39), although they show some stylistic variation, can probably also be placed in this group.

Group III contains works expressing independent Meroitic features. All are official, and date from the fourth or early third century B.C.[21] These works demonstrate with particular clarity the changes in iconography and in the proportions of the human figure that accompanied the development of Meroitic art.

Group IV comprises the so-called *ba*-statues and reserve heads, almost all of which were found in Lower Nubia. They represent officials and priests, personages who were not members of the royal family. Since they reflect a local burial practice, they belong to the sphere of unofficial art.[22] They cannot be compared stylistically with any other Meroitic art form. These statues and heads present a great variety of types and display no stylistic unity. On the basis of our current knowledge, we must place the *ba*-statues somewhere in the period between the first and the fourth century A.D.; most of them probably date from the second or third centuries.

Group V, apparently produced during a short span of time, was strongly influenced by Hellenistic art, principally from Alexandria.[23] These works probably reflect a passing fashion.

The common denominator in the works of these five, often disparate, stylistic groups is not simply the fact that they were created during the Meroitic Period by Meroites in the Kingdom of Kush. Just as we were able to determine specific stylistic characteristics of Kushite art of the Napatan Period, we can also recognize specific features in Meroitic art. In sculpture and relief representations of human beings, we find such features as exceptionally broad, usually level shoulders, long, columnar necks, and round heads. These features appear in all five stylistic groups, albeit employed with great variation.[24]

The reasons for stylistic variation are manifold, an important one being the clear distinction between the art of the south, from whence most official works come, and that of the north. This distinction does not preclude the creation of official works in the north; it merely reflects the fact that such works are rare.[25]

Meroitic artists were unusually receptive to external influences. Such receptivity, a basic feature of their art, is another reason for its lack of stylistic unity, especially in Group V. Unusual architectural forms, such as column-statues and animal-form bases, may perhaps be traced to influences from the Near East, but Meroitic artists knew how to absorb, adapt, and combine foreign elements to create new works of undeniably Meroitic character.

Meroitic art has a limited repertoire. Although more types may emerge with the excavation of cemeteries and settlements south of the Second Cataract, the picture will probably not be altered significantly.

Another notable feature of Meroitic art is the rarity of inscriptions. This is particularly striking when compared with Egyptian and earlier Kushite art. While inscriptions are found with some frequency on temple walls, they are usually very brief, and inscriptions on statues are extremely rare. This circumstance has contributed to the uncertainty of interpretation and dating of Meroitic works.

Finally, Meroitic art is characterized by the creation of new themes and motifs. A description of several motifs may help to emphasize the creativity of Meroitic artists and to reveal the basic qualities of their art.

Column-statues, which first appear in this period, serve an architectural purpose, though they should be regarded as sculptures.[26] They always represent the deities Sebiumeker and Arensnuphis, two Meroitic gods who functioned as protectors of temples, always standing as a pair at temple entrances (Fig. 40; Wenig 1974; see p. 85).[27]

Column bases in the form of animals, which have so far been discovered only in the Great Enclosure at Musawwarat es-Sufra (Fig. 38), are also an outstanding development of Meroitic art. We know, however, that animals appeared as column bases in earlier works from the Near East. Meroitic artists endowed such figures with their own peculiar stylistic forms. The animal-form bases quite possibly represent a type of art that was limited exclusively to Musawwarat es-Sufra. We should note, however, that bases in the form of lions and elephants, like the column-statues, appeared at a time when the Kushite art of Napata was still flourishing. The base from Room 108 of the Great Enclosure at Musawwarat

Fig. 38. Unfinished column base in the form of an elephant and a lion in the Great Enclosure at Musawwarat es-Sufra, Meroitic Period, fourth to early third century B.C.

Fig. 39. Kandake Amanitore before the ram-headed Amun, from Temple M720 at Meroe, Meroitic Period, early first century A.D. *(Khartoum, Sudan National Museum).*

Fig. 40. Reconstruction of the facade of Temple 300 in the Great Enclosure at Musawwarat es-Sufra, with statues of the gods Arensnuphis and Sebiumeker, Meroitic Period, late third century B.C.

Fig. 41. Triple-protome from the Apedemak Temple at Musawwarat es-Sufra, Meroitic Period, probably second century B.C. *(Khartoum 18890).*

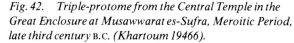

Fig. 42. Triple-protome from the Central Temple in the Great Enclosure at Musawwarat es-Sufra, Meroitic Period, late third century B.C. *(Khartoum 19466).*

es-Sufra (Fig. 38) is contemporary with the column-statues from the same room.[28]

Also unique are the so-called triple-protomes, rectangular blocks with sculpted human and animal heads, that were set into the walls above temple entrances. Like the animal-form bases, they have been discovered only at Musawwarat es-Sufra, where they were found not only in the Great Enclosure but also in the Apedemak Temple of Arnekhamani. Two of these triple-protomes from the Apedemak Temple (Cat. 145; Vol. I, Fig. 65; and Khartoum 18890; Fig. 41) consist of a ram's head flanked by lion's heads. The lions represent the gods Arensnuphis and Sebiumeker and, like the column-statues, they functioned as protectors of temples. The inclusion of the ram, the sacred animal of Amun, is explained by this deity's position as the Meroitic state god. Another triple-protome shows the ram's head flanked by the human heads of Arensnuphis and Sebiumeker (Khartoum 19466; Fig. 42). Still another work juxtaposes the heads of two goddesses, probably Hathor and Isis, with that of the ram. We shall be able to determine whether or not these triple-protomes represent a local art form only when sites such as Naqa have been excavated.

A hypothesis alleging Indian influence on the art of Meroe is based chiefly on three isolated representations. One, a god riding an elephant, appears on a column in the Temple of Apedemak at Musawwarat es-Sufra. Another, on the rear wall of the Temple of Apedemak at Naqa, is probably the most unusual work in all of Meroitic art. It shows the god Apedemak with four arms and three heads (Fig. 43). King Natakamani and Kandake (Queen) Amanitore approach the deity from left and right, each accompanied by the crown prince. There are absolutely no grounds for supposing that this representation was influenced by Indian art (Wenig 1973a; Žabkar 1975a). The scene suggests, rather, a combination of two figures standing back to back to receive the royal persons. Such representations are known in Egyptian art and are frequently found on royal Napatan stelae (see p. 60 and Cat. 72). Looking at this work more carefully, we can see that the two figures have not merely been joined together but have been fused into one, and for aesthetic reasons, a third head, rendered in front view, has been added to conceal the joining of the other two heads. It should be remembered, moreover, that deities with multiple heads were not unknown to the Meroites, and they were frequently represented in Egypt. This sculpture illustrates, however, a significant artistic achievement in that two figures, once placed back to back for purposes of symmetry, were fused into one figure. Neither Egyptian nor Napatan artists had undertaken such a synthesis.

The third example thought to indicate Indian influence occurs on the narrow side of a pylon in the Temple of Apedemak at Naqa. It shows a lion-headed serpent (Fig. 44) rising from the calyx of a flower. However, the combination of a lion's head and a serpent's body is a purely Meroitic motif, which has also been

Fig. 43. The god Apedemak shown with four arms and three heads on the outside back wall of the Apedemak Temple at Naqa, Meroitic Period, early first century A.D.

found at Semna (Žabkar 1975a,44ff.). The motif of a god on a flower had been known in Egypt from earliest times. Thus, if we are to speak of influence, we should probably look to Egyptian and not to Indian sources. In any event, Meroitic artists reshaped and adapted the flower-and-serpent motif in a highly individualistic manner.

Scenes which depict apparently sacred activities also occur in Meroitic art. A frieze from the north interior wall of the Apedemak Temple at Musawwarat es-Sufra shows men holding a large piece of cloth and standing beside a cow. The activity hidden by the cloth is inexplicable. The scene is reminiscent of the painting of a naked couple on a pot fragment found at Meroe (Cat. 220), where some sort of action is also obscured by a piece of fabric.

Among the iconographic innovations in Meroitic art is the faithful rendition of the royal costume. We must, however, regard representations of kings wearing the Egyptian royal kilt as holdovers, for this garment had long been out of fashion in Egypt as well as in Meroe. On the walls of the Apedemak Temple at Musawwarat es-Sufra, a king is represented wearing what became the costume of ruling kings and queens (Fig. 45). It consists of a long gown reaching to the ankles, a narrowly pleated sash draped across the right shoulder and covering the chest, and long tasseled stjamers, which hang from the shoulders and reach, in front and back, to the calves. In addition, the king wears typically Meroitic jewelry, such as a band with a scaraboid on the upper arm. Such scaraboids sometimes show four ram's heads and two frog's legs (Fig. 45). The royal headdress usually consists of a diadem with two uraei at the forehead and two wide streamers in back. Other crowns are sometimes also worn.

The lack of stylistic unity in Meroitic art does not mean that there was no stylistic development. This is most clearly visible in works of Group III, in which native Meroitic features are most prominent.

There appears to have been a gradual simplification of forms combined with increasing emphasis on a few specific elements. In the rendering of faces, increased stress was placed upon eyes, a process culminating in the *ba*-statues. Naturalism was abandoned in favor of simplification moving toward abstraction. This process is clearly evident when one compares the lion heads of Cat. 145 with that of Cat. 147. In the first case, the details are clearly, if schematically, rendered. In Cat. 147, however, the animal's face has been reduced to an abstracted form, and is therefore datable to the late Meroitic Period.

The amplitude of queens' figures is characteristic of later Meroitic (compare Fig. 46 with Cat. 135).[29] In contrast, the figures of goddesses are always slender.

In the first century B.C., works of Group I, the continuation of the Napatan style, become rare. At the same time, significant changes occur in the proportions of

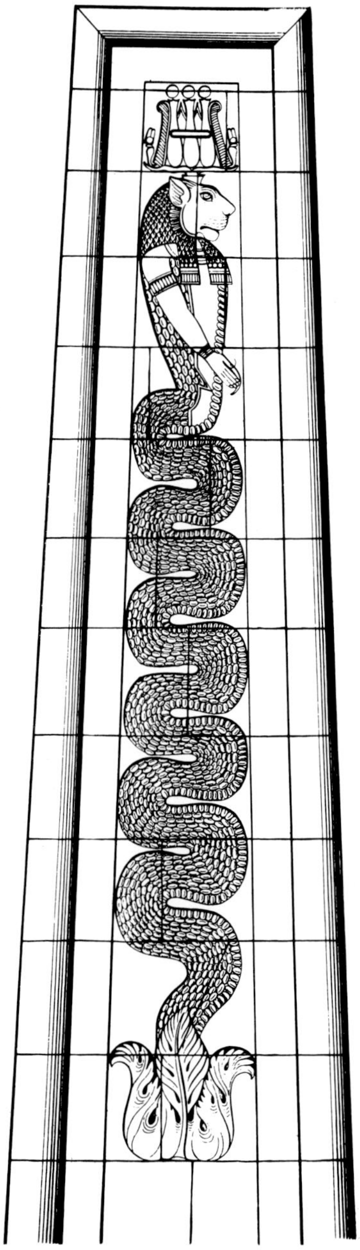

Fig. 44. Lion-headed serpent rising from a flower on the south side of the south tower of the pylon of the Apedemak Temple at Naqa, Meroitic Period, early first century A.D.

Fig. 45. Representation of King Arnekhamani wearing the costume of ruling kings and queens on the south outside wall of the Apedemak Temple at Musawwarat es-Sufra, Meroitic Period, 235-218 B.C.

Fig. 46. Kandake Amanitore on the rear outside wall of the Apedemak Temple at Naqa, Meroitic Period, early first century A.D.

human figures in both relief and in statuary, which provide important criteria for dating. Originally, figures were slender, frequently much more slender than is consistent with nature. Such attenuation can be seen mainly in works dating from the third and second centuries B.C.,[30] but in the first century B.C. figures become more compressed and compact, producing a rather dumpy effect.[31]

Iconography is a very important factor in tracing the development of Meroitic art and in identifying individual objects. We have learned, for example, that many details, especially types of clothing, were restricted to certain personages. Robes with trains usually signified gods, and with a single exception, kings were never represented as bearded (Wenig 1974). In the course of time, changes occurred, not only in style and proportion, but also in iconographic details. Conclusions can be drawn regarding date once such changes are recognized. Even the ceremonial attire of Meroitic rulers was subject to change. The royal sash was originally very narrow,[32] but during the course of the first century B.C. it grew wider in keeping with the new proportions of the figures, and achieved its greatest width in the first century A.D.[33]

Further iconographic study will allow many as yet undated objects to be placed in sequence, and this in turn will make it easier to trace and evaluate the development of Meroitic art.

ARCHITECTURE

Evidence of secular architecture comes primarily from scattered dwellings and a few settlements in Lower Nubia. Most of the population probably lived in round huts with roofs of straw or grass, similar to those of their ancestors (and those still being built today).[34]

It was only as a result of excavations undertaken in connection with the recent archaeological campaign that Meroitic settlements with more ambitious structures were uncovered. Two unusual building complexes were found on the Island of Gaminarti in the region of the Second Cataract (Adams—Nordström 1963,26-27). These asymmetrical complexes containing, respectively, eleven and twenty-one rooms were constructed of mud-brick. The walls were approximately thirty-five centimeters thick and perhaps originally reached a height of two meters. In both installations were living units consisting of one long and one short room. The entrance to the living unit was generally in the exterior wall, there being no interior connection between the apartments. In the larger room of each unit were hearth and cooking vessels. Careful investigation of the walls of these installations proved that the living units were built at different times, which explains the asymmetrical ground plan of the complexes.[35]

Two other Lower Nubian settlements of the first to the third centuries A.D. at Arminna West (Trigger 1967) and Ash-Shaukan present a somewhat different picture.[36]

The houses of the latter settlement have symmetrical, rectangular ground plans containing three to five rooms and a court. According to Jacquet (1971,121ff.), the houses of Ash-Shaukan, carefully constructed of sun-dried mud-bricks approximately sixty centimeters in width, lay very close to one another, separated by a few centimeters only. Narrow pathways provided access to the living quarters. The foundations were sometimes of brick, sometimes of stone. The rooms were plastered and whitewashed; the floors were of firmly tamped earth; the spring-vaulted roof was made of bricks approximately five centimeters in thickness. Barrel-shaped houses existed in Nubia as early as the New Kingdom and continued to be built there until very recently. The door frames were carefully made of wood or stone. Window-like slits placed fairly high on the walls of the narrow sides of the rooms provided light and air. Some, probably official, buildings had much larger windows.[37]

The interior walls of the living quarters at Ash-Shaukan contained many niches of varied form (Jacquet 1971,125, fig. 31), most of which served as repositories for household objects. Some, however, were shallow and placed out of reach; these were devoted no doubt to other purposes. Jacquet believes that these latter may have played some part in the house cult. Traces of red bands have been found on the upper parts of interior walls and also outlining the niches in imitation of wooden frames.

A simpler kind of house, found in both the north and the south, had walls made of layers of flat stones. Such houses, mostly from the late Meroitic Period, were less carefully built than the brick structures. Houses found in the city of Meroe, belonging to high officials and priests, were substantially larger than those described above. Stone bathtubs bespeak a level of comfort not previously known beyond the precincts of the royal residence.

Houses and workrooms of late Meroitic ironsmiths, which Shinnie found during his excavations, have not yet been published but will undoubtedly yield much new information concerning the little-known living conditions of workmen.

Palace installations were found by Garstang at Meroe and by Vercoutter at Wad Ban Naqa (Vercoutter 1962,263ff., esp. 278ff.). The buildings in the Meroe residence were constructed mainly of hewn sandstone blocks, which apparently replaced the small blocks used during the Napatan Period. Since almost no relief decoration was found in Meroitic palaces, we must assume that the inner walls of these buildings were plastered and painted (Cat. 132).

The palace of Wad Ban Naqa had unusually thick walls of sun-dried brick. The structure was approximately square in plan, each side about sixty-one meters long. More than forty, mostly rectangular, rooms were found on the ground floor, in addition to many narrow passages. Each side of the structure had an entrance, but the main portal was on the south. It led into an entrance hall containing six sandstone columns with capitals in the form of lotus flowers, similar to those found in Egypt. Some of the capitals are provided with four groups of three closely spaced ram's heads crowned with sun disks. To judge from the large finds of ivory, wood, and pottery, most of the rooms uncovered probably served as storerooms. The living quarters must have been situated on the upper floor. Part of a staircase, as well as fragments of fallen sandstone columns, permit the assumption that the building was at least two stories high. Although we have no idea how the upper story looked, it must have included a relatively large columned hall, which perhaps served as an audience chamber. That thin relief slabs covered with gold leaf probably lined the walls of this hall is evident from preserved fragments, one of which depicts a queen offering a necklace (Vercoutter 1962, fig. 11 on 282); another shows the head of a royal personage (Cat. 123) and bears remnants of Meroitic inscriptions with the name of Queen Amanishakheto (ibid. fig. 12 on 283). On the basis of this evidence, the palace has been dated to the late first century B.C.

Another secular building found at Wad Ban Naqa is a large round structure with walls 3.70 meters thick and an inner diameter of 12.70 meters. These walls, preserved to a height of about 5 meters, are made of fired and unfired brick, plastered only on the outside. The building, probably once domed, is approached by a ramp on the west side (Vercoutter 1962,274). The purpose of this unique structure remains a mystery. The excavator believes that it was in some way associated with the nearby Temple of Isis; he considers parallels to Indian temple towers (ibid. 298-99), but this interpretation is not plausible (Wenig 1973a). Certain investigators believe the building to be a granary (Nur 1962,76) or an observatory. Neither view can be verified. All we can say at present is that nothing comparable exists anywhere else in the Nile Valley.

Funerary architecture survives primarily in the form of pyramids belonging to rulers and their families, most of which were erected quite near the city of Meroe (Fig. 47). For a brief period during the first century B.C., the royal cemetery was once again transferred to Gebel Barkal (Wenig 1973b), a move probably undertaken in connection with certain policies of the royal house directed toward the northern part of the kingdom.

The Meroitic pyramids are not distinguished in any essential way from those of the Napatan Period; there are only superficial changes in form and construction. The most important innovation appeared in the course of the first century A.D., when outside access to the burial chamber was eliminated. Since the burial chamber was directly under the pyramid, construction of the superstructure could not begin until after the burial had taken place. In the course of time, the royal burial installations grew steadily smaller and less carefully constructed. This did not preserve them, however, from tomb robbers; they were all plundered, and so we know very little about their equipment and offerings. A few

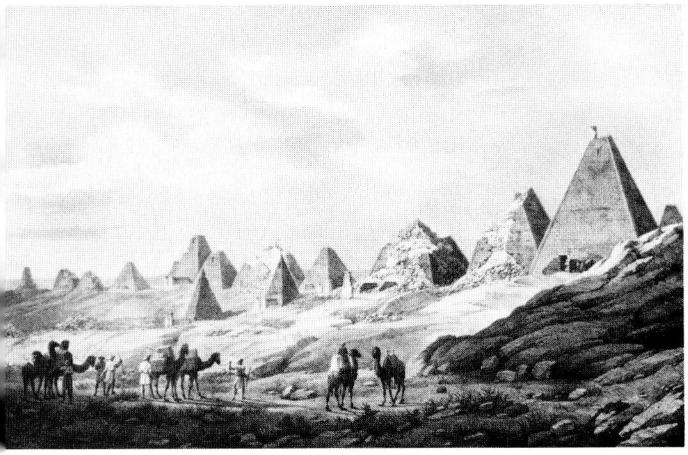

Fig. 47. Pyramids in the North Cemetery at Meroe as they appeared to nineteenth-century travelers (after Cailliaud 1826).

Fig. 48. Typical Lower Nubian burial, Meroitic Period, second to third century A.D. (after Emery 1965).

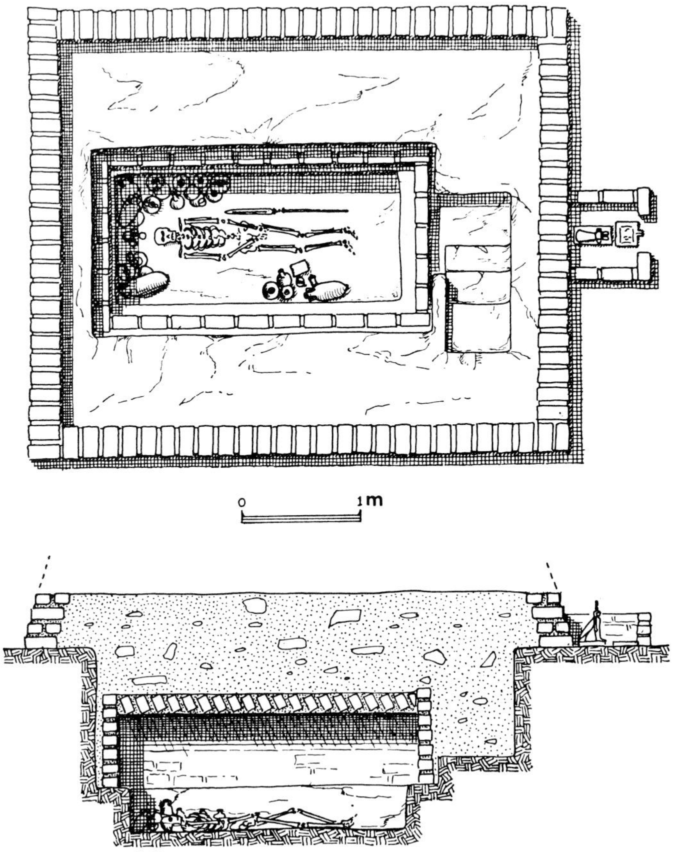

skeletal remains indicate that human sacrifice was still practiced during the late Meroitic Period. Animals were also buried with the deceased.

The superstructures of graves belonging to the Meroitic upper classes in both Lower and Upper Nubia apparently consisted of mastabas as well as pyramids (Vila 1967,315-16) although not a single superstructure has survived intact. The burial chamber generally consisted of nothing more than a narrow shaft, which occasionally broadened out to form a niche at the lower end (Fig. 48). More elaborate forms of niche graves were very rare.

A cemetery with tumuli, excavated near the city of Meroe, may well belong to the post-Meroitic Period. Since tumuli became customary once again in the Ballana and Tanqasi cultures, the discovery of this cemetery strongly suggests the continuity of the local population from the Kerma culture to post-Meroitic times. As bed burial was again revived in the post-Meroitic Period, it is possible that this custom may have persisted among non-royal persons during the Meroitic Period. In the absence of evidence, however, this remains supposition.

Temples are the most important Meroitic constructions. Official art, as well as the state religion, is reflected in sacred architecture, which includes, in addition to temples, such buildings designed for cult use as the so-called Great Enclosure at Musawwarat es-Sufra, a complex erected by the ruler and the priesthood.

The good relations between Kush and Egypt that prevailed at the end of the third century B.C. made it possible for Meroitic kings to authorize construction in the northernmost part of Lower Nubia and on the Island of Philae, where a temple dedicated to the god Arensnuphis was built.[38] A few reliefs for this temple, showing the king offering, were authorized in the name of the Meroitic ruler Ergamenes II (218-200 B.C., Gen. 37), but they say as little about the nature of Meroitic art as do the same king's constructions in Dakka and Kalabsha, where blocks bearing his name were found reused as building material. Similarly uninformative is the temple of the Meroitic King Adikhalamani (200-190 B.C., Gen. 38) at Dabod, which contains purely Egyptian representations. Of course, while such works as these suggest close contact between the two countries, they may also indicate a resettlement of Lower Nubia in the late third century B.C. At Qasr Ibrim, poorly preserved remains of a temple, the northernmost known, have been uncovered.

Meroitic temple architecture is concentrated south of the Second Cataract. Near Amara, approximately one hundred kilometers south of Wadi Halfa, King Natakamani (0-20 A.D., Gen. 53) built a sanctuary for the god Amun. Farther south, at Kawa, Argo, Sanam, and Gebel Barkal, structures of Dynasty XXV were refined and enlarged during the Meroitic Period. Most of the new temples were in the Butana; but in most cases no more than ground plans remain.[39]

Fig. 49. The Amun Temple at Naqa built by King Natakamani, Meroitic Period, early first century A.D.

Meroitic temple constructions can be divided into two groups. The first group consists of multi-chambered temples, which were designed exclusively for the cult of Egyptian deities. Temples existed at Meroe, Naqa, and Amara for Amun. A many-roomed temple at Wad Ban Naqa, of which only the foundation walls survive, was dedicated to the goddess Isis. This type of temple construction is Egyptian, derived from the temples of the early Napatan Period, albeit on a much smaller scale. The Egyptian custom that relief scenes should reflect the room's function was maintained here.

The Amun Temple built by Natakamani at Naqa is well preserved (Fig. 49). In conformity with Egyptian prototypes, it contains five rooms: festival court, hall of appearances (hypostyle hall), offering room (pronaos), bark room (sanctuary), and statue room. The representations appearing on the three remaining stone portals illustrate the rites performed in the various rooms.

On the first portal, Amun, represented in both his human- and ram-headed forms, is pictured holding the king and queen by the elbow, which indicates that the royal couple has been chosen and received by the gods at the temple gate, to be led into the interior and endowed by the gods with life. The royal pair was then led into the second hall, where their coronation took place. They already appear with crowns, however, on the second portal. These first two rooms were the public part of the temple, only the king and some of the higher clergy being permitted to go beyond them. The scenes on the third portal represent various rites that were celebrated in these rooms.

The representations are reflections of the coronation ritual, which took place in the Great Temple of Amun at Meroe. This ritual was probably repeated when the king visited Naqa. Provincial localities were in this way able to participate in the activities of the capital.

Since Meroites followed definite rules in the decoration of their multi-roomed temples, it is possible to reconstruct the original position of the columns of the Amun Temple at Amara. It has been determined that these columns (known through publication but now lost) once belonged to the first hall of the temple (Wenig 1977). The reliefs on them relate to the rites performed in that room and show, in the two main vertical registers, King Natakamani and Kandake Amanitore in the company of gods.

The second type of temple consisted of only one room, which, on occasion, was subdivided into a naos and a pronaos. Either four or six columns supported the roof, and, in a few instances, columned passages encircled the cella. Little more can be said, for in most cases only ground plans survive. The two well-preserved one-room temples at Musawwarat es-Sufra and Naqa, dedicated to the Meroitic god Apedemak, suggest that all one-room Meroitic temples were designed exclusively for the worship of Meroitic deities.

The oldest known building of this type was erected by King Arnekhamani (235-218 B.C., Gen. 36) at Musawwarat es-Sufra during the late third century B.C. It is in this structure that representations of Meroitic gods first appear. The other well-preserved one-room temple was built about two hundred and fifty years later by Natakamani at Naqa (Fig. 50).

The source of the characteristically Meroitic one-room temple can probably be traced to the shrines built by Taharqo and Aspelta at Kawa and Sanam. The Meroitic gods worshipped in these temples did not demand the kind of Egyptian-inspired decorative scheme that still was, for the most part, used in the multi-roomed temples. Hence, the style of the reliefs and the iconography are purely Meroitic. With regard to the development of Meroitic art, a comparison of the two Apedemak temples is important because the changes in the proportions of relief figures can be dated, but with only these two examples surviving, it is difficult to discern the rules of decoration. The available space was limited, but the rule that the gods on the inner and outer walls face the entrance was always observed.[40] So, too, was the tradition that the royal personages be shown facing the gods.

Astronomical orientation played an important role in the layout of Meroitic temples. All Apedemak temples are oriented east-southeast. At Musawwarat es-Sufra, the alignment was 135 degrees, at Basa 132 degrees, and at Naqa 120 degrees. These alignments strongly suggest that the star or planet used by the architects in determining the orientation of these temples was a fast-moving one.[41] In any case, this fact can be used to confirm the relative dates of these temples. The Musawwarat es-Sufra temple is the oldest, the Naqa temple the youngest, and the Apedemak Temple at Basa falls between them. On the basis of their dates, it can be dated to somewhere between the late third century B.C. and the early first century A.D.[42]

A building complex unique in the Nile Valley is the Great Enclosure at Musawwarat es-Sufra, which has been variously regarded as the summer palace of a queen, a school for cadets, a place for the taming of elephants, and a seminary for priests. It was actually a pilgrimage center composed of several temples (Fig. 51). The Great Enclosure consists of numerous large and small courts, corridors, and small rooms. It also includes three temples, of which the Central Temple, built on a terrace, and Temple 300 are of special interest.

The buildings of the Great Enclosure were by and large undecorated. In the Central Temple, however, three triple-protomes with sculpted heads of animals and gods (Fig. 42), which were placed above the portals, survive. Columns with relief decoration stood in front of the Central Temple on bases of animal form (Fig. 38). It is impossible to tell if the walls of the Great Enclosure, which were once covered with a layer of white stucco, were decorated with paintings.

The Central Temple contained four columns, built-in niches, and a columned ambulatory with entrances on three sides. It is not known what god was worshipped here, but the ground plan strongly suggests that it was a Meroitic rather than an Egyptian deity.

The Great Enclosure was built in several stages. Its origins date back to the Napatan Period, while the final additions and renovations date from the late Meroitic Period. Hundreds of graffiti of the most varied motifs (see p. 80) were found on the walls. These pictures, made by pilgrims, provide important evidence of a Meroitic folk art. The pilgrims came to the sacred festivals at Musawwarat es-Sufra from all parts of the countryside

Fig. 50. Pylon of the Apedemak Temple of Natakamani at Naqa, Meroitic Period, early first century A.D.

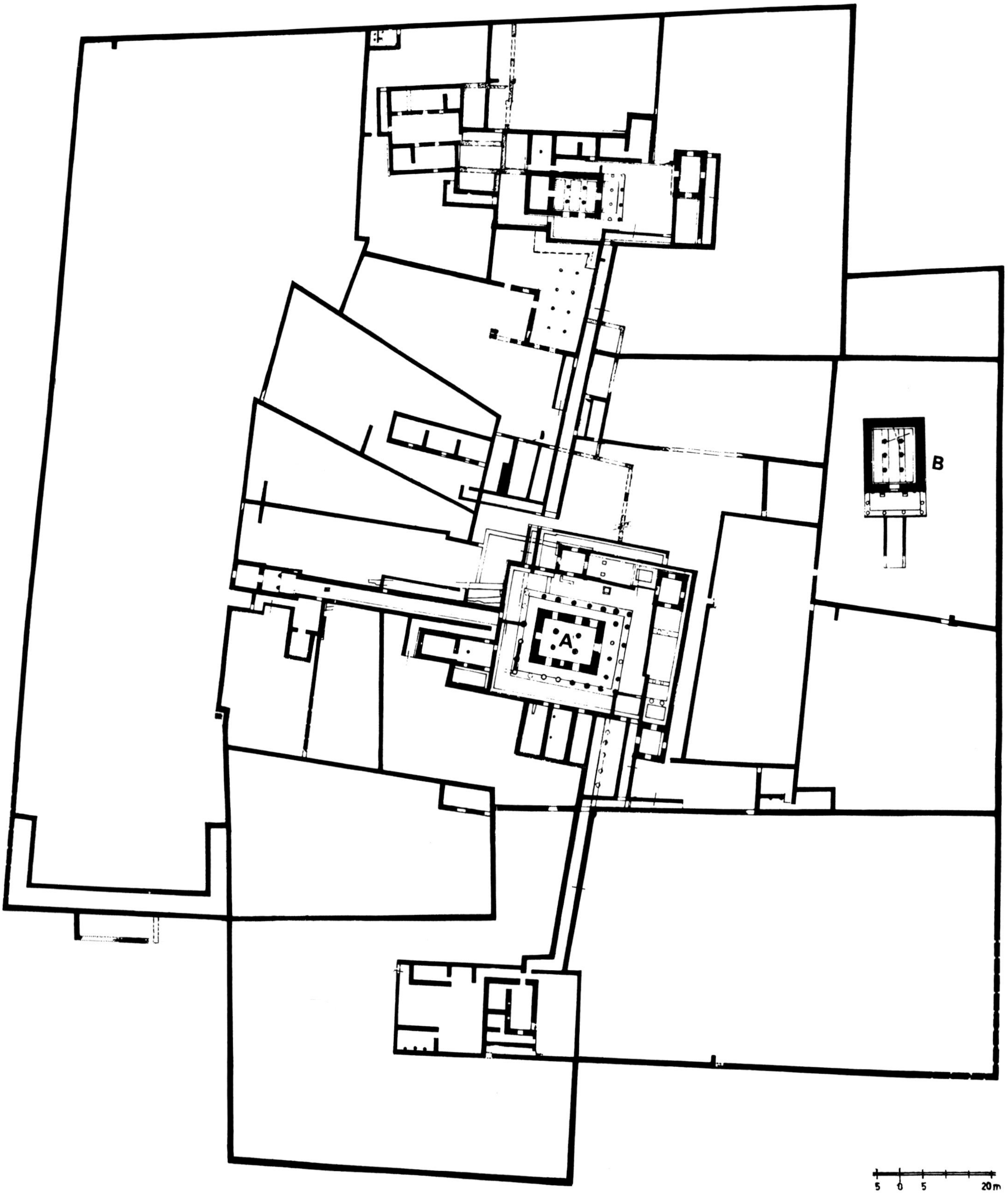

Fig. 51. Groundplan of the Great Enclosure at Musawwarat es-Sufra; building activity lasted from the Napatan Period until the late Meroitic Period.

on their camels and donkeys, and, during the festivals they lived with these animals in the great courts of the Enclosure, which were not unlike the Oriental caravanserai in which later travelers and their animals found lodging. Provisions for the pilgrims were probably brought from Naqa and from Wad Ban Naqa. There was an elaborate water system with wells and reservoirs, or *hafirs*, which consisted of an excavated circular basin surrounded by an earth embankment with an opening for water running down from the surrounding hills during the rainy season. The reservoir at Musawwarat es-Sufra was approximately two hundred and fifty meters in diameter and could store enough water to insure an adequate supply for the pilgrims. Lion sculptures were often found near these *hafirs*, suggesting that this animal was not only sacred to Apedemak but was also, along with the frog, a symbol of fertility.

The unique architectural detail of the Central Temple at Musawwarat es-Sufra of a wall projection in the form of an elephant and other numerous representations of elephants at the same site suggest that this animal was the object of local cult worship. This does not appear to have been the case in other Meroitic centers.

In summarizing the achievements of Meroitic architecture, one must mention the practical, outward-looking, eclectic attitude of the architects, who combined motifs freely, unencumbered by millennia of religious tradition that governed stone buildings in Egypt. The three ram's heads crowned by sun disks, used to decorate capitals, and the square column bases would have been unthinkable in Egypt. Various building techniques also bear witness to the architects' abilities to create, out of their eclecticism, a practical style of their own.

RELIEF SCULPTURE

As with architecture, Meroitic official reliefs developed from Egyptian prototypes by way of Kushite art of the Napatan Period. In the course of the third century B.C., however, relief achieved a degree of independence.

Reliefs form the largest group of extant Meroitic art. The greatest number come from the pyramid chapels of Meroe and Gebel Barkal and are closely associated with funerary establishments. The inner long walls of the pyramid chapels show the deceased enthroned (Fig. 52) in the company or under the protection of a winged goddess,

Fig. 52. King Amanitenmemide protected by a winged goddess, from his pyramid chapel at Meroe (Beg. N. 17), Meroitic Period, A.D. *50-62 (Berlin/DDR 2261).*

who stands behind him. Before him stands a priest offering incense or water. In the middle Meroitic Period, the deities Isis and Anubis occasionally replace the priest. These pictures served a magical function, assuring life after death.

The funerary chapels are the only group of monuments providing a continuous sequence throughout the Meroitic Period. With few exceptions, the sequential order of pyramids is firmly established, thereby providing a tool for dating reliefs from the chapels. A developmental process which can be traced in the reliefs themselves, especially in iconographic details, provides us with a point of departure for dating other works of art. But it is much more difficult to determine stylistic changes, for the scenes are more or less prescribed and the style is very often conventional. The combination of scenes shown on narrow friezes placed in front of the deceased, however, appears to have undergone modification from time to time. We can assign these changes to three sequential groups.[43]

The first group reflect a continuation of the Napatan tradition. These reliefs were created from approximately 270 B.C. until the early part of the second century B.C. Many Egyptian scenes are included in the second group, which derive from Egyptian temples or from other Egyptian religious sources. The close ties between Egypt and Meroe at this time are probably responsible for this. This group ends with the pyramids of Queen Amanishakheto (Beg. N. 6) and of Kandake Amanitore (Beg. N. 1). Natakamani introduced a new type in his pyramid (Beg. N. 22) which lasted from the beginning of the first century A.D. to the end of the kingdom. It is no accident that such changes occurred during his reign. Other indicia point to significant changes in Meroitic art during this period, but the causes for such changes have not yet been determined.

It can be said, in general, that the reliefs of the pyramid chapels are more closely tied to the Napatan tradition, in both content and style, than are other classes of Meroitic art. This conservatism is a natural result of their religious subject matter. Thus they belong to Style Group I. Meroitic stylistic elements, which are so evident in works of Group III, cannot be attested before the reign of Queen Amanishakheto, at the end of the first century B.C. This does not preclude the existence of Meroitic iconographic elements, however, in earlier times.

Temple reliefs are not so numerous as pyramid chapel reliefs. Recent excavations at Musawwarat es-Sufra and Meroe allow us to assume, however, that systematic excavations, especially in the Butana, will yield much more material.

Of all the temple reliefs, those found in the Apedemak temples at Musawwarat es-Sufra (Fig. 45) and Naqa (Figs. 53-54) play a key role. Since the two structures are fairly accurately dated to the late third century B.C. and the beginning of the first century A.D., respectively, they provide fixed points to work from.

Fig. 53. The god Apedemak, from the south outside wall of his temple at Naqa, Meroitic Period, early first century A.D.

Fig. 54. King Natakamani worshipping the god Apedemak, on the south outside wall of the Apedemak Temple at Naqa, Meroitic Period, early first century A.D.

The changes in style, iconography, and proportions for the human figure that are reflected in these two temples (see pp. 70-71) demonstrate the stylistic development of Meroitic art. Temple F, built at Naqa by Queen Shanakdakhete (170-150 B.C., Gen. 41), is the only sanctuary containing representations datable to a definite time between the two Apedemak temples, but its reliefs, because of their poor state of preservation and their compositional irregularities,[44] are of little help in determining stylistic development.

The "Egyptian-like" reliefs of Style Group II all date from the reign of King Natakamani and are found exclusively in temples dedicated to the Egyptian gods Amun and Isis at Naqa, Wad Ban Naqa, and Amara. In referring to these reliefs as "Egyptian-like," we emphasize only their iconographic dependence upon Egyptian examples. Meroitic characteristics are also clearly expressed, for example, in the rendition of obese female figures with pendulous breasts. The bark pedestal from the Isis Temple of Wad Ban Naqa (Berlin/DDR 7261) provides a characteristic example of this well-rounded female type (Vol. I, Fig. 74). Goddesses portrayed here and elsewhere, however, are depicted with slender figures. Somewhat different are the reliefs found recently by Shinnie at Meroe (Fig. 39). They are related to Group II but also exhibit some of the features peculiar to Group III.

In addition to reliefs from pyramid chapels and temples, palace reliefs have been found. At Wad Ban Naqa, a few rooms in the palace were lined with thin sandstone relief slabs covered in gold leaf (Cat. 123). The many relief-decorated blocks found by Garstang at Meroe probably date mostly from the Napatan Period. Early Meroitic palaces may also have contained reliefs. The rooms of the palaces of Meroe were, however, usually decorated with paintings. Copies of the best of them were made, but only one survives (Cat. 132),[45] which shows a very unusual motif: a squat, naked youth with a yoke across his shoulders from each end of which a small elephant is suspended. The proportions of this figure suggest that it is later than the reign of Natakamani.[46]

There are few other paintings attributable to the Meroitic Period. It is possible that the walls of the Great Enclosure at Musawwarat es-Sufra and the brick walls of temples were painted. We know that these walls were plastered. Although a few grave stelae from Lower Nubia were painted (Cats. 127, 128), the number of painted stelae is small. Meroitic tombs were not decorated with paintings, as was the custom in Egypt; they provided no space for wall decoration.

In addition to reliefs from pyramid chapels, temples, and palaces, several scattered reliefs have been found. A small number are preserved on royal stelae (Cat. 122). Others are on the funerary stelae of members of the royal family (Cats. 118, 120) and of private persons. The latter so far have been found only in Lower Nubia (Cats. 127-129). In addition, there are offering tablets with the names of kings and members of the royal house (Cat. 119) as well as of private persons. These tablets employ two primary motifs, one depicting various offerings and the other showing two libating deities, Isis and Anubis, placed at the sides of the tablet (Cat. 119). A few of the other types of objects which bear relief decoration are described in Cats. 121 and 125.

Many reliefs can be dated only if they are inscribed with the name of a ruler or other known person. Votive tablets, stelae, and the undated relief work may, in certain instances, be given a relative date on the basis of stylistic comparisons.

The techniques of raised, sunk, and incised relief were employed according to the general Egyptian principle: the outer walls of buildings were decorated in sunk relief and the interior walls in raised relief. There are many cases where this rule was not followed. Columns, for example, were decorated in raised relief no matter where they stood. Raised and incised relief sometimes occur together (stela of Tanyidamani, Boston 23.736; Vol. I, Fig. 71). In general, incised relief appears to have been the preferred method of decoration.

Reliefs also include rock drawings and graffiti. The latter include incised sketches and simple scribblings on the walls of buildings such as the pyramid chapels at Meroe (Fig. 55) and, more frequently, in the Great Enclosure at Musawwarat es-Sufra (Figs. 56-57). They

Fig. 55. Block found at Meroe with representation of a royal head bearing marks of scarification, Meroitic Period, first century B.C. *to third century* A.D.

Fig. 56. Graffito of a royal winged sphinx vanquishing an enemy, Great Enclosure at Musawwarat es-Sufra, Meroitic Period, probably second century B.C.

Fig. 57. Copy of graffito of a mounted warrior, Great Enclosure at Musawwarat es-Sufra, late Meroitic Period or post-Meroitic Period, second to fourth century A.D.

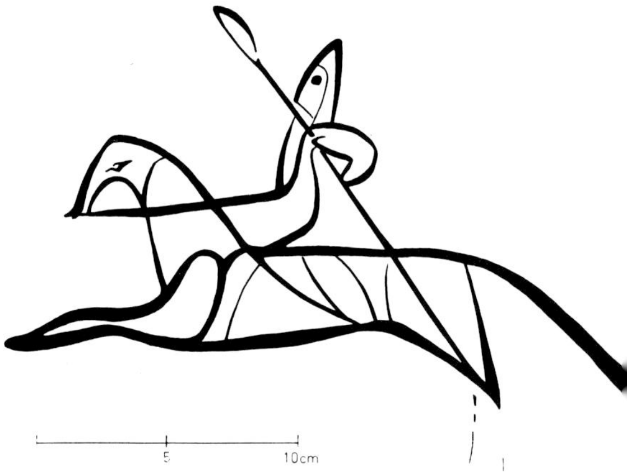

show various religious motifs, and some are certainly to be regarded as votive dedications. Certain graffiti depict activities such as stick-fencing, dogs chasing hares, and mounted figures. Generally, however, these drawings represent single animals, such as donkeys, lions, cattle, and giraffes, or human heads. They are documents of a folk art that stands in sharp contrast to the official art of the period in both style and subject.

Attention should be drawn to the incised representation of King Shorkaror (first century A.D., Fig. 58) carved into the cliff of Gebel Qeili in the Butana, a work that must be regarded as belonging to official art. The scene includes a god with a halo and nimbus, two details appropriated from the sacred iconography of Classical antiquity. The representation of the king shows us regalia as well as weapons that are unknown in other monuments. Of special importance, however, is the representation of the king's enemies, who are pictured as falling from a cliff. The liveliness with which the figures are depicted and the graphic manner in which the dislocation of limbs is shown are unparalleled in the Meroitic Period.

An incised drawing whose technique is reminiscent of the rock drawings was found on a wall of the Great Enclosure at Musawwarat es-Sufra (Fig. 59). It is a very unusual picture of unknown meaning, showing a man and a woman standing face to face. The naked female is represented in front view with her head in profile. The lower part of her body is dotted, perhaps to indicate tattooing. To her right stands a man with an erect penis; his loincloth is open and the ends of his loosened belt hang down. A long cloak floats at his back. The man embraces the woman with both hands; his head touches hers, probably in the act of kissing. The woman holds the corners of a large cloth in her outstretched arms, which is probably meant to conceal the two figures. This incised representation is certainly not a document of official art, but in spite of the awkwardness of its details, the scene speaks eloquently of the ability of its creator.

A study of Meroitic relief shows that the artists freely adopted and adapted foreign elements to create a vivid style imbued with spirit and action.

SCULPTURE IN THE ROUND

Substantially more sculpture in the round survives from the Meroitic Period than from the Napatan Period, which is probably indicative of increased artistic productivity, although the total number of preserved sculptures is still quite small. They can be divided into two principal groups. The first consists of human figures, such as gods, kings, and private persons. The second comprises animal representations.[47]

A limited number of types were employed for human figures. Individual standing figures are most frequent,

Fig. 58. Copy of an incised drawing of King Shorkaror conquering his enemies with the help of a god, Gebel Qeili, Meroitic Period, A.D. *20-30.*

Fig. 59. Copy of incised drawing of a man and a woman, Great Enclosure at Musawwarat es-Sufra, Meroitic Period, probably second century B.C.

Fig. 60. Small faience figurine of a woman bending forward, from Meroe, Meroitic Period (Copenhagen NCG 1321).

Fig. 61. Sandstone and painted plaster statue of a reclining man, from the Royal Baths at Meroe, Meroitic Period, second to third century A.D. *(Copenhagen NCG 1484).*

many of the male figures being shown as striding with left leg advanced. A few standing groups are also known. Most of them represent private individuals; Cat. 135 is the only example belonging to the sphere of official art. A few seated individual and group sculptures are known, mainly depicting gods[48] or a ruler in the company of a god. So far as is known, figures in other positions were extremely rare in the Meroitic Period (Fig. 60). A unique sculpture of a man reclining on a couch, from the Royal Baths at Meroe (Copenhagen NCG 1484; Fig. 61), appropriates a Roman motif.

Individual heads were also created during this period. The most famous of these is the head of a black African from the Royal Baths at Meroe; it belongs to Style Group V (Copenhagen NCG 1336; Fig. 62). There are several reserve heads from Lower Nubia (see p. 89), and, finally, there are architectural elements in the form of the human heads of the gods Arensnuphis and Sebiumeker flanking a ram's head.

Small sculptures constitute a relatively minor part of the whole. At most, about one-third of Meroitic sculptures in the round of human figures consist of statuettes, mostly in bronze, that functioned either as votive offerings in temples or as temple equipment (Cats. 136-138). There are also a few colossal statues, all depicting gods.

Fig. 62. Sandstone head of a black African, from the Royal Baths at Meroe, Meroitic Period, second century A.D. *(Copenhagen NCG 1336).*

Sculptures of human figures can be divided into five categories:

1. Statues of royal persons, that is, kings and reigning queens, are known. These all belong to the sphere of official art.[49] Two life-size statues from Naqa (Shinnie 1953,95) probably depict princes and are to be regarded as exceptions. No statues of non-reigning queens or of princesses have been found.

2. Statues and statuettes of deities, mostly male, are preserved. These, too, belong to the sphere of official art. In addition to the approximately three dozen representations of deities, there are numerous figurative amulets, mostly in faience. It is not certain whether the few figurines made of clay (Cats. 142,143) belong to this group because their meaning is still obscure, but it is clear that they belong to the category of unofficial rather than official art.

3. This group consists of sculptures from the Royal Baths at Meroe. These works encompass a wide variety of subjects, but, because they are derivative of Alexandrian art, they form a separate stylistic group of about thirty statues (Style Group V).

4. A few figures of captives, of which Cats. 139 and 140 are characteristic examples, belong to the sphere of official art.

5. This category comprises representations of non-royal persons and includes the *ba*-statues, almost all of which were found in Lower Nubia, as well as a few reserve heads. These works belong to the sphere of unofficial art and form their own stylistic group (Style Group IV). No private sculptures from the south have come to light.[50]

The material used for sculpture in the round was generally sandstone, of very variable quality. Granite, steatite, graywacke, gold, bronze, and faience were also sometimes used.

Excluding the amulets, there are fewer than fifty statues, including fragments, that can be placed in the first two categories, but numerous fragments of smashed statues recently found at Tebo reveal that there must have been many sculptures of gods and kings (Maystre 1973,197).

Considerably more examples of unofficial art have been preserved than of official art. This large group of private sculpture is made up of a few clay figurines (Cats. 142,143), somewhat reminiscent of those produced by the A- and C-group cultures, a large number of *ba*-statues, and some reserve heads. By way of illustration, if one were to divide known sculptures belonging to official art equally over the entire Meroitic Period, there would be fewer than three royal sculptures and perhaps six figures of deities per century, while there would be some seventy-five *ba*-statues per century from the golden age of Lower Nubia (first to fourth centuries A.D.).

The difficulties involved in dating are much greater for sculpture in the round than for relief, and the absence of inscriptions on sculpture further complicates attribution.[51] Royal sculpture can be dated with the aid of stylistic and iconographic comparison. Parallels can be found in dated temple and pyramid chapel reliefs. The situation is far more complicated in the case of sculptures of gods, animals, and *ba*-figures. Given the present state of our knowledge, there is no way in which these sculptures can be precisely dated. Only the statues belonging to Style Group V, from the Royal Baths at Meroe, can be securely attributed to the second to third century A.D.

In the absence of inscriptions or special attributes, it is difficult in many cases to determine whether a sculpture represents a god or a king. Nevertheless, iconographic analysis has revealed that there are ways of distinguishing between them. With the exception of Cat. 122, Meroitic kings are never shown wearing strapped garments. Moreover, they are never bearded unless they are meant to be perceived as gods (Wenig 1973a; 1974). *Ankh*-signs are carried only by gods; the one possible exception to this rule is Cat. 136.

Three royal sculptures have been included in this catalogue. The figurine, Cat. 136, the earliest known Meroitic royal sculpture, has stylistic parallels in the sculpture of early Ptolemaic Egypt and can therefore be dated to the late third century B.C.

The group statue, Cat. 135, is dated on the basis of iconography and style to the middle of the second century B.C. (Wenig 1969a). The queen must therefore be Shanakdakhete, the only sovereign queen of that period. This sculpture vividly illustrates the absence of stylistic unity in Meroitic art. The faces of the two figures are so different from one another that if the heads had been found separately, they would not have been

Fig. 63. Bronze statue of an unknown king, from the Island of Argo, Meroitic Period, probably first century A.D. *(Khartoum, Sudan National Museum 24705).*

Fig. 64. Colossal granite statue of a god, from the Island of Argo, Meroitic Period, probably third century B.C. *(Khartoum 23983).*

Fig. 65. Sandstone column-statue of the god Sebiumeker from Meroe, Meroitic Period, first century A.D. *(Copenhagen NCG 1082).*

considered contemporary. Nevertheless, this group statue may be ranked among the best works produced during the Meroitic Period.

The third royal example is a statuette of a queen in ceremonial dress (Cat. 137) from the first century B.C. This figurine, which shows the slender physical forms of early Meroitic sculpture, was created just before the introduction of the new canon of proportions in the late first century B.C.

A very important discovery, made on the Island of Argo during the 1973-74 season, was a well-preserved bronze statue of an unknown Meroitic king (Fig. 63), found in the Temple of Tebo (Leclant 1975b,234, pl. XXV, fig. 24). Approximately fifty centimeters in height, it is the largest bronze sculpture discovered to date in Kush. There is no doubt that the work was made within the kingdom, though there are as yet no known parallels. Although the waist is sharply constricted, this figure, with its broad, straight shoulders and powerful limbs, gives a stockier, more compact impression than do other known royal representations. The change of proportions of the late first century B.C. is already reflected in this figure, and can also be seen in other sculptures such as the Argo deity figures (Fig. 64) and the two column-statues found at Meroe (Fig. 65). This royal representation therefore belongs to the late first century B.C. It is the only known example of Meroitic large-scale bronze sculpture and illustrates the high level of sophistication achieved by Meroitic artists.

There are no parallels for the two headless sculptures made of dark sandstone found at Naqa. These are approximately life-size, uninscribed figures of standing males, probably princes, dressed identically. Both wear garments gathered up in the left hand below the belt line. The garment crosses the right shoulder, leaving the left bare. A vertical border adorns the front. This type of statue was adopted from Egypt, but the garment is found elsewhere in Kush. On the walls of the Temple of Apedemak at Naqa, built by Natakamani, the crown prince is represented in a very similar pleated robe. The two headless statues are therefore identified as representations of princes. Whether or not they belong to the period of King Natakamani cannot be proved for the time being. Where these largest of all non-divine statues once stood is unknown, possibly in a palace or, less likely, in a temple.

Statues of gods are more common than those of kings and, like them, belong exclusively to the sphere of official art. Small sculptures of deities are relatively rare. More frequent are works of medium size representing either groups of gods (sometimes with a king or queen) or individual figures. In general, the group statues stood in pyramid chapels, while single figures were placed within temples. Larger-than-life temple statues are not uncommon, and always stood in pairs beside entrances. Of the five pairs extant, four represent Arensnuphis and Sebiumeker, protectors of temples.[52] That these statues represent gods rather than kings, as was once assumed, is

Fig. 66. The kiosk at Naqa, Meroitic Period, third century A.D. *(after Cailliaud 1826).*

Fig. 67. Sandstone and painted plaster statue of a harpist in the Royal Baths at Meroe, Meroitic Period, second to third century A.D.

confirmed by the fact that they are bearded and wear strapped garments (Fig. 65).

For the same reason, the two colossal granite figures from Argo (Khartoum 23983; Fig. 64) must be regarded as representing gods. These statues, approximately seven meters in height, are the largest surviving Meroitic sculptures. They provide no concrete clues to their exact date, but they are Meroitic works, not least of all because of their proportions and stylistic features (Wenig 1974). Which deities they represent is not known; they have no attributes of Arensnuphis and Sebiumeker, except for the Double Crown. One of them wears around his crown a wreath of lanceolate leaves resembling a laurel wreath, and his uraeus has a ram's head. This figure is more typically Meroitic than the other, the eyes being large and bulging in the flattish face. The cleft of the mouth curves upward, giving the impression of a smile. The other figure has almond-shaped eyes and a straight mouth with more tubelike lips. There are further differences in costume. Beside the knee of the latter colossus is a small figure holding the index finger of his right hand to his mouth.

It would be most difficult to assume different periods of origin for the two colossi, since it is probable that they were meant to be set up together. Here again, then, we find a clear expression of the lack of stylistic unity characteristic of Meroitic art. As for the dating of these two statues, we find ourselves once again largely in the

Fig. 68. Sandstone and painted plaster statue of a woman, found near the Royal Baths at Meroe, Meroitic Period, second to third century A.D. *(Khartoum 538).*

realm of supposition. Dunham (1947,65) has suggested the reign of Natakamani, but the rather stocky proportions of both figures suggest that they might as easily date from the late first century B.C.[53]

The statues found in the Royal Baths at Meroe constitute a special group. The hybrid style, a combination of Alexandrian and Meroitic elements, occurs only in these statues, in the kiosk of Naqa (Fig. 66), and in a few faience objects and reliefs. Kraus (1964) has dated the kiosk to the third century A.D. The statues, however, need not all be dated to this century; some of them may have been made earlier. Classical archaeologists familiar with the Alexandrian school believe that the head of a black African (Copenhagen NCG 1336; Fig. 62) was made in the second century A.D. These sculptures reflect a short-lived fashion, which was apparently limited to Meroe and Naqa. They show no inner connection with one another and probably had no other meaning than room decoration (Fig. 67). Because they were all placed at the edge of the large pool, and because the bath installation also contained a semicircular room with three apselike niches which may have functioned as thrones or seats, we are inclined to view the whole structure as, perhaps, a splendid, ornate imitation of a Hellenistic villa, complete with a swimming pool.

The close relationship that existed between the Kingdom of Kush and the Classical world, with Rome and especially with Alexandria (Kraus 1969), stimulated the Meroites to re-create in their royal city things they had heard existed in other great cities of the ancient world. We have no idea why the Meroites adopted certain motifs and chose to ignore others. The transformation of prototypes taken from Classical antiquity and their adaptation to the indigenous artistic tradition clearly demonstrate the continued creativity of Meroitic artists.

The most famous work from the baths of Meroe is the figure of a man reclining on a blue couch (Copenhagen NCG 1484; Fig. 61). His skin is red brown in color, and he is dressed in a richly pleated robe. The soft Nubian sandstone of which this figure is made as well as the technique of applying a thick plaster coat prove that the piece was created by a Nubian artist, and this is confirmed by many of the details, such as the straight shoulders, the gentle, curving forms, and the headband. The motif of a reclining figure comes from Roman art, where it was used to decorate urns and sarcophagi, but since this statue was erected at the edge of the Royal Baths, it seems that only the form and not the meaning was adopted by the Meroites. It has been suggested that the figure represents a Nile god, but, except for the blue couch, there is no evidence to support this attribution. More likely it represents a man reclining on a couch during a banquet.[54]

The so-called Venus of Meroe (Cat. 161) clearly illustrates a Meroitic adaptation of a Classical theme. The curve of the figure, with head and torso turned to one side in imitation of movement, is directly translated from the Classical world, and the translation has brought a characteristic Meroitic fullness to the female form.

Two sandstone statues found near the baths are fashioned in a different style but are related to the figures from the baths. The first statue is of a naked female, covered with a thick layer of plaster and painted red brown (Khartoum 538; Fig. 68). The effect of movement is achieved by the position of the arms. The eyes and eyebrows are inlaid in a different material. The figure's hips are strongly emphasized in accord with the Meroitic ideal of beauty. The shoulders are straight; the neck is relatively long and vertical. The second statue (Khartoum 537) shows a man with red-brown skin dressed in a white kilt. The head is inclined upward; eyes and eyebrows are inlaid. The arms here, too, are freely worked. Nothing is known about the relation of these two statues to the others of Style Group V.

Prisoners appear in many variations in Meroitic art (Cats. 236, 237), but only a few figures were sculpted in the round. Large statues such as Cat. 140 or other, less well preserved works found by Garstang in the Apedemak Temple at Meroe (Garstang 1911, pl. XXI,2 and 7) probably stood in front of temples. This hypothesis is supported by Cat. 140, which shows a prisoner whose torso is bent sharply backward. There is a deep hole in the chest, where a standard was once placed. The same motif appears in relief on the side of the pylon of the Temple of Apedemak built by Natakamani at Naqa, probably replacing a statue. The small bronze figure, Cat. 139, was attached to a footstool. Here we see an underlying Egyptian idea to the effect that the king tramples his enemies underfoot.

Most of the funerary figures, or *ba*-statues, from Meroitic tombs come from Lower Nubia.[55] These are usually representations of winged human figures, often with sun disks on their heads.[56] The *ba*-statues never represent royal persons. They were made for civil servants, frequently viceroys, as well as for high priests and wives of members of the Meroitic upper class in Lower Nubia. The few extant group statues show a man and a woman, or sometimes two men. The *ba*-statue stood either in a small cult chapel placed to the east of the elaborated superstructure of the tomb or in a niche above the chapel entrance.[57] Since the tombs have not been securely dated, it is difficult to date the *ba*-statues precisely. Traditionally, they have been attributed to the second and third centuries A.D., but it is possible that they are both older and more recent.

Ba-statues are, for the most part, similar in posture, the main difference being generally in the position of the arms. Viceroys (Cat. 153) are shown with forearms horizontally extended, a position apparently reserved for them. Female figures (Cat. 151) are shown with both arms held to the sides, but a few male figures are also represented this way. There are other arm positions as well. Although it does not appear that they had any particular significance, except for the viceroys, some arm positions occur only in male or female figures while others are used for both sexes.

Iconographic distinctions are observable only in clothing, which is usually very simple. Only viceroys wear elaborate garments; Cat. 153 is an impressive example. The deceased are sometimes shown with or sometimes without sandals, which may or may not represent a social distinction. Jewelry, which is chiefly worn by the viceroys, consists mainly of a bead collar and sometimes a pendant amulet. Men frequently wear a hairband or diadem (Cats. 153, 154) and often carry a fly-whisk. Viceroys and civil servants carry short or long staffs and, in one instance, a pine cone or fruit.

A few *ba*-statues were made with great care and can be regarded as important works of art (Cats. 151, 153). Many of them, however, appear crude and awkward (Cats. 154, 155, 157, 159). And yet, an important stylistic tendency is expressed in precisely these works. In them, we can see most clearly the Meroitic impulse toward stylization that approaches abstraction in the reduction of form to its essentials.

Nothing about these statues is Egyptian except the idea, nor can Hellenistic or Roman elements be seen. They are very different in both style and content from all other Meroitic works, constituting a localized style group of their own. They provide impressive evidence of the artistic division of the country.

It has so far been impossible to outline the stylistic development of the *ba*-statues. The distinctions observable in the heads from Shablul (Cats. 157, 159), those from Karanog (Cats. 154, 155), and those from Faras (Cat. 156) need not necessarily reflect different periods. Local traditions, the varying skill of individual sculptors, and the differences between provincial (Shablul) and metropolitan areas (Faras and Aniba) probably contributed to such distinctions. Some of the faces are round, others are oval-shaped, and a large number are tapered or pointed. In all cases, however, the eyes are strongly emphasized. The enlargement of the eyes probably represents the only point of stylistic unity to be found in these statues. The figures with pointed faces have extremely schematic eyes, with tubelike lids. Such heads have been found in Karanog and even more frequently in Shablul, but to judge from the still incomplete excavation report, they were unknown at Faras.

The eye sockets are sharply etched, with the orbital ridge emphasized. Eyebrows are not shown, except on the head from Faras (Cat. 156), in which symmetrically arching eyebrows are plastically rendered, and the head from Karanog (Cat. 154), in which the bulging plastic eyebrows serve also to define the upper contours of the eyes.

The mouth is rendered in various ways. In some cases, it is small and consists of a single line; in others, it is wide, with thick, puffy lips. The hair is generally represented as an unarticulated mass with clearly marked edges. The ears are generally large and often not completely formed, but in a few instances, even auditory canals have been drilled. The female figures always have pendulous breasts rendered in high relief.

Incised lines on the forehead, and three vertical strokes on the cheeks of a few heads (Cats. 151, 154, 159), pose a special problem. In one statue from Karanog (Cairo JE 40233), a vertical row of three incised dots is drilled on the forehead. The forehead lines are sometimes horizontal and sometimes slightly upcurving. They are found on the statues of viceroys (Cat. 153) as well as on those of private individuals (Cats. 151, 159). They do not appear to reflect a local custom, since they appear on statues from Shablul, Karanog, Faras, and Argin (Cat. 160). Painted faces on ceramics with similar forehead lines are also known.

These markings cannot be explained as a temporary fashion. The three vertical cheek marks, which perhaps are related to the forehead lines, appear on several Meroitic works and are not confined to the second and third centuries A.D. The vertical cheek lines are found even today in the Sudan, where they can be decorative or symbolic. In Kush, such markings were not limited to viceroys and civil servants from Lower Nubia. Queen Amanishakheto, for example, bore such markings.[58] King Natakamani's facial markings appear on a relief in the Apedemak Temple at Naqa. Even enemies are sometimes shown with the three cheek marks, as can be seen in a representation on a vessel (Cat. 232) showing a lion, a symbol of the king, attacking a man.

The *ba*-statues of Lower Nubia, which represent a special, geographically limited funerary custom within the borders of the Meroitic kingdom, were restricted to a few persons of the upper class. The reason why only a few people were buried with *ba*-statues appears not to have been economic. In Meroitic times, the population of Lower Nubia enjoyed considerable prosperity. The statues must have been made only for those members of the upper class who actually ruled the non-Meroitic inhabitants of the northern part of the Kingdom of Kush. One generally assumes that such rulers were Meroites, for the civil servants emphasize in their offering tables their close ties to Napata and Meroe, and several viceroys stress their connection to the royal house. Why these Meroites who governed Lower Nubia adopted burial customs that differed from those practiced in the Meroitic heartland is unknown.

Fig. 69. Sandstone head from Abri East, Meroitic Period, second to third century A.D. *(Khartoum 24144).*

A few examples of heads survive that were finished smoothly under the neck and were never intended to form part of a complete statue. These substitutes for *ba*-statues are known as reserve heads.[59] The finest of them was found at Argin (Cat. 160). Although the underside of the neck is not completely smooth, the size of the head (26.7 centimeters) precludes its having been part of a larger figure. Traces of color indicate that the work was once painted or at least plastered. The importance of this head, which is fundamentally different from all other heads of *ba*-statues, lies in its high artistic quality. The expression of the face, the result primarily of the unconventionally formed eyes, is extraordinary and found in no other Meroitic sculpture.

Completely different in style is another reserve head with an exaggeratedly long neck that spreads out at the base, suggesting a bust (Fig. 69). This head was found in a child's grave dated to the late Meroitic Period.[60] It is fashioned in hard pinkish-white sandstone and is fifty-nine centimeters high, about the size of the average *ba*-statue. The pointed face with its small mouth and deemphasized nose is carved softly, creating a very introspective effect. On the forehead is an incised horizontal line. The hair is rendered in low relief in the form of small curls.

The few examples of reserve heads differ greatly in style from the *ba*-statues as well as from one another.[61] Their diversity points to the artistic variety of Lower Nubia. We will know more about the artistic and stylistic development of sculpture in Lower Nubia when the many *ba*-statues found during the 1960s in this area, as well as in a few places south of the Second Cataract, are published.

Any survey of Meroitic sculpture would be incomplete without a brief mention of the many animal sculptures. These figures pose special dating problems; with the exception of three animal statues from Basa, Soba, and Qasr Ibrim,[62] all animal sculptures are uninscribed. A few of them, the two lion statues in the Apedemak Temple at Musawwarat es-Sufra, for example, and the ram figures in the Amun Temples at

Fig. 70. Sandstone statue of a lion attacking a bound captive, from Basa, Meroitic Period, first century B.C. *(Khartoum, Sudan National Museum).*

Fig. 71. Sandstone statuette of a lion from Meroe, Meroitic Period, first century B.C. *to first century* A.D. *(Liverpool SAOS 8003).*

Naqa and Meroe, can be dated because they were probably created at the same time as the temples.

It is difficult to explain why there are so many more figures of animals than of gods and kings. Of course, animals played an important part in Meroitic religion. The ram and the lion were sacred to Amun as well as to the Meroitic deities Apedemak, Arensnuphis, and Sebiumeker, although it is impossible to say which god is represented in most cases. The lion as sacred animal of Apedemak is attested by several temple reliefs, but the gods Arensnuphis and Sebiumeker are also accompanied by lions.[63] As in Egypt, the lion was a symbol of the king. This is proved by two statue groups from Basa, which show lions attacking a prisoner (Fig. 70) and trampling enemies. That lions were probably related to a fertility cult is supported by several lion sculptures found near the *hafirs* at Basa, Umm Usuda, and Musawwarat es-Sufra. The date and meaning of small lion figures such as Cat. 146, found in the palace of Wad Ban Naqa, and another quite different sculpture from Meroe (Liverpool SAOS 8003; Fig. 71) are not clear. Waterspouts in the form of lion heads placed below the roof on the long walls of temples are appropriated from Egyptian models. Cat. 147, a lion whose hindquarters are only roughly formed, may have been a mock waterspout with a purely decorative function. Another sacred animal represented in sculpture is the falcon, symbol of the Egyptian god Horus, who was introduced into the Meroitic pantheon. The unusual colossal figures of frogs or toads found in the *hafir* at Basa (Crowfoot 1911, pl.VII,14-15; Khartoum, museum garden) were symbols of fertility. Figures of monkeys and apes, such as Cat. 149, are rare; one statue of this animal of outstanding quality was found in 1974 in a temple at Meroe (Fig. 72).

Since Meroitic art displayed a decided tendency toward simplification and abstraction, the naturalistic animal figures are probably to be dated in the early and middle Meroitic Period. This has been confirmed by the more or less securely dated triple-protomes from Musawwarat es-Sufra (Cat. 145 and Khartoum 18890; Fig. 41), and the lion-headed Apedemak figure bearing the name of King Tanyidamani (Louvre E. 11657b; Fig. 73). Cat. 147, on the other hand, illustrates the style of the late Meroitic Period, when reduction of form approaching abstraction prevailed.

MINOR ARTS

The design and production of jewelry reached a high level in the Meroitic Period. Jewelry is perhaps the best represented of the minor arts since, paradoxically, many examples have survived. Reisner found several pieces of gold jewelry in his excavation of the royal pyramids. The largest cache, however, was discovered by the Italian adventurer and treasure hunter G. Ferlini in the early nineteenth century. In the course of tearing down a pyramid in the North Cemetery at Meroe (Beg. N. 6), he chanced upon a small gold treasure walled up in two hiding places. These pieces demonstrate that the art of the Meroitic goldsmith maintained or even surpassed the high level of the Napatan Period (Cats. 162-171, 173-175, 181-189; Fig. 74; Vol. I, Figs. 63-64). Most of the objects found by Ferlini date from the time of Queen Amanishakheto (end of the first century B.C.), although a few pieces were heirlooms (Cat. 185).

Much of this jewelry was designed for the queen; the shield-rings in particular (Cats. 164, 166-168, 171; Fig. 74) were undoubtedly meant for a woman. Most of these rings were worn on the fingers. They appear frequently in reliefs of the period.

The most important Meroitic jewelry-making techniques were embossment, granulation, and glass inlay, often applied in cloisonne (Cats. 163, 165, 169-171; Fig. 75; Vol. I, Fig. 64). The glass inlays are most frequently white, dark blue, and green; red and black also appear. Many of the signet rings found by Ferlini and by others are significant both historically and artistically. They sometimes show the artist's appropriation of Hellenistic motifs (Cat. 186). Rings depicting the legend of the king's divine birth (Cats. 181-184) are based on Egyptian prototypes. Indigenous motifs also appear (Cats. 187, 188). Many of the earrings, pendants, chains, armbands, and other ornaments such as those found in the royal cemeteries at Meroe are comparable in quality to those produced in contemporary Egypt or Greece. In their mastery of a variety of forms as well as in their invention of new shapes, the royal jewelers of the Meroitic kingdom were unparalleled.

Several large, thick-walled, hollow faience cylinders found by Garstang at Meroe have so far received little attention, but they also illustrate the richness of the minor arts of this period (Garstang 1914a,3,10-11, table IV,1). One of them has a projecting base, and they are all decorated with vertical relief registers of striding rams and lions (Toronto 921.4.1; Fig. 76) or libating winged goddesses.[64] The purpose of these cylinders is not known. It is possible that they were stacked one on top of another, but they cannot have formed a column since faience would not be strong enough for such use. Perhaps they were used as column caps for wooden posts.

The many other minor arts of the Meroitic Period cannot be discussed here. It should be mentioned, however, that jewelry belonging to non-royal persons was usually worked in bronze rather than precious metal. Bronze was also used for lamps, which resemble similar objects imported from the Classical world (Cat. 200; Fig. 77). These lamps, and many other objects, such as the bronze figurine of a kneeling man with offering table (Cat. 141), are outstanding examples of metalworking and clearly illustrate the independent character of Meroitic art.

CERAMICS

The Meroites undoubtedly accomplished one of their most independent artistic achievements in the field of ceramics. General observations regarding pottery making can be found elsewhere (Vol. I, Chap. 9). The

Fig. 72. Sandstone statuette of a baboon from Meroe, Meroitic Period, first century B.C. *to first century* A.D. *(Khartoum, Sudan National Museum).*

Fig. 73. Sandstone figure of the god Apedemak inscribed with the name of King Tanyidamani, Meroitic Period, 110-90 B.C. *(Louvre E. 11657b).*

Fig. 74. Gold shield-ring with ram's head in front of a temple portal (Cat. 164), from the pyramid of Queen Amanishakheto at Meroe (Beg. N. 6), Meroitic Period, late first century B.C. *(Munich Ant. 2446b).*

Fig. 75. Gold armlet with glass inlays (Cat. 170), from the pyramid of Queen Amanishakheto at Meroe (Beg. N. 6), Meroitic Period, late first century B.C. *(Munich Ant. 2455).*

Fig. 76. Faience cylinder decorated with figures of striding rams and lions, from Meroe, Meroitic Period, second to third century A.D. *(Toronto 921.4.1).*

Fig. 77. Bronze oil lamp with heads of elephants, from Meroe (Tomb W. 102), Meroitic Period, second to third century A.D. *(Khartoum 1947).*

following pages will concentrate on the considerable artistic achievement of the Meroites.

Many ceramic wares were produced in the Meroitic kingdom. There are at least two kinds of handmade wares, from Lower Nubia and the southern part of the kingdom. The wheel-made pottery can be divided into three groups. One is found only in the south, mainly at Musawwarat es-Sufra; it is relatively crude and generally undecorated (Otto 1973; Adams 1973,237). The two other types, or "families," as Adams calls them (1973,210-11), are considered typically Meroitic and represent the high point of pottery making not only in Nubia and the Sudan but in the entire Nile Valley. The "Meroitic fine wares" consist of delicate, thin-walled bowls, beakers, and cups (the so-called "eggshell wares") while the "Meroitic ordinary wares" consist of larger vessels, in various forms, fabrics, and decoration. This Meroitic decorated pottery is distinctive and cannot be confused with pottery of any other period.

Both wares are found mostly in Lower Nubia; they were discovered first at Areika and Karanog and later at Faras. Because of their connections to Egyptian pottery, especially in their painted decoration, their first discoverers, Woolley and Randall-MacIver, termed them "Romano-Nubian." The relatively few examples of this decorated pottery found in the southern part of the kingdom come mainly from Kerma, Wad Ban Naqa, and the pyramids at Gebel Barkal and Meroe. Many fragments, mostly of painted or stamped eggshell wares, were excavated in the royal quarter of Meroe. At Musawwarat es-Sufra, examples of Meroitic fine ware are scarce.

The concentration of the fine wares in the north and their presumed limitation to the late Meroitic Period have suggested to some that they might be a specialized Lower Nubian product, exported as a luxury good to the south. Therefore, they cannot be considered "Meroitic" in the true sense of the word (Adams 1973,237). There is evidence, however, that these wares were not limited in time or place. Meroitic fine wares were manufactured during the whole period in both parts of the kingdom. Sherds of a large, thick-walled vessel from Musawwarat es-Sufra (Cat. 219) have painted decoration — palms, vine tendrils, and an archer — which is reminiscent of Ptolemaic pottery painting, according to M. Bietak (oral communication). Since these sherds were found in the landfill of the terrace on which the Central Temple of the Great Enclosure was erected, they must date to the third century B.C. This important recent find suggests that painted Meroitic pottery originated earlier than has been assumed. But it also proves that painted pottery was first produced in the southern part of the kingdom. Although exact dates for the resettlement of Lower Nubia are lacking, the Meroitic building activity there during the third century B.C. and the northward-directed policy of the Meroitic rulers in the first century B.C. point to an earlier date for the resettlement. Adams (1964a, 164-65; 1973,198) believes that the Meroitic fine wares were not produced in Lower Nubia until the second century A.D. But the production of decorated Meroitic pottery in Lower Nubia is probably connected with its resettlement and could have started at a much earlier date. Griffith (1925; 1926) has proposed that ceramic production began in the first century B.C. That these fine wares originated in the south but later became more common in the north is a still unexplained paradox.

Fine Meroitic wares are generally decorated with paintings that show some Hellenistic influences borrowed from contemporary Egypt. The technique of decorating bowls and beakers with impressed designs had roots in indigenous traditions, but the arrangement of the motifs was new. Serpents or squares, for example, were impressed into the soft clay in friezes or covered the body of the vessel completely. Although this technique was used in Lower Nubia, it is more frequent in the south. This and the fact that there are other clear differences between painted pottery from the two regions show that fine Meroitic wares were also produced in the south. The vessels found at Kerma and in both the city and royal pyramids at Meroe have generally a whitish or light gray slip, while vessels found in Lower Nubia are usually red brown to yellow in color. Pots from the north more frequently depict scenes, while ornamental decoration appears to have been preferred in the south. The vessels from the south are also generally more delicate and more carefully executed, probably because the capital had superior workshops. It is highly improbable that the painted pottery found in the south was imported from Lower Nubia. Not only are the distances great, but the journey around the cataracts is hazardous, which would make the transportation of ceramics from Lower Nubia to Meroe expensive and risky.

Almost nothing is known of the development of painted Meroitic pottery. Neither the studies of Griffith nor the pioneering works of Adams have solved the problems of dating. We are still unable to say in general which ceramic paintings are earlier and which later. The wealth of motifs and ideas expressed in ceramic painting is such that very few vessels have identical decoration. Even when motifs are repeated, they vary in detail. A comparison of material from Karanog and Faras shows that vessels definitely painted by the same artist were found in cemeteries seventy kilometers apart. This confirms Adams' view that there were centers of ceramic production in Lower Nubia. Vessels such as beakers, cups, pots, jugs, amphorae, bowls, and the like were produced in such centers and then distributed. Whether this distribution was undertaken by the artists or by middlemen is not known. It seems most likely that the trade was carried on by agents, but the possibility that the potters moved from place to place cannot be completely dismissed. Their movements would have been limited, however, by the availability of clay and kilns.

Since similarities in certain painting styles often appear, they probably represent "schools" of painting. In many of these schools, particular patterns, and in many cases vessel forms as well, were preferred. The possibility that painter and potter were not the same suggests a high level of specialization in ceramic decoration.

One of the most common schools is distinguished by the use of certain specific motifs delineated with particularly exact, carefully executed lines. Because of the care and precision with which these motifs are drawn, and their linear style, this school should be called the "academic school." This decoration appears only on spherical vessels and beakers. The academic school was extremely productive. More surviving painted vessels from Karanog and Faras are attributable to this school than to any other.

In one group of vessels of the academic school, the decoration is divided into several registers. These registers can be subdivided, as in Cat. 239. The ball-bead motif appearing on the upper shoulder of this vessel is found on many others from Karanog and Faras. In this case, the slant-striped circles are joined by narrow bars. This ball-bead chain may well be the characteristic motif of the academic school.

In another group of vessels from the same school, there is a wide, undivided register of decoration on the body, which may be filled with plant or figural motifs. In Cat. 240, it is filled with two rows of stars. A uraeus frieze appears on the shoulder, and the ball-bead chain is just below the neck. In Cat. 241, the main register extends from the neck and covers about two-thirds of the body. Only the careful execution of the decoration bespeaks the academic style.

In addition to these two groups of ceramic decoration belonging to the academic school, several more have been ascertained. Sometimes only the upper third of the vessel is painted. These pots are common at Karanog. Other painters who used the academic style preferred the beaker form.[65]

Another group of painters, whose products have been found at Karanog and Faras, show a clear predilection for vine-leaf decoration. Artists of this school also limited their choice of vessel forms. One group of pots of the "vine-leaf school" have a wide body and a small, concave neck. The vessel is divided into two zones of decoration by colored stripes encircling the neck, the shoulder, and the lower body. Sometimes the shoulder is further subdivided into two registers (Cat. 224). Vine tendrils always encircle these pots at the shoulder, although they are rendered differently each time. A wide variety of motifs is used on the bodies. Cats. 221-224 (Fig. 78; Vol. I, Fig. 96) belong to the vine-leaf school. Handled jugs such as Cat. 244 were also decorated by artists of this school.

Enough vessels of this school survive for us to distinguish the hands of individual artists. The vines that appear on the shoulder are distinct, as are the other motifs, and careful study of these has, for the first time, allowed us to identify individual personalities. One painter showed a preference for the horned-altar motif. At least three works from this "Altar Painter" are known,

Fig. 78. Vessel with vine-leaf decoration and an antelope in flight (Cat. 221), Meroitic Period, second to third century A.D. *(Brooklyn 71.84).*

Fig. 79. Beaker with scalelike pattern and floral-star design (Cat. 251), Meroitic Period, second to third century A.D. *(Boston 23.1469).*

all from the same grave (Karanog 712) and now in Philadelphia (E 8156, E 8182, and Cat. 224; Vol. I, Fig.96). But it is worth noting that the execution of the vine pattern is different in each case.

The "Antelope Painter" is also known from three vessels, all featuring the motif of springing antelopes. Two come from Karanog (Cats. 222, 223); the origin of the third (Cat. 221; Fig. 78) is not known. There can be no doubt that Cat. 223 was painted by this artist, although the vessel has two handles, while Cats. 221 and 222 are without handles. These three pots also have representations, in a distinctive hand, of birds whose tail feathers are spread out and separately indicated. The same bird is found on a pot from Faras (Grave 2091; Berlin/DDR 20967). The antelope does not appear on this pot — proof that artists did not limit themselves exclusively to one subject.

Motifs alone are not the sole criterion in attribution of a vessel to a particular artist; technique and style must also be considered. The presence of such individuality in painting reflects the high level of achievement reached by ceramic artists in Lower Nubia.

Some painters did not limit themselves to special vessel forms. The tall, long-necked, ovoid pot from Faras, Cat. 236, shows giraffes, trees, and a bound prisoner. The details, particularly the delineation of eye and ear with a continuous line, make it clear that this pot and the cylindrical vessel from Faras, Cat. 237, were painted by the same artist.[66] The technique and style of the "Prisoner Painter" are too distinctive to be imitated.

Another artist painted Cat. 234 from Faras and Cat. 235 from Karanog. On both vessels, men stand in front of tall, stylized lotus stalks. This painter, too, varied his motifs. On one pot, he placed three men in front of a plant; on the other, he divided the scene into parts and placed each man in front of a different lotus plant.[67]

The identification of these artists is a great step toward the creation of a ceramic chronology. Tombs that yield vessels produced by the same artist must be of roughly the same date. It is possible, therefore, that a relative chronology can be worked out.

Fewer examples of painted pottery have come to light in the southern part of the kingdom. Those pots which are known, moreover, indicate that there existed in the south an independent tradition.

The unique rim fragment from Meroe, Cat. 220, with the representation of a naked couple, reflects the influence of Alexandrian art and can be placed within Style Group V (see p. 65). The goblet, Cat. 250, with impressed *ankh*-signs and the tall beaker, Cat. 249, with impressed geometric patterns are probably products of the royal workshops. Both were found in pyramids belonging to members of the royal house. Vessels of this distinctive form and brick red color have been found only in the south. The beaker from a pyramid at Meroe, Cat. 251 (Fig. 79), with its painted floral stars and the beaker from Kerma, Cat. 252, painted with halfmoons are works of unusual quality, perhaps the most beautiful examples of fine Meroitic ceramics. Stylistically, Cat. 252 is related to the academic school of Lower Nubia, but its superior quality suggests that it is more likely a product of the royal workshops. For Cat. 251 only one parallel has been found in Lower Nubia: a graduated beaker from Grave 738 at Karanog (Philadelphia E 8457). It may well have come from one of the pottery centers of the south, which would suggest that wares from the royal workshops found their way to Lower Nubia.

Among the few ceramic motifs appropriated from the sphere of official art are *udjat*-eyes, *ankh*-signs, winged and wingless cobras, vultures with spread wings, offering tables, horned altars, and lion heads representing the god Apedemak. Fabled beings, dancing fauns, grape clusters, and vine-tendril patterns are adapted from Egypt and the Classical world. Apart from these motifs, ceramic painting reflects a rich, probably folk art tradition. Many different kinds of human representations are known. Generally, the face is shown full front, often with scarifications indicated. But the most common motifs are animals or geometric or floral patterns.[68]

A few narrative scenes were painted on vessels (Cat. 233; Vol. I, Fig. 97). There is the rim fragment found at Meroe (Cat. 220) with a naked man and woman holding a cloth in front of themselves. The shoulder painting of Cat. 232 depicts lions attacking fallen men, a royal triumph motif that appears very rarely in ceramic art. Also outstanding is the hunting scene, Cat. 219.[69]

The creative richness of ceramic decoration in the Meroitic Period is equaled by the richness of forms. The Meroitic potter, like the sculptor, both borrowed and invented. Among the new forms are the barrel-shaped vessel (Cat. 226), the ring-flask (Cat. 225; Vol. I, Fig. 95), which appears to go back to a form known in Egypt in Dynasty XVIII, and two unique openwork vessels (Cats. 242, 243). Cat. 259 is an example of a very different tradition known as barbotine ware, in which small lumps of clay are applied as ornamentation. This Roman decorative technique developed in the first century A.D. and was very popular, making its way even to England. The relative frequency of vessels of this type in Lower Nubia, especially Faras, suggests that barbotine vessels were manufactured in Nubia. It is hard to believe they were imported from Egypt. Egyptian vessels, which arrived in Nubia as early as the late fourth millennium B.C., were containers for oils, beer, or wine. The vessels themselves were never imported, since the Nubians were capable of manufacturing their own.

Handmade domestic wares were probably produced by women. These wares can be traced as far back as the Neolithic Period, and similar pots are still being produced in the Sudan today. From an artistic point of view, the black or blackish-brown polished ware with incised (more rarely, impressed) decoration is the most ambitious. It has been found in Lower Nubia (Cats. 260, 261, 263, 265) as well as in the south of the kingdom (Cats. 262, 264), and reflects the continuity of tradition from the C-group and the Kerma culture (Adams 1964a,161). These pots prove that the population of Nubia and the northern Sudan remained substantially unchanged. This high-quality household ware is less common than the painted ceramics.

A more detailed examination of Meroitic ceramic painting cannot be undertaken here. The pots included in the catalogue, however, illustrate its rich variety. Meroitic ceramics are the finest ever produced in the Nile Valley.

SUMMARY

We have tried here to define the character of Meroitic art. In this attempt, certain aspects have been discussed in far more detail than others. In summation, Meroitic art developed from Napatan art. While retaining the established principles of official art, Meroitic art subsequent to the third century B.C. increasingly departed from its roots to incorporate independent features, consisting of iconographic elements that had either developed within Kush itself or were borrowed and adapted. The essential features of Meroitic art include stylistic variety, receptivity to external influences, a general absence of inscriptions, limitation to a few genres, distinct separation of official and unofficial art, and, finally, an artistic division between the north and the south. The most important achievements of Meroitic artisans undoubtedly lay in the field of unofficial art, in which independence is most markedly expressed.

Meroitic art had its origins in both the Eygptian and African worlds. Its character is creatively eclectic. It represents an early contact point where elements of Western and African culture met and were integrated into a literate civilization. (Many features of Meroitic art — and Nubian art in general — are African in character, though certainly not in the generally accepted sense of African art. However, in order not to overburden the continuing discussion of the concept "African," we have consciously refrained from emphasizing this aspect. We have made a distinction between "African" and "Egyptian" in spite of the fact that Egypt is located in Africa. Egypt has always occupied both culturally and ethnically a special position between Africa and Asia.)

The ability of Meroitic artists to free themselves from foreign models and create an art expressing the Meroitic-Nubian sensibility is one of their important contributions to civilization.

17. The last Meroitic works are Pyramids Beg. N. 24, N. 25, and N. 26, located in the North Cemetery of Meroe. In Lower Nubia, works in the Meroitic style were probably produced even somewhat later. The prolonged existence of Meroitic art in the north is associated with the political history of the kingdom.
18. Addison (1950, 18-19) believes that near Sennar was a large Meroitic city. Dixon (1963, 234) thinks that the Meroitic kingdom extended even farther south.
19. The stela of King Nastasen (Cat. 72) and the tomb stela of Queen Sakhmakh (Cat. 73), which date from the late fourth century, come from Gebel Barkal and are still in the style of the Napatan Period.
20. These structures are the two Amun Temples at Amara and Naqa and the bark pedestal from the Isis Temple of Wad Ban Naqa (Berlin/DDR 7261; Vol. I, fig. 74). It is unclear whether or not the statue of King Natakamani, made of graywacke (Liverpool MCM 49.47.709) should be placed within this group. Unfortunately, only a single fragment of this statue bearing the king's name has been found.
21. The earliest are the column base from the Great Enclosure (Fig. 38) and the Apedemak Temple of King Arnekhamani, both from Musawwarat es-Sufra (Fig. 45; Vol. I, Fig. 69). Also belonging to this group are sculptures (Cat. 137), including a group statue (Cat. 135), statues of gods from the Isis Temple at Meroe now in Edinburgh and Copenhagen (Fig. 65), colossal figures from Argo now in Khartoum (Fig. 64), a votive tablet (Cat. 121), a relief (Cat. 125), and the triple-protomes found at Musawwarat es-Sufra (Cat. 145).
22. The primary reason for placing *ba*-statues and reserve heads in this group is the fact that they are geographically restricted, though they depict private individuals who happened to belong to the Meroitic ruling class in Lower Nubia (viceroys and priests). They did not therefore represent official art nor, indeed, were they made for all members of this class.
23. These works include a single temple construction, the Roman kiosk at Naqa (Fig. 66), whose dependence on Alexandrian art has been clearly demonstrated (Kraus 1964). Other works belonging to Group V are statues from the Royal Baths at Meroe (Cat. 161 and Figs. 61,62,67) and two reliefs on columns of the Central Temple of the Great Enclosure at Musawwarat es-Sufra. On one of these reliefs is a row of dancing youths; on the other, in raised relief, are both Egyptian and Meroitic deities in front view.
24. Thus the shoulders of one queen (Cat. 135) are broad, while those of another (Cat. 137) are completely unemphasized.
25. To the first group belong works authorized by the royal house and the ruling class: temples, palaces, pyramids, and likenesses of gods and kings, all of which represent the power of the sovereign and the permanency of the kingdom. In contrast are such unofficial works as decorated ceramics and figural graffiti (secondary pictures), small sculptures (Cats. 142,143), and amuletic figures of gods.
26. The oldest pair of columns with sculpted fronts have come to light in Room 108 of the Great Enclosure at Musawwarat es-Sufra and thus probably still belong in the fourth century B.C. (Hintze 1968b).
27. A second pair from a much later time also represent these gods. Garstang found them reused as building material in the foundations of the Isis Temple at Meroe (now Edinburgh and Copenhagen; Fig. 65).
28. See note 26.
29. As can be seen in the representations of Queen

Amanishakheto and of Queen Amanitore (Fig. 46).

30. As one can see in reliefs from the Apedemak Temple of Musawwarat es-Sufra, the group statue, Cat. 135, and the funerary stelae, Cats 118, 120.
31. It is exemplified by the statuette of Queen Nawidemak (Cat. 137), the reliefs of the early first century A.D. from the Apedemak Temple at Naqa (Figs. 43,46,53,54), the relief from King Amanitenmemide's pyramid chapel (Fig. 52), the colossal figures from Argo (Fig. 64), and the column-statues in Edinburgh and Copenhagen (Fig. 65).
32. As is evident in the Apedemak Temple reliefs from Musawwarat es-Sufra (Fig. 45) and from the group statue, Cat. 135.
33. Reliefs from the Apedemak Temple at Naqa (Fig. 46) and representations of King Amanitenmemide (Fig. 52) support this. On the basis of the sash, the statuette, Cat. 137, was attributed to the first century B.C. (Shinnie 1953,95), and this dating has been confirmed by an inscription on its base bearing the name of Queen Nawidemak.
34. The representation of a round hut on a bronze bowl from Karanog (Cat. 196) and the relief of a village scene from the Temple of Apedemak at Meroe (Garstang 1911, pl.XXI,6) confirm the existence of these huts in Meroitic times. The Gebel Barkal shrine containing an image of a god (Cat. 131) is an imitation of this type of dwelling.
35. This method of construction may reflect social conditions. The excavators believe that new living quarters were perhaps added to the old with the acquisition of a new wife, who received a separate apartment for herself and her children, which suggests the practice of polygamy. Additional units, however, may have been given to married children, who were thus provided with their own living quarters in the house of their parents.
36. The latter locality, lying approximately two kilometers to the north of Abu Simbel, was excavated by a Dutch expedition under A. Klasens in 1962-63.
37. A sandstone window grill was found at Faras (Michałowski 1965,180, pl.XXXVIIIb), which was carved in the form of the squatting ibis-headed god Thoth. A similar grill, recently found at Qasr Ibrim, is in the form of a naked man bearing an elephant on his shoulders (Plumley 1970a, pl.XXIII,4).
38. Although this god is probably of Meroitic origin, he was introduced into the Egyptian pantheon during the early part of the third century B.C. His cult did not extend north of Philae (Winter 1974; Wenig 1974).
39. Garstang found several temples at Meroe (1909-14) dedicated to Amun, Apedemak, and Isis. P. L. Shinnie has since uncovered additional sacred buildings there. Sanctuaries also existed at Musawwarat es-Sufra, Naqa, Wad Ban Naqa, Duanib, and Basa, to name but a few sites.
40. For some unknown reason, this rule was not followed in Temple F at Naqa, built by Queen Shanakdakhete during the second century B.C. (Hintze 1959, pls.V-VIII), where there appears to be an internal division in which the gods face the rear wall in the first half of the temple and the entrance in the other.
41. Changes in the orientation of the Central Temple in the Great Enclosure at Musawwarat es-Sufra are probably the result of a change in position of the star or planet with which the temple was aligned.
42. The Temple of Basa can also be dated to the first century B.C. on the basis of a colossal lion bearing the name of King Amanikhabale (Khartoum 24393a).
43. Investigation of the sequential schemes of pyramid reliefs has supported changes in dating pyramids and led to greater precision in the relative chronology of the period (Wenig 1964; 1967).
44. See note 40.
45. Photographs of two other wall paintings from palaces at Meroe are preserved but still unpublished. One shows a prince on a lotus blossom and is similar to a scene in Temple F of Queen Shanakdakhete at Naqa (Hintze 1959, pl.I); the other depicts an enthroned king, his feet on a footstool with representations of prisoners on the side. Gods and several men are also included in this scene. Unfortunately, the paintings (which might have provided us with information regarding a genre of art for which there is scarcely any other evidence in Kush) have remained unpublished. Should the drawings, which disappeared immediately after the end of the Second World War in 1945, ever be found, they would be received with great interest.
46. The same motif has been found at Qasr Ibrim in a window grill. See note 37.
47. We have only one example of a god with the head of an animal and the body of a human being. This is the upper part of a statuette depicting the god Apedemak; it also bears a Meroitic inscription naming King Tanyidamani (Louvre E. 11657b; Fig. 73).
48. The seated individual and group statues that we possess can be easily listed. In Musawwarat es-Sufra, three individual figures (two men and one woman) have been found; these may well have been cult representations but are quite poorly preserved. A large granite statue of Isis with a child comes from Gebel Barkal (Berlin/DDR 2258: Griffith 1912,2ff.). In Meroe, Garstang found the lower portion of a statuette of the same type (Liverpool MCM 47.49.711) and the lower part of a female figure dressed in a long skirt and carrying an *ankh*-sign in her left hand (Liverpool SAOS 224). There were also seated groups from several pyramids at Meroe and Gebel Barkal; these depicted either Osiris between two goddesses, or rulers and deities. It is not certain whether or not the figurine, Cat. 144, is a seated sculpture. If the figure is to be regarded as seated, then it must be a representation of a deity. A few seated sculptures from the baths at Meroe belong to Style Group V (see p. 87).
49. Approximately fifteen statues are known. Among them is the fragment of a statue of King Natakamani found at Meroe, with the king's name inscribed in Egyptian hieroglyphs (Liverpool MCM 49.47.709), which is possibly to be placed within Style Group II, a group to which otherwise only the reliefs belong. The reasons for this classification lie in its Egyptian inscription as well as in its material. The green stone is not otherwise known in Meroe and was therefore probably imported.
50. Three small faience figurines which come from Meroe and are difficult to assign or interpret (Copenhagen NCG 1321; Brussels E. 3550) depict women bending forward and grasping with their left hands a vertical slab standing before them; the right hands all lie upon the body (Fig. 60). It is not known if they are products of official or unofficial art, but they are of a type unknown in the north.
51. Only six objects bear an inscription: the Apedemak statuette in the Louvre (Fig. 73); the golden statuette of

Queen Nawidemak (Cat. 137); the fragment of a statue of Natakamani in Liverpool (see note 49); a lion from Basa (now Khartoum) bearing the name of King Amanikhabale; a ram figure from Soba inscribed with the name of King [Mnkh] reqerem (Khartoum 24393a); and a fragment of a lion sculpture from Qasr Ibrim bearing the name of King Yesbokheamani.

52. The two figures standing in front of Temple 300 at Musawwarat es-Sufra must belong to the fourth or third century B.C. Both gods are accompanied by lions on a leash. In Room 108 of the Great Enclosure at Musawwarat es-Sufra are two more figures that were found broken into many small fragments; these were in the form of column-statues and belong also to the fourth or third century B.C. In Naqa, the remains of two similar figures were excavated (Hintze 1960a,376-81), for which no dates can be given. The fourth pair of statues are the column-statues of Meroe which, on the basis of their proportions, are to be dated subsequent to King Natakamani (Edinburgh 1910.110.36; Copenhagen NCG 1082; Fig. 65).
53. It was originally hypothesized that these figures belonged in the third century B.C. (Wenig 1973a); it now appears more likely that they are somewhat later.
54. Among the sculptures from the Royal Baths, which are mostly unpublished, is the figure of a naked boy playing a double flute (Wellcome Historical Medical Museum EG. 1.63; now London, University College [A400,036]: Dixon —Wachsmann 1964). Still standing in the partially restored baths is the statue of a man clad in a pleated robe playing a Pan-flute and the figure of a harpist (Garstang 1913b, pl. VI) dressed in a pleated robe and wearing a headband (Fig. 67). Garstang also found fragments of a so-called armored statue (Garstang 1912a,10, pl.X), which is a Roman type (Kraus 1969,55), as well as a seated man holding a papyrus roll, reminiscent of Classical philosopher statues. The most interesting of these is a group statue of a couple who are shown lying on their stomachs, their upper torsos raised, supported by their elbows. The lower half of both figures is covered. The woman holds a bowl. Heads of several statues from the baths are in various museums; the finest represents a black African (Copenhagen NCG 1336; Fig. 62). Traces of color show that this head was once a deep black.
55. The term *ba*-statue, first used by Randall-MacIver—Woolley (1909,29), only reflects the fact that these sculptures are faintly similar to Egyptian representations of the soul, called the *ba*. This Egyptian form was taken over in Lower Nubia and a few places south of the Second Cataract (Žabkar 1968,84), though it is doubtful that it had the same meaning in Nubia as in Egypt. In fact, similar statues were never made in Egypt to depict the deceased. Only Emery (1965,229) has raised doubts concerning the interpretation of these figures as representations of the *ba*. This new tradition of tomb equipment, found only in the northern part of the Kingdom of Kush, is probably to be explained as a new custom taken over by the ruling Meroites.
56. Other figures represent falcons and birds with a human head, sometimes shown with human feet. These three types were grouped by the first excavators of such statues found at Shablul and Karanog (Randall-MacIver—Woolley 1909, 28-29, pls. 16-20; Woolley—Randall-MacIver 1910, 46-48, pls. 1-10).
57. Woolley—Randall-MacIver 1910,10-11, pl. 114 left; Almagro 1965b, 19, Fig. 4; Simpson 1964,18; Emery 1965,228-29, Fig. 42.
58. Represented on the pylon of her pyramid chapel at Meroe, Beg. N. 6, now Berlin/DDR 2244.
59. The fact that the heads were made as complete works and were undoubtedly placed in or on top of the cult chapel of pyramid or nastaba tombs is reminiscent of an Egyptian custom practiced during Dynasties IV and V, when heads rather than complete statues were placed in tomb shafts. These heads are called reserve heads and it seems justifiable to use the same term to describe the Meroitic works of this kind.
60. Cemetery 2-W-3; Find Number 2-W-3/1/1; Khartoum 24144. It was discovered in Amir Abdallah, District of Abri East, by a Franco-Sudanese expedition under the leadership of A. Vila.
61. Further examples were found by Bates at Gemai (Grave U 3.1: Bates—Dunham 1927, pl.36,2-3). Another head was discovered during the excavations at Sedeinga (Leclant 1966, pl. XXXII, Fig. 55).
62. See note 51.
63. In front of Temple 300 at Musawwarat es-Sufra (Fig. 40) and, therefore, it is presumed the lions appearing at either side of the ram's head on the two triple-protomes found in the Apedemak Temple at Musawwarat es-Sufra (Cat. 145 and Khartoum 18890; Fig. 41) represent the same gods (Wenig 1974).
64. One cylinder, however, does show representations reminiscent of Hellenistic-Roman art and can be placed in Style Group V. In another case, the upper part of a girl's body is shown; the figure turns to the left, and the head, rendered in profile, is somewhat inclined. This posture is similar to those of figures of women found on Greek grave reliefs.
65. Several vessels found at Karanog are clearly imitations of the academic school. They are characterized by the attempt to achieve linear form in their decoration; however, the paintings are less precise and less careful than in the academic style.
66. Another vessel from Faras (Grave 2006; London 51561) corresponds in form to Cat. 236 and also depicts giraffes standing in front of trees as well as a prisoner. In other words, we see here a variant of the same motif. The details of the decoration are identical.
67. The representation of an animal seen in Cat. 235, which is perhaps meant to be a dog, is reminiscent of a caricature; whether or not this was intended is difficult to say. However, the main motif must have possessed a particular meaning; it was certainly not merely decoration.
68. Among the animals we find monkeys, crocodiles, frogs, serpents (carrying branches or *ankh*-signs in their mouths), giraffes, cattle, antelope, geese, chickens, and dogs. Finally, there also appear stars, floral stars, halfmoons, and many other such motifs.
69. In contrast, the later representation of a hunter found on a two-handled vase from Faras (Griffith 1924, pl. XLVIII,7; London 51515) appears quite awkward. The figure shows very little animation and is by no means to be regarded as having reached the same artistic level as that revealed by the earlier work.

4

The Art of the Ballana Culture

After the fall of the Meroitic kingdom about A.D. 320, Meroitic art and writing lived on for a while in Lower Nubia. It seems that the old political order also survived in that part of the country for a few decades after the fall of the capital. But by the end of the fourth century at the latest, changes occurred, especially in ceramics and jewelry. How these changes affected other areas of art is not yet known.

Meroitic art forms died out as the result of a change in the political structure. The Meroites gradually lost power to the Noba and the Nobadae, groups probably of southern origin. The latter had been settled in the Dodekashoinos by the Emperor Diocletian in A.D. 297.[70] Early in the fifth century, groups of Blemmyes from the Eastern Desert also settled temporarily in several places in Lower Nubia. These groups had their own artistic traditions, which brought about the end of Meroitic art. It can no longer be believed that a new ethnic group brought the Ballana culture. Junker (1925,85) long ago stated that the cultures of Meroe and the Ballana Period were segments of the same cultural continuum, a view now generally accepted (Adams 1965a; 1965b; Trigger 1965; 1967; 1969a; Török 1974).

The dates of the Ballana Period remain uncertain. It has been rather generally dated from the third to the sixth century (Emery 1948,26), but studies by Bissing (1939a; 1939b; [1939-41]; 1941) and Török (1974,361 ff.) suggest that a dating between the late fourth century and the beginning of the sixth would be more accurate. On the basis of the relationship between minor art objects from the royal tombs at Ballana and Qustul and those of Egypt, especially of Alexandria, Bissing assigned the Ballana culture to the fourth or fifth century, rejecting the view of Emery and Kirwan that it lasted to the sixth century. Török, working from a few pieces of jewelry found in Tombs B 47 at Ballana and Q 14 at Qustul and in the late Meroitic Pyramid Beg. W. 130, concluded that the objects dated from the second half of the fourth century. A few coins discovered in Lower Nubia also support the dating of the Ballana culture to the fourth and fifth centuries.

Political changes in Lower Nubia and its lack of communication with the south resulted in greater dependence upon Egypt (Adams 1964b; 1965a; Trigger 1968,117). The Hellenistic art of Greece, Rome, and Alexandria, and the emergent Coptic art of Egypt, all contributed to a pervasive northern influence. It is not surprising that early Byzantine art left traces in Nubia, for Egypt had been part of the Byzantine Empire since A.D. 395. However, the Meroitic influence was still strong, as several scholars, recently also Kirwan (1963,72f.), have pointed out. Thus the art of the Ballana culture was an admixture of old and new, the new including indigenous developments as well as influences from the north. This situation makes an evaluation of Ballana art difficult. Several authors have claimed that the best of minor art objects from this period found in Lower Nubia were imported from Egypt and Byzantium, which was certainly not the case. Bissing began the task of tracing the origins of the Ballana culture in the series of articles cited above, which deal with minor objects found in the royal tombs of Ballana and Qustul. He was chiefly concerned with tracing the relationship between selected objects from the royal necropolis and the art of Alexandria. His conclusions have, in most cases, been adopted here.

In sheer quantity, the Ballana finds are impressive, although they are limited to jewelry, ceramics, and other small objects. Most of the surviving objects come from the royal cemeteries at Ballana and Qustul, but fine works of art have been found also at Gemai, south of the Second Cataract, and at Ferka, Gebel Adda, and other places. Qasr Ibrim was once a great administrative center but is today merely an island in the huge Lake Nasser. The site has yielded a great deal of information about Nubian history and art.[71]

Our knowledge of the Ballana culture is rather one-sided. The tempting conclusion is that art production was limited to objects of daily use for the consumption of the affluent upper classes. Almost no relief, sculpture, or painting has been discovered, and such architecture as has come to light appears to be an impoverished reflection of the past. Sophisticated architecture seems to have been limited in general to houses and tombs (see Vol. I, pp. 109-15). The tumulus burials at Ballana reflect the old Nubian burial customs first seen at Kerma. The existence of human sacrifice indicates the survival of an ancient tradition, and bed burials were common, as they were at both Meroe and Kerma. Links with Meroe can be discerned in the approaches to the royal tombs, and tumuli such as those at Gebel Adda are covered with pebbles like those at Kerma. These mounds vary greatly in size, their diameters ranging from two to fourteen meters (Millet 1963,150).

To date, no temples of the Ballana Period have been discovered. They must have existed, for religion had always played an important part in Nubian life and required developed cult constructions. Perhaps temples were built less solidly in this period of political change than in more settled times and have therefore not survived. Certainly during the early Christian Period, any such structures as remained would have been destroyed by zealots of the new faith. Objects found in the cemeteries of Ballana and Qustul, especially in the tombs of royal persons, bear motifs derived from the old Meroitic religion. Although these motifs may have been largely incomprehensible to the persons for whom the objects were made, they undoubtedly had some religious significance. The worship of the goddess Isis at Philae by Nubians and Blemmyes proves that organized religion was still practiced in this period, and so we may presume the existence of temples preserving the remnants of a dying cult.

Sculptures and reliefs of the Ballana Period are almost entirely lacking. One of the few surviving examples of relief is on the four sides of the stone capital of a vanished column from Qasr Ibrim (Cat. 283). The style of these reliefs, so very different from that of Meroitic examples, suggests that Ballana artists developed an individual form of expression.

MINOR ARTS

It is in the minor arts — jewelry, bronze work, and ceramics — that the skill and inventiveness of Ballana craftsmen are most apparent. Among the important finds in the royal cemeteries at Ballana and Qustul are the diadems and crowns of the kings and queens who were buried there. Ten crowns have come to light, all of them evidently of local manufacture. These and many heavy rings, necklaces, and bracelets, as well as silver plates and jugs, demonstrate that the silversmiths of Ballana were familiar with most techniques known in antiquity.

The crowns are reminiscent of Meroitic crowns. These wide silver circlets are decorated in bold relief with Egyptian motifs: Hathor heads, Horus hawks (Cat. 267), *udjat*-eyes (Cat. 266), and striding kings bearing offerings. Uraei cut out of thin sheets of silver are sometimes attached to the upper edges (Cat. 267). Some crowns are encrusted with precious and semi-precious stones. Over the forehead on three of the kings' crowns (B 80, B 95, and B 114) is mounted the ram's head of Amun, fully in the round, and above it rises the feathered crest of the pharaohs derived from the *atef*-crown, flanked by uraei. We see here the adaptation of a form that originated in Egypt and was later appropriated by the Meroites. In one instance, the feathered crown rests on a crescent on a shaft (Cat. 267). Much later the crescent on a shaft became an insignium of office for the eparchs of the Christian Era, who are pictured in church frescoes (Cat. 293).

These crowns testify to the great skill of the Ballana silversmiths. The practice of setting jewels *en cabochon* has been discussed by Bissing (1939a; 1941), who proves that the technique originated in the Black Sea region and was further developed in Alexandria, from whence it spread to Nubia. This by no means implies that the crowns themselves were made in Alexandria or any other place outside of Nubia. While the technique may have come from the north, it is evident that the objects in which it was used were of local manufacture. The sheer abundance of silverwork at Ballana — rings, bracelets, necklaces, and innumerable horse trappings — bespeaks a large-scale industry in Lower Nubia, an industry that produced not only jewelry but silver vessels for the use of princes.

Török (1974,362ff.) based his study upon two armlets from a queen's tomb (B 47) and a finger ring from a tomb at Qustul (Q 14). He concludes, on the basis of two similar bracelets found in Pyramid W. 130 at Meroe, that the royal cemetery at Meroe continued to be used until the second half of the fourth century. We know that his conclusion is historically impossible because Pyramid W. 130 at Meroe is earlier than the burials B 47 and Q 14 of the Ballana Period. Török's study suggests, however, that the Meroitic bracelets with their cabochon stones came from the same workshop as the objects from the Ballana tombs. Hence, there could not have been a long time span separating the Ballana Period from the end of the Meroitic Period.

No other Nubian epoch has yielded so many copper, iron, and bronze objects as the Ballana Period. Hundreds of examples have been found in the royal tombs at Ballana and Qustul, and many other sites in Lower Nubia — Qasr Ibrim, Ferka, Gemai, among them — have added to the abundance. Almost without exception, these metal objects served a practical purpose. They include goblets, pitchers, bowls (Cat. 281), bottles, cooking vessels, and articles of furniture, such as lamps and lamp stands (Cats. 277-280), chests or decoration for chests, small tables, and frames for folding chairs.

Most of these metal objects display great technical skill and artistic invention, and it has been frequently stated that they must be either imports from the Graeco-Roman north or slavish imitations of Hellenistic models. It is entirely possible that certain pieces of metalwork found at Ballana came to Nubia in trade or as booty and that others may have been inspired by Graeco-Roman models. It cannot be doubted, however, that many — perhaps most — of the metal objects discovered at Ballana were made in Nubia by Nubian craftsmen. As was seen at Meroe, there was a long tradition of bronze working in Nubia that had shown a native inventiveness along with adaptation of Graeco-Roman forms. There are always multiple examples of metal objects. Almost identical bronze bowls were found at Qasr Ibrim (Cat. 281), Ballana, Gemai, and elsewhere. Only a few objects can be definitely identified as imports from the north; most of these came from Alexandria. Whatever their stylistic sources may be, the Ballana bronze objects testify to the continuing ability of Nubian craftsmen to imitate, absorb, and adapt, and to produce works of technical perfection.

In addition to bronze objects, Ballana burials yielded other articles for household use. Among them were wooden chests, some with elaborate ivory inlays. Such chests were already in use in Meroe (Cats. 208, 209), but the Ballana examples show more care in construction and greater variety in decoration. In some cases, the wood has disintegrated, leaving only the inlays (Cat. 284), but a few almost intact examples survive. An impressive chest discovered at Gebel Adda (Millet 1964,9, pl.IV, figs.9-10) is decorated with Classical deities, such as Venus, rendered in Hellenistic style and Egyptian deities and motifs, including the divine child Harpocrates and Hathor heads, rendered in the style of Egypt. The largest and best-preserved chest of this type comes from Ballana (Fig. 80). It is one meter high, and the front is carved in the form of a richly decorated, many-storied house facade. There are six registers inlaid with ivory panels, each with the incised figure of a deity. The gods are a catholic

Fig. 80. Large wooden chest in the form of a multi-storied house, from Ballana, Ballana culture, late fourth century A.D. *(Cairo JE 71191).*

Fig. 81. Hemispherical bowl with stylized birds, from Wadi Kitna, near Kalabsha, Ballana Period, fourth century A. D. *(Prague, Náprstkovo Muzeum).*

Fig. 82. Goblet with "wavy line pattern," from Wadi Kitna, near Kalabsha, Ballana Period, fourth century A. D. *(Prague, Náprstkovo Muzeum).*

mixture, including Pan, Zeus, Aphrodite, and the Egyptian dwarf-god Bes.

Millet (1964,9) believes that these chests were made in Byzantine Egypt and came to Lower Nubia as trade or booty; in this, he follows Bissing's opinion (1941,24,n.76). Kirwan, on the other hand (1963,67), regards the chests as the work of Nubian artisans. It is true that similar works have been found in Egypt, but considering the skill demonstrated by Ballana craftsmen in such objects as the royal crowns, it is certainly possible that local artisans were capable of producing these chests. The peculiar mixture of Egyptian and Greek gods argues for their local creation.

A completely different type of wooden chest turned up in 1963 at Gebel Adda (Millet 1964,9, pl.IV, fig.11). On its lid is carved a lion in high relief, shown in frontal view, with falcon head and wings pointed upward. He wears a misunderstood Egyptian *hemhem*-crown, and below him is a frieze of uraei. It can hardly be doubted that this creature represents the Meroitic god Apedemak and that the chest is, as the excavator regarded it, an indigenous Nubian product. It indeed documents an unbroken tradition from the Meroitic past, though with some iconographic and stylistic changes. Such changes are also evident in a wooden cosmetic container in the form of a seated sphinx (Cat. 282). Both pieces typify the essence of Ballana, with its close ties to Egypt and its roots deep-sunk in Nubian soil.

A few pieces of jewelry and small objects in stone from Ballana burials reflect a very different stylistic tradition. Two such bracelets were found in Tomb B 80 on the arm of a sacrificed retainer (Cat. 272). They are decorated with colored inlays in simple geometric designs and show careful, experienced workmanship. Colorful inlay occurs also on some of the numerous stone archer's thumb-guards found at Ballana and Sesebi (Cat. 273). Although similar pieces were found at Meroe (Cat. 217), they were undecorated. This jewelry is probably not in the Meroitic tradition but is rather a product of one of the ethnic groups that inhabited Lower Nubia in the Ballana Period.

The same process of innovation is observable in ceramics. Typical Ballana ceramics are discussed elsewhere (Vol. I, p. 131), but it should be recalled that Ballana pottery developed from Meroitic pottery and acquired an independent character only after the fourth century A. D. A recently identified ware that has nothing to do with Ballana ware, but that seems to be of considerable importance in assessing the artistic diversity of Lower Nubia during the Ballana Period, was discovered in the 1960s near Kalabsha by a Czechoslovakian expedition. It has no recorded parallels. This pottery can probably be accurately dated to the fourth century on the basis of associated finds, which included a glass plate of that period and a single coin of Constantius II (A. D. 337-61). These vessels are predominantly red brown or dark brown in color, more rarely black or grayish black, and are mostly polished. They include chiefly hemispherical bowls (Fig. 81) and simple goblets (Fig. 82). They bear incised decoration, contained between lines or simple ornamented borders. Stylized birds, similar to those that decorate crude C-group ware or the ordinary black Meroitic pottery, appear on a hemispherical bowl; another motif taken from painted Meroitic ceramics is imitated on a goblet; lozenges, wavy lines, stylized fish, and other motifs are all traceable to earlier sources. However, these works have a well-defined character of their own for which nothing comparable has come to light. Probably they are products of the Nobadae who were settled in this region by Diocletian in A.D. 297. These people had experienced earlier contact with Meroe but had retained their cultural independence.

It is precisely such unexpected discoveries as this which reveal the tangled traditions of Lower Nubia in the post-Meroitic Period.

70. That the Noba and the Nobadae were two different ethnic groups has been proved by a document (still unpublished) found at Qasr Ibrim in 1976.
71. There, the excavations of the Egypt Exploration Society have unearthed not only works of art but documents written in Meroitic, Coptic, Arabic, Greek, and Old Nubian, which implies that a large section of the population could read and write. Other finds, including numerous bronze utensils, testify to the material culture of the people of the region. However, as of this writing, we have only preliminary reports of the British excavation at Qasr Ibrim (Plumley 1964; 1966; 1967; 1970a; 1975) and must await full publication to form a complete picture of this center of Nubian culture.

5

The Art of Christian Nubia

The end of the Ballana culture marked the close of the second major phase of Nubian history, which had begun in the eighth century B.C. with the establishment of the Kingdom of Kush. The third phase dawned in the late fifth or early sixth century A.D. with the introduction of Christianity into the region south of the First Cataract (Dinkler 1970). The new faith spread with considerable rapidity, and in the course of the sixth century there arose in the Upper Nile Valley three kingdoms in which Christianity became the official religion: Nobatia, Makuria, and Alwa. Nubia remained henceforth a Christian land until the advance of Islam in the fourteenth and fifteenth centuries.

The art of the Christian Era reveals a complete break with that of the Ballana culture. The rupture, however, signifies an ideological rather than an ethnological change. The same people inhabited Nubia; and these early Christian Nubians were very like their descendants still living in the region today, as can be seen in the portrayals of bishops and dignitaries (Cats. 292, 293) on the walls of ancient churches.

It is no mystery that Christianity brought to Nubia new techniques and iconography, which replaced the old traditions. The new canons were inspired in part by Christian Egypt, in part by Christian Syria and Palestine. Although Christian art in Nubia later acquired a specifically Nubian character, it never completely lost touch with its foreign sources. We have included here a few outstanding objects which show that Nubia in the Middle Ages once again became an important artistic center.

Dinkler (1970,8) has stated that "Nubian art in the Christian Period is Christian in theme but not in essence, that is, Christian in its representational material though not in its style or structural principles." Thus in Nubia the term "Christian art" involves a reversal of the concepts that govern pre-Christian art in Nubia, for it was precisely style and structural principles rather than themes and representational material that constituted the essence of Kushite art.

The question of whether there is actually a Nubian Christian art that differs from the Christian art of other regions has aroused widely divergent opinions. Plumley (1970b,133) believes that the Christian art of Nubia has a character of its own, and Michałowski holds that even the earliest of the Nubian Christian frescoes show stylistic elements that are unknown to the art of other Christian countries.

Under K. Michałowski's leadership, Polish expeditions in the 1960s conducted extensive excavations at Faras, in Lower Nubia, which has a long history as a bishop's seat. Their investigations yielded much information concerning wall paintings and church architecture (Adams 1965c, 87ff.; Grossmann 1971,330ff.). According to Adams, church architecture had reached its zenith by the eighth century (Fig. 83), much earlier than painting.

So far as we know, there were no wall paintings in the earliest churches of Nubia; the walls of the earliest cathedral at Faras, built in the seventh century, were decorated only with panels and friezes carved in high relief. The sandstone relief, Cat. 289, comes from such a frieze in the apse of the cathedral. Its subject, the dove, is one of the most important Christian symbols. Along with reliefs, icons were probably hung on the walls, and were later replaced by wall paintings (Michałowski 1974,33). Interestingly, local practices varied; there is no evidence that the cathedral located in the important administrative center at Qasr Ibrim ever contained frescoes. Works in wood and stone continued to fill the needs of the cult.

From the eighth century, the originally undecorated walls of the Great Cathedral at Faras were completely covered with frescoes. Michałowski (1974,35) believes that the painters were Coptic monks who had fled Egypt to escape Arab persecution, and that they used as models the icons they had brought with them. Since there were no centers for the training of painters in Nubia in the seventh and eighth centuries, it seems very likely that only such priestly émigrés could have created the earliest Nubian frescoes. It was not until the later emergence of Faras and Qasr Ibrim as important administrative centers that a new tradition could take root.

There are many remnants of Christian Nubian art: decorated column capitals and reliefs from churches (Cat. 289), tombstones, crosses, and small objects (Cat. 290). One drawing from a Nubian manuscript has survived (Cat. 291), and of course there are a large number of painted ceramics (Cats. 294, 295). Christian Nubian art is, however, best defined by the frescoes that decorated the walls of churches from the eighth century on.

It should be noted that these wall paintings were not mere decoration but an essential part of the cult. Like the earlier icons, they reflect the liturgy, and according to Weitzmann one can read in them the history of liturgical development. The frescoes of the Great Cathedral at Faras (which are today in the museums at Warsaw and Khartoum) have been particularly valuable in determining the development of Nubian wall painting. Since many of these frescoes were superimposed one upon the other, it has been possible to determine their chronological sequence as well as to preserve a number of them more or less intact. Inscriptions from the cathedral provide additional evidence for dating the paintings.

The significance of the Faras frescoes, however, is not limited to the local process of development. It transcends the borders of Nubia, for what has been learned from the Faras paintings can be applied, for example, to the art of Coptic Egypt. This is particularly important because no similar finds have been made in Egypt, and as a result the dating and significance of Coptic frescoes and panel paintings are often imprecise or unknown. Since the Christian art of Nubia was largely derived from Egypt, Syria, and Palestine, the new discoveries in Nubia take on far-reaching significance.

The stylistic sequence of the Faras frescoes is largely based on the colors used. Thus, light and dark violet and steel gray predominate in the paintings of the earliest style, dated to a period from the early eighth to the middle of the ninth century. The second style, characterized by the extensive use of white, reached its peak in the late ninth century with the painting of Bishop Kyros (ca. 866), which is now in Khartoum, and continued into the early eleventh century. In the second half of the tenth century, the red and yellow style became dominant. To this style belong the portrait of Bishop Petros (Cat. 292) and the Biblical scene of the three youths in the fiery furnace (now in Khartoum). The ascension of Bishop Johannes to the episcopal throne in 997 brought with it a new style in which a wide range of colors was used. A work in this polychromatic style is the portrait of Bishop Marianos (Warsaw 234036; Vol. I, Fig.93), who died at Qasr Ibrim in 1037. As we see from his brown skin, this dignitary was certainly a Nubian.

The polychromatic style reached its zenith in the middle of the twelfth century (Cat. 293; Fig. 84). It is probable that the cathedral at Faras was destroyed shortly thereafter, during the Arab incursion into Nubia in the year 1175, and this brought a halt to the development of painting in Nubia. Such works that survive from later times show clear signs of decline, which must have been a corollary of the political decline of the Christian kingdoms. The last Christian frescoes in Nubia date probably from the fifteenth century, long after the majority of the population had turned to Islam.

Since the Christian art of Nubia did not develop out of local tradition, some inquiry into its origins seems to be in order. Weitzmann (1970,325ff.) believes that it stems from three great artistic sources: the Coptic art of Egypt, the art of Syrian Palestine (especially Antioch and Jerusalem), and the Byzantine art of Constantinople. It was from the latter city that the Christianization of the royal courts of the three Nubian kingdoms proceeded.

Michałowski (1974,36), referring to the most recent investigations of du Bourguet (1970,303ff.), has noted that certain characteristics of the violet style, which was derived from the Coptic art of Egypt, appear only in the wall paintings of Faras, suggesting that some stylistic elements developed locally. Michałowski (1966,11-12) has been able to distinguish the work of at least three different artists painting in the violet style.

Weitzmann and Michałowski have traced the white style to Palestinian painting. In the white-style paintings in the apse at Faras, Michałowski has discerned the hands of several masters belonging to different generations. Here, he holds, style cannot be defined on the basis of color alone; a new stylistic element — a "tendency toward realism" — must also be considered (Michałowski 1974,37). This tendency is clearly expressed in the portrait of Bishop Kyros.

Nubian church painting as a whole is not based on any single concept, and the styles that have been identified

Fig. 83. Ground plan of the Great Cathedral at Faras, Christian Period, early eighth century A.D.

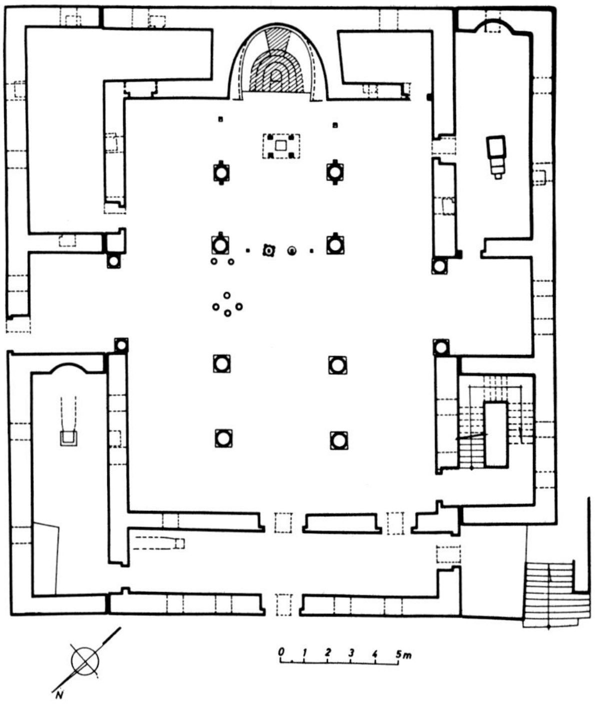

overlapped in time. Some works in the violet style, for example, date from a period in which the white style was already established. Michalowski (1974,39) believes the yellow-red style to be an independent phase, but Weitzmann does not. Red became the dominant color only under Bishop Petros (974-99). A fresco containing his likeness (Cat. 292), dated to about A. D. 975, is a major work in this style, but here the realism that characterized the paintings of the white style has again given way to idealization.

Nubian art in the Christian Era offers a variegated picture. Although largely dependent upon external artistic centers, it nevertheless developed independent features, as are evident in Cat. 290, a wooden object used as a pectoral.

Painted pottery from the Christian Period provides the clearest indication that the Nubian ceramic tradition was unbroken. Although there were changes in shape, decoration, and technique, the ceramics of the Christian Period are clearly linked to the past (see Vol. I, pp.131-33). A pilgrim's bottle (Cat. 294) decorated with two entwined serpents reveals that motifs of the Ballana Period were still used in late Christian ceramics. The motif of a giraffe found on a vessel fragment of the Christian Era (Cat. 295) goes back still further to Meroitic ceramic painting. The development of ceramics in Christian Nubia has been investigated by Adams (1962a,245ff.; 1970,111ff.; and Vol. I, pp.131-33), whose work offers scholars a most important aid to understanding the development of Nubian art during the Christian Period.

The art of Christian Nubia had long been known but had received little attention from serious scholars of early Christian art until the dramatic discoveries made during the recent campaign to save the Nubian monuments. Today, although much of the work done in the 1960s remains unpublished, the art of Christian Nubia has been acknowledged as an important tool in the comparative study of early Christian art. The thousand-year-long period produced a great deal of material and makes rich the prospects of further discoveries.

Fig. 84. *Detail of a fresco painting of Christ protecting an eparch (Cat. 293), from Faras, Christian Period, first half of twelfth century* A.D. *(Warsaw 234033).*

The Catalogue

■ indicates an object that does not appear in the exhibition

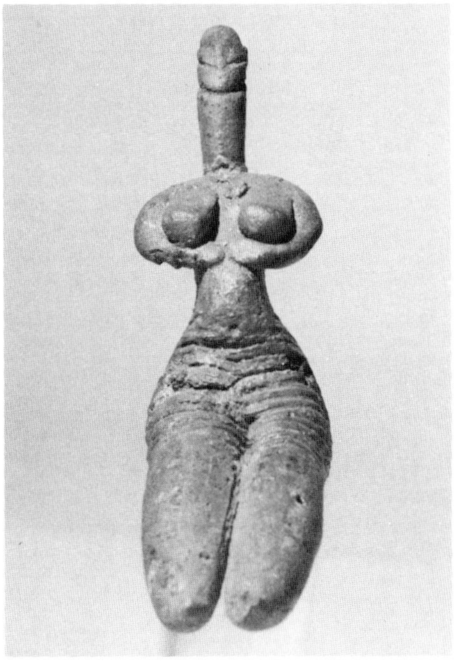

1
Seated Woman

About 3000 B.C.
MATERIAL: Unfired clay.
COLLECTION: *Khartoum, Sudan National Museum 13729.*

DESCRIPTION: A seated steatopygous woman is represented, her arms folded on her chest. Head and neck are summarily modeled in cylindrical form, an incised curve setting off the head. Oblique notches mark the eyes, and the nose is indicated by a slight knob. The navel is recessed. The long legs end in rounded stumps, without feet, and are, like the buttocks, divided by a deep indentation. Roughly parallel curved lines cover the abdomen and part of the thighs.

COLOR: Brownish gray.
CONDITION: Complete; minor damages.
MEASUREMENTS: Height 8.4 cm. Length 8.6 cm. Width 3.2 cm. Height of head and neck 1.3 cm.
PROVENANCE: Halfa Degheim, Site 277, Grave 16 B (Scandinavian Joint Expedition 1963-64, Find no. 277/16 B:3).
BIBLIOGRAPHY: Keating 1964,26-27; Leclant 1965a,209, fig. 33; Nordström 1972,127,196, pls. 56:3,197; Säve-Söderbergh 1965, fig. 31; Säve-Söderbergh 1973,228, pl. XLIII; Huard 1973,109 (fig. 8,9-10),110.

This female figure was found with a statuette of a young girl in a grave which contained the skeletons of a woman and a girl. This unusual discovery, the first to reveal artistically significant A-group statuettes, provides an important clue to the meaning of such figures. They were, perhaps, intended as a magical assurance of life after death (Säve-Söderbergh 1973,228). Significant parallels might thus be drawn with Egyptian funerary sculpture.

The lines incised on the abdomen have been interpreted as the indication of a garment (Nordström 1972,127), but it seems to me that a garment would probably have been represented in some other way; besides, the back of the figure is only partially covered with these lines. I consider it more likely that they represent the folds of fat customary in steatopygia. They might also represent tattooing or body decoration. Although we have no similar examples from Nubia, C-group statuettes (Cats. 13,15, and 18, for example) confirm that the representation of body ornamentation, in a different form, was not unusual. Nordström now interprets these lines as an indication of body decoration (letter of May 10, 1976).

In an article intended to demonstrate the connections of the C-group with the central Sahara (Chad, Ennedi, Borkou, Tibesti, Fezzan), Huard illustrated this figure (erroneously regarding two photos of the same figure in the *Unesco Courier* of December 1964 as two different figures). The fact that all the female representations are steatopygous and exhibit either body decoration or tattooing is not in itself sufficient to claim cultural connections between the central Nile Valley and the Sahara. However, comparisons of cattle representations from the two areas are more convincing (see commentary to Cat. 20).

Hippopotamus Head (Cat. 3).

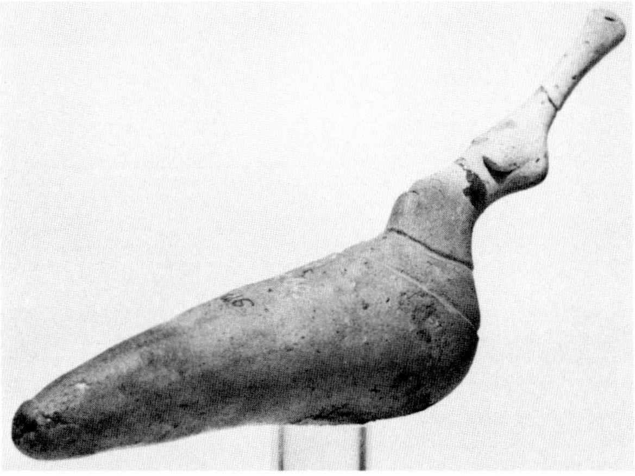

2 ■
Armless Woman

Probably before 3000 B.C.
MATERIAL: Fired clay.
COLLECTION: *Aswan Museum 346.*

DESCRIPTION: A seated woman, with a small beaked head set without transition atop a long, thin neck, leans far back from the waist. Short oblique slits indicate the eyes. The neck merges into the shoulders which, together with the trunk, form a lozenge-shaped figure. The arms are not indicated. The breasts were modeled separately and applied. The navel is marked by an incised impression, above which runs a short horizontal line. Beneath the tightly constricted waist and protruding abdomen, the lower part of the body swells to give heavy emphasis to the buttocks. The unmodeled, shapeless legs taper to rounded points. Two horizontal lines run round the hips, upper and lower lines being looped together at each side of the back, although the two loops do not touch.

COLOR: Grayish brown.
CONDITION: Broken and repaired at neck and waist; right breast (modeled separately) missing; corroded spots on left hip and buttocks; damaged and discolored in places.
MEASUREMENTS: Height 9.6 cm. Length 21.2 cm. Width 4.1 cm.
PROVENANCE: Dakka, Cemetery 102, Grave 102 (Firth 1909-10, Field no. 102/102/8).
BIBLIOGRAPHY: Firth 1915,61, pl. 11f; Ucko 1968,405; Helck 1971,20 with n. 75; Nordström 1972,27.

This female figurine was found in a child's grave, as evidenced by the skeleton. The grave offerings unequivocally date the piece in the A-group. Although stylistic similarities with statuettes of this type found in Egypt are established, this is definitely a Nubian product. It is not, however, of the same artistic quality as Cat. 1.

3
Hippopotamus Head

After 3000 B.C.
MATERIAL: Fired clay.
COLLECTION: *Chicago (Illinois), Oriental Institute Museum 23845.*

DESCRIPTION: The hollow head of the animal is highly stylized, with plastically formed eyes, ears, and incisors. Skin folds are represented above the eyes. The opening of the wide mouth is shown as a deeply incised line, and the nostrils are impressed.

COLOR: Light reddish brown.
CONDITION: Head broken off at neck; part of left side beneath eye lost; right ear damaged and left one missing.
MEASUREMENTS: Height 19.7 cm. Width 17.1 cm. Depth 17.6 cm.
PROVENANCE: Qustul, Cemetery L, Grave 19 (Seele 1963-64, Field no. B-1501).
BIBLIOGRAPHY: Seele 1974,33, fig. 18.

The first find of an animal sculpture from the A-group period was made in the richly furnished Grave 19 of Qustul Cemetery L. Seele, on the basis of typical A-group ceramics (Cat. 8), dates it to early Dynasty I. In the opinion of the excavator, the head was probably part of a complete statue which—if that assumption is correct—must have been of extraordinary size.

Illustrated in color on page 115.

4
Stone Vessel with Relief Decoration

About 3000 B.C.
MATERIAL: Limestone.
COLLECTION: *Chicago (Illinois), Oriental Institute Museum 24069.*

DESCRIPTION: A scene in sunk relief on the outside of a conical vessel shows a palace facade and three boats. A man stands behind a cabin on the first boat, and a crocodile, whose head only is preserved, is visible below it. Traces of prow and stern remain of the second boat. Behind it is a harpoon (?) and a goat standing on its hind legs, followed by a man wearing a scanty loincloth. He faces the third boat, one of his arms raised. On the third boat is a large quadruped, and under it is a fish pierced by a harpoon (?). Above the scene are incised hatchings. The flat rim of the vessel is decorated with hatched triangles.

COLOR: Dull buff.
CONDITION: Pieced together from many fragments; large portions missing; discolored brown in places.
MEASUREMENTS: Height 8.8 cm. Diameter at top 14.9 cm., at base 13.5 cm.
PROVENANCE: Qustul, Cemetery L, Grave 24 (Seele 1963-64, Field no. B-1728).
BIBLIOGRAPHY: Seele 1974,36-37 (figs. 21a-e,22),38-39; DeVries 1973/74,39-41 (fig.); DeVries 1975,21.

The excavator considered this unique object, which is dated roughly to Dynasty I, to be the cylinder seal of a prince or high official that was smashed at his death to prevent its misuse. Seele's interpretation rests mainly on the decoration in sunk relief, a technique known in Egypt only from Dynasty IV on, but appearing earlier on cylinder seals from the period of Dynasty I.

Cylinder seals were found in A-group graves (Firth 1912, pl. 37a[1-3]; Björkman—Säve-Söderbergh in Nordström 1972,117f.; Mills—Nordström 1966,8, fig. 3,15 on 9), but the identification of this object as such seems doubtful primarily because of its depressed top and its slightly inclined wall, which one would not expect in a cylinder seal.

Several similar objects in sandstone as well as limestone have been found in A-group excavations (Säve-Söderbergh 1964,29, pl. IIIa; Nordström 1972,119f.; Nordström 1962, 58, pl. Xa; Griffith 1921,9, pl. IV,3; Reisner 1910,277, pl. 64h). They are either undecorated or have only incised lines. Other pieces from Qustul Cemetery L and now in Chicago (Oriental Institute Museum 23684, 23709, 23717, 23719, 24058) have for the most part only a shallow depression on top, and several show traces of burning inside.

These vessels have been regarded as censers (Firth), as lamps (Säve-Söderbergh 1964,29; Nordström 1972, 119f.), and as dishes for grinding pigments, since an object of this kind found in Grave L 19 shows traces of red dye (Seele 1974,29-30,33-34). They might have had nothing to do with cylinder seals, the similarity of form being purely coincidental.

The present object should be classified with the pieces cited, which may well include some censers, although others were certainly used as mortars. The fact that the vessel is decorated is a sign of its owner's high position in society. Although the limestone was imported from Egypt, the decoration appears to be the work of a Nubian stonecutter. Similar boat representations are frequently found in rock drawings in Nubia (Landström 1970, figs. 73-74 on 25). The goat is a buck of the common domestic type, with twisted horns (Brentjes 1962,14ff.). The fish is more difficult to identify since its tail fin is not plainly visible; Brentjes thinks it may be a Nile perch (*Lates niloticus*). He identifies the quadruped standing on the third boat as a baboon, based on the proportions of the extremities, the form of the hind legs, the simian long tail and dorsal line, and the shape of the head (by letter). According to this exact view, we must regard Nubia as the country of origin of the relief, since baboons still existed there when this object was made. Egyptian parallels are lacking.

5
Bowl with Zigzag Decoration

Probably late fourth millennium B.C.
MATERIAL: Fired clay.
COLLECTION: *Brooklyn (New York), The Brooklyn Museum 07.447.404.*

DESCRIPTION: A narrow zigzag band encircles the rim of a deep conical bowl. On the body, tall rectangular panels composed of four horizontal rows of overlapping zigzags alternate with irregular red polished areas. A broad zigzag band runs round the bottom of the vessel. On the inside, six zigzag panels taper down from the rim to the center of the floor; the intermediate areas are red polished.

COLOR: Light to dark brown; polished areas dark red.
CONDITION: Broken into four pieces and repaired; damages near bottom; red polished areas partly discolored black and painted in modern times.
MEASUREMENTS: Height 8.9 cm. Diameter 19.2 cm., inner diameter at mouth 18.5 cm.
PROVENANCE: Ma'amariya (Upper Egypt, West Bank, opposite Elkab), Grave 2 (Morgan 1907).
BIBLIOGRAPHY: Morgan 1909,266; Morgan 1912,32; Arkell 1955a, 95f., pls. XI-XII; Hofmann 1967,68-69; Baumgartel 1970,199.

The decoration of this bowl from an Upper Egyptian grave reflects Nubian workmanship. Patterns created by the use of rocker-stamps frequently appear in late Neolithic Sudan and in Nubia right up to the A-group (Nordström 1972,76, pl. 25, Group 1,16-22). However, there is some disagreement about the date of the vessel. The pottery figurine of a woman with raised arms (Brooklyn 07.447.505) from the same grave has usually been ascribed to the Naqada I Period, by, among others, Arkell (1955a,96), Wolf (1957,60), Ucko (1963,100, no. 72), Bothmer (1970,12: "about 4000 B.C."; 1974,12: "about 4000-3500 B.C."), and Nordström (1972,26). H. W. Müller (1970b, no. 4) attributes the figure to the later Naqada culture, "second half of the fourth millennium." Baumgartel first (1960,69, pl. V,4) placed the figure in Naqada I, but later (1970,199) dated it to the end of Naqada II or early in the Dynastic Period because she considered the bowl an A-group product. Hofmann (1967,68-69) regarded the bowl as Neolithic.

The red decoration on the bowl points toward the A-group, when painted ceramics first appeared and which in its early form is contemporary with the developed Naqada I culture of Egypt (Kaiser's Naqada Ic; cf. Nordström 1972,28). On the other hand, zigzag decoration is more in evidence in the late Neolithic Esh-Shaheinab culture. As Arkell himself also pointed out (1955a,95), the alternation of polished bands with areas of basketwork pattern is Protodynastic or late Predynastic. It should be noted, however, that W. Y. Adams (letter to B. V. Bothmer) and Nordström assign the bowl an earlier date.

On the subject of the bowl, Nordström (letter of May 10, 1976) remarks: "The dating of the decorated bowl from Ma'ameria . . . will be a matter of dispute until someone has carried out a technical analysis of the ceramic material of the vessel. . . . Personally I think that the bowl belongs to the Abkan/Shaheinab tradition of pottery making and not to the Nubian A-group. This conclusion is based on the layout of the decorative pattern, the pattern elements, and the technique of decoration—all these properties seem to fit better into the stage preceding the A-group. . . . The bowl from Ma'ameria may very well be an 'Egyptian' product but the southern influence from the Abkan or from the wider concept of what I have called the Khartoum technocomplex is unmistakable."

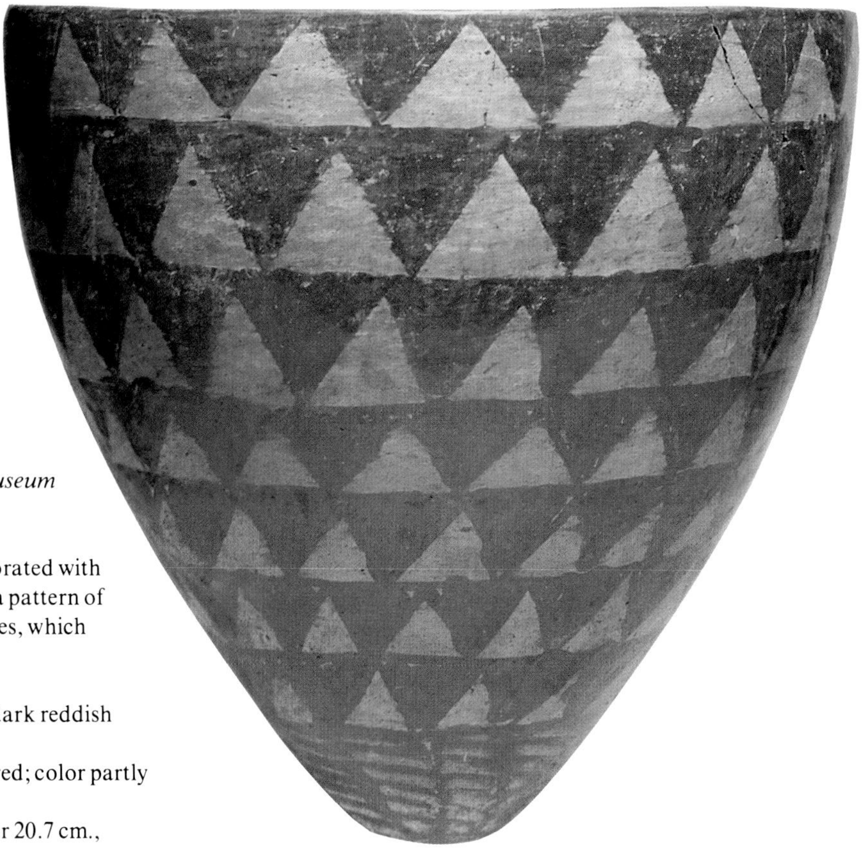

6

Jar with Geometric Decoration

Early third millennium B.C.
MATERIAL: Fired clay.
COLLECTION: *Cambridge, Fitzwilliam Museum EGA. 4668.1943.*

DESCRIPTION: A polished ovoid jar is decorated with seven rows of inverted triangles. Below is a pattern of adjoining vertical rows of horizontal dashes, which become shorter toward the bottom.

COLOR: Painted light brown; decoration dark reddish brown; interior black polished.
CONDITION: Complete; broken and repaired; color partly obliterated.
MEASUREMENTS: Height 19.4 cm. Diameter 20.7 cm., inner diameter at mouth 19.8 cm.
PROVENANCE: Not known. Gift of Gayer-Anderson.
BIBLIOGRAPHY: None.

Among the rich and varied ceramics of the A-group is a class of polished vessels, very thin-walled, which are painted brown outside with reddish-brown decoration while the interior is black polished. This jar, belonging to the classic A-group, is of the same type as a vessel found by the Scandinavian Joint Expedition in Sahaba (Site 401, Grave 49: Nordström 1972, 188). Nordström classifies these vessels with his type AVIIIa of the "brown-and-black 'eggshell' ware" (ibid. 88, pl. 42); the painting corresponds to his Group 4, no. 5 (basketwork pattern) and no. 9 (triangles: ibid. 77, pl. 25).

7

Jar with Basketwork Decoration

Early third millennium B.C.
MATERIAL: Fired clay.
COLLECTION: *Chicago (Illinois), Oriental Institute Museum 21877.*

DESCRIPTION: A polished ovoid jar is decorated with vertical rows of small curves.

COLOR: Painted light brown; decoration dark red; interior black polished.
CONDITION: Numerous breaks, repaired; small chips missing; surface on one side corroded by weathering and covered with whitish deposit.
MEASUREMENTS: Height 18.2 cm. Diameter 22.1 cm. Wall thickness 0.4 cm.
PROVENANCE: Qustul, Cemetery V, Grave 67 (Seele 1963-64, Field no. Q-2126).
BIBLIOGRAPHY: None.

This jar corresponds in shape and type to Cat. 6. The thinness of its wall and the dark red decoration on a light brown ground make it a typical example of a category of A-group ceramics which Nordström classifies under his type AVIIIa ("brown-and-black 'eggshell' ware": Nordström 1972, pl. 42); the painting corresponds to his Group 4, no. 5 (basketwork pattern: ibid. pl. 25).

8

Jar with Cross-Hatched Bands

Early third millennium B.C.
MATERIAL: Fired clay.
COLLECTION: *Chicago (Illinois), Oriental Institute Museum 24259.*

DESCRIPTION: Five painted cross-hatched bands alternating with undecorated bands cover this tall polished jar from its rim to its small base.

COLOR: Yellowish brown; decoration red; interior black polished.
CONDITION: Broken into several pieces and repaired; one small and two fairly large pieces missing; surface on one side corroded and discolored in places.
MEASUREMENTS: Height 17.2 cm. Diameter 17.4 cm. Wall thickness 0.5 cm.
PROVENANCE: Qustul, Cemetery L, Grave 19 (Seele 1963-64, Field no. B-1878).
BIBLIOGRAPHY: None.

This typical A-group jar comes from a richly furnished grave in which were found, among other items, a cylindrical Egyptian alabaster vessel of early Dynasty I, a vessel for pigment grinding, similar in shape to Cat. 4, and a hippopotamus head (Cat. 3). The vase belongs to Nordström's type AVIIIa (Nordström 1972, pl. 42), but he did not discuss this kind of painting, which was not found in the Scandinavian Joint Expedition's concession.

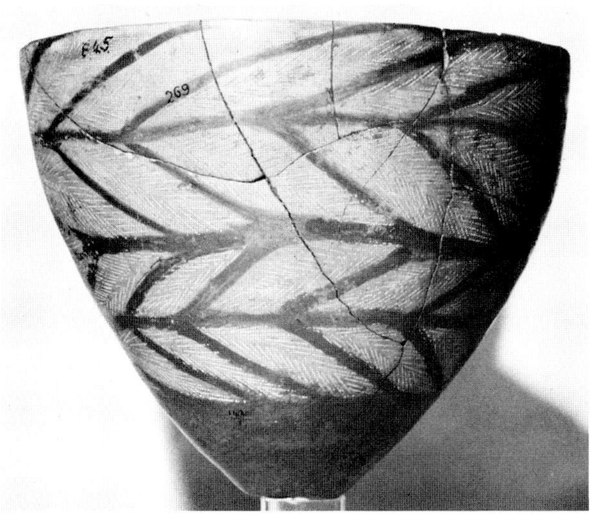

9 ■
Pot with Herringbone Decoration

Early third millennium B.C.
MATERIAL: Fired clay.
COLLECTION: *Aswan Museum 269.*

DESCRIPTION: The polished ovoid pot has a thin, flaring wall and a small base. Two rows of connected herringbone pattern are painted in red on the light ground. The unpainted areas between the herringbones are filled with impressed decoration. The lower part of the pot is painted red.

COLOR: Light brown; decoration dark red.
CONDITION: Complete; broken into several pieces and repaired.
MEASUREMENTS: Height 19.9 cm. Diameter 24.8 cm., at base ca. 4.0 cm. Wall thickness 0.35 cm.
PROVENANCE: Naga Wadi, Cemetery 142, Grave 1 (Firth 1910-11, Field no. 142/1/22).
BIBLIOGRAPHY: Firth 1927,214, pl. 19c, no. 2.

The shape of this pot is typical for the A-group. It belongs to Nordström's type AVIIIa (Nordström 1972, pl. 42); he, however, did not deal with this kind of decoration, which was not found in the Scandinavian Joint Expedition's concession.

Illustrated in color, Volume I, page 54.

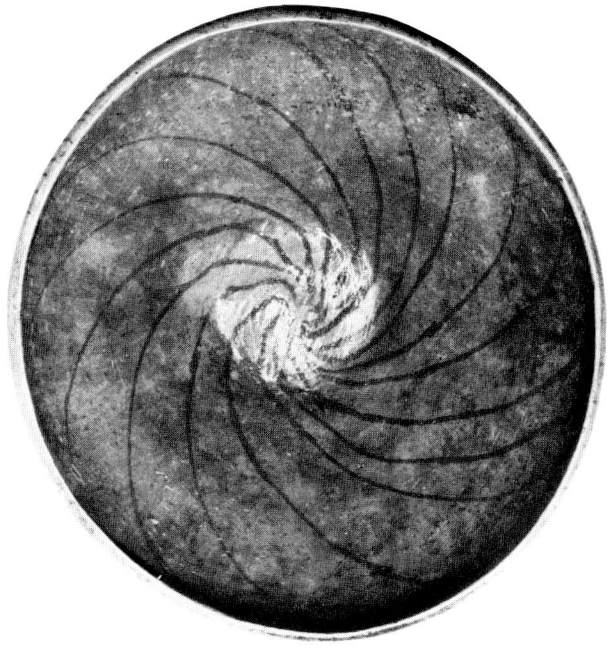

10
Bowl with Painted Designs

Early third millennium B.C.
MATERIAL: Fired clay.
COLLECTION: *Chicago (Illinois), Oriental Institute Museum 23772.*

DESCRIPTION: A thin-walled bowl, polished inside and out, is flattened at the bottom and slightly constricted at the rim. On the outside, four fields of irregular parallel chevrons alternate with undecorated areas. On the inside, numerous curved lines spiral from the center to the rim.

COLOR: Light brown; red painted decoration inside and out.
CONDITION: Complete; discolored in places.
MEASUREMENTS: Height 12.1 cm. Diameter 22.7 cm. Wall thickness 0.6 cm.
PROVENANCE: Qustul, Cemetery W, Grave 11 (Seele 1963-64, Field no. B-1428).
BIBLIOGRAPHY: None.

The light brown color of this bowl, both inside and out, places it in Nordström's type AII ("brown 'eggshell' ware") of A-group ceramics, which is further characterized by thin walls (Nordström 1972,84, pl. 39); most vessels of this kind are undecorated. Nordström's classification of painted motifs includes neither the outside pattern nor the inside spiral motif. The dating into the late A-group is based on parallel material from other graves. In the same grave as this bowl was found an Egyptian vessel with a secondary incised pattern similar to that on the Egyptian wine vessel, Cat. 11.

11
Egyptian Storage Vessel

Early third millennium B.C.
MATERIAL: Fired clay.
COLLECTION: *Chicago (Illinois), Oriental Institute Museum 23763.*

DESCRIPTION: Groups of horizontal wavy lines decorate the broad shoulder of a tapering vessel. In addition, a remarkable candelabra-like design was shallowly incised, partly overlapping the wavy lines.

COLOR: Light brown; decoration red.
CONDITION: Complete.
MEASUREMENTS: Height 57.5 cm. Diameter 42.4 cm.
PROVENANCE: Qustul, Cemetery W, Grave 10 (Seele 1963-64, Field no. B-1418).
BIBLIOGRAPHY: None.

Imported Egyptian storage jars for wine and other liquids have been found in many A-group graves of Lower Nubia which must be dated between the Naqada II Period and the beginning of the Dynastic Period. But on only two of these vessels (the other was found in Grave W 11; now Chicago, Oriental Institute Museum 23764) was a stylized pattern incised afterwards. It must have been done by an A-group artist since it is completely non-Egyptian. However, because it is unique, an interpretation is still difficult. A remote resemblance may be glimpsed to the extremely unusual geometric patterns on two early C-group bowls with incised designs (Cat. 27 and Berlin West 14969); their dominant patterns correspond somewhat to the incised decoration on this vessel. It is possible that the secondary incision is a sign of ownership.

12
Animal-Headed Human Figure

Between 1900 and 1550 B.C.
MATERIAL: Fired clay.
COLLECTION: *Los Angeles, University of California, Museum of Cultural History 400-1541.*

DESCRIPTION: Only the figure's upper part is preserved. The modeling is summarily done and merely renders the principal parts of the body in stylized form. The pointed animal head rests on a solid, unmodulated neck, which is encircled by incised lines. Eyes, ears, and nostrils are indicated by impressed holes, and the mouth is marked by a cleft. The round shoulders curve into stumpy arms that taper to points at waist level. The amorphous body is almost round; only the stomach protrudes prominently. A double line of dots crosses the breast from shoulder to shoulder. What remains of the buttocks is steatopygous. Several incised lines run across the lower part of the abdomen and toward the back of the body, approaching each other at the sides.

COLOR: Reddish brown.
CONDITION: Broken off beneath abdomen; discolored black in places.
MEASUREMENTS: Height 10.0 cm. Width at shoulders 5.1 cm. Depth 3.7 cm.
PROVENANCE: Askut, outside the fortress, eastern part of the southeast sector, Room SE 32A (Badawy 1963-64, Find no. 1541).
BIBLIOGRAPHY: Badawy 1964,88, fig. 9; Badawy 1965,130 (fig.),131; Badawy, unpubl. ms.

This figure is one of the most astonishing small sculptures of the C-group found in Lower Nubia. It can be attributed to that culture because the upper settlement stratum from which it came apparently dates to a period more recent than the Middle Kingdom. However, the buildings were certainly inhabited by members of the native population, not by Egyptians, who lived in the fortress. Moreover, the shape of

the shoulders and the tapering stumpy arms indicate that the figure is a typical C-group product. Similar details are found in other sculptures discovered in a clear C-group context, such as Cats. 13, 15, 16, and 18; further examples from Aniba are illustrated in Steindorff (1935, pls. 71-72). Although the Kerma culture might theoretically be considered in connection with this figure, a relationship is very unlikely since no similar figures are known from Kerma burials or from the site of Kerma itself.

The little figure was found in a chamber with a shrine, so it must be regarded as a cult object or as a votive offering. From A. Badawy's unpublished manuscript on the Askut excavation, kindly made available to me by the author, we have the following facts: A brick altar, added later, was built against the east wall of Room SE 32A. Its back wall, 70 cm. high and 87 cm. wide, was crowned by a projecting cornice and had a central niche, measuring 16 by 25 cm., which contained an Egyptian sandstone stela. Traces of two round posts indicated that the altar could be closed. The offering place in front of it, approximately square in plan, was enclosed on two sides by low, round-topped baffle walls. A gutter led to a receptacle sunk into the floor in front of the offering place.

The figure clearly has a sheep's head, which is stylistically closely related to the head of the sheep, Cat. 19. The only other animal-headed human figures from the Nile Valley known to me, apart from the animal-headed representations of the gods of Egypt and Kush, belong to the Predynastic Period. They include, for example, female figures with bird's heads (Brooklyn 07.447.505; see commentary to Cat. 5). There is also the A-group figurine with a beaklike head, Cat. 2. No stylistic connections can be drawn among the Brooklyn figure, Cat. 2, and the present figurine, yet it is conceivable that—despite the chronological disparity—all three spring from the same source.

Although breasts are not indicated, it is almost certain that the figurine represents a woman, who is shown as pregnant (Badawy 1964; 1965). Since images of pregnant women are very rare in Egyptian art, and then are highly idealized, the figurine must be regarded as unique also in this respect. It must represent a goddess, as the animal head indicates. Badawy has discussed it as a fertility goddess, which is plausible, for a sheep can be a symbol of fecundity. Perhaps there are some connections to the ram's head found at Kerma, Cat. 44, which is probably an image of an animal deity. Furthermore, the ram sacred to Amun from before the early New Kingdom originally came from Nubia (Wildung 1973), and may have been worshipped by both the C-group people and those of the Kerma culture.

Illustrated in color on page 28.

13
Tattooed Woman

Between 1900 and 1550 B.C.
MATERIAL: Fired clay.
COLLECTION: *Cairo, Egyptian Museum JE 65192.*

DESCRIPTION: The body of this seated woman is bent back from the waist. The head is relatively large, and the face flat except for the nose and mouth, which form a beaklike unit. The eyes are indicated by horizontal slits. The hair, framing the face, is marked by hatchings. Six lines surround the long, thin neck. The rounded shoulders merge into short, pointed arms. Slanting lines are incised on the shoulders, and similar incisions appear on the preserved left arm. Four comparatively long vertical lines adorn the breast; nipples and navel were indicated by deeply punched points. On the slightly protruding stomach, beneath the navel, three horizontal lines are incised round the body; the lowest line loops back on each side to separate hips from thighs and mark the pubic area. The buttocks are steatopygous. The legs are modeled as a homogeneous mass, tapering sharply and ending bluntly, their separation being indicated by a troughlike depression. Both thighs carry incised ornamentation reaching to the ends of the legs. Short incised lines indicate the toes.

COLOR: Grayish brown.
CONDITION: End of right arm missing; neck broken and repaired; discolored in places.
MEASUREMENTS: Height 11.6 cm. Width 5.0 cm. Depth 9.4 cm. Height of head 2.2 cm.
PROVENANCE: Aniba, Cemetery N, in the sand (Steindorff 1930-31).
BIBLIOGRAPHY: Steindorff 1935,120, pl. 71,2a-b; Sameh 1975,59 (fig.).

This almost perfectly preserved figure of a seated woman is one of the most impressive minor sculptures from the C-group culture. The attitude of the body, the accentuated thighs, and the rudimentary arms are reminiscent of A-group figurines (Cats. 1 and 2), although several details, above all some details of the head, indicate that the figure belongs to a later period. Similarities are revealed here to the two separately discovered small heads, Cats. 14 and 17. The tattooing, which appears much more frequently in the C-group than in the A-group, is also different from that of Cat. 1; only the looplike formations of the lower line on the abdomen are similar to those in Cats. 1 and 2. Above all, the stumpy arms arching out from the shoulders and ending in points are indicative of the C-group.

The chronological attribution is based on Bietak (1968,104,112), who has meticulously established that small sculptures occur only in his phases II/a and II/b but are not, however, more precisely datable.

Illustrated in color on page 127.

14
Female Head

Between 1900 and 1550 B.C.
MATERIAL: Fired clay.
COLLECTION: *Leipzig, Karl-Marx-Universität, Ägyptisches Museum 4396.*

DESCRIPTION: The smooth features of this highly stylized little head are only superficially modeled. Vertical incisions carried back at the temples define the sides of the face, and a curving line across the forehead sets it off from the hair. The nose is modeled as a faint protuberance; two horizontal incisions on each side indicate the eyes. The mouth is not marked. Rows of parallel dashes—two at the forehead and one on each side—and deeply incised holes indicate the hair. There is a plug hole for attachment in the underside.

COLOR: Reddish brown.
CONDITION: Complete; fine cracks on face, left side, and back of head; dark discoloration in places.
MEASUREMENTS: Height 6.4 cm. Width 6.4 cm. Depth 5.8 cm.
PROVENANCE: Aniba, Cemetery N, Grave 133 (Steindorff 1914).
BIBLIOGRAPHY: Steindorff 1935, 121 (no. 12), 134 (N 133), pl. 72, 12a-b.

This piece was found beside the body of a young girl, together with another head in the same style (Cat. 17). The hole in the underside leads one to assume that the head was meant to be affixed to a body or perhaps a staff; however, no traces of such a body were found in the grave. The rows of short parallel incisions around the face may indicate that the coiffure was a wig; the deep holes may have been used for the insertion of real hair.

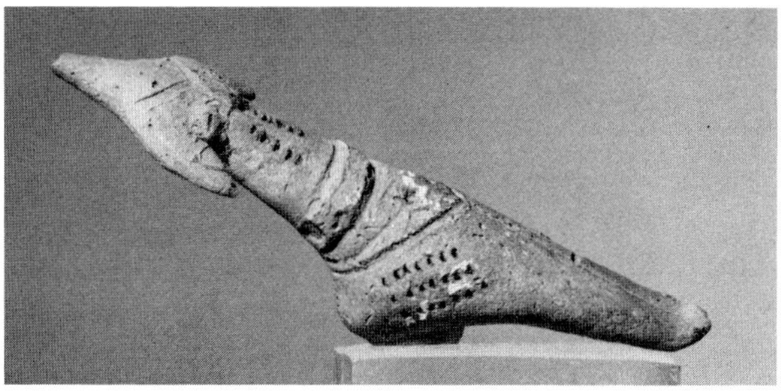

15
Standing Woman

Between 1900 and 1550 B.C.
MATERIAL: Fired clay.
COLLECTION: *Khartoum, Sudan National Museum 62/12/66.*

DESCRIPTION: The upper part of the body appears to be leaning back, yet the figure is conceived as standing. The conical neck must have supported a separately modeled head. The drooping shoulders merge into the short arms, which end in pointed stumps. The torso beneath the arms is cylindrical, the lower part broad with wide hips. The legs are formed as a single unit, without feet; lines incised in front and back indicate the division between them. There are incised lines around the neck, on the chest, and around the waist and hips. On the abdomen and right thigh are impressed dots. A wavy line appears on the left thigh.

COLOR: Light to dark brown.
CONDITION: Head missing; broken beneath arms and repaired; darkish discoloration in places.
MEASUREMENTS: Height 8.3 cm. Width 2.4 cm. Depth 2.1 cm.
PROVENANCE: Shirfadik (Serra East District), Site 179, Grave 80 (Scandinavian Joint Expedition 1961-62, Find no. 179/080:2).
BIBLIOGRAPHY: None.

This C-group statuette, found with the fragment of a similar figure in the disturbed shaft of a grave, brings to light a type of female figurine not previously known. One assumes that the woman is standing. The lines scored or incised in the soft clay of the neck and waist represent a necklace with pendant and a belt (a loincloth is very unlikely). The body designs are remotely reminiscent of decorations on other female figurines (Cat. 16), although none exactly like this have been found. Here again, the question arises as to whether they represent tattooing or body decoration. Nordström (by letter) attributes the figure to Bietak's phases II/a-b of the C-group.

Steindorff (1935,118), discussing a similar piece, asked whether the decoration might be a purely aesthetic embellishment, analogous to the decoration of objects such as pottery. This suggestion is hardly credible. Certainly all these figurines were burial equipment, intended to fulfill a magical purpose.

16
Flat-Chested Woman

Between 1900 and 1550 B.C.
MATERIAL: Fired clay.
COLLECTION: *Leipzig, Karl-Marx-Universität, Ägyptisches Museum 4403.*

DESCRIPTION: The simply modeled figurine represents a standing (?) steatopygous woman with a flat chest. The head, made separately, fits onto a thin neck. Nose and mouth form a beaklike unit; long horizontal slits mark the eyes. Of the limbs, only the upper arms and thighs have been formed, and appear as if cut off short. The division between the legs is indicated front and back. Nipples and navel are impressed. Incised lines round neck and hips represent necklaces and a waistband.

COLOR: Dark brown.
CONDITION: Complete; neck broken and repaired; discolored in places.
MEASUREMENTS: Length 10.5 cm. Width 5.0 cm.
PROVENANCE: Aniba, Cemetery N, Grave 390 (Steindorff 1914).
BIBLIOGRAPHY: Steindorff 1935,122 (no. 16),150 (N 390), pl. 72,16; Bietak 1968, pl. 13 (II/b/21); Leipzig 1976,38 (no. 51/11).

The woman's sexual characteristics are not emphasized. The buttocks are prominent, as in all female figurines of the A-group (Cats. 1 and 2) and the C-group (Cats. 12, 13, 15, 18) and in most figures of this kind from Predynastic Egypt. The figurine was found in the grave of a young girl.

Tattooed Woman (Cat. 13).

17
Small Female Head

Between 1900 and 1550 B.C.
MATERIAL: Fired clay.
COLLECTION: *Leipzig, Karl-Marx-Universität, Ägyptisches Museum 4395.*

DESCRIPTION: This almost spherical little head is flattened underneath. The face is set off from the hair by straight lines at the sides and a curved line above the high forehead. The features are in very low relief. The eyes are represented by simple long strokes; the nostrils are incised; and a short horizontal gash marks the mouth. The hair, which is in low relief, is indicated by deeply pressed holes; a narrow band of delicate hatching can be seen on the forehead. There is a plug hole for attachment in the underside.

COLOR: Reddish brown.
CONDITION: Broken and repaired; break runs through right half of face to middle of forehead; chipped from eye upward and on reverse of break; dark discoloration in places.
MEASUREMENTS: Height 5.4 cm. Width 5.8 cm. Depth 5.2 cm.
PROVENANCE: Aniba, Cemetery N, Grave 133 (Steindorff 1914).
BIBLIOGRAPHY: Steindorff 1935,121-22 (no. 13), 134 (N 133), pl. 72,13; Leipzig 1976,38 (no. 51/12).

This head and Cat. 14 were found in the same girl's grave. They belong to the same type, but stylistic differences are discernible in the treatment of the mouth, eyes, and hair. Here, too, one assumes a wig is intended.

A very similar head was found in the Meroitic Grave 225 at Karanog (Philadelphia E 7729: Woolley—Randall-MacIver 1910, pl. 96). It would be taken unquestionably for a C-group object if the context did not make that impossible. Thus, it seems that the style of these heads was maintained right into the Meroitic Period and reappears in unofficial art. However, the head may have come to Karanog when the grave was robbed and is possibly not Meroitic at all.

Illustrated in color, Volume I, page 54.

18 ■
Broad-Chested Woman

Between 1900 and 1550 B.C.
MATERIAL: Unfired clay.
COLLECTION: *Chicago (Illinois), Oriental Institute Museum 23202.*

DESCRIPTION: This unusual broad-chested figurine resembles a dressmaker's dummy. The upper part of the body leans backward. The globular, simply modeled head rests on the truncated cone of the neck. Short vertical strokes indicate the hair. The eyes are marked by parallel slits, the mouth by a single slit. The nose is faintly shaped and the nostrils impressed. Drooping shoulders merge into tapering arm stumps. Under the constricted waist, the body spreads out to end in an abrupt flat surface. The nipples are marked by short horizontal strokes, the navel by an impressed hole. A lozenge pattern consisting of incised dots decorates the neck, torso, and right arm; the lozenge shapes are arranged either vertically or at a slant. Usually there are two, sometimes three, interlinked lozenges on the breast. Above the navel is a circular area with incised holes.

COLOR: Light to grayish brown; traces of whitish pigment.
CONDITION: Complete; broken into three pieces and repaired; surface of front of lower torso chipped; dark discoloration in places.
MEASUREMENTS: Height 9.7 cm. Width 5.1 cm., at base 3.9 cm. Depth 4.7 cm. Height of head 1.9 cm.
PROVENANCE: Adindan, Cemetery T, Grave 51 (Seele 1963-64, Field no. B-846).
BIBLIOGRAPHY: None.

Parallels for this kind of small sculpture were not found until the 1960s in the Nubian Campaign (for example, in Askut, Cat. 12, though with the head of a sheep). For an interpretation, and a discussion of the problem of tattooing, see commentary to Cat. 15.

19
Sheep Figurine

Between 1900 and 1550 B.C.
MATERIAL: Fired clay.
COLLECTION: *Leipzig, Karl-Marx-Universität, Ägyptisches Museum 4389.*

DESCRIPTION: The attenuated body is only superficially modeled, without indications of sex or species. Eyes, ears, goatee, and dewlap are plastically formed. The tail is short and broad.

COLOR: Light brown.
CONDITION: Goatee and tip of tail missing; legs broken off; blackish discoloration in places.
MEASUREMENTS: Height 8.2 cm. Length 11.4 cm. Width 3.0 cm.
PROVENANCE: Aniba, Cemetery N, near Grave 214, with other animal figures (Steindorff 1914).
BIBLIOGRAPHY: Steindorff 1935,123 (no. 37), 140 (N 214), pl. 73,37.

The dating of the figure is based on Bietak's attribution of all small sculptures to phases II/a and II/b. In contrast to numerous cattle representations (Cats. 21 and 22), sheep figurines rarely occur in the C-group. The piece was found with a bovine figure, Cat. 22.

20
Animal with Head Ornament

Between 1900 and 1550 B.C.
MATERIAL: Fired clay.
COLLECTION: *Leipzig, Karl-Marx-Universität, Ägyptisches Museum 4373.*

DESCRIPTION: The animal's body is poorly modeled, without indications of sex. Horns project laterally from the pointed head. The tail has a broad base. A spherical object with holes punched into it rests on the head.

COLOR: Light brown.
CONDITION: Right horn missing; tip of left horn broken off; discolored in places.
MEASUREMENTS: Height 5.1 cm. Length 6.8 cm. Width 2.7 cm.
PROVENANCE: Aniba, Cemetery N, found in the sand with seven other figures (Steindorff 1914).
BIBLIOGRAPHY: Steindorff 1935,123 (no. 34), pl. 73,34; Huard 1973,106-07 (fig. 7,25); Leipzig 1976,38 (no. 51/14).

Steindorff regarded this figure as a bovine animal. Huard thought it was a sheep (*ovine*), an opinion which might be supported by the broad base of the tail. However, the shape of the body and the tapering head occur in bovine figures from Aniba, so that Steindorff's interpretation is more probable. The unique object on the head is curious. Huard (1973, fig. 7,18-19,26) found rock drawings at Borkou and Tibesti in which cattle have round or discoid formations between their horns, but he cannot explain what they represent. Since this C-group figure is probably related to the rock drawings of the Libyan Desert, the spherical object cannot have been intended to represent the sun, which is always conceived as disk-shaped, at least in Egypt. In any case, some magical import must be considered. Related elements found in the C-group and in eastern Saharan rock drawings suggest a link between the people settled there and the C-group. Both were cattle breeders who lived in these regions in the late third and early second millennia B.C.

21
Bull Figurine

Between 1900 and 1550 B.C.
MATERIAL: Fired clay.
COLLECTION: *Leipzig, Karl-Marx-Universität, Ägyptisches Museum 2757.*

DESCRIPTION: A bull figurine is modeled very naturalistically, with a massive body supported by amorphous, tapering, slightly splayed legs. Powerful horns spring laterally from the slender head. The eyes are oval in shape and look as if they had been modeled separately and applied. The dewlap is prominent, as is the rump with the base of the tail. Sexual organs are indicated.

COLOR: Dark brown to black.
CONDITION: Tail missing; left horn broken off and replaced; minor damages.
MEASUREMENTS: Height 10.0 cm. Length 15.8 cm. Width across horns 10.3 cm.
PROVENANCE: Aniba, Main Cemetery, Grave S 31 (H 12), superstructure, anteroom, northwest corner (Steindorff 1914).
BIBLIOGRAPHY: Steindorff 1937,86,168, pl. 46,5; Berlin 1963,19 (with incorrect grave number); Hintze 1966, pl. 49 bottom; Hintze 1968a, pl. 47 bottom; Eggebrecht 1975,399, pl. 401a left.

This bull figurine is the only one of its kind found in the Egyptian cemetery at Aniba. There can be no doubt, however, that it belongs with similar cattle figurines, such as those found in many Aniba C-group graves (Cat. 22). It is not clear how the piece came to this particular place. Steindorff (1937,86) discusses it among the "magic figures."

22
Bovine Animal

Between 1900 and 1550 B.C.
MATERIAL: Fired clay.
COLLECTION: *Leipzig, Karl-Marx-Universitat, Agyptisches Museum 4387.*

DESCRIPTION: The body of a bovine animal is only slightly modeled. The powerful horns spring upward and then curve back at the tips. Eyes and ears are indicated plastically. The nostrils are impressed and the mouth marked by a horizontal cleft. Chin beard and dewlap are indicated; sexual organs are not.

COLOR: Brown to grayish brown.
CONDITION: Tips of horns, tail, and parts of forelegs missing; hind legs broken off and restored; breaks on neck and horns, repaired; dark discoloration in places.
MEASUREMENTS: Height 12.2 cm. Length 13.3 cm. Width across horns 5.2 cm.
PROVENANCE: Aniba, Cemetery N, near Grave 214 with other animal figures (Steindorff 1914).
BIBLIOGRAPHY: Steindorff 1935,123 (no. 25),140 (N 214), pl. 73,25; Berlin 1963,19; Hintze 1966, pl. 49 bottom; Hintze 1968a, pl. 47 bottom; Bietak 1968, pl. 8 (II/a/25/β); Eggebrecht 1975,399, pl. 401a right; Leipzig 1976,38 (no. 51/15).

This figurine, found with the sheep, Cat. 19, is one of the rare Nubian representations of a long-horned animal. Horns and head are exquisitely modeled, in contrast to the very sketchy body and legs. Bietak (1968,104) has established that these clay figurines should be dated to his phases II/a-b.

Illustrated in color on page 132.

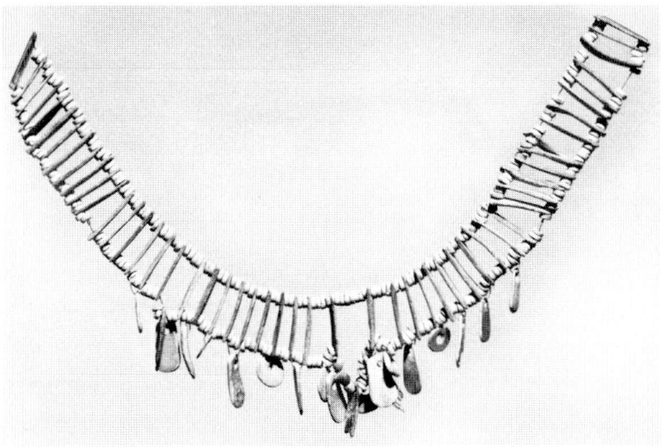

23
Two-Strand Necklace

Between 1700 and 1550 B.C.
MATERIAL: Ostrich shell, mother-of-pearl, and faience.
COLLECTION: *Leipzig, Karl-Marx-Universität, Ägyptisches Museum 4444.*

DESCRIPTION: Two strands of small disk beads are linked by rectangular plaques. A few needle-like and spatulate beads and some large pierced disks were strung into the lower strand. The necklace was assembled in modern times, but the arrangement is very plausible.

COLOR: Yellowish brown; green faience beads (one darkly discolored).
CONDITION: Strung in modern times.
MEASUREMENTS: Length ca. 30 cm.
PROVENANCE: Aniba, Cemetery N, Graves 65 and 66 (Steindorff 1914).
BIBLIOGRAPHY: Steindorff 1935,46ff.,130 (N 65, N 66); Berlin 1963,22; Hintze 1966, pl. 49 top; Hintze 1968a, pl. 47 top; Leipzig 1976,38 (no. 51/21).

A necklace has been strung from beads found in two C-group graves of the North Cemetery at Aniba. Most of these beads were in use all during the C-group period. The small rectangular plaques, which belong to the late C-group, are typical products of the Pan-grave culture (Junker 1930,31; Bietak 1968,122) and appear in C-group graves from Bietak's phase II/b on.

24
Stone Armband

Presumably between 2200 and 2000 B.C.
MATERIAL: Calcite.
COLLECTION: *Leipzig, Karl-Marx-Universität, Ägyptisches Museum 4617.*

DESCRIPTION: An armband is almost flat on the inside; the outside is curved. The surface was very carefully finished.

COLOR: Whitish yellow.
CONDITION: Complete; slightly chipped and traces of wear on outer surface.
MEASUREMENTS: Height 2.4 cm. Outer diameter 10.2 cm. Inner diameter 7.5 cm. Thickness 1.4 cm.
PROVENANCE: Aniba, Cemetery N, Grave 455 (Steindorff 1914).
BIBLIOGRAPHY: Steindorff 1935,60-61,154 (N 455); Berlin 1963,22.

Steindorff assumed that this type of armband was probably worn only by men, and generally on the upper left arm. They were all found in graves of the early C-group (Bietak's phase I/a).

Bovine Animal (Cat. 22).

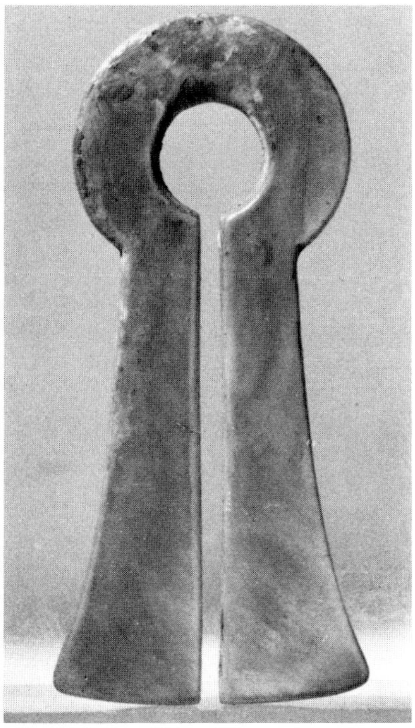

25
Hair Clip

Between 1700 and 1550 B.C.
MATERIAL: Mother-of-pearl.
COLLECTION: *Leipzig, Karl-Marx-Universität, Ägyptisches Museum 4598.*

DESCRIPTION: A hair clip consists of a round perforated disk with a slot and two long shanks.

COLOR: Yellowish light brown.
CONDITION: Complete; slightly scratched and discolored.
MEASUREMENTS: Height 4.9 cm. Width 2.3 cm. Thickness 0.23 cm.
PROVENANCE: Aniba, Cemetery N, Grave 59 (Steindorff 1914).
BIBLIOGRAPHY: Steindorff 1935,63,130 (N 59); Berlin 1963,22.

Hair clips of this kind, mostly of mother-of-pearl but sometimes of ivory, are known exclusively from the C-group and were presumably worn only by women. They may have become fashionable rather late since they have been found only in late C-group graves. Because of the fragile material, they were easily breakable, and many repaired examples have been found, with holes bored at the sides of the break so a thread or wire could be drawn through. These hair clips were initially taken for earrings. They were identified as clips by Junker (1920a,86) and later by Steindorff (1935,63). The hair was drawn through the slot and then bunched in the hole (Steindorff 1935,63, fig. 14).

26
Hair Clip

Between 1700 and 1550 B.C.
MATERIAL: Mother-of-pearl.
COLLECTION: *Leipzig, Karl-Marx-Universität, Ägyptisches Museum 4601.*

DESCRIPTION: The hair clip is almost identical to Cat. 25.

COLOR: Yellowish light brown.
CONDITION: Complete; heavy traces of weathering on one side; slightly scratched and discolored.
MEASUREMENTS: Height 4.5 cm. Width 2.1 cm. Thickness 0.27 cm.
PROVENANCE: Aniba, Cemetery N, Grave 200 (Steindorff 1914).
BIBLIOGRAPHY: Steindorff 1935,63,139 (N 200), pl. 32,23; Berlin 1963,22; Hintze 1966, pl. 44; Hintze 1968a, pl. 42.

See the commentary to Cat. 25.

27
Bowl with Interconnected Rectangles

Between 2200 and 2000 B.C.
MATERIAL: Fired clay.
COLLECTION: *Chicago (Illinois), Oriental Institute Museum 24264.*

DESCRIPTION: On a shallow, polished bowl, undecorated bands create a pattern of interconnected horizontal rectangles, open at top and bottom. Within each rectangle is a long, undecorated horizontal band. The background is finely hatched. Two wavy lines meeting at regular intervals run round the rim. The inside is combed.

COLOR: Black.
CONDITION: Restored from many fragments; rim damaged, with small gaps.
MEASUREMENTS: Height 6.5 cm. Diameter 20.8 cm. Wall thickness 0.3 cm.
PROVENANCE: Adindan, Cemetery T, Grave 101 (Seele 1962-63, Field no. B-1883).
BIBLIOGRAPHY: Seele 1974,27, fig. 13.

The unique decoration was published too late to be included in Bietak's type catalogue, but the shallow form of the bowl assures its attribution to his phase I/a, that is to say in the early C-group. In 1901, L. Borchardt bought an early C-group polished bowl in Luxor, with incised geometric decoration which is also without parallel (Berlin West 14969). Such decorations have no prototype in Nubia nor even in Egypt, yet one is remotely reminded of the unusual secondary incisions on Egyptian-type vessels from A-group graves, such as Cat. 11, which has a similar geometric motif. It seems doubtful that there are any connections here. Yet the fact remains that extraordinary patterns occur in both the A-group and the C-group, which cannot be explained without the publication of further excavated material from Lower Nubia. The incisions were at one time filled with white.

28
Bowl with Halfmoon Decoration

Between 2200 and 2000 B.C.
MATERIAL: Fired clay.
COLLECTION: *Leipzig, Karl-Marx-Universität, Ägyptisches Museum 4232.*

DESCRIPTION: Incised lines divide the surface of a shallow polished bowl into a grid. Two opposite sides of each square serve as baselines for segments of circles outlined within the square and connected by parallel hatchings; the rest of the square is filled with hatchings running in the opposite direction. Since the segments of circles in adjacent squares are offset by ninety degrees, the impression is of symmetrical curves. Wavy lines meeting at regular intervals encircle the rim. The unpolished interior of the bowl is combed.

COLOR: Dark brown.
CONDITION: Complete; rim slightly chipped; traces of white pigment.
MEASUREMENTS: Height 6.0 cm. Diameter 15.3 cm. Wall thickness 0.5 cm.
PROVENANCE: Aniba, Cemetery N, Grave 478 (Steindorff 1914).
BIBLIOGRAPHY: Steindorff 1935,67 (Heidenreich),156 (N 478), pl. 33,7; Bietak 1968,95 (I/a/10),167 (table 1), pl. 2 upper right; Leipzig 1976,37 (no. 51/4).

Heidenreich dated this bowl to the earliest C-group, and Bietak attributes it to his phase I/a. The unusual design has been found on only three objects (sherds from Aniba: Steindorff 1935, pl. 64,32; from Faras: Griffith 1921, pl. XII,17). The significant point of this pattern is the use of curved lines in the form of segments of circles, which were later completely abandoned for geometric designs (Cats. 29, 30, 33-38). The rim pattern, which is similar to that of Cat. 29, was later relinquished in favor of the zigzag band. The incisions were filled with white.

29
Bowl with Basketweave Pattern

Between 2000 and 1900 B.C.
MATERIAL: Fired clay.
COLLECTION: *Leipzig, Karl-Marx-Universität, Ägyptisches Museum 4231.*

DESCRIPTION: A polished bowl is decorated with incised basketweave decoration. The basic pattern element is a band composed of four alternating smooth and hatched stripes. Two of these bands, intersecting at the bottom of the vessel, divide the surface into four panels, each of which is filled with alternating smooth and hatched stripes running in various directions. Another four-stripe band encircling the vessel just below the rim is interrupted by the intersecting bands. Around the rim are wavy lines meeting at intervals.

COLOR: Brown; inside black.
CONDITION: Small portion of rim missing; inside cracked.
MEASUREMENTS: Height 10.0 cm. Diameter 21.0 cm. Wall thickness 0.7 cm.
PROVENANCE: Aniba, Cemetery N, Grave 473 (Steindorff 1914).
BIBLIOGRAPHY: Steindorff 1935,71 (Heidenreich),156 (N 473), pl. 49,1; Bietak 1968,97 with n. 483.

Heidenreich dated the bowl to the early C-group, but Bietak attributes it to his phase I/b and regards the decoration as a special form of the developed basketwork pattern (1968,97, n. 483). This was originally formed from only one pair of stripes, from which a band of stripes then developed. The zones are again subdivided so that the number of panels increases, making the whole more complex. The decoration of the rim is similar to that of Cat. 28. The incisions were at one time filled with white.

30
Bowl with Lozenge Decoration

Between 2000 and 1900 B.C.
MATERIAL: Fired clay.
COLLECTION: *London, British Museum 51218.*

DESCRIPTION: A brown hemispherical bowl with blackened rim and interior is decorated with a lozenge pattern that developed out of the so-called square pattern of the C-group. Like most C-group ceramic decoration, it proceeds from the bottom up. Four large lozenges, composed of alternating smooth and hatched bands, extend to the rim of the vessel. The panels between them, below the rim, are filled with the same pattern. A double zigzag line running round the rim is composed of impressions made in the soft clay by a triangular stamp.

COLOR: Light to medium brown.
CONDITION: Complete; a few cracks visible on inside; discolored in places.
MEASUREMENTS: Height 9.8 cm. Diameter 17.6 cm. Wall thickness 0.6 cm.
PROVENANCE: Faras, Cemetery 2, Grave 238 (Griffith 1912, Find no. 2/238/1).
BIBLIOGRAPHY: None.

According to Bietak (1968,97), this type of lozenge pattern belongs in phase I/b and can also be related to the basketwork pattern. Its use extends into phase II/a. Bietak's examples on his pl. 3 (I/b/5/α) should be compared. The incisions were filled with white.

31

Bowl with Cattle Representations

Between 1900 and 1650 B.C.
MATERIAL: Fired clay.
COLLECTION: *Cairo, Egyptian Museum JE 89989.*

DESCRIPTION: Three rows of horned and unhorned cattle, decreasing in scale from top to bottom, decorate a hemispherical bowl. In the top row, small animals appear among the large ones. Front and back legs are not separated, nor are sexual organs indicated. Spotted hide is suggested by areas of closely juxtaposed incisions. The background is grooved. An incised line encircles the flat bottom of the vessel, which is divided into four panels, alternately smooth and hatched. Around the rim are a plain band and three zigzag lines produced by impressed triangles. The inside of the bowl is combed.

COLOR: Grayish black.
CONDITION: Complete; inside cracked.
MEASUREMENTS: Height 11.3 cm. Diameter 15.7 cm. Wall thickness ca. 0.6 cm.
PROVENANCE: Adindan, Cemetery T, Grave 230 (Seele 1963-64, Field no. B-1099).
BIBLIOGRAPHY: Yoyotte 1966,188 (fig. 2),190; Dakar —Paris 1966, no. 454; Seele 1974,27; DeVries 1975,18.

C-group vessels with figurative decoration were found for the first time in 1963. On this bowl and a second, very similar example from the same cemetery (Cat. 32), the potter first drew the contours of the animals, then filled in the spot pattern and furrowed the background with short, closely set strokes. Because they lack detail, the animals seem crude and clumsy, whereas rock drawings of cattle from the same period (Fig. 7), with which these representations can be compared, give a definitely elegant impression. The reason for this, it seems to me, is that there was no tradition for decorating vessels with figurative representations; C-group ceramics display incised geometric patterns almost exclusively.

In any case, we may admire the courage of this potter who ventured on such new motifs for the decoration of ceramics. When Bietak published his study on the chronology of the C-group, which was based on the evolution of ceramic decoration, vessels with incised figurative motifs had not yet been published; later another C-group vessel of this type was found, which was decorated with female figures (Lal 1967,114, pl. XXXVII). My dating in Bietak's phase II/a rests solely on the fact that small fired clay figurines (Cats. 12-22) originated in the late phase of C-group culture and should probably be considered in connection with the representations on pottery. The incisions were at one time filled with white.

32
Bowl with Cattle Representations

Between 1900 and 1650 B.C.
MATERIAL: Fired clay.
COLLECTION: *Chicago (Illinois), Oriental Institute Museum 23452.*

DESCRIPTION: The vessel is very similar to Cat. 31. There are only two zigzag lines produced by impressed triangles around the rim. An incised line encircles the flat bottom, which is divided into four panels by intersecting hatched bands.

COLOR: Dark brown to black.
CONDITION: Complete; cracked; partly discolored with reddish patches.
MEASUREMENTS: Height 10.2 cm. Diameter 13.9 cm. Wall thickness 0.7 cm.
PROVENANCE: Adindan, Cemetery T, Grave 223 (Seele 1963-64, Field no. B-1098).
BIBLIOGRAPHY: Seele 1974,27,28 (fig. 14); DeVries 1975,18.

In shape and decoration, this vessel is so similar to Cat. 31 that we may assume they were made by the same potter. The attribution to Bietak's phase II/a is explained in the commentary to Cat. 31. The incisions were originally filled with white.

33
Bowl with Zigzag Bands

Between 1900 and 1650 B.C.
MATERIAL: Fired clay.
COLLECTION: *Leipzig, Karl-Marx-Universität, Ägyptisches Museum 4196.*

DESCRIPTION: The decoration of a flat-bottomed hemispherical bowl consists of five smooth zigzag bands touching at the tips. The resulting irregular diamond shapes are roughly hatched. The flat bottom is encircled by an incised line from which spring two rows of hatched, partly overlapping triangles. A smooth band and a double zigzag line produced by impressed triangles encircle the rim.

COLOR: Black; incisions filled with white.
CONDITION: Small piece of rim missing.
MEASUREMENTS: Height 8.8 cm. Diameter 11.6 cm., at mouth 10.5 cm. Wall thickness 0.6 cm.
PROVENANCE: Aniba, Cemetery N, Grave 385 (Steindorff 1914).
BIBLIOGRAPHY: Steindorff 1935,79 (Heidenreich),150 (N 385), pl. 44,3; Bietak 1968,100-101 with n. 562 (II/a/9), pl. 6 top right.

Bietak dated the vessel to his phase II/a on the basis of the flat bottom, which is found only in this period. The zigzag pattern produced by adjoining diamonds is characteristic of this phase (which also includes other styles of decoration). Bietak (1968,101) could find only one example of the use of this pattern in phase II/b; we may assume, therefore, that it was abandoned in the course of time.

34
Bowl with Herringbone Decoration

Between 1900 and 1650 B.C.
MATERIAL: Fired clay.
COLLECTION: *Leipzig, Karl-Marx-Universität, Ägyptisches Museum 4189.*

DESCRIPTION: Around the rim of a polished bowl are a band of fine oblique hatching, an incised line, a smooth stripe, and a dotted line. On the body, smooth vertical stripes alternate with rows of arrow-like angles pointing downward, which have been designated as herringbone pattern. An incised line encircles the bottom; within it are two parallel lines. The interior is smooth.

COLOR: Grayish black; some incisions filled with white.
CONDITION: Complete; small piece broken from rim and replaced; small chips.
MEASUREMENTS: Height 6.95 cm. Diameter 11.6 cm. Wall thickness 0.55 cm.
PROVENANCE: Aniba, Cemetery N, Grave 131 (Steindorff 914).
BIBLIOGRAPHY: Steindorff 1935,77 (Heidenreich), 134 (N 131), pl. 414; Bietak 1968,103, pl. 7 (II/a/19).

Heidenreich regarded this decoration as a misunderstood star pattern; Bietak described it, without further commentary, as herringbone. The pattern is not incised, as in the overwhelming majority of C-group vessels, but impressed, probably with a rocker-stamp. The herringbone pattern is rare in the C-group; a second example was found at Aniba, Grave N 232 (Steindorff 1935,77, pl. 41,5). Bietak (1968,103) refers to a further example from Toshka. He dates these bowls with herringbone decoration to his phase II/a.

35
Bowl with Incised Patterns

Between 1900 and 1650 B.C.
MATERIAL: Fired clay.
COLLECTION: *Leipzig, Karl-Marx-Universität, Ägyptisches Museum 4206.*

DESCRIPTION: The surface of a polished bowl is divided into two areas of decoration. Rising from the bottom are four rows of horizontally hatched inverted triangles. Above are hatched zigzag bands that touch at the tips to form lozenges. Around the rim are a zigzag line and a smooth stripe. The interior is smooth.

COLOR: Dark brown to black; incisions filled with white.
CONDITION: Small piece of rim missing.
MEASUREMENTS: Height 7.8 cm. Diameter 10.9 cm. Wall thickness 0.4 cm.
PROVENANCE: Aniba, Cemetery N, Grave 153 (Steindorff 1914).
BIBLIOGRAPHY: Steindorff 1935,80 (Heidenreich), 136 (N 153), pl. 46,7.

The pattern on the lower part of the bowl corresponds to Bietak's phase II/a/8 (triangle pattern: Bietak 1968,100); he does not list the upper pattern. It might be a variant of his zigzag pattern II/a/9, with, however, the reversal of the customary principle of leaving the zigzag line smooth.

36
Bowl with Diamond Pattern

Between 1900 and 1650 B.C.
MATERIAL: Fired clay.
COLLECTION: *Leipzig, Karl-Marx-Universität, Ägyptisches Museum 4207.*

DESCRIPTION: A polished bowl with a carinated wall has a pattern of diamonds on a hatched background. Around the rim are an impressed pattern, an incised line, and a smooth band. Another smooth band beneath the middle of the vessel divides the decoration into two areas.

COLOR: Dark brown.
CONDITION: Rim slightly chipped.
MEASUREMENTS: Height 8.6 cm. Diameter 11.8 cm. Wall thickness 0.5 cm.
PROVENANCE: Aniba, Cemetery N, Grave 402 (Steindorff 1914).
BIBLIOGRAPHY: Steindorff 1935,80-81 (Heidenreich),151 (N 402), pl. 46,5; Bietak 1968,102, pl. 7 (II/a/17); Leipzig 1976,37 (no. 51/2).

Bietak placed the bowl in his phase II/a/17. Carinated vessels are infrequent in the C-group.

37 ■
Goblet-Shaped Vessel

Between 1700 and 1550 B.C.
MATERIAL: Fired clay.
COLLECTION: *Aswan Museum 587.*

DESCRIPTION: This spherical polished vessel is drawn in at the wide mouth and has a flaring foot. Around the rim is a zigzag line of impressed triangles above a plain band. The body decoration consists of horizontal lozenges, which, in the first and third rows, have double contour lines; in the second row, they are filled with scored lines. Below are a zigzag band, another row of lozenges, and finally a smooth band. On the foot of the vessel, a zigzag line is bounded above and below by hatched bands. The incisions were filled with white and red pigment.

COLOR: Black; traces of white and red pigment in lozenges.
CONDITION: Complete; discolored in places.
MEASUREMENTS: Height 10.9 cm. Diameter 9.8 cm., at foot 7.5 cm., at mouth 6.5 cm.
PROVENANCE: Koshtamna, Cemetery 87, Grave 21 (Firth 1908-09, Field no. 87/21/2).
BIBLIOGRAPHY: Firth 1912,162, pl. 39f, no. 2; Firth 1915, pl. 39, no. 2; Bietak 1968,111 with n. 723, 177-78 (tables 11, 12), pl. 12.

According to Bietak (1968,110), horizontal lozenges are the most frequent and characteristic decorative motif of phase II/b. Vessels with an attached foot have been found only rarely; besides this piece, which Bietak classifies as II/b/16, he lists two other objects from Aniba and Toshka that have the same pattern. A fourth vessel of this type from Aniba has triangle patterns (Bietak 1968,111).

Illustrated in color on page 141.

38
Bowl with Horizontal Lozenges

Between 1700 and 1550 B.C.
MATERIAL: Fired clay.
COLLECTION: *Leipzig, Karl-Marx-Universität, Ägyptisches Museum 4212.*

DESCRIPTION: The decoration of a polished bowl proceeds from the bottom up. A plain band running round the flat bottom creates a circle that is almost filled by broad plain crossed bands; the corners are decorated. Above are horizontal lozenges filled with various patterns. A row of impressed triangles and a smooth band encircle the rim. The inside of the vessel is deeply combed.

COLOR: Brownish black; traces of red, white, and yellow pigment in lozenges.
CONDITION: Complete; minor scratches.
MEASUREMENTS: Height 8.0 cm. Diameter 10.8 cm., at mouth 9.8 cm. Wall thickness 0.7 cm.
PROVENANCE: Aniba, Cemetery N, Grave 322 (Steindorff 1914).
BIBLIOGRAPHY: Steindorff 1935,81 (Heidenreich),148 (N 322), pl. 47,6; Leipzig 1976,37 (no. 51/7).

According to Bietak (1968,110), the use of horizontal lozenges belongs exclusively to his phase II/b, although the motif should be construed as a variant of the upright lozenges typical of phase II/a. The pattern on the base of the vessel has the form of the Egyptian hieroglyph for "town" but has no connection with it.

Goblet-Shaped Vessel (Cat. 37).

39
Bowl with Cross-Hatched Bands

Between 1900 and 1550 B.C.
MATERIAL: Fired clay.
COLLECTION: *Chicago (Illinois), Oriental Institute Museum 23241.*

DESCRIPTION: An unpolished hemispherical vessel has a wide cross-hatched band around the bottom. On the body are two rows of seven or eight irregular panels bounded by contour lines and filled with cross-hatching. An impressed zigzag line encircles the rim. The incisions were filled with white pigment.

COLOR: Dark to blackish brown; traces of white pigment in incisions.
CONDITION: Complete; cracked in places.
MEASUREMENTS: Height 8.7 cm. Diameter 12.2 cm. Wall thickness 0.6 cm.
PROVENANCE: Adindan, Cemetery T, Grave 64 (Seele 1963-64, Field no. B-885).
BIBLIOGRAPHY: None.

Its shape and incrustation relate this C-group vessel to the incised-pattern bowls, but the decoration is unique. The bowl thus represents connections between the incised-pattern bowls and the coarse native wares.

40
Bowl with Impressed Decoration

Between 1900 and 1550 B.C.
MATERIAL: Fired clay.
COLLECTION: *Leipzig, Karl-Marx-Universität, Ägyptisches Museum 4219.*

DESCRIPTION: A polished bowl corresponds in form to the usual incised-pattern vessels, but the decoration is impressed. Around the body are tall rectangular panels, connected by lines at top and bottom. Below are a zigzag line, a double row of short horizontal strokes, and another zigzag line standing on a contour line that sets off the bottom of the vessel and gives it particular emphasis. Around the rim is a double row of impressed triangles.

COLOR: Brown.
CONDITION: Two small pieces of rim missing; blackish discoloration in places.
MEASUREMENTS: Height 8.7 cm. Diameter 12.0 cm., at mouth 11.2 cm. Wall thickness 0.6 cm.
PROVENANCE: Aniba, Cemetery N, Grave 412 (Steindorff 1914).
BIBLIOGRAPHY: Steindorff 1935,84 (Heidenreich),152 (N 412), pl. 51,1.

Heidenreich classifies this bowl among the special forms of incised-pattern pottery. In reality, however, the decoration was impressed in a manner similar to that of Cat. 41, except that in this case styluses were probably used to produce the pricked dots and triangles. Its form and incrustation relate the bowl to the customary incised-pattern vessels; on the other hand, the technique of impressed decoration is familiar in Nubia and the northern Sudan from the Neolithic age (Cat. 5) and is found in the C-group especially in coarse native wares (Cat. 41), so that this vessel establishes a certain connection between the two types of ceramics. The decoration is unusual in the C-group except for the impressed triangles around the rim.

41
Dish with Tripod

Between 1900 and 1550 B.C.
MATERIAL: Fired clay.
COLLECTION: *Leipzig, Karl-Marx-Universität, Ägyptisches Museum 4179-80.*

DESCRIPTION: A dish rests on a cylindrical support with a concave flaring top and three bulky feet, decorated with vertical rows of impressed lozenges. Below the rim of the dish are two incised zigzag lines. On the underside are two rows of incised hatched lozenges, and between them are pricked four birds (?), shaped like lozenges with feet added. On the inside of the bowl are several rows of double lozenges, all designed differently, pointing inward from the rim.

COLOR: Light to dark brown.
CONDITION: Complete; bottom of tripod cracked; two feet broken off and repaired (with defects); small damages on uneven dish; discolored.
MEASUREMENTS: Height of tripod 9.7 cm. Width 5.0 to 5.9 cm. Height of dish 3.4 cm. Diameter 11.5 cm. Height of dish and tripod 12.7 cm.
PROVENANCE: Aniba, Cemetery N, between Graves 4 and 10 (Steindorff 1914).
BIBLIOGRAPHY: Steindorff 1935,95 (Heidenreich),126 (N 10), pl. 58,17; Berlin 1963,18.

This rare C-group example of a tripod stand with a small dish is related in both technique and decoration to the coarse native ware, which is fundamentally distinct from the incised-pattern vessels.

42
Red Polished Bowl

Between 1900 and 1550 B.C.
MATERIAL: Fired clay.
COLLECTION: *Cairo, Egyptian Museum JE 65145.*

DESCRIPTION: A bowl with a small base and outward-slanting wall is red polished with a black top and a black interior. Below the rim runs a broad band of double lozenges. On the body is a series of double festoons, bounded by incised lines and finely hatched. The same pattern, in reverse, springs from the base of the vessel. A few subsidiary incised lines on the underside were used to lay out the decoration.

COLOR: Red; rim and interior black.
CONDITION: Small fragment missing from rim; blackish discoloration in places.
MEASUREMENTS: Height 12.5 cm. Diameter 24.5 cm. Wall thickness 0.9 cm.
PROVENANCE: Aniba, Cemetery N, in the sand (Steindorff 1930-31).
BIBLIOGRAPHY: Steindorff 1935,84 (Heidenreich), pl. 50,2.

This bowl is extraordinary in many respects. The base is quite untypical of C-group incised-pattern vessels. It is among the largest incrusted vessels of this culture, which were only rarely found in graves; furthermore, it is red polished and has a black top. Although this type of ceramic has been found in Nubia from the late Neolithic on, it is seldom decorated with incised patterns. Finally, the festoon decoration is without parallel. Heidenreich thought the vessel might belong to the later C-group; Bietak does not list it, but a dating in his phases II/a to II/b is plausible.

43
Bird-Shaped Vessel

Probably between 1700 and 1550 B.C.
MATERIAL: Fired clay.
COLLECTION: *Philadelphia (Pennsylvania), University Museum E 10604a.*

DESCRIPTION: An unpolished vessel is in the form of a legless bird with a tublike body, the bird's elongated beak serving as the spout. On top of the body is a cylindrical filling hole. Two small birds (one is now broken off) were perched on each wing.

COLOR: Reddish brown.
CONDITION: Part of left wing missing; beak broken and repaired; minor surface damages.
MEASUREMENTS: Height 8.9 cm. Diameter 7.9 cm. Length 20.0 cm.
PROVENANCE: Buhen, Tomb J 28 (Randall-MacIver—Woolley 1909-10).
BIBLIOGRAPHY: Randall-MacIver—Woolley 1911,132,230.

The excavators dated Buhen Cemetery J to Dynasty XVIII. Twenty-five graves, containing 346 skeletons, were opened. All had been plundered; only small objects and a great deal of pottery were found. In Tomb J 28, which consisted of a chamber with an approach 2.80 meters long, were the bones of an adult and a child. In addition to scarabs and other minor objects, the funerary gifts included three bird-shaped vessels with nestlings perched on the wings. Traces of red and white pigment are preserved on the wings of one of these vessels (Philadelphia E 10604 B: Randall-MacIver—Woolley 1911,132, where the number is erroneously given as 10605).

This kind of vessel, probably given for the child rather than the adult, is otherwise unknown from Nubia. They must have been produced by native potters, since nothing comparable is known from Egypt. It cannot be said with certainty, however, whether they should be attributed to the C-group people, who were native to Lower Nubia, or to representatives of the Kerma culture, who had conquered Lower Nubia during the Second Intermediate Period. No parallels to the bird vessels are known from either culture. Reference may be made, however, to the so-called Kerma teapots with animal-headed spouts, such as Cat. 65. Although this and the bird-shaped vessel are not directly comparable, some common fundamental concepts are evident. We may surmise, therefore, that the bird-shaped vessels from Buhen belong to the ceramic tradition of the Kerma culture, especially since fancy forms of vessels are relatively frequent there.

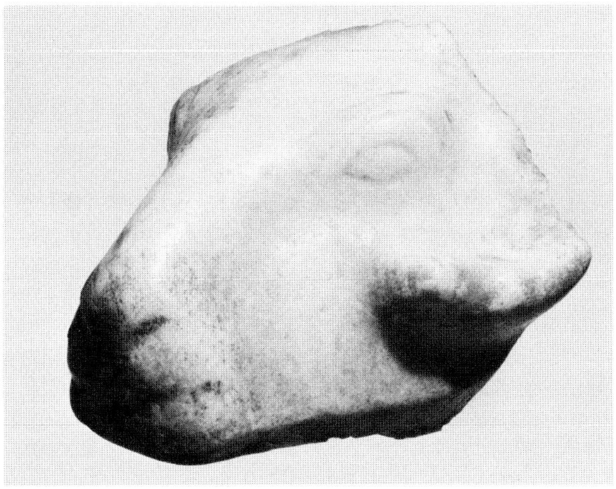

44
Ram's Head

Between 1750 and 1550 B.C.
MATERIAL: Quartz.
COLLECTION: *Boston (Massachusetts), Museum of Fine Arts 20.1180.*

DESCRIPTION: The head, approximately half life size, was originally glazed. The back is severed, but the remains of the left ear and the tip of the horn are visible. The details are softly modeled. Nostrils and mouth are shown by faint indentations, and the almond-shaped eyes and skin folds above them are indicated by narrow grooves.

COLOR: Grayish white; traces of blue pigment.
CONDITION: Back of head missing, the break running through the right eye and the underside severed on a single plane; brownish discoloration in places.
MEASUREMENTS: Height 9.4 cm. Width 10.6 cm. Depth 8.3 cm.
PROVENANCE: Kerma, Tumulus K III, comp. 17/3 (Reisner 1913, Location no. K III:XIII, Object no. S 13-12-785).
BIBLIOGRAPHY: Reisner 1923a, 139(f), xiii; Reisner 1923b, 51, pl. 37,4.

The only breed of sheep known in Egypt in the Old Kingdom was the Cretan sheep, which had laterally spreading horns. In the Middle Kingdom, new breeds were imported, probably from Syria. They must have spread southward rapidly, since they are known shortly afterward from the C-group and the Kerma culture. These new breeds had horns that curled around the ears, as in this sculpture from Kerma. We may assume that sheep already had some religious significance in Nubia, since statuettes of these animals, to which a cultic or ritual function must be attributed, were made so soon after their introduction. A typical C-group figure in the form of a pregnant woman with a sheep's head (Cat. 12), found at Askut, points toward a Nubian sheep cult.

The present ram's head may have been made at

Kerma, where the manufacture of works in glazed quartz was more common than in Egypt (Reisner 1923b,50). The style, however, is Egyptian. Wildung (1973) has shown that the ram which from before the beginning of the New Kingdom was sacred to Amun reached Egypt from Nubia. Whether the ram was already connected, in the Kerma culture, with a native deity corresponding to the Egyptian god cannot be determined. It is important, however, that Egypt adopted impulses from the south, as the ram of Amun demonstrates.

I am indebted to B. Brentjes for zoological information.

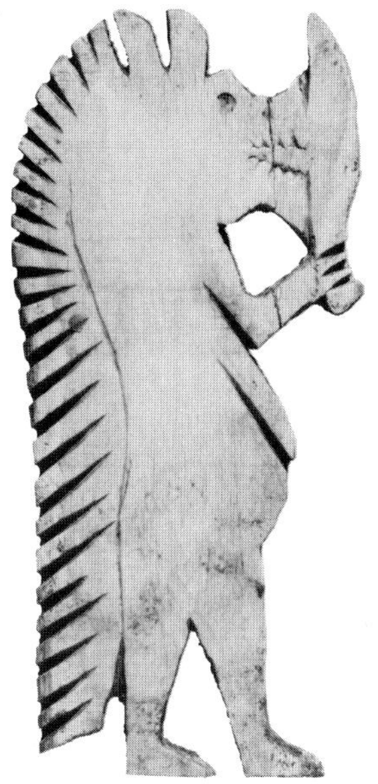

45
Inlay in the Form of a Mythical Creature with Crest

Between 1750 and 1550 B.C.
MATERIAL: Ivory.
COLLECTION: *Boston (Massachusetts), Museum of Fine Arts 13.4220c.*

DESCRIPTION: A standing female figure with human hands and feet, swollen belly, pendulous breasts, and a hippopotamus head represents a mythical creature. A serrated crest ending in a long tail runs from the forehead down the back. The creature holds a knife in her hands.

COLOR: Light brown.
CONDITION: Complete; front of head with forearm and knife broken off and repaired; discolored in places.
MEASUREMENTS: Height 9.9 cm. Width 4.4 cm. Thickness ca. 0.3 cm.
PROVENANCE: Kerma, Tumulus K X, Grave 1053 (Reisner 1913, Location no. K 1053:1, Object no. SU 1073).
BIBLIOGRAPHY: Reisner 1914,20, fig. 22; Reisner 1923b,267,270 (no. 27), pl. 55,1(4).

Three rows of ivory inlays decorated the inside of the footboard of a bed: ibexes (Cat. 47); eight female mythical creatures, including the present one; and hyenas (Cat. 48). Reisner (1923b,266ff.) considered these mythical creatures, which are sometimes shown with a loincloth, as representations of the Egyptian hippopotamus-goddess Taweret, who, with a knife held in her human hands and a crocodile tail running down her back, was reputed to ward off evil by her awesome appearance. Frequently found on beds discovered in Egypt, she was considered above all as protectress of women in labor.

46
Inlay in the Form of a Mythical Creature

Between 1750 and 1550 B.C.
MATERIAL: Ivory.
COLLECTION: *Boston (Massachusetts), Museum of Fine Arts 20.2027.*

DESCRIPTION: A female creature in human form has the head of a hippopotamus and pendulous breasts. Her ears are upright, jaws open, and tongue extended. She wears a skirt and holds a knife in her hands.

COLOR: Dark brown.
CONDITION: Broken in several places and repaired; long piece missing from back; cracked and discolored.
MEASUREMENTS: Height 9.7 cm. Width 4.2 cm. Thickness 0.2 cm.
PROVENANCE: Kerma, Tumulus K IV, Grave 439, Bed A (Reisner 1914, Location no. K 439:II, Object no. between S 14-1-249 and -258).
BIBLIOGRAPHY: Reisner 1923a,228; Reisner 1923b,267,269 (no. 14), pl. 56,2; Roveri 1963,570-76, fig. 728.

Like Cat. 45, this inlay represents the Egyptian goddess Taweret, in this case wearing a skirt consisting of separate strips. The piece has an unequivocally apotropaic character; see commentary to Cat. 45. In this representation, the analogy to Egyptian images of the goddess is particularly clear; see, for example, two ornate axes from about the same period (Kühnert-Eggebrecht 1969, pl. XX).

The decoration of the footboard of the bed consisted of an upper row of four vultures with wings outspread (object nos. S 14-1-245 to -248), a row of five pairs of Taweret figures standing back to back, and a row of five pairs of goats ascending small trees to browse the upper leaves (object nos. S 14-1-259 to -263).

47
Inlay in the Form of an Ibex

Between 1750 and 1550 B.C.
MATERIAL: Ivory.
COLLECTION: *Boston (Massachusetts), Museum of Fine Arts 13.4219e.*

DESCRIPTION: An inlay from the footboard of a bed is in the form of an ibex, its powerful horns arching back over the body.

COLOR: Grayish brown.
CONDITION: Complete; discolored.
MEASUREMENTS: Height 6.7 cm. Length 7.4 cm. Thickness ca. 0.4 cm.
PROVENANCE: Kerma, Tumulus K X, Grave 1053 (Reisner 1913, Location no. K 1053:1, Object no. SU 1073).
BIBLIOGRAPHY: Reisner 1914,20, fig. 22; Reisner 1923b, 267-68 (described as an antelope),270 (no. 27, here called a gazelle), pl. 55,1(3); Smith 1954, fig. 26.

The inlay comes from the same bed as Cats. 45 and 48; see commentary to Cat. 45.

48
Inlay in the Form of a Hyena

Between 1750 and 1550 B.C.
MATERIAL: Ivory.
COLLECTION: *Boston (Massachusetts), Museum of Fine Arts 13.4221e.*

DESCRIPTION: An inlay in the form of a hyena comes from the footboard of a bed. Anatomical details are indicated by incisions and notches.

COLOR: Dark brown.
CONDITION: Complete; discolored.
MEASUREMENTS: Height 4.2 cm. Length 11.2 cm. Thickness ca. 0.5 cm.
PROVENANCE: Kerma, Tumulus K X, Grave 1053 (Reisner 1913, Location no. K 1053:1, Object no. SU 1073).
BIBLIOGRAPHY: Reisner 1914,20, fig. 22; Reisner 1923b, 267,268,270 (no. 27), pl. 55,1(5); Smith 1954, fig. 26.

The inlay comes from the same bed as Cats. 45 and 47; see commentary to Cat. 45.

Illustrated in color, Volume I, page 59.

49
Inlay in the Form of a Bustard

Between 1750 and 1550 B.C.
MATERIAL: Ivory.
COLLECTION: *Boston (Massachusetts), Museum of Fine Arts 20.2028.*

DESCRIPTION: A bird with long legs and curved beak has a crest, pointed tail feathers, and uplifted, separately made wings. There are notches on the beak, crest, tail feathers, and wings; the eye is drilled. These details create an interior design.

COLOR: Dark brown.
CONDITION: Complete; wings made separately; discolored and spotty.
MEASUREMENTS: Height 8.5 cm. Width 6.3 cm. Thickness 0.4 cm.
PROVENANCE: Kerma, Tumulus K X, Grave 1096 (Reisner 1914, Location no. K 1096:11 ff., Object no. between S 14-3-706 and -743).
BIBLIOGRAPHY: Reisner 1923a,369; Reisner 1923b,268,270 (no. 33), pl. 54,1; Dunham 1958,89, fig. 63f.

The decoration on the footboard of the bed found in Grave 1096 consisted of a row of six bustards (identified by Reisner), nine ostriches with uplifted wings, and nine giraffes; all of the animals face right.

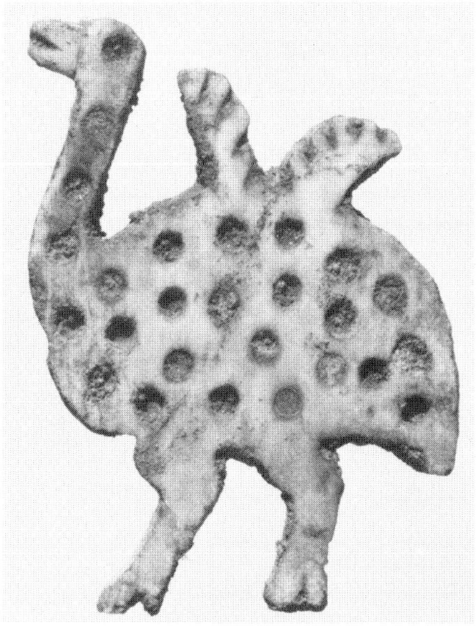

50
Inlay in the Form of an Ostrich Chick

Between 1750 and 1550 B.C.
MATERIAL: Ivory.
COLLECTION: *Boston (Massachusetts), Museum of Fine Arts 13.4211.*

DESCRIPTION: An ostrich chick has small upright wings rising from its back. Neck and body are covered with drilled holes.

COLOR: Dark to blackish brown.
CONDITION: Complete; foreleg broken and repaired; discolored.
MEASUREMENTS: Height 3.9 cm. Width 3.0 cm. Thickness ca. 0.3 cm.
PROVENANCE: Kerma, Tumulus K X, Grave 1050 (Reisner 1913, Location no. K 1050:II, Object no. SU 920).
BIBLIOGRAPHY: Reisner 1914,20, fig. 22; Reisner 1923a,340; Reisner 1923b,267 (no. 26),268,270 (no. 26), pl. 55,1(7).

The inlays on the footboard of a bed found in Grave 1050 included several ostrich chicks, facing right and left, and six bees. A reconstruction of the decoration is no longer possible because of the footboard's poor state of preservation.

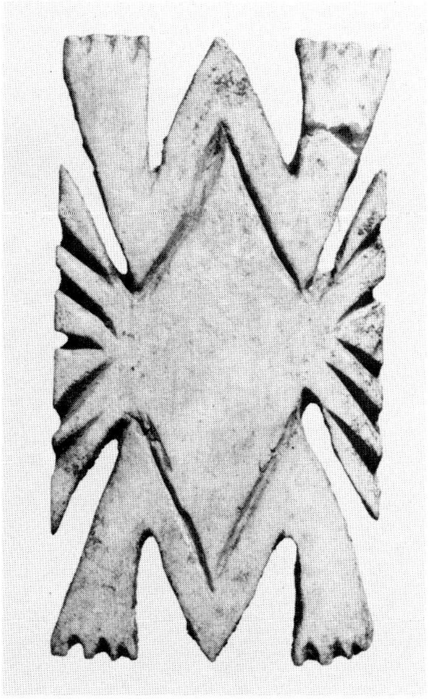

51
Inlay in the Form of a Stylized Motif

Between 1750 and 1550 B.C.
MATERIAL: Ivory.
COLLECTION: *Boston (Massachusetts), Museum of Fine Arts 13.4222g.*

DESCRIPTION: A small oblong plaque is carved in a symmetrical shape, with interior incisions and notches at the side edges.

COLOR: Light brown.
CONDITION: Complete; one leg broken off and repaired; discolored in places.
MEASUREMENTS: Height 4.6 cm. Width 2.6 cm. Thickness 0.2 cm.
PROVENANCE: Kerma, probably from Tumulus K X, Grave 1053 (Reisner 1913, Location no. K 1053-la-b, Object no. SU 1073).
BIBLIOGRAPHY: Reisner 1923b,266,270 (no. 27), pl. 55,2.

Inlays such as this were placed around the side edges of the footboards of beds; it is not known what they represent. Reisner (1923b,266) interpreted them as plant motifs. It appears to me that one can recognize animal legs with a suggestion of toes, so that we have here an abstract rendition of a quadruped. Perhaps the hide is represented, or the animal as seen from underneath. A similar inlay was curved over the lower corner of the footboard. See Fig. 13, the reconstruction of an inlaid bed in the Museum of Fine Arts, Boston.

52
Inlay in the Form of a Striding Lion

Between 1750 and 1550 B.C.
MATERIAL: Copper.
COLLECTION: *Liverpool, University SAOS 1566.*

DESCRIPTION: The massive figure of a striding lion, its taut tail curling upward at the tip, is cut out of thin copper sheet.

COLOR: Dark reddish brown.
CONDITION: Complete; discolored and oxidized in places.
MEASUREMENTS: Height 6.8 cm. Length 15.2 cm. Thickness 0.5 cm.
PROVENANCE: Kerma, Tumulus K III, Grave 334 (Reisner 1914, Location no. K 334:14, Object no. S 14-2-674).
BIBLIOGRAPHY: Reisner 1923a,170-71; Reisner 1923b,204.

Sixteen copper lions had been inlaid in four rows on the outside of a bed footboard that measured 26-27 cm. by 77 cm. The two inner lions in each row faced each other; the outer ones faced out; the animals' tails were close together. Altogether, eighteen lion figures belong to this find; two were applied to the inside of the footboard. Sheet copper inlays have been found nowhere else in Kerma.

53
Ornament in the Form of a Stylized Plant

Between 1750 and 1550 B.C.
MATERIAL: Mica.
COLLECTION: *Leipzig, Karl-Marx-Universität, Ägyptisches Museum 3793.*

DESCRIPTION: The tall rectangular plaque, a highly stylized plant representation, is in the form of four overlapping inverted triangles. There are sewing holes at top and bottom.

COLOR: Light to dark brown; partly transparent.
CONDITION: Complete.
MEASUREMENTS: Height 7.6 cm. Width 4.0 cm.
PROVENANCE: Kerma, Tumulus K X, Grave 1044, near the skull of Skeleton A (Reisner 1913, Location no. K 1044:8, Object no. SU 826).
BIBLIOGRAPHY: Reisner 1923a,36; Reisner 1923b,273(n), 278-79 (no. 21), pl. 56,4; Berlin 1963,21; Hintze 1966, pl. 54; Hintze 1968a, pl. 52; Eggebrecht 1975,399, pl. 401b left; Leipzig 1976,35 (no. 50/19).

This ornament was sewn onto the cap of a sacrificial victim; Cat. 56 comes from the same cap. The motif, found more than once with this skeleton and in other Kerma graves, probably represents a stylized bunch of flowers. Reisner interprets it as a bush or tree. In any case, it recalls the *Stabstrauss*, or formal bouquet, that was common in Egyptian art and was often highly stylized. The motif continued to be popular in Meroitic times, when it likewise represented a bunch of flowers or plants. As to the present piece, the question arises whether the motif originated in Egypt or evolved independently in Kerma, the similarity to the stylized Egyptian formal bouquet being purely coincidental.

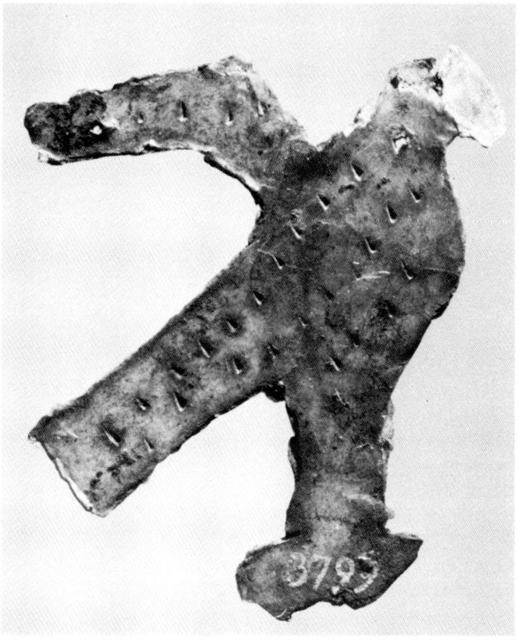

54
Ornament in the Form of a Standing Bird

Between 1750 and 1550 B.C.
MATERIAL: Mica.
COLLECTION: *Leipzig, Karl-Marx-Universität, Ägyptisches Museum 3799.*

DESCRIPTION: Standing on a base is a bird with swelling breast, long tail, and upright twisted wings. On the surface is a pattern of triangular holes, with further holes at the edges for sewing.

COLOR: Light to dark brown.
CONDITION: Head partly missing; surface chipped; discolored in places.
MEASUREMENTS: Height 6.7 cm. Width 5.5 cm.
PROVENANCE: Kerma, Tumulus K III, Grave 323, Skeleton A (Reisner 1914, Location no. K 323:7, Object no. S 14-2-977).
BIBLIOGRAPHY: Reisner 1923a,161; Reisner 1923b,273(c), 277 (no. 1), pl. 57,1(4); Berlin 1963,21; Hintze 1966, pl. 54; Hintze 1968a, pl. 52; Eggebrecht 1975,399, pl. 401b right; Leipzig 1976,36 (no. 50/21).

On the leather cap of a sacrificial victim were sewn eleven mica ornaments, a rosette and ten birds, reminiscent of the Egyptian *rekhyt*-birds, with which Reisner (1923b,273) has identified them. It might, however, be a falcon; a connection with the Egyptian *rekhyt* hieroglyph appears questionable to me. The motif does not occur among the ivory bed inlays.

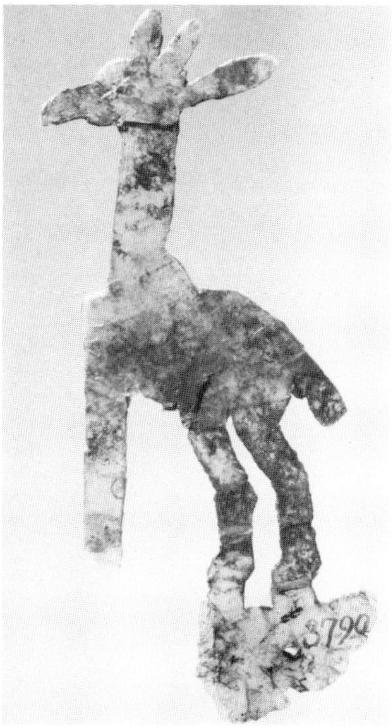

55
Ornament in the Form of a Giraffe

Between 1750 and 1550 B.C.
MATERIAL: Mica.
COLLECTION: *Leipzig, Karl-Marx-Universität, Ägyptisches Museum 3790.*

DESCRIPTION: A giraffe, standing on a now fragmentary base, has a columnar neck that is too short in proportion to the body; the head is rendered more naturalistically. Holes along the edges served for sewing.

COLOR: Light to dark brown; transparent in places.
CONDITION: One foreleg, lower part of the other, and most of base missing; discolored in places.
MEASUREMENTS: Height 9.1 cm. Width 4.1 cm.
PROVENANCE: Kerma, Tumulus K X, Corridor B, Body EI (Reisner 1914, Location no. K X B 339a, Object no. S 14-3-517).
BIBLIOGRAPHY: Reisner 1923a,301; Reisner 1923b,273,278 (no. 19), pl. 58,1(1); Berlin 1963,21; Leipzig 1976,35 (no. 50/15).

Small plaques of various shapes and eight standing giraffes were sewn onto the cap of a sacrificial victim. This motif is found also among ivory bed inlays (Reisner 1923b,270, nos. 28, 33).

56
Ornament in the Form of Four Lion's Heads

Between 1750 and 1550 B.C.
MATERIAL: Mica.
COLLECTION: *Leipzig, Karl-Marx-Universität, Ägyptisches Museum 3792.*

DESCRIPTION: Four lion's heads in superimposed pairs emerge from a common trunk. The eyes are cut out in the shape of diamonds, and the open mouths are wedge-shaped. There are sewing holes at the edges.

COLOR: Dark to blackish brown; transparent in places.
CONDITION: Top right head missing; ears broken off top left head; discolored in places.
MEASUREMENTS: Height 5.6 cm. Width 5.5 cm.
PROVENANCE: Kerma, Tumulus K X, Grave 1044, near the skull of Skeleton A (Reisner 1913, Location no. K 1044:8, Object no. SU 826).
BIBLIOGRAPHY: Reisner 1923a,336; Reisner 1923b,273(m), 278 (no. 31), pl. 56,4.

The motif of four lion's heads appears only in the art of Kerma; it does not occur in ivory inlays. Nine ornaments of this type were sewn onto the cap of a sacrificial victim. Cat. 53 was found with the same skeleton.

57
Half of a Double Eagle Ornament

Between 1750 and 1550 B.C.
MATERIAL: Mica.
COLLECTION: *Leipzig, Karl-Marx-Universität, Ägyptisches Museum 3796.*

DESCRIPTION: This piece is the left half of a double-headed eagle; the other head was turned to the right. The wings curve upward, and the legs spread beneath. There are sewing holes at the edges.

COLOR: Light to dark brown.
CONDITION: Only left half of ornament preserved; discolored in places.
MEASUREMENTS: Height 7.4 cm. Width 4.2 cm.
PROVENANCE: Kerma, Tumulus K XIV (Reisner 1914, Location no. K XIV:X, Object no. S 14-1-646).
BIBLIOGRAPHY: Reisner 1923a, 478; Reisner 1923b,273(i), 279 (no. 38, with incorrect no. K XIV:XIV), pl. 59,2(3); Berlin 1963,21; Smith 1965a, pl. 83(B).

The two-headed eagle with outspread wings (Smith 1965a,120, considers the birds vultures) is an independent product of Kerma art and is found only there; it does not occur as an ivory bed inlay. Bissing (1928,54) thinks the motif reflects strong Egyptian influence. I believe it arose spontaneously in the Sudan.

58
Necklace of Carnelian and Gold Beads

Between 1750 and 1550 B.C.
MATERIAL: Carnelian and sheet gold.
COLLECTION: *Khartoum, Sudan National Museum 1139.*

DESCRIPTION: Fifty small carnelian ball beads and twelve hollow gold biconical beads were restrung in modern times.

COLOR: Carnelian beads dark red.
CONDITION: Complete; a few of the gold beads have small perforations or are crushed.
MEASUREMENTS: Length of necklace ca. 76.0 cm. Length of gold beads 3.0-3.2 cm., width 2.9 cm. Diameter of carnelian beads 0.8-1.1 cm.
PROVENANCE: Kerma, Tumulus K XIX, chief burial, southern room, found in the debris 90.0 cm. above floor level, in a basket, the impression of which is preserved (Reisner 1914, Location no. K XIX:X [Reisner 1923b,99] or K XIX:IX [Reisner 1923a,460; 1923b,116], Object no. S 14-1-613).
BIBLIOGRAPHY: Reisner 1923a,459-60; Reisner 1923b,99 (no. 10),116,120.

According to Reisner, the necklace lying in a basket was overlooked when the grave was plundered and was thrown into the rubble; he also thinks it conceivable that the thief hid the necklace in a basket but had no opportunity to pick up his loot. Carnelian ball beads were found in abundance in Kerma (Reisner 1923b,116); biconical beads were less frequent and were mostly of faience or carnelian. The necklace elements described here are the only ones of gold found at Kerma (Reisner 1923b,119-20).

59
Strand of Ball Beads

Between 1750 and 1550 B.C.
MATERIAL: Faience, glazed.
COLLECTION: *Leipzig, Karl-Marx-Universität, Ägyptisches Museum 3845.*

DESCRIPTION: The strand consists of fourteen blue faience ball beads of different sizes.

COLOR: Blue to dark blue.
CONDITION: All beads complete; glaze rubbed off some; discolored in places.
MEASUREMENTS: Diameter of beads 2.5 - 3.7 cm.
PROVENANCE: Kerma, Tumulus K III, Grave 317, found in the debris (Reisner 1914, Location no. K 317:I, Object no. S 14-1-594).
BIBLIOGRAPHY: Reisner 1923a,156; Reisner 1923b,113; Berlin 1963,21.

According to Reisner's report on the finds (1923a,156), there were formerly fifteen ball beads, which were found with the bed interment in Grave 317. Faience ball beads, mostly blue but sometimes black, were frequently found, particularly in this tumulus, along with beads of glazed crystal, quartz, gold, stone, and semi-precious stones. Strands of ball beads of this kind represented one of the most important elements of adornment in Meroitic times. Their use from the time of the Kerma culture until the third and fourth centuries A.D. is probably to be regarded as evidence for the continuity of population in Upper Nubia.

60
Plaque with Sculptured Scorpion

Between 1750 and 1550 B.C.
MATERIAL: Faience.
COLLECTION: *Khartoum, Sudan National Museum 1036.*

DESCRIPTION: On a plaque corresponding to the animal's contour lies a sculptured scorpion, its tail turned to one side. On the upper edge, over the animal's head, is a hole, and two holes are drilled on each side of the tail. The back of the plaque is smooth.

COLOR: Blue green.
CONDITION: Complete; tail broken off and repaired in ancient times; surface slightly corroded.
MEASUREMENTS: Length 6.5 cm. Width 5.4 cm. Thickness 1.7 cm.
PROVENANCE: Kerma, Tumulus K X, Corridor B, no. 134, on the stomach of Body PB (Reisner 1914, Location no. K X B:134, Object no. S 14-3-292).
BIBLIOGRAPHY: Reisner 1915,81 (fig. 16); Reisner 1923b,131, pl. 44,2(19).

On the stomach of a sacrificial victim were two very similar scorpion pendants; the upper hole in each case probably served for attachment to a garment. In both pieces, the tail had been broken off in antiquity and reattached by means of a thread drawn through the holes bored on each side of the break. Scorpion amulets had a certain distribution in Predynastic and Early Dynastic times, in Lower Nubia (A-group) as well as in Egypt.

61
Black-Topped Red Polished Beaker

Between 1750 and 1550 B.C.
MATERIAL: Fired clay.
COLLECTION: *Boston (Massachusetts), Museum of Fine Arts S 14-2-1197.*

DESCRIPTION: A polished beaker with flat base and slightly projecting rim has the form of a tulip. Between the red of the lower vessel and the black of the upper body is a gray transition zone.

COLOR: Dark red-brown bottom and deep black top with dark gray transition zone.
CONDITION: Complete.
MEASUREMENTS: Height 10.0 cm. Diameter 12.1 cm. Wall thickness 0.2 cm.
PROVENANCE: Kerma, Tumulus K III, Grave 339 (Reisner 1914, Location no. K 339:5, Object no. S 14-2-1197).
BIBLIOGRAPHY: Reisner 1923a,176; Reisner 1923b,334f.

These very elegant, extremely thin-walled beakers with flaring rim, sometimes flat-based, belong to the class of black-topped red polished ware (Reisner: Bkt. Type II). They are the most typical, most widely distributed vessels of the Kerma culture. Hundreds, with only slight variations, have been found in Kerma burials of Upper and Lower Nubia as well as at the site of Kerma itself.

62
Pot with Long Spout

Between 1750 and 1550 B.C.
MATERIAL: Fired clay.
COLLECTION: *Boston (Massachusetts), Museum of Fine Arts 13.4102.*

DESCRIPTION: An almost oval polished vessel has a wide, concave neck and a flaring lip that is stepped on the outside. On the shoulder are two handles in the form of perched falcons, with a perforation between legs and tail. The long spout rises from the same level.

COLOR: Dark red bottom and black top with mottled gray transition zone.
CONDITION: One handle missing; multiple breaks, repaired.
MEASUREMENTS: Height 14.8 cm. Diameter 12.3 cm., at mouth 9.7 cm. Length of spout 10.1 cm.
PROVENANCE: Kerma, Tumulus K X, Grave 1052 (Reisner 1913, Location no. K 1052:17, Object no. SU 876).
BIBLIOGRAPHY: Reisner 1914,10ff.; Reisner 1923a,341; Reisner 1923b,364, fig. 244,1.

Twelve examples of this type of vessel (Reisner: Bkt. Type XVIII-1) of the black-topped red polished ware were found at Kerma, specifically in Tumuli K IV, K X, K XVI, and K XXXIX, as well as in two graves of Cemetery B. They are thus of the greatest importance for the internal chronology of the Kerma graves. The perforations in the handles served for suspension.

Illustrated in color on page 39.

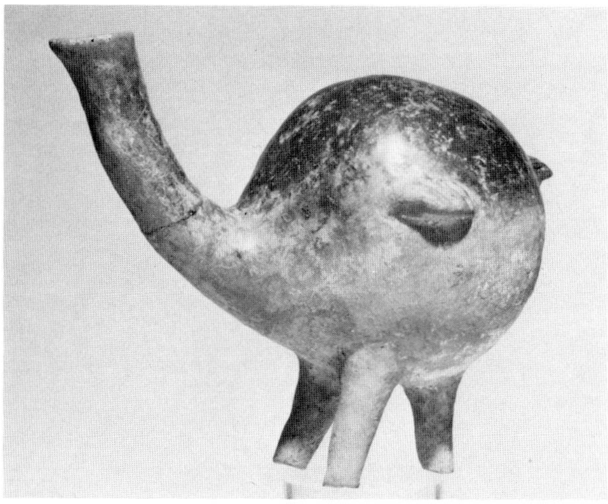

63 ■
Vessel in the Form of an Ostrich

Between 1750 and 1550 B.C.
MATERIAL: Fired clay.
COLLECTION: *Khartoum, Sudan National Museum 1134.*

DESCRIPTION: The rudimentary wings and tail of an ostrich are attached to a spherical polished vessel standing on three legs and closed on top. The upcurving spout represents the animal's neck, with a suggestion of the head.

COLOR: Reddish-brown bottom and black top with dark gray transition zone.
CONDITION: Neck broken off and repaired.
MEASUREMENTS: Height 15.5 cm. Diameter 19.0 cm. Wingspread 12.5 cm.
PROVENANCE: Kerma, Tumulus K XIV, Chapel A (Reisner 1914, Location no. K 1400 A:12, Object no. S 14-1-721).
BIBLIOGRAPHY: Reisner 1915,77 (fig. 10); Reisner 1923b,374, fig. 253, pl. 71,1.

Two pots in the form of an ostrich were found at Kerma, both in Chapel A of Tumulus K XIV. Like Cats. 61 and 62, they belong to the group of black-topped red polished vessels (Reisner: Bkt. Type XXIX-1). Several vessels of fancy form were found at Kerma, but it is not necessary to consider them toys, as Reisner did in this case because he regarded as a plaything a dagger found with the two ostrich-shaped pots. The size of the vessel is normal, and it has three feet so that it can be conveniently put down. The so-called teapots (designated by Reisner) were not regarded as playthings. This vessel is unique in that the spout was used for filling as well as pouring.

64
Vessel with Long Spout

Between 1750 and 1550 B.C.
MATERIAL: Fired clay.
COLLECTION: *Boston (Massachusetts), Museum of Fine Arts S 14-3-285.*

DESCRIPTION: The lower part of this polished vessel is dish-shaped; the upper part is faintly convex. A wide, slightly convex lip, decorated with two grooves, rises from a concave neck. The vessel has a small ring base and a long spout.

COLOR: Dark red; traces of black pigment at tip of spout.
CONDITION: Complete; neck and lip broken and repaired.
MEASUREMENTS: Height 7.9 cm. Diameter 10.4 cm., at mouth 5.8 cm. Length of spout 7.3 cm.
PROVENANCE: Kerma, Tumulus K X, Corridor B, with Skeleton AB (Reisner 1914, Location no. K X B:127, Object no. S 14-3-285).
BIBLIOGRAPHY: Reisner 1923a,288, no. 127 (with incorrect no. S 14-3-288); Reisner 1923b,404 (no. 89), fig. 281.

Reisner classified this unusual little pot in his group R.P. Type XXVI-1. The form is unique, but the thin-walled red polished ware is typical for Kerma.

65
Pot with Ram's Head

Between 1750 and 1550 B.C.
MATERIAL: Fired clay.
COLLECTION: *Boston (Massachusetts), Museum of Fine Arts 20.1714.*

DESCRIPTION: A handle with ridged edges curves over the opening of an almost spherical polished vessel, the ridges merging into the body to form a rim around the opening. At the same level from which the handle springs is a ram's head with curling horns and a long neck with a pouring hole on the underside.

COLOR: Brick red.
CONDITION: Multiple breaks, repaired; small chip missing to right of spout; discolored and abraded in places.
MEASUREMENTS: Height 22.0 cm. Diameter 20.4 cm.
PROVENANCE: Kerma, Tumulus K III, Grave 325 (Reisner 1914, Location no. 325:3, Object no. S 14-2-772).
BIBLIOGRAPHY: Reisner 1923b,405 (no. 101),406, fig. 284 (no. 101).

This vessel (Reisner: R.P. Type XXXII-5) was regarded as a luxury object by the excavator. Its round shape, wide opening overspread by a handle, and applied animal's head are characteristic of the Kerma culture. Other pots of this type, found in Tumuli K III, K IV, K X, and K XIV, have spouts in the form of other animals, and some are decorated with animal heads in relief (Fig. 16). These vessels were dubbed "teapots" by Reisner.

Illustrated in color on page 158.

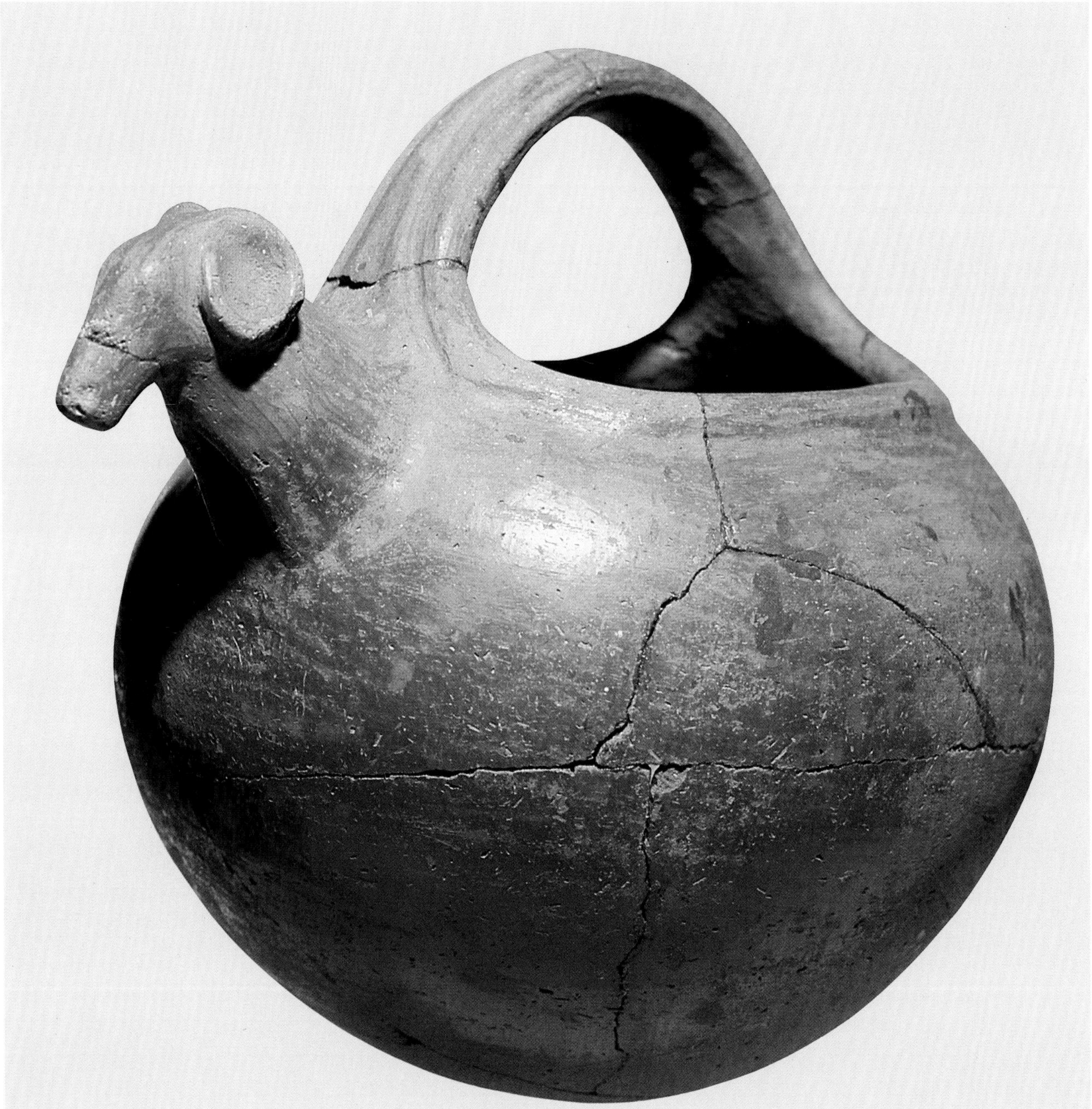

Pot with Ram's Head (Cat. 65).

66
Jar with Narrow Neck and Flaring Lip

Between 1750 and 1550 B.C.
MATERIAL: Fired clay.
COLLECTION: *Boston (Massachusetts), Museum of Fine Arts S 13-12-522.*

DESCRIPTION: A polished, egg-shaped vessel has no base. The slender neck flares to a thick lip.

COLOR: Dark red.
CONDITION: Complete.
MEASUREMENTS: Height 18.4 cm. Diameter 12.8 cm.
PROVENANCE: Kerma, Tumulus K III, Chamber DD,I (Reisner 1913, Location no. K III, Comp. DD:XXI, Object no. S 13-12-522).
BIBLIOGRAPHY: Reisner 1923a,140; Reisner 1923b,396 (fig. 272, no. 61), 398 (no. 61).

Although this little pot of red polished ware (Reisner: R.P. Type XIII-8) has Egyptian prototypes, it has no parallels in Egypt in this particular form and must be regarded as an indigenous product of the Kerma culture. A considerable number of these vessels have been found in graves.

67
Tall Beaker with Stepped Wall

Between 1750 and 1550 B.C.
MATERIAL: Fired clay.
COLLECTION: *Boston (Massachusetts), Museum of Fine Arts 20.2005.*

DESCRIPTION: The wall of a tall, slender beaker curves up from an offset base and is drawn in to form a series of six steps. The vessel widens slightly to the gently flaring lip.

COLOR: Black.
CONDITION: Complete; broken in several places and repaired.
MEASUREMENTS: Height 22.6 cm. Diameter at mouth 12.7 cm. Wall thickness 0.4 cm.
PROVENANCE: Kerma, Tumulus K III, Grave 319 (Reisner 1914, Location no. K 319:20, Object no. S 14-2-284).
BIBLIOGRAPHY: Reisner 1923a,158; Reisner 1923b,377 (no. 26),378 (fig. 260, no. 26), pl. 73,2; Smith 1946,88 (fig. 56); Dunham 1958,87, fig. 61d; Smith 1960,98, fig. 61.

This type of stepped-wall beaker occurs in two groups of black polished ware (Reisner: B.P. Types X, XI, and XIII, from Tumulus K III and contemporary graves of Kerma Cemetery B; and B.P. Type XII, from Tumuli K XVI, K XIX, and K XX). Altogether, some thirty examples have been found, as well as eight conical lids (Reisner: B.P. Type XV), in Tumuli K III, K IV, K X, K XXXIIIA, and in Cemetery B. Although the occurrence of these lidded beakers is comparatively rare, they extend over the entire third phase of the Kerma culture.

According to A. J. Mills, this vessel form, which is unique to the Kerma culture, represents a stack of nested cups, such as Cat. 61, and served as an inexpensive replacement for the set of pots that was often deposited in graves (verbal communication).

68

Painted Vessel in the Form of a Basket with Lid

Between 1750 and 1550 B.C.
MATERIAL: Fired clay.
COLLECTION: *Khartoum, Sudan National Museum 1119.*

DESCRIPTION: Seven black zigzag lines are painted on the light-colored slip of a vessel with a gently curving wall and a concave base; the rest of the body is red and the rim is white. In the center of the overhanging lid is a red circle, from which radiate bands of checkerboard pattern, the squares painted yellow and white, alternating with red and white trapezoidal panels. There are four holes below the rim of the vessel and another on the lid.

COLOR: Brown, spotted black in places; decoration red, black, and yellow on whitish slip.
CONDITION: Complete; colors blurred and abraded in places.
MEASUREMENTS: Height 10.6 cm., with lid 14.4 cm. Diameter 13.7 cm., of lid 14.4 cm.
PROVENANCE: Kerma, Tumulus K III, Grave 315 (Reisner 1913, Location no. K 315:6, Object no. S 13-12-898).
BIBLIOGRAPHY: Reisner 1915,78 (fig. 11); Reisner 1923b,471 (no. 1), 472,473 (fig. 340); Dunham 1958,87 (fig. 62b); Smith 1965a, pl. 81(A); Davidson 1972,46 (color).

Of Kerma painted ware, which is uncommon, there are two primary groups (Reisner: W.S.R. and R.P.). This vessel belongs to the first group, a red ware with a whitish slip (Reisner's Type I-1). According to Reisner (1923b,472), the imitation of a basket is evident because of the wicker-pattern decoration. However, the similarity to the circular hut with overhanging roof (*tukkol*) still in use in large areas of Africa is striking, and that association may have been in the mind of the potter when this beautiful vessel was made.

69

Three-Legged Bowl

Between 1750 and 1550 B.C.
MATERIAL: Fired clay.
COLLECTION: *Boston (Massachusetts), Museum of Fine Arts S 14-2-1213.*

DESCRIPTION: An unpolished hemispherical bowl rests on three solid columnar legs. Encircling the rim is a row of impressed dots. The underside of the bowl and the places where the legs are attached are adorned with irregular incisions that give the effect of wrinkled elephant hide.

COLOR: Gray brown.
CONDITION: Complete; discolored in places.
MEASUREMENTS: Height 9.0 cm., of legs 5.0 cm. Diameter 8.9 cm., of bowl 5.4 cm.
PROVENANCE: Kerma, Great Deposit K XXXIII A (Reisner 1914, Location no. K 33A:5, Object no. S 14-2-1213).
BIBLIOGRAPHY: Reisner 1923a,470ff., esp. 473 top; Reisner 1923b,455 (no. 34), fig. 328 (no. 34).

This type of vessel belongs with the coarse native products, which have not been found in quantity at Kerma but which always occur in conjunction with the highly classical wares. Many of them are smoke-blackened and are plainly to be considered as cooking pots. This bowl, representing a rare type (Reisner: Blk. W. Type XXV-1), was found in front of Chapel K XXXIII A, with some two hundred other vessels. Reisner suggests that they might have been collected there by grave robbers or they may have been votive offerings, just as funerary offerings in the C-group were deposited outside the tomb. This latter interpretation might well be preferred. In that case, one would see here the penetration of C-group burial customs into Kerma. U. Hintze reminds me that this vessel might have been a drum (verbal communication).

70
King Shabaqo Offering Wine

Dynasty XXV, late eighth century B.C. (Gen. 3).
MATERIAL: Sandstone.
COLLECTION: *Berlin/DDR, Ägyptisches Museum 2103.*

DESCRIPTION: The very shallow sunk relief shows the king offering two wine vessels to the no longer extant image of the god Ptah. The king wears a short kilt and a cap encircled by a diadem with two uraei at the forehead and two streamers at the back. The inscription states that the ruler is offering wine to the god.

COLOR: Light to dark brown; traces of red pigment on head and vessels.
CONDITION: Original edges of stone at top and right; broken in several places and repaired; minor surface damage; streaky discolorations.
MEASUREMENTS: Height 67.4 cm. Width 67.8 cm. Thickness ca. 9.0 cm.
PROVENANCE: Karnak, Temple of Ptah, Second (Jubilee) Gate, back of south wall, east end (Lepsius 1843).
BIBLIOGRAPHY: Berlin 1899,243; LD T III,6; Leclant 1965b,38 (with further biblio.),40, pl. XV B; P—M II 1972,197.

Shabaqo, a frequent builder at Thebes, erected a gate in front of the Temple of Ptah built by Tuthmosis III. He is represented on its walls performing various activities, including offering wine to Amun and Mut as well as to Ptah, Hathor, and Imentet. The facial features on this relief, whose surface was roughened so that stucco would stick to it better, are those of a Kushite. Noteworthy are the round head and straight neck, this last being an element of style that endures well into the Meroitic Period.

71
King in the Care of a Goddess

Dynasty XXV, early seventh century B.C.
MATERIAL: Sandstone.
COLLECTION: *Brooklyn (New York), The Brooklyn Museum 70.1.*

DESCRIPTION: The representation in sunk relief shows a king as a child before a goddess who embraces him protectively. The ruler wears a cap encircled by a diadem, with a uraeus at the forehead, and an amulet on a long band around his neck. His head is turned toward the face of the goddess, on whose lap he is probably sitting. She wears a broad collar and a haltered garment.

COLOR: Gray brown; traces of red pigment on torso and hand of goddess.
CONDITION: Right side of block sawed; superficial chips and abrasions; back of block trimmed in modern times.
MEASUREMENTS: Height 23.7 cm. Width 29.4 cm. Thickness 2.9 cm.
PROVENANCE: Not known.
BIBLIOGRAPHY: Russmann 1969-70, 145ff.,144 (fig. 1); Russmann 1974,23,36; Wenig 1975a,407, pl. 404.

Although the king is shown as a child, he wears the insignia of a pharaoh; it is the ruler who plays the role of a child in relation to the goddess. The subject was a common one in Dynasty XXV (see p. 56).

The king's head has the characteristic round shape of all Kushite likenesses. The neck rises straight, as in Cat. 70, but is very short. Russmann (1969-70,145ff.) attempted to attribute the relief to Taharqo, in view of the difficulty in identifying this king with Shabaqo or Shebitqo, whose likenesses are more individualized. One must follow this suggestion, although conclusive evidence is lacking.

72
Stela of King Nastasen

335-315 B.C. (Gen. 27).
MATERIAL: Granite.
COLLECTION: *Berlin/DDR, Ägyptisches Museum 2268.*

DESCRIPTION: On the front of a large, polished, round-topped stela is a double scene with several figures above the first twenty-six lines of a sixty-eight-line text in Egyptian hieroglyphs, which is continued on the back of the stela. Over the scene is a winged sun disk from which extend two uraei, wearing the crowns of Upper and Lower Egypt and enclosing a cartouche with the name of the king. The scene below is divided by two columns of hieroglyphs. On each side is a figure of the god Amun, shown on the left with a human head and on the right with a ram's head. Both figures hold a *was*-scepter in one outstretched hand and an *ankh*-sign in the other. On each side, King Nastasen approaches the god and offers a ball-bead necklace and a pectoral hanging from a long band. The king wears a pointed Egyptian kilt, a diadem with uraeus and streamers, a broad collar, and wide armlets and bracelets. An animal's tail hangs from his belt. On the left, he is accompanied by his mother, Pelekh; on the right, his wife, Sakhmakh, follows him. Both women wear ankle-length garments that come to a point in back, and each has a diadem with a uraeus. They both hold a sistrum in one hand and pour a libation with the other. The hieroglyphic captions give the names and titles of the figures and describe their action.

COLOR: Black, mottled.
CONDITION: Complete; surface slightly chipped in places; set tightly into base.
MEASUREMENTS: Height 163.0 cm. Width 127.0 cm. Thickness 16.5 cm. Height of figure of king on right 29.8 cm.
PROVENANCE: Found at Dongola in 1853 by Count W. von Schlieffen; given to Kaiser Friedrich Wilhelm IV by Abbas Pasha and deposited in Staatliche Museen (then Königliche Museen) in 1871.
BIBLIOGRAPHY: LD V,16a-b; Berlin 1899,402-04; Schäfer 1901; Schäfer 1905,137ff.; Budge 1912,140ff.; P—M VII 1951,193; Hintze 1959,17-20; Berlin 1963,23-27; Hintze 1966, pls. 76-77; Hintze 1968a,21, pls. 74-75; Wenig 1975a, pl. 405; Leclant 1976, 120, 122, fig. 123.

Although it was found at Dongola, the stela of King Nastasen probably comes from the Great Temple of Amun at Gebel Barkal (Schäfer 1901,1-6), where five similar stelae, now in Cairo, were found. The present stela is not only an important artistic monument of the later Napatan Period, it is a major historical document as well. Reisner's (1923d) chronology of the kings of the late fourth century B.C., based on the architectural history of the pyramids of Nuri and Meroe, was confirmed, above all, by Hintze (1959,17-20), who established that the hostile Prince Khambes-wten who is named in the inscription of this stela is the same as the King Khababash who ruled Egypt for a short time, ca. 338-335 B.C.

The inscription is dated in the eighth regnal year of the king and contains the annals of his reign. It begins with a list of the king's titles. The text then describes how Nastasen learned that he had been called to the throne by the god Amun of Napata and how he traveled to Napata to be crowned in the Amun Temple there. A huge feast in the coronation city was followed by a royal progress to Gematon (Kawa), Pnubs (Tebo), back to Napata, and finally to a place called Tar. Then follows a list of offerings made by the king to Amun. Most of the inscription consists of a detailed description of the king's wars and compaigns against numerous enemies; in the first of these wars is mentioned a battle against Khababash. It must have been a difficult one for Nastasen, for after his victory he made offerings to the gods. Other enemies were nomads from the surrounding deserts, who had often caused trouble to the inhabitants of the Nile Valley and against whose incursions Nastasen had to protect his land. The inscription ends with praise for Amun, to whom the king owes his victories.

73
Stela of Queen Sakhmakh

Late fourth century B.C. (Gen. 27).
MATERIAL: Granite.
COLLECTION: *Khartoum, Sudan National Museum 1853.*

DESCRIPTION: On the pediment of this round-topped stela is a winged sun disk over a five-column inscription containing an offering formula. The main body of the stela is designed as a chapel; a polished strip imitates the torus molding, and slightly sunk horizontal strips represent pilasters. A winged sun disk takes the place of the cavetto cornice below the upper "torus" and is repeated above it. The whole is crowned by a frieze of uraei, as in divine shrines. A cult scene is incised in the more deeply sunk central panel. On the right stands a queen wearing a long robe and two tall feathers on her head. She holds a sistrum, apparently lion-headed, in one raised hand and pours a libation with the other. In front of her is enthroned the god Osiris, an *atef*-crown on his head and crook and flail in his hands. Behind him stands the goddess Isis with an *ankh*-sign in her left hand and her right hand raised in salutation. The scene is surmounted by incised captions similar to those on the "pilasters." Beneath the scene, on a polished raised panel, is a five-line inscription with an offering formula.

COLOR: Gray black, mottled.
CONDITION: Top edge damaged; back only roughly dressed.
MEASUREMENTS: Height 60.1 cm. Width 37.9 cm. Thickness 9.0 cm.
PROVENANCE: Gebel Barkal, Great Temple of Amun (B 551), discovered walled up (Reisner 1920, not registered).
BIBLIOGRAPHY: Reisner 1931,83, no. 59; Dunham—Macadam 1949,146, no. 65; P—M VII 1951,216; Wenig 1967,13; Dunham 1970,34, no. 23, pl. XXXIV.

The stela has the usual form, with rounded top and winged sun disk, but the design of the surface as a chapel, imitating the back wall of a Meroitic funerary chapel, is without parallel and betrays a lively artistic imagination.

Sakhmakh was a wife of King Nastasen. He was buried in Pyramid Nuri 15, and a large stela for him (Cat. 72) was erected in the Great Temple of Amun at Gebel Barkal. Since it would be unreasonable to imagine that Sakhmakh's stela, which, considering the subject represented, must have belonged to her tomb, was hauled from Nuri across the river to Gebel Barkal about ten kilometers away merely to be reused as building material, we must assume that Sakhmakh, unlike her spouse, was buried not at Nuri but in one of the pyramids of the period at Gebel Barkal. The form of the hieroglyphs is so similar on both stelae that one suspects they were carved by the same stonemason.

74
Stela of Queen Batahaliye

Early fourth century B.C. (Gen. 23).
MATERIAL: Granite.
COLLECTION: *Boston (Massachusetts), Museum of Fine Arts 21.3231.*

DESCRIPTION: In the upper part of the round-topped funerary stela, the queen is shown in bold raised relief in front of the enthroned Osiris and Isis standing behind him. A food-laden altar stands before Osiris. The queen wears a long, ample robe, a crown with two tall feathers, and a uraeus. She has a collar, bracelets on her raised arms, and sandals. Over the scene is a winged sun disk with two uraei. The inscriptions above the figures give the names of the queen and the deities in Egyptian hieroglyphs. Below the scene is another Egyptian inscription, consisting of eight lines with an offering formula containing an invocation to the gods Osiris and Isis. The surface of the stela is only slightly polished.

COLOR: Dark gray.
CONDITION: Complete; minor damages at edges.
MEASUREMENTS: Height 61.4 cm. Width 34.1 cm. Thickness ca. 19.0 cm.
PROVENANCE: Nuri, Pyramid Nu. 44, in rubble left by plunderers in entrance passage, Chamber A (Reisner 1917, Object no. S 17-4-76).
BIBLIOGRAPHY: Reisner 1918,78 (fig.); Dunham—Macadam 1949,143, pl. XV; P—M VII 1951,232; Dunham 1955,230 (fig. 177),231, pl. LXX B.

The stela of Queen Batahaliye, a wife of King Harsiyotef, belongs to a group of gray granite funerary stelae, all with bold raised relief in the pediment and inscriptions in faulty Egyptian, which were made in the fourth century B.C. This relief has a crisp effect, since the edges are sharply cut; the representation is on the whole somewhat unskilled. The scenes on the stela of King Harsiyotef (Cairo JE 48864), which was erected in the Great Temple of Amun at Gebel Barkal, show quite a different style, relating to that of the older stelae of Aspelta or the more recent one of Nastasen (Cat. 72), proving that two stylistic trends existed side by side.

75
King Shabaqo Offering

Dynasty XXV, late eighth century B.C. (Gen. 3).
MATERIAL: Bronze, solid cast.
COLLECTION: *Athens, National Museum 632.*

DESCRIPTION: King Shabaqo kneels in an attitude of offering, his hands open and palms vertical. He wears a short kilt with a patterned belt and his name on the buckle. On his head is a close-fitting cap patterned with incised circles, ringed by a diadem with a uraeus frieze and a winged sun disk incised on the back. The two uraei on his forehead wind across his head to the nape of the neck, and two long streamers hang from the crown. His rounded sideburns are also patterned with incised circles. Around his neck is a cord, its ends falling onto his chest, with three pendant ram's heads. He has wide bracelets and armlets.

The king's neck is straight and his torso powerful and well modeled, with smoothly shaped nipples and a marked navel. The face is full and round, the eyes relatively large below elongated eyebrows that are horizontal at the root of the nose. Above the distended lips is a trace of the philtrum and perhaps a mustache. The Kushite fold, running horizontally from the sides of the nose, is especially distinct and is accentuated by the high cheekbones.

COLOR: Dark brown to gray black.
CONDITION: Complete; slight damage to kilt, below cartouche.
MEASUREMENTS: Height 15.6 cm. Width 3.4 cm. Depth 10.0 cm.
PROVENANCE: Not known.
BIBLIOGRAPHY: Cavvadias 1894,35, no. 168; Russmann 1968-69,93f., figs. 7-9; Russmann 1969-70,153,n. 37 and passim; Boufides 1970,279,284, figs. 4-5; Russmann 1974, 12f.,57, app. II, no. 1, fig. 1; Wenig 1975a,411, pl. 416a; Leclant 1976, 92, figs. 73, 74.

This statuette, one of the finest works of royal sculpture in the round from Dynasty XXV, is also one of the few secure likenesses of King Shabaqo. The details are all carefully executed. The ram's heads, which are represented in a manner typical of Dynasty XXV and the later periods of the Kingdom of Kush, show the elongated head of the animal seen from above, with long horns and horizontal ears. There is a sun disk above the animal's head and a uraeus (usually two are represented; see Cat. 77). The king's torso is meticulously modeled; shoulders, upper arms, and chest make an athletic impression. This, too, is typical of the likenesses of Kushite rulers.

Scholarly opinion is divided on the subject of the sideburns. Some consider them to be natural hair, as I do. Others (including B. V. Bothmer and E. Russmann) consider them to be tabs extending from the cap. But nowhere do we have a clear depiction of a cap with tabs. On the contrary, a sandstone stela of King Piye found at Gebel Barkal (Reisner 1931, pls. V-VI) supports the other interpretation.

76 ■
Head of King Taharqo

Dynasty XXV, 690-664 B.C. (Gen. 5).
MATERIAL: Diorite.
COLLECTION: *Cairo, Egyptian Museum CG 560.*

DESCRIPTION: The polished head is over life size. The face is round, with the typical Kushite fold merely intimated beneath the accentuated cheekbones. The eyes are somewhat bulging, with plastic upper lids and sharp-cut lower lids; the eyeballs are only slightly polished. The arching brows are plastically formed. The lips are thin and the chin not stressed. The well-modeled ears lie flat. Stylized hair emerges from beneath the close-fitting cap. The crown base, cap, and necklace, traces of which are visible on the back of the neck, were left rough. On the tapering back pillar is a hieroglyphic inscription in sunk relief with one of the king's names.

COLOR: Black, mottled.
CONDITION: Head broken from torso along horizontal plane at base of neck; nose, crown, and uraei missing; lips and ears badly damaged; back pillar extensively chipped.
MEASUREMENTS: Height 41.5 cm. Height of face ca. 15.0 cm. Width 23.8 cm. Depth 33.8 cm. Width of back pillar at top 17.8 cm., at bottom 18.0 cm. Width of inscription 10.7 - 10.8 cm.
PROVENANCE: Luxor (in the market).
BIBLIOGRAPHY: Schäfer 1895,115, pl. 7; Bissing 1914, pls. 60-61; Borchardt 1925,108, pl. 94; Bosse 1936,76, no. 211, pl. XIIa; Scharff 1939,616; Cairo 1949, no. 167; Sauneron—Yoyotte 1952,193, n. 4; Desroches-Noblecourt 1954,48 (fig. 9); Smith 1958,241, pl. 178; Aldred 1961,153, pl. 73; Pirenne 1963, pl. 21; Dixon 1964,130, n. 9; Smith 1965a, pl. 178(A-B); Yoyotte 1968,195 (with incorrect no. 650); Russmann 1968-69,96; Müller 1970b, pl. 164; P—M II 1972,533; Russmann 1974,16-17,47, app. I, no. 9, figs. 8-9; Wenig 1975a,409, pl. 408; Leclant 1976, 98, fig. 81.

The head may have belonged to a standing statue of Taharqo that was set up in a Theban temple. The Sudanese features of the king are unmistakable, but the foreign aspect is here subdued and idealized. In other likenesses of this king, e.g., the head in Copenhagen (Fig. 26) attributed to him, the Kushite element is more strongly expressed. In the colossal statue (Fig. 27) found at Gebel Barkal, the king wears the four-feather crown, which this head, too, probably wore (not the Double Crown nor the two feathers of Amun, as some writers think). The facial features of the Gebel Barkal statue are much more formalistically modeled and clearly indicate another stylistic direction; see p. 51 and Cat. 85. That the likeness of a king from the Sudan was strongly idealized (for a non-idealizing likeness of Taharqo, see his sphinx from Kawa, Cat. 77) while his foreignness was not denied indicates that the kings of Dynasty XXV were proud of their origin; indeed, they maintained close connections to their homeland.

77
Sphinx of King Taharqo

Dynasty XXV, 690-664 B.C. (Gen. 5).
MATERIAL: Granite.
COLLECTION: *London, British Museum 1770.*

DESCRIPTION: A sphinx wearing a headcloth with two uraei rests on a rectangular base. The face is bordered by a collarlike mane; the ears are those of a lion. Beneath the low edge of the headcloth, the eyebrows arch over the bulging eyes in an extremely round, fleshy face. The mouth is very wide and the lips unusually thick, with deeply pinched corners. The Kushite fold is very visible here; the broad chin juts forward slightly. There are apparently indications of a mustache. On the chest is a cartouche with the prenomen of King Taharqo.

COLOR: Discolored yellowish brown.
CONDITION: Complete; slight chips on head of left uraeus and on front corners of base.
MEASUREMENTS: Height 40.0 cm. Width 28.5 cm. Length 74.7 cm. Height of base 7.5 cm.
PROVENANCE: Kawa, Temple T, Dais Room E, between the altar and the north wall (Griffith 1930-31, Object no. 0732).
BIBLIOGRAPHY: Glanville 1932-33,46, pl. XIXb; Macadam 1949,87; Macadam 1955,97,139, pl. LXXIV; P—M VII 1951,190; Russmann 1968-69,89, n. 6; Russmann 1974,18,24,50, app. I, no. 18, fig. 12; Wenig 1975a,411, colorpl. LVIII; Leclant 1976,98, figs. 85,86.

A brutal realism, noticeable chiefly in a few private sculptures of Dynasty XXV (see p. 53 and Cat. 83), is here more apparent than in any other royal likeness of the period. The Kawa sphinx evokes the memory of royal representations of the Old Kingdom, a relationship that may have been intended. The workmen active at Kawa were in fact brought there from Memphis by Taharqo, as we learn from an inscription (stela Kawa IV, 20-22; see p. 56). Some of the reliefs in Taharqo's Temple T at Kawa were copied from the walls of royal funerary temples of the Old Kingdom, an indication that people were very concerned with that bygone era (Russmann 1974,22ff.). On the other hand, Macadam (1955,97) and Russmann (1974,24) have drawn attention to the fact that this sphinx in its brutality is reminiscent of two of King Amenemhat III's sphinxes (Cairo CG 393, CG 394). Whether such a connection was intentional is still a question. K.-H. Priese thinks the brutal expression, as in the sphinxes of Amenemhat III, may be connected with the representation of the king as a lion (verbal communication).

Illustrated in color on page 50.

78
Shawabti of King Taharqo

Dynasty XXV, 690-664 B.C. (Gen. 5).
MATERIAL: Calcite.
COLLECTION: *Brooklyn (New York), The Brooklyn Museum, Charles Edwin Wilbour Fund 39.4.*

DESCRIPTION: The mummiform statuette represents King Taharqo holding hoes in both hands. He wears a *khat*-headcloth that reaches to the shoulders and is gathered at the back into a pigtail, and has a uraeus at the forehead. The somewhat protruding eyes are sharply contoured, while the eyebrows are modeled naturalistically. The nose, like the face, is very broad; the lips are thick. The chin is adorned with a long, blocklike beard, broad at the base and curled at the end. On the body is a ten-line inscription, without dividers, containing excerpts from Chapter Six of the Book of the Dead. On its back, the figure carries bags, rendered as rectangles with cross-hatching in low relief, suspended from straps hanging from the shoulders.

COLOR: Creamy white.
CONDITION: Complete; lips abraded.
MEASUREMENTS: Height 33.3 cm. Height of head 4.5 cm. Width 11.5 cm. Depth at base 6.5 cm.
PROVENANCE: Nuri, Pyramid Nu. 1 (Reisner 1916-17, Object no. S 17-2-451).
BIBLIOGRAPHY: None.

Shawabtis are small figures that, from the time of the Middle Kingdom on, were placed in the tomb and were intended to perform work as the proxies of the deceased in the hereafter. For this reason, they have hoes in their hands and sacks on their backs for carrying sand. The word *shawabti* (or *ushabti*) means "responder," for the figures respond for the deceased at the call to daily work in the afterlife. The *shawabtis* found in the pyramids of the kings of Dynasty XXV and of the Napatan Period (Cats. 79, 87) differ for the most part from Egyptian *shawabtis* in that they are frequently very broad in the upper torso. In the present figure, the elbows are clearly marked beneath the garment, and the torso is trapezoidal in form. The king's features are similar to those in other representations of Taharqo, such as the Kawa sphinx (Cat. 77).

In Taharqo's pyramid were found 1,070 intact *shawabtis* and many fragments. They stood in at least three rows along the walls of the burial chamber. They are between 25.0 and 60.0 cm. high, inscribed, made from calcite, green ankerite, and black granite, and can be classified into five different types (Dunham 1955,10, fig. 197,199, pl. CXL). Cat. 79 comes from the same tomb.

79
Shawabti of King Taharqo

Dynasty XXV, 690-664 B.C. (Gen. 5).
MATERIAL: Ankerite.
COLLECTION: *Brooklyn (New York), The Brooklyn Museum, Charles Edwin Wilbour Fund 39.3.*

DESCRIPTION: The *shawabti* is very similar to Cat. 78, although the facial features are somewhat different. The inscription is nine lines long.

COLOR: Brown, mottled.
CONDITION: Complete; back worn.
MEASUREMENTS: Height 39.0 cm. Width 12.2 cm. Depth at base 8.3 cm.
PROVENANCE: Nuri, Pyramid Nu. 1 (Reisner 1916-17, not registered).
BIBLIOGRAPHY: Fazzini 1971, no. 8.

W. J. Young, of the Museum of Fine Arts, Boston, and scientists of the Massachusetts Institute of Technology have identified the material as jade green ankerite. The present brown color is the result of the *shawabti's* immersion in ground water that temporarily flooded the floor of the tomb. See commentary to Cat. 78, from the same tomb.

80
Small Head of a Kushite Ruler

Probably late eighth century B.C.
MATERIAL: Schist.
COLLECTION: *Brooklyn (New York), The Brooklyn Museum, Charles Edwin Wilbour Fund 60.74.*

DESCRIPTION: The king's head is polished, but the cap, diadem, and uraei were left rough. Eyes and eyebrows were inlaid in the full, round face. The thick lips and weak chin bulge, and there are traces of folds from the sides of the nose to the corners of the mouth. The head rests on a short, thick neck. The sideburns are rounded.

COLOR: Dark green.
CONDITION: Head severed below chin in diagonal break; beginning of shoulder visible; only vestiges of uraei, which appear to have been added at a later date; small chips on both ears, nose, upper lip, and upper eyelids; inlays missing.
MEASUREMENTS: Height 7.2 cm. Width 5.3 cm. Depth 6.6 cm.
PROVENANCE: Not known.
BIBLIOGRAPHY: Russmann 1968-69, 97-101, figs. 10-12; Russmann 1974, 14-15, 52-53, app. I, no. 27, fig. 5; Fazzini 1975, 101, 109, 137, cat. 90; Berlin 1976, cat. 65; Leclant 1976, 92, fig. 72.

With some reservations, Russmann (1968-69; 1974) attributed the head to King Shabaqo, because a miniature faience head of that ruler in the Louvre (A.F. 6639) has a similarly full face, but principally because a torso in the Louvre (N. 2541) bearing the name of Shabaqo is made of the same material and could, in its measurements, fit this head. The inlaid eyes and eyebrows are unparalleled in sculpture of Dynasty XXV, but the two uraei and rounded sideburns, resembling those of Cat. 76, are typical for likenesses of Kushite rulers.

81
Sphinx Head of a Kushite Ruler

Dynasty XXV, probably first half of seventh century B.C.
MATERIAL: Fine-grained diorite.
COLLECTION: *Brooklyn (New York), The Brooklyn Museum 05.316.*

DESCRIPTION: The small, boldly modeled head, broken off at the forehead and at the base of the comparatively long neck, is framed by a *nemes*-headdress. The thick upper eyelids end in cosmetic lines; the elongated eyebrows are in low relief. The cheeks are round and the cheekbones are emphasized, as are the Kushite folds running from the fleshy nostrils to the sides of the mouth. On the short chin can be seen the beginning of a beard, fastened with a chin strap indicated by two incised lines.

COLOR: Black.
CONDITION: Broken off at forehead and base of neck; left ear, top of right ear, and left side of chin missing; nose, left cheek, and both eyebrows chipped.
MEASUREMENTS: Height 9.3 cm. Width 10.1 cm. Depth 14.9 cm.
PROVENANCE: Not known; acquired in Cairo in 1905 by Flinders Petrie for The Brooklyn Museum.
BIBLIOGRAPHY: Vandier 1958,504, n. 6; Russmann 1968-69, 101ff., figs. 15-16; Russmann 1974,52, app. I, no. 26.

There can be no doubt that this is a Kushite royal portrait. Comparison with a securely dated Dynasty XXV likeness, such as the bronze statuette of Shabaqo, Cat. 75, points up considerable similarities, which are to be regarded, however, as common racial characteristics rather than as portrait indicators. Russmann (1968-69,101ff.) suggested, with some reservations, that this head be attributed to Tanwetamani, but since we have no secure likenesses of that king, the attribution remains hypothetical. It seems to me, however, that Cat. 82 could represent Tanwetamani. Consequently, some other ruler may be represented here, if we assume that features are rendered identically in bronze and stone.

82
Statuette of an Unknown King

Dynasty XXV, probably mid-seventh century B.C.
MATERIAL: Bronze, solid cast.
COLLECTION: *Christos G. Bastis, on loan to Brooklyn (New York), The Brooklyn Museum L75.6.6.*

DESCRIPTION: A kneeling king with both arms stretched forward wears the royal kilt and a cap encircled by a diadem with uraei and two streamers. He has a round, plump-cheeked face, high cheekbones, narrow, almond-shaped eyes, a pointed nose, and a small mouth. He wore around his neck a cord with three pendant ram's heads; only traces of this ornament remain. The belt of his pleated kilt is decorated with panels of alternating vertical and horizontal stripes.

COLOR: Reddish brown.
CONDITION: Both forearms missing; one uraeus and neck cord with pendants partially effaced.
MEASUREMENTS: Height 7.2 cm. Width 3.3 cm. Depth 3.7 cm.
PROVENANCE: Not known.
BIBLIOGRAPHY: None.

The paucity of dated bronze figures of Kushite kings makes an attribution of this statuette almost impossible. From published material, similarities can be established only with a statuette in Cairo (temp. no. 8/4/70/10: Russmann 1974,61, app. II, no. 13, fig. 20), which has the same full face and almond-shaped eyes; unfortunately, the name is not preserved, but it is reasonable to assume that both pieces came from the same find, a deposit of bronze figurines possibly all belonging to a divine bark.

The statuette cannot represent Shabaqo or Taharqo, who have quite different features. There remain Shebitqo and Tanwetamani. If one agrees with Russmann (1974,53, no. 29) that the granite head in Cairo (Fig. 25) represents Shebitqo, this figure must represent Tanwetamani. In that case, the attribution of the sphinx head, Cat. 81, to Tanwetamani is impossible, since its features are completely different.

83
Iriketakana

Late first half of seventh century B.C.
MATERIAL: Granite.
COLLECTION: *Cairo, Egyptian Museum JE 38018.*

DESCRIPTION: The high official Iriketakana stands with left leg advanced on a rectangular base, his arms close to his sides and his hands holding emblematic staves. He wears a long garment, indicated by incised lines, that leaves his left breast and shoulder bare. The fringed edge of the cloth is shown on his right side, and its ends fall over his right shoulder. His head is shaved. He has a receding forehead, prominent high cheekbones, and a very broad nose. The eyebrows are indicated by incised double lines; the eyes are narrow. The lips appear pursed. The short neck is very thick and the breasts almost feminine. Inscriptions on the back pillar and on all four sides of the base give Iriketakana's titles.

COLOR: Gray black.
CONDITION: Broken at base of neck and at hem of garment and repaired; right temple, upper right arm, right breast, nose, body, back pillar, and corners of base damaged.
MEASUREMENTS: Height 44.2 cm. Height of head 5.7 cm. Height of face 4.0 cm. Height of base 4.0 cm., width 11.4 cm., depth 21.6 cm.
PROVENANCE: Karnak, Cachette (1905), K. 650.
BIBLIOGRAPHY: Kuentz 1934,144-45, pls. I-II; Kirwan 1934,373-77; Bosse 1936, no. 2, pl. Ia; Cairo 1949, pl. 173; Wolf 1957,618f. (fig. 635); Leclant 1965b,434; Lapis 1966,105, fig. 3; Priese 1968,188; Donadoni 1969,150-51; P—M II 1972,153; Wenig 1975a,410, pl. 413; Leclant 1967, 116; fig. 115; Bothmer 1978, pl. 13.

Iriketakana, who came to Egypt as an official of the king of Kush, bore honorary titles in use since ancient Egyptian times, such as "Prince, Count, King's Friend," which did not describe the man's true function. In this statue, formerly set up in the Temple of Amun at Thebes, he had himself portrayed as a stout old man with pendulous breasts and a protruding abdomen. His face, too, shows the signs of age. To me, it certainly has the appearance of portraiture. Few statues of Dynasty XXV show as clearly as this one a brutal realism in which there is nothing of the customary Egyptian idealization. In this respect, we can compare the head with the Taharqo sphinx from Kawa, Cat. 77.

The former reading of the name was Irigadiganen, but Priese (1968,188; 1973,156, n. 1) has shown that the name is purely Meroitic and is to be read in the form used here.

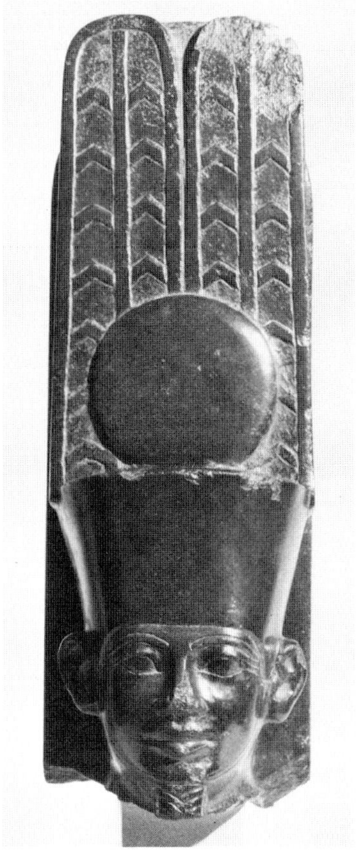

84
Head of Amun

Dynasty XXV, about 660 B.C. (Gen. 6).
MATERIAL: Fine-grained quartzite.
COLLECTION: *Oxford, Ashmolean Museum 1922.157.*

DESCRIPTION: The polished head, broken off at the neck, wears a crown with a sun disk and two plumes rising from a tall base. A back pillar, rounded at the top, rises almost to the tip of the crown and bears the title of King Tanwetamani, of which only the beginning is preserved. The god has a full, symmetrical face, with large eyes and arching, elongated eyebrows. The contours of the brows and the upper lids are incised, and the pupils are indicated in low relief. The nostrils are drilled. A slight philtrum is visible above the mouth, which is straight with deep corners. The broad chin is not emphasized. The chin strap is rendered by two incised parallel lines ending at the base of the braided beard.

COLOR: Dark brown.
CONDITION: Head broken from torso along irregular plane; nose, mouth, chin, left ear, upper edge of crown base, and tip of left feather chipped.
MEASUREMENTS: Height 33.6 cm. Height of head 14.0 cm. Width of back pillar 12.3 cm. Depth ca. 15.8 cm.
PROVENANCE: Sanam, Temple of Taharqo, Chamber H (Griffith 1912-13).
BIBLIOGRAPHY: Griffith 1922,86, pl. XIII,1-2; P—M VII 1951,202; Russmann 1968-69,106,107 (fig. 18).

Images of the gods were idealized in Dynasty XXV, as in the past. Since the features of ruling monarchs were not, in this period, transferred to divine images, it is impossible to attribute them with certainty to particular reigns in the absence of inscriptions. On the iconography of Tanwetamani, whose title appears on the back pillar of this head, see the commentary to Cat. 81.

According to B. V. Bothmer (verbal communication), the representation of eyebrows by incised lines is common in Dynasty XXV (e.g., in the statues of Mentuemhat, Cairo CG 42236; Khem-Hor, Cairo CG 42234; and Iriketakana, Cat. 83), but the rendering of the pupil of the eye is extremely rare and appears again only in the statue of the Divine Consort Amenirdas I (Cairo CG 565).

85
King Senkamanisken

643-623 B.C. (Gen. 8).
MATERIAL: Granite.
COLLECTION: *Boston (Massachusetts), Museum of Fine Arts 23.731.*

DESCRIPTION: The king, clad in a short kilt and sandals, stands with left leg advanced on a high base that is rounded in front. His arms are held at his sides, and he has emblematic staves in his hands. He wears a close-fitting cap with a diadem and two uraei that extend over the top of his head to the nape of the neck. His ornaments consist of a necklace with three pendant ram's heads, armlets, bracelets, and anklets. His title is inscribed on the back pillar, which reaches to his head. Most of the statue is polished.

COLOR: Gray, mottled.
CONDITION: Found broken into pieces and repaired; left shoulder missing; back pillar at neck level, top of base, and right foot damaged; chipped in many places.
MEASUREMENTS: Height 147.8 cm. Width ca. 38.5 cm. Width of base 28.2 cm. Depth ca. 50.1 cm.
PROVENANCE: Gebel Barkal, Great Temple of Amun (B 500-A) (head) and B 904 (body and base) (Reisner 1916, Object no. S 16-4-32).
BIBLIOGRAPHY: Reisner 1917b,30; Reisner 1920,251f., pl. XXXIII; Reisner 1931,82, no. 38; Smith 1946,146; P—M VII 1951,221; Smith 1960,165; Russmann 1968-69,96, n. 27; Dunham 1970,21, no. 6, pl. XII; Leclant 1976, 116, figs. 116, 119.

Senkamanisken was responsible for much building activity at Gebel Barkal (Temple B 700). Besides a sphinx (Cat. 86) from the Great Temple of Amun, he left three colossal statues, which were discovered in two places, broken into pieces, together with statues of Taharqo (Fig. 27), Tanwetamani (Toledo 49.105, Khartoum 1846), Anlamani (Boston 23.732, Khartoum 1845), and Aspelta (Boston 23.730). Two of the statues of Senkamanisken show the king as priest, clad in the panther skin (Khartoum 1842, Richmond 53-30-2). All three are in the stylistic tradition identified with Gebel Barkal from the time of Taharqo and exemplified in his statue in Khartoum (Fig. 27). In all, kilt, ornaments, diademed cap, and sandals were left rough to take gilding. Nevertheless, the statues are not to be regarded as mere replicas of some colossal prototype (thus Russmann 1974,17, n. 4, referring to the head of Taharqo, Cat. 76), but represent a stylistic variant, although they lack the inner tension that appears in the Taharqo heads from Egypt.

86 ■
Sphinx of King Senkamanisken

643-623 B.C. (Gen. 8).
MATERIAL: Granite.
COLLECTION: *Khartoum, Sudan National Museum 1852.*

DESCRIPTION: A lion sphinx wearing a *nemes*-headdress and a Double Crown with two uraei rests on a base with rounded back corners. The extended forelegs end in human hands that hold a conical vessel with the king's name in two cartouches.

COLOR: Gray, mottled.
CONDITION: Complete; nose, crown, rim of vessel, and corners of base chipped; brownish discoloration in places.
MEASUREMENTS: Height 53.9 cm. Width 25.5 cm. Length 88.3 cm.
PROVENANCE: Gebel Barkal, Great Temple of Amun (B 501) (Reisner 1920, Object no. S 20-1-274).
BIBLIOGRAPHY: Reisner 1931,82, no. 41; P—M VII 1951,216; Dunham 1970,33, no. 18, fig. 28, pl. XXXII A-C.

This representation of King Senkamanisken, one of the rare Napatan Period sphinxes, is wholly in the Egyptian tradition. Sphinxes in which the forelegs end in hands holding a receptacle are known from Dynasty XXV (e.g., Berlin/ DDR 7972, sphinx of the Divine Consort Shepenwepet II) but portrayals of the king with Double Crown and beard are rare in Napatan art. The sculpture is stylistically similar to Cat. 85, found at Gebel Barkal. We see the same almond-shaped eyes within lids that are not contoured (so-called buttonhole eyes). The modeling of the round face with its high cheekbones is also similar, but the sphinx has somewhat more emphatically arched eyebrows and thinner lips.

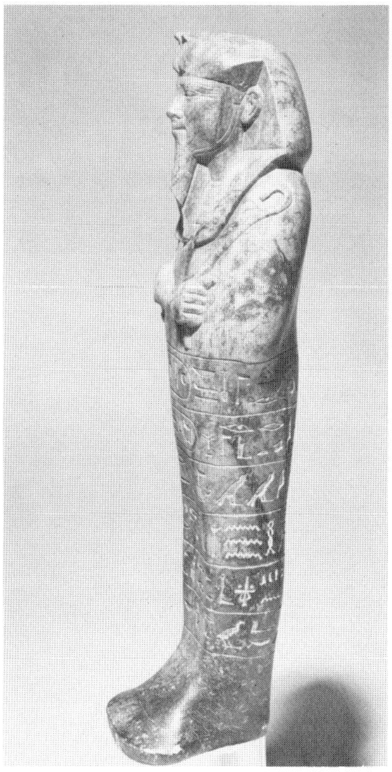

87
Shawabti of King Senkamanisken

643-623 B.C. (Gen. 8).
MATERIAL: Steatite.
COLLECTION: *Brooklyn (New York), The Brooklyn Museum, Charles Edwin Wilbour Fund 39.5.*

DESCRIPTION: The mummiform statuette represents King Senkamanisken holding crook and flail. He wears a *nemes*-headdress and two uraei. The elongated face is highly stylized. The lids of the almond-shaped eyes have incised contours and extend to long cosmetic lines. The plastic eyebrows are elongated. The braided beard, very broad at the base, is fastened with a chin strap. A broad collar is visible. On the body is an inscription of six lines separated by dividers, giving excerpts from Chapter Six of the Book of the Dead.

COLOR: Gray.
CONDITION: Lower part of beard missing.
MEASUREMENTS: Height 22.6 cm. Height of head 3.5 cm. Width 7.3 cm. Depth at base 5.3 cm.
PROVENANCE: Nuri, Pyramid Nu. 3 (Reisner 1916-17, Object no. illegible).
BIBLIOGRAPHY: Cooney 1939,45 (illus.).

This *shawabti* strongly resembles Egyptian prototypes and thus differs from the Taharqo *shawabtis,* Cats. 78 and 79. The treatment of the head is also different. The facial features of this king are, however, un-Egyptian.

At least 410 steatite (Dunham 1955,43, says serpentine) and 867 faience *shawabtis* were found in the Senkamanisken pyramid. Like Taharqo's *shawabtis* (see commentary to Cat. 78), these can be classified into several types. Instead of hoes, as in Cats. 78 and 79, the king in this case carries a crook and flail as insignia of royal authority; some of these *shawabtis* do, however, have hoes.

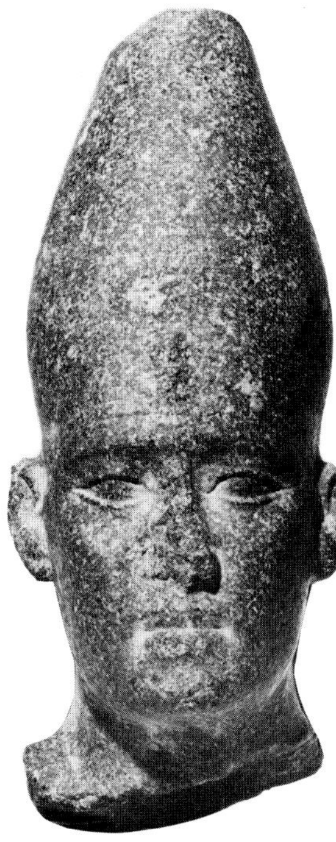

88
Royal Head with White Crown

Probably fifth to fourth century B.C.
MATERIAL: Granite.
COLLECTION: *Berlin/DDR, Ägyptisches Museum 13188.*

DESCRIPTION: This head of an unknown king with very shallowly modeled features comes from a statue that was somewhat smaller than life size. The corners of the mouth are depressed, the eyelids protuberant, and the high cheekbones emphasized. The beginnings of the shoulders are visible. The tapering, uninscribed back pillar reaches to the tip of the crown.

COLOR: Gray black, mottled.
CONDITION: Tips of crown and back pillar missing; relatively small uraeus and nose broken off; both ears chipped.
MEASUREMENTS: Height 28.3 cm. Width 12.0 cm. Depth 14.2 cm.
PROVENANCE: Bought in Wadi Halfa but allegedly discovered farther south; acquired in 1896 as a gift of Baron Max von Oppenheim.
BIBLIOGRAPHY: Berlin 1899,401; P—M VII 1951,141.

The head was originally attributed to the Napatan Period (Berlin 1899,401), to Dynasty XXV (P—M VII 1951,141), and later (by the museum), without proof, to the Middle Kingdom. The flat, simply modeled face, the softness of the features, and the strange shape of the back pillar indicate that the head was made during a so-called intermediate period or else outside of Egypt. Since it is stylistically not comparable to the plentiful material preserved from the First and Second Intermediate Periods, we must assume that it originated somewhere outside of Egypt, which must have been, considering the site at which it was found, in Nubia. Because of the wide stylistic variations that occur in the Napatan Period, it seems to me possible that the head can be dated later than Dynasty XXV and probably reveals indications of the Meroitic. For that reason, an attribution to the late Napatan Period has been considered.

That only one uraeus is present instead of two is rare but not extraordinary. Two parallels from the Meroitic Period can be cited for the White Crown: an unpublished sandstone head from Wad Ban Naqa (now in Khartoum) and an unfinished statuette of a standing king, also from Wad Ban Naqa (Khartoum 62/9/101), which is frequently regarded as a man with an elephant's head (Vercoutter 1962,275, fig. 6, 276; see also 285, fig. 14).

It should be noted that B. V. Bothmer does not consider the head ancient, for stylistic reasons and because there exist no parallels.

89 ■
Ram-Headed Amun

Presumably sixth to fourth century B.C.
MATERIAL: Granite.
COLLECTION: *Khartoum, Sudan National Museum 1844.*

DESCRIPTION: A ram-headed Amun wearing a royal kilt stands with left leg advanced on a rectangular base, his arms close to his sides. He holds an *ankh*-sign in his left hand and an emblematic stave in the right. On his head is a long striated wig and a round crown support with a rectangular hole in the center. The horns rest, as usual, on the face. The circular eyes are drilled. The navel is faintly indicated, and the waist is constricted. The back pillar reaches to the shoulders and ends in a truncated pyramid.

COLOR: Dark gray; discolorations in the stone.
CONDITION: Complete; right horn broken off and repaired, with slight defects; crown support and right shoulder chipped.
MEASUREMENTS: Height ca. 60.0 cm. Width 15.7 cm. Width of base 11.5 cm., depth 20.5 cm. Hole in crown support 1.6 by 2.6 by 2.4 cm.
PROVENANCE: Gebel Barkal, Temple B 704 (Reisner 1916, Object no. S 16-3-203).
BIBLIOGRAPHY: Reisner 1918a,101-02; Dunham 1970,69, pl. LVI.

The eyes of this well-fashioned sculpture were originally inlaid, a feature that occurs in only one other Napatan sculpture, a royal head (Cat. 80) that is certainly Kushite. The god probably wore the two tall Amun plumes, which, like the eyes, must have been made from some other material. The lack of parallels makes an exact dating of this statue impossible. It can only be assumed that the work was made in the later Napatan Period, when, as in Meroitic times, sculptures in the round of gods in human form with animal heads were very rare. Reisner (1918a,101) considered the sculpture Meroitic.

90
Swimming Girl with Basin

Eighth to seventh century B.C.
MATERIAL: Faience.
COLLECTION: *Oxford, Ashmolean Museum 1921.735.*

DESCRIPTION: A naked girl lying prone, with long hair tied in a ribbon, pierced earlobes, and pronounced hips, holds in her outstretched hands a small rectangular basin with sloping walls. Between the wrists and the basin are vertical holes. Ankle bands are indicated in low relief.

COLOR: Yellowish brown; hair on head and pubic hair black; ribbon light colored.
CONDITION: Complete; broken in several places (perhaps in recent times) and repaired.
MEASUREMENTS: Length 10.8 cm. Height 2.8 cm. Width 2.3 cm.
PROVENANCE: Sanam, Grave 963 (Griffith 1912-13, Object no. 1/963/5).
BIBLIOGRAPHY: Oxford 1914,5; Griffith 1923,105,120, pl. XXIII; Oxford 1951,44, pl. XXIX B; Boardman 1964, 143, fig. 43a; Wallert 1967,39-40,136 (no. O 11), pl. 34; Oxford 1970,59, fig. 28.

Objects of this type were previously designated as ointment spoons, since they were regarded as toilet articles, but recent research (Wallert 1967) indicates that they were used in burial and cult ceremonies for dispensing myrrh or wine. The girl's prominent hips, her coiffure, which faintly resembles that of a Kushite lady of rank (e.g., Cats. 128 and 196, from the Meroitic Period), and her features, which are in a non-Egyptian artistic tradition, indicate that the piece might be Kushite in origin. The upper arms are too short.

Illustrated in color on page 178.

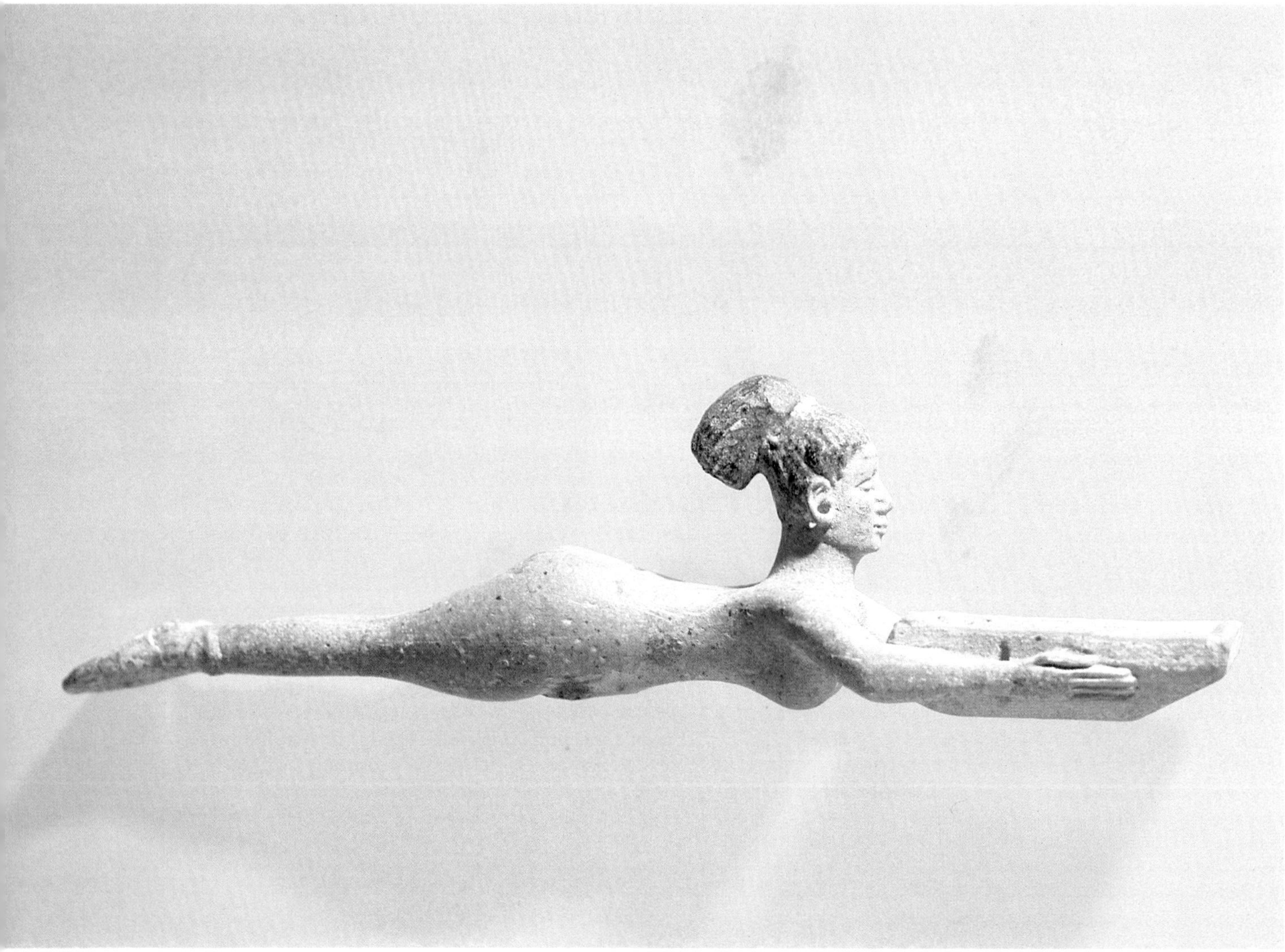

Swimming Girl with Basin (Cat. 90).

91
Bed Leg in the Form of a Goose

Beginning of seventh century B.C. (Gen. 4).
MATERIAL: Bronze.
COLLECTION: *Boston (Massachusetts), Museum of Fine Arts 21.2815.*

DESCRIPTION: A goose, its feathers carefully incised, squats on a base shaped like a truncated pyramid and decorated on all four sides with the Egyptian papyrus plant motif. Above the animal rises a round-topped bedpost with square holes for fastening to the bedstead.

COLOR: Deep gray green.
CONDITION: Complete; corroded and discolored in places.
MEASUREMENTS: Height 56.1 cm. Height of base 13.9 cm. Height of goose 19.6 cm. Width 13.0 cm. Depth ca. 30.5 cm.
PROVENANCE: El Kurru, Tomb Ku. 72 (Reisner 1919, Object no. S 19-3-1544).
BIBLIOGRAPHY: Reisner 1921b,37 (fig.); Dunham 1946,382, pl. XXXIa; Smith 1946,153; Dunham 1950,104,107 (fig. 35f), pl. LVIII B; Dunham 1953,90 (fig.); Smith 1960,171 (fig. 108),175; Los Angeles 1974, no. 64 (illus.).

Bed burials, a characteristic feature of the Kerma culture (see pp. 31-32), were also found in the early tombs of El Kurru, which points to a continuity of population in Upper Nubia. Two identical examples of these bronze bed legs were found (the second is Khartoum 1900). They were still standing in the holes at the corners of a stone bench in the burial chamber on which the funeral bed rested. In this bed leg, Egyptian formal elements have been combined for an un-Egyptian function. The collar, Cat. 96, comes from the same tomb of a queen of the time of Shebitqo.

Illustrated in color on page 46.

92
Offering Stand

747-716 B.C. (Gen. 2).
MATERIAL: Bronze.
COLLECTION: *Boston (Massachusetts), Museum of Fine Arts 21.3238.*

DESCRIPTION: A tall base in the form of an inverted horn supports a traylike table. A palm column in the center holds a small bowl, while four flower-shaped cups are equally spaced around the rim.

COLOR: Brown.
CONDITION: Found badly crushed and restored; numerous defects and cracks.
MEASUREMENTS: Height 81.1 cm. Diameter of base ca. 45.0 cm., of table ca. 41.0 cm.
PROVENANCE: El Kurru, Pyramid Ku. 17 (Reisner 1919, Object no. S 19-2-674).
BIBLIOGRAPHY: Smith 1946,153; Dunham 1948,98ff., figs. 1-4; ILN 1950,699, figs. 1-4; Dunham 1950,65,66 (fig. 22d), pls. XL A-C, XXII B; Monnet 1952,93, fig. 2; P—M VII 1951,197; Dunham 1953,90 (fig.); Smith 1960, 174-75; Wenig 1975a,412, pl. 417.

This offering table from the tomb of King Piye, so designated because it resembles many representations of offering tables, is without parallels. K.-H. Priese thinks it may be a lamp stand, an interpretation not easily dismissed (verbal communication); there must at one time have been stone or pottery receptacles to hold the oil inside the flower-shaped cups. The reappearance in Dynasty XXV of palm-leaf capitals, which were used in Egypt for the first time in Dynasty V, is evidence of the pronounced archaizing tendency of the later period (see also Cat. 94).

93
Rock Crystal Ball with Hathor Head

Late eighth century B.C. (Gen. 2).
MATERIAL: Gold and rock crystal.
COLLECTION: *Boston (Massachusetts), Museum of Fine Arts 21.321.*

DESCRIPTION: A rock crystal ball flattened at top and bottom is surmounted by the head of the goddess Hathor worked in gold. The face is framed by a wig. There is a uraeus at the forehead and a crown base with cow horns and sun disk on the head. The ball is drilled vertically to receive a gold sleeve, to which the Hathor head and the base plate are firmly affixed. A loop for suspension is attached to the back of the crown.

CONDITION: Complete.
MEASUREMENTS: Height 5.3 cm. Height of ball 2.0 cm. Diameter 3.2 cm.
PROVENANCE: El Kurru, Tomb Ku. 55 (Reisner 1919, not registered).
BIBLIOGRAPHY: Reisner 1921b,30 (fig.); Smith 1946,148,150 (fig. 92); Dunham 1950,94, pl. LX E-G; Dunham 1958, 108,114 (fig. 83); Smith 1960,169 (fig. 105),170; Terrace 1968,117ff.

This unique object was found in the tomb of a queen, who, according to Reisner, belonged to the period of King Piye. The loop attached to the back of the crown suggests that the piece was an amulet. The combination of a translucent ball with a head of a goddess is unparalleled in Egypt. Although the head looks very Egyptian, the composition as a whole is most probably a native conception. Cat. 94 was found in the same tomb.

Illustrated in color as frontispiece to Volume I.

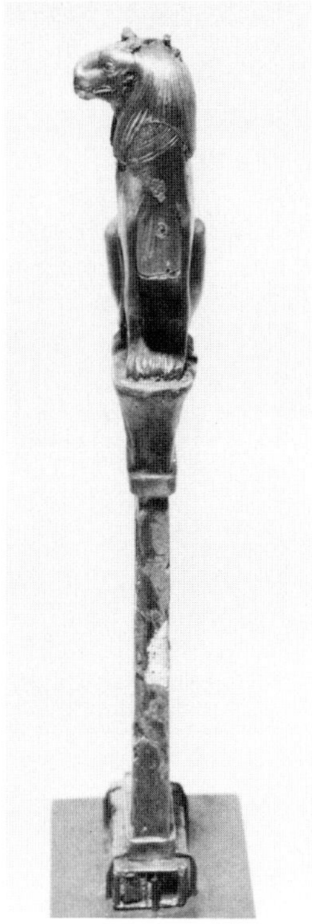

94
Criosphinx on a Column

Late eighth century B.C. (Gen. 2).
MATERIAL: Electrum with glass inlays.
COLLECTION: *Boston (Massachusetts), Museum of Fine Arts 24.972.*

DESCRIPTION: A lion with a ram's head turned to one side is seated on a column that is richly decorated with fused-glass inlays set in cloisonné technique, with a palm-leaf capital and a small base. The animal's head is framed by a voluminous wig, and a wide collar encircles the neck. The hide is beautifully incised. A suspension loop is affixed to the back of the head.

COLOR: Red, light blue, and dark blue inlays.
CONDITION: Left horn and suspension ring broken off; some inlays missing; column capital partly restored; animal's head and back and column chipped.
MEASUREMENTS: Height 10.3 cm. Width 3.0 cm. Depth 1.5 cm.
PROVENANCE: El Kurru, Tomb Ku. 55 (Reisner 1919, Object no. S 19-3-1434c).
BIBLIOGRAPHY: Smith 1946,148,151 (fig. 93); Dunham 1950,94,97 (fig. 31f), pl. LXI A-C; Smith 1960,169 (fig. 106 left),170; Terrace 1968,117ff.

The purpose of this funerary object, which presumably belonged to a queen, is not clear; it may have served as an amulet. Its exquisite workmanship ranks it, with the other objects shown here from El Kurru, as among the best goldsmith's products of Dynasty XXV. A ram-headed lion made of electrum and seated on a stone pillar (Boston 24.974) was found in the same tomb, along with Cat. 93.

Illustrated in color as frontispiece.

95
Isis Suckling a Queen

Late eighth century B.C. (Gen. 3).
MATERIAL: Silver gilt.
COLLECTION: *Boston (Massachusetts), Museum of Fine Arts 24.928.*

DESCRIPTION: An openwork amulet, which once had a suspension loop at the back, shows the goddess Isis suckling a queen, who is represented in much smaller scale. The goddess wears a long robe and a vulture headdress with cow horns and sun disk. The queen, who carries an *ankh*-sign in her left hand, wears a long pleated robe, a collar, and a short wig encircled by a diadem. A vulture hovers over her head.

CONDITION: Tips of cow horns on goddess's crown and suspension loop missing; gilt worn off.
MEASUREMENTS: Height 5.1 cm. Width 1.8 cm. Thickness 2.0 cm.
PROVENANCE: El Kurru, Tomb Ku. 52 (Reisner 1919, Object no. S 19-3-1145).
BIBLIOGRAPHY: Smith 1946,150; Dunham 1950,82, pls. LX C, LXX B top left; Hofmann 1971,37,48, pl. 3(a).

The amulet comes from the tomb of Queen Nefru-ka-Kashta, a wife of King Piye. The motif of a goddess suckling a monarch had been common in Egypt since the Old Kingdom, although the monarch was always a pharaoh, never a queen. The theme reappeared during Dynasty XXV. On the counterpoise of an aegis of King Kashta (private collection, Leclant 1963,78ff.), the ruler is suckled by the goddess Mut. On a faience *menat* in the Metropolitan Museum of Art (41.160.104), Taharqo stands before Ubastet. The motif appears frequently in Dynasty XXV reliefs; see Cat. 71. In this amulet, a queen (identified as such by Hofmann 1971,37) appears in the role for the first time, which suggests an extraordinary position for Nefru-ka-Kashta. Cats. 104 and 105 come from the same tomb.

96
Queen's Collar

Beginning of seventh century B.C. (Gen. 4).
MATERIAL: Gold.
COLLECTION: *Boston (Massachusetts), Museum of Fine Arts 21.307.*

DESCRIPTION: The collar is made of two crescent-shaped sheets of gold joined with hinges. On the larger crescent is the representation of a kneeling winged goddess with sun disk on her head, and on the smaller crescent is a scarab, both motifs being in raised relief.

CONDITION: Complete; slightly dented in places.
MEASUREMENTS: Outer diameter 16.9 cm. (height), 16.0 cm. (width). Width of collar 2.5 cm.
PROVENANCE: El Kurru, Tomb Ku. 72, in debris in burial chamber (Reisner 1919, not registered).
BIBLIOGRAPHY: Reisner 1921b,35 (fig.); Smith 1946,150,151 (fig. 94); Dunham 1950,104, pl. LXIII A; Dunham 1958, 107-08,112 (fig. 80); Los Angeles 1974, no. 65.

This collar, found in the tomb of a queen of the time of King Shebitqo, is unique, like many others from the royal tombs of Dynasty XXV and the Napatan Period. It could be opened and closed by means of the hinges. No Egyptian prototypes are known. The bronze bed leg, Cat. 91, comes from the same tomb.

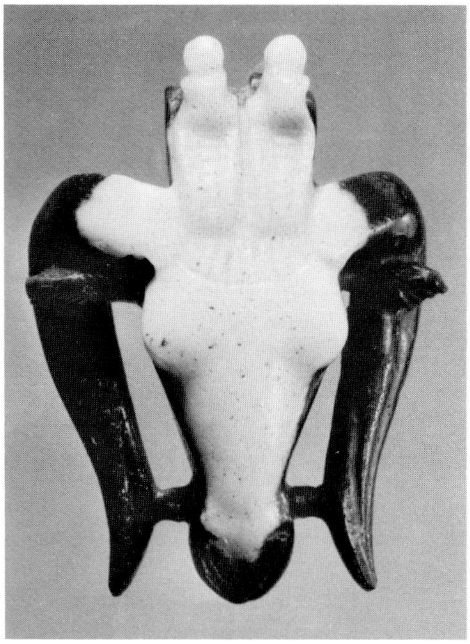

97
Ram's-Head Amulet

Presumably eighth to sixth century B.C.
MATERIAL: Jasper.
COLLECTION: *Brooklyn (New York), The Brooklyn Museum, Charles Edwin Wilbour Fund 54.198.*

DESCRIPTION: A ram's head with two uraei is made of bichrome banded Egyptian jasper. The freely modeled horns follow the contour of the head, to which they are joined by bridges near the tips. The small ears extend horizontally. A wide, semicircular piece has been left standing for support behind the uraei. There is a transverse hole and small holes at the base of the horns and ears.

COLOR: Blackish green and white.
CONDITION: Complete; tip of right ear chipped.
MEASUREMENTS: Height 3.7 cm. Width 2.8 cm. Depth 1.7 cm.
PROVENANCE: Not known; allegedly from Mitrahineh.
BIBLIOGRAPHY: Brooklyn 1956,55, no. 68, pl. 86; Russmann 1968-69,92, n. 11; Russmann 1974,26; Fazzini 1975,110,137, cat. 91.

The selection of the stone, with its white banding used for the top of the head, is evidence of Kushite taste and feeling for style. This very beautiful piece is an example of exceptional craftsmanship.

98
Ram's-Head Earring

Middle to end of sixth century B.C. (Gen. 12-15?).
MATERIAL: Gold.
COLLECTION: *Boston (Massachusetts), Museum of Fine Arts 23.333.*

DESCRIPTION: The earring consists of two parts. The hollow front is in the form of a slender ram's head framed by separately made, carefully incised horns. On the forehead are two crowned uraei, and a sun disk is on the head. The back is a concave disk with rosette decoration. The two parts are connected by interlocking tubes.

CONDITION: Complete.
MEASUREMENTS: Height 2.9 cm. Width 1.6 cm. Depth 1.3 cm.
PROVENANCE: Meroe, West Cemetery, Pyramid Beg. W. 443 (Reisner 1923, Object no. S 23-2-278).
BIBLIOGRAPHY: Dunham 1963,277 (fig. 173,12),278.

The workmanship is exceptionally meticulous and fine. Stylistically, the earring differs considerably from the approximately contemporary ornament, Cat. 99.

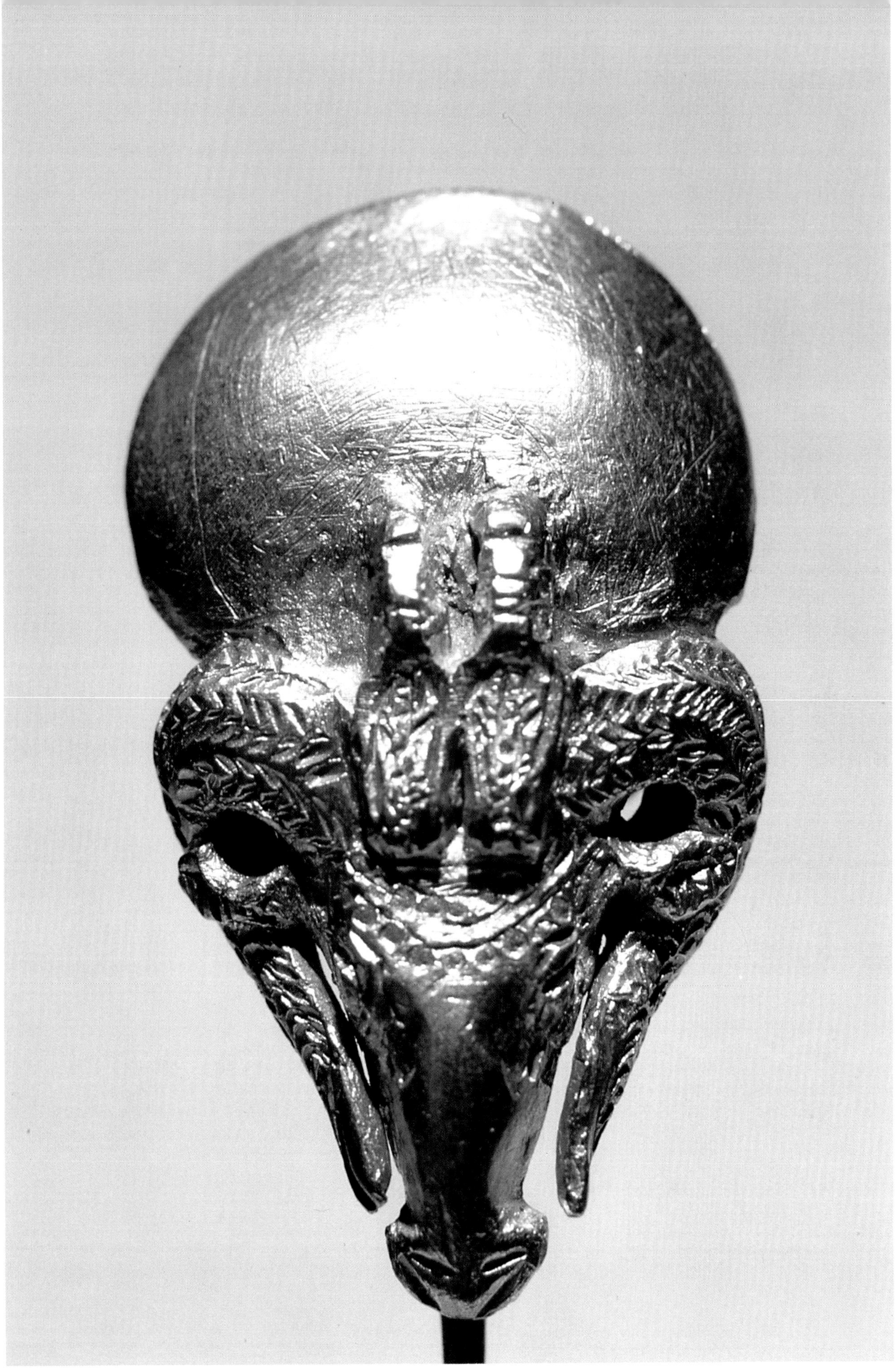

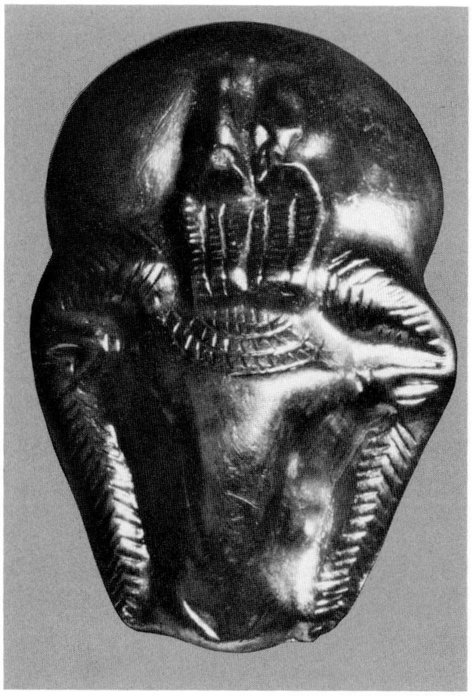

99
Ram's-Head Ornament

Middle of sixth century B.C. (Gen. 13).
MATERIAL: Gold.
COLLECTION: *Boston (Massachusetts), Museum of Fine Arts 20.269.*

DESCRIPTION: A ram's head from the pyramid of King Analmaaye is crowned with a sun disk. Two broad uraei on the forehead wear the crowns of Upper and Lower Egypt. On the back is a long clasp with a catch.

CONDITION: Complete.
MEASUREMENTS: Height 3.9 cm. Width 2.2 cm. Total depth 1.5 cm.
PROVENANCE: Nuri, Pyramid Nu. 18, in rubble left by plunderers in Chamber A (Reisner 1917, Object no. S 17-3-138).
BIBLIOGRAPHY: Reisner 1918b,72 (fig.); Smith 1946,150,151 (fig. 93); Dunham 1955,152 (fig. 174),153, pl. CXII E; Smith 1960,169 (fig. 106 center),171; Terrace 1968,117ff.

The form of the clasp suggests that the piece was fastened onto a garment somewhat in the manner of a brooch. Since it was found with other small gold objects in the debris left by robbers, we cannot say with certainty whether it belonged to the furnishings of this relatively poor tomb or whether it had been left there for some other reason and then forgotten. The ornament is less carefully fashioned than the gold ram's head from Meroe, Cat. 98, and has a broader head. Since the two objects are probably approximately contemporary, it becomes clear that stylistic criteria cannot always be used for dating, although they provide clues to provenance.

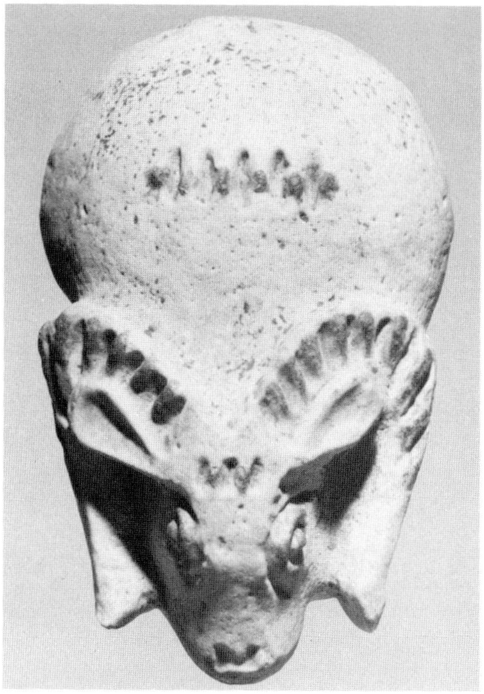

100
Object in the Form of a Ram's Head

Third to first century B.C.(?).
MATERIAL: Faience.
COLLECTION: *Khartoum, Sudan National Museum 690.*

DESCRIPTION: A ram's head with two powerful horns curving round the ears is surmounted by a disproportionately large sun disk, on which are five short vertical incisions. A transverse hole runs through a pointed projection on the smooth back of the ornament.

COLOR: Light blue green; indications of horns, eyes, and "uraei" dark.
CONDITION: Complete; whitish discoloration in places.
MEASUREMENTS: Height 8.8 cm. Width 5.7 cm. Thickness 2.9 cm.
PROVENANCE: Meroe (Garstang 1913).
BIBLIOGRAPHY: None. Garstang Photo M. 664.

Several examples of these faience objects in the form of ram's heads were found at Meroe. The way the back is fashioned suggests that they served as wall inlays, a thread or wire being drawn through the hole for attachment. The tiles on the door panels of the Pyramid of Zoser at Saqqara were similarly secured. The five vertical incisions in the center of the sun disk may represent a highly simplified frieze of uraei. The circumstances of the find are not known. For stylistic reasons, the object has been attributed to the early Meroitic Period, although certainty is impossible without further finds. The gold ram's heads from the Napatan Period (Cats. 98,99), however, are stylistically quite different.

101
Necklace Spacer

Middle of sixth century B.C. (Gen. 11).
MATERIAL: Gold.
COLLECTION: *Brooklyn (New York), The Brooklyn Museum, Charles Edwin Wilbour Fund 49.29.*

DESCRIPTION: A hollow trapezoidal object made of sheet gold is pierced by seven transverse holes. Egyptian hieroglyphic inscriptions cover front and back surfaces. On the front: "Son of Ra, Lord of the Crowns, Aramatelqo, may he live forever; Beloved of Hathor, Lady of Dendera, Mistress of the Gods, may she give life." On the back: "King of Upper and of Lower Egypt, Lord of the Two Lands, Wadj-ka-ra, may he live for ever; Beloved of Ra-Harakhte, the Great God, Master of Heaven, may he give life."

CONDITION: Complete; scratched on both sides.
MEASUREMENTS: Height 4.5 cm. Height of cartouches 1.8 cm. Width at base 2.7 cm., at top 1.9 cm. Thickness 0.9 cm.
PROVENANCE: Meroe, Building 294 (Garstang 1911). Formerly in the MacGregor, Wm. R. Hearst, J. Brummer, and A. B. Martin collections.
BIBLIOGRAPHY: Garstang 1912b,49-50; Sayce 1912,59; MacGregor Coll. 1922,194, no. 1502, pls. XX, XXXVIII; Dunham — Macadam 1949,142, no. 12; Keimer 1951,227, pl. IX C; P — M VII 1951,240; Cooney 1963,26 (fig. 8), 27; Shinnie 1967,123, fig. 43. Garstang Photo M. 862.

To judge from the Garstang photograph, this object was found with two very similar ones and several finger rings, together with gold dust and gold nuggets, in a vessel underneath the foundation of a wall. The three objects are the only ones of their kind. They are probably collar spacers, the threads of the individual strands being drawn through the holes so that the collar would lie flat. The two other spacers are now in Khartoum (511/1). One of them is a counterpart to the Brooklyn object, with an identical inscription. The other bears the name of King Malonaqen, Aramatelqo's successor. Although the inscriptions are in faultless Egyptian, the objects themselves may be entirely Kushite in form.

Garstang found comparatively large quantities of gold nuggets at Meroe, which he shared with the Sudanese Antiquities Service. From his share, he had a goldsmith make an unknown number of replicas of the collar spacers, and presented them to friends and sponsors of his work (Cooney 1963). The Brooklyn Museum owns two of them (63.35.1-.2); three are in Liverpool (SAOS 8041-8043).

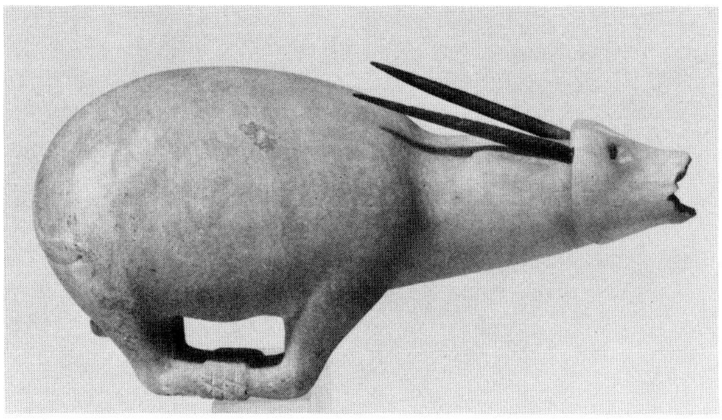

102
Jar in the Form of a Bound Antelope

Beginning of seventh century B.C. (Gen. 4-5).
MATERIAL: Calcite.
COLLECTION: *Boston (Massachusetts), Museum of Fine Arts 24.879.*

DESCRIPTION: An antelope with bound feet has two holes in its head to receive long, straight horns made of some other material. The open muzzle serves as the mouth of the jar. The head was made separately. The testicles are modeled in the round; tail and ears are faintly indicated. The eyes were inlaid, and there is an inlaid triangle of reddish material above the nose. The horns are modern.

COLOR: Creamy white.
CONDITION: Complete; slightly chipped at mouth; inlays missing.
MEASUREMENTS: Height 8.2 cm. Length 17.3 cm. Width 6.5 cm.
PROVENANCE: Meroe, West Cemetery, Pyramid Beg. W. 609 (Reisner 1923, Object no. S 23-3-407b).
BIBLIOGRAPHY: Reisner 1925,21 (fig.); Smith 1946,154,156 (fig. 100); Dunham 1958,121 (fig. 93),125; Dunham 1963,30 (fig. 21c,f),35 (with incorrect no. S 23-3-407a, which is in Khartoum).

Three alabaster jars in the form of bound antelopes, which served for the storage of liquids, probably perfumes, were found in a pyramid that belonged to a woman. The bound-antelope motif for ointment vessels was common in Egypt in the New Kingdom and reappeared later in Nubia. Whether this vessel is an Egyptian import or the work of Kushite craftsmen cannot be determined.

Illustrated in color, Volume I, page 83.

103
Amulet in the Form of a Lion-Headed Goddess

Late eighth century B.C. (Gen. 3).
MATERIAL: Faience.
COLLECTION: *Boston (Massachusetts), Museum of Fine Arts 24.616.*

DESCRIPTION: A winged, lion-headed goddess wearing a long wig, a uraeus, and a sun disk stands on a narrow base. On each arm is a uraeus crowned with cow horns and sun disk. The back pillar is inscribed. Behind the goddess's sun disk is a horizontal attachment hole.

COLOR: Blue.
CONDITION: Complete.
MEASUREMENTS: Height 8.5 cm. Width 6.3 cm.
PROVENANCE: El Kurru, Tomb Ku. 51 (Reisner 1919, Object no. S 19-3-993).
BIBLIOGRAPHY: Dunham 1950,78, pl. LV A top row, extreme left; Dunham 1958,114-15 (fig. 82 lower row, extreme right).

The amulet, possibly representing the goddess Sakhmet, comes from the tomb of a queen of the time of Piye or Shabaqo. Such amulets were very popular with female royalty in the early days of the Kushite domination of Egypt and have been found in many tombs (see the same motif from El Kurru Tomb Ku. 52, Cat. 105). The full, somewhat pendulous breasts and large hips reflect an African ideal of beauty, which was later prominently expressed in the Meroitic Period (see, for example, Fig. 46).

Amulet in the Form of a Winged Goddess (Cat. 104).

104
Amulet in the Form of a Winged Goddess

Late eighth century B.C. (Gen. 3).
MATERIAL: Faience.
COLLECTION: *Boston (Massachusetts), Museum of Fine Arts 24.639.*

DESCRIPTION: A winged goddess wearing a broad collar and a crown with cow horns, sun disk, and two plumes stands on a narrow base. On each arm is a crowned uraeus. Three circular forms in relief are visible on her forehead. The navel is deeply impressed. The back of the amulet is covered with hieroglyphs. A transverse attachment hole runs through the uraei and the head of the goddess.

COLOR: Blue.
CONDITION: Complete; broken into several pieces and repaired.
MEASUREMENTS: Height 9.0 cm. Width 6.0 cm. Depth 1.4 cm.
PROVENANCE: El Kurru, Tomb Ku. 52 (Reisner 1919, Object no. S 19-3-1116).
BIBLIOGRAPHY: Reisner 1921b,32 (fig.); Dunham 1950,82, pl. LIV A-B bottom row.

Like Cats. 95 and 105, the amulet comes from the tomb of Queen Nefru-ka-Kashta, a wife of King Piye. The goddess resembles Cat. 103. Such winged goddesses appeared also in Egypt, frequently at the corners of royal sarcophagi. Whether this image represents Isis or Hathor is uncertain; the inscription on the back is of no help. As in Cat. 103, the uraei on the upper arms are unusual. The motif appears also on an unpublished Meroitic Period architectural block from Musawwarat es-Sufra.

Illustrated in color on page 187.

105
Amulet in the Form of a Goddess with Sun Disk

Late eighth century B.C. (Gen. 3).
MATERIAL: Faience.
COLLECTION: *Boston (Massachusetts), Museum of Fine Arts 24.670.*

DESCRIPTION: A winged, lion-headed goddess, facing right, stands on a narrow base. She wears a large sun disk without uraeus. Papyrus stalks are incised on the back of her wings, and there is an incised design on the back pillar. Behind the sun disk is a transverse attachment hole.

COLOR: Blue.
CONDITION: Complete; broken into several pieces and repaired, with small defects.
MEASUREMENTS: Height 10.3 cm. Width 5.4 cm. Depth 1.2 cm.
PROVENANCE: El Kurru, Tomb Ku. 52 (Reisner 1919, Object no. S 19-3-1086).
BIBLIOGRAPHY: Dunham 1950,82, pl. LIII A-B top row.

An amulet from the tomb of Nefru-ka-Kashta, a wife of King Piye, is in the form of a goddess who was frequently represented in reliefs right up to the late Meroitic Period; it is uncertain whether she is Sakhmet or Tefnut. Cats. 95 and 104 come from the same tomb.

106
Amulet in the Form of a Dwarflike God

Late eighth century B.C. (Gen. 2).
MATERIAL: Faience.
COLLECTION: *Boston (Massachusetts), Museum of Fine Arts 24.688.*

DESCRIPTION: A naked male figure with thick, bandy legs, inflated paunch, large, prominent ears, and a scarab on his head stands on two crocodiles. He holds two knives and two serpents, whose heads rest against his cheeks. Armlets are visible on the upper arms. The back pillar carries an inscription.

COLOR: Blue green.
CONDITION: Complete; badly discolored in places.
MEASUREMENTS: Height 7.1 cm. Width 3.3 cm. Depth 2.5 cm.
PROVENANCE: El Kurru, Tomb Ku. 53 (Reisner 1919, Object no. S 19-3-1297).
BIBLIOGRAPHY: Dunham 1950,87, pl. L A-B lower row center.

This figure from the tomb of Queen Tabiry, one of King Piye's wives, could at first sight be taken for a representation of the god Bes, but his characteristic features, such as the aged face, animal ears, and plumed crown, are missing. The motif, a naked being standing on two crocodiles, holding knives and snakes in his hands as conqueror over evil powers, and wearing a scarab on his head, is very similar to that of the steloform pendant, Cat. 107, so perhaps this amulet, too, represents Horus on the crocodiles.

Illustrated in color on page 190.

Amulet in the Form of a Dwarflike God (Cat. 106).

107
Steloform Pendant

Seventh century B.C. (Gen. 5-8).
MATERIAL: Faience.
COLLECTION: *Boston (Massachusetts), Museum of Fine Arts 24.781.*

DESCRIPTION: In raised relief on the front of a round-topped steloform pendant is a naked megacephalic boy with bandy legs standing on two crocodiles and holding serpents and knives in his hands. A heart-shaped amulet is suspended from a cord around his neck. On his head is a winged sun disk with a scarab. On the back of the stela is incised a long-tailed spotted jackal standing behind a stylized tree. Behind the animal's head is a patterned disk (?) with a serpent, and below the disk is a horizontal rectangle.

COLOR: Blue.
CONDITION: Complete; broken in several places and repaired, with small defects; suspension ring at back broken off; surface worn and discolored.
MEASUREMENTS: Height 10.5 cm. Width 6.9 cm. Thickness 1.1 cm.
PROVENANCE: Meroe, West Cemetery, Pyramid Beg. W. 805 (Reisner 1923, Object no. S 23-M-591).
BIBLIOGRAPHY: Dunham 1963,323 (fig. 184,14),325.

The boy's physical characteristics recall those of a *pataikos*, a youthful, stunted creature, who, like the gods Bes and Horus, protects the amulet's wearer from harm. Here, however, we may have a representation of the young Horus on the crocodiles. It is certain that some Egyptian deity is represented, who could frighten malignant demons by his appearance; compare Cat. 106. The enigmatic representation on the back of the amulet is without parallels.

108
Winged Dwarflike Figurine

Probably eighth to seventh century B.C.
MATERIAL: Faience.
COLLECTION: *Brooklyn (New York), The Brooklyn Museum, Charles Edwin Wilbour Fund 75.166.*

DESCRIPTION: A naked megacephalic boy holding knives stands on a rectangular base. He wears a broad collar and a large cap on top of which are traces of some object now broken off. He has large eyes, a broad nose, thick lips, and prominent ears. Median line and navel are clearly indicated. On the back are two pairs of wings with a scalelike pattern on top and striped below. The back pillar, reaching to the top of the head, is divided into eight registers, in which traces of signs can be recognized. At neck level is drilled a transverse hole for attachment.

COLOR: Blue.
CONDITION: Object on cap and tip of back pillar broken off; chipped and abraded in places; base coated with dark material.
MEASUREMENTS: Height 8.05 cm. Width 2.7 cm. Depth 2.45 cm. Height of face 1.2 cm.
PROVENANCE: Not known.
BIBLIOGRAPHY: None.

The figure is very similar to Cat. 106, although here it is not Horus on the crocodiles who is represented but some other youthful god, a *pataikos* (see commentary to Cat. 106). The object that was once attached to the top of the cap is impossible to identify. Its provenance is not known, but stylistically the piece resembles many amulets found in Dynasty XXV tombs at El Kurru, so that a Kushite origin seems assured.

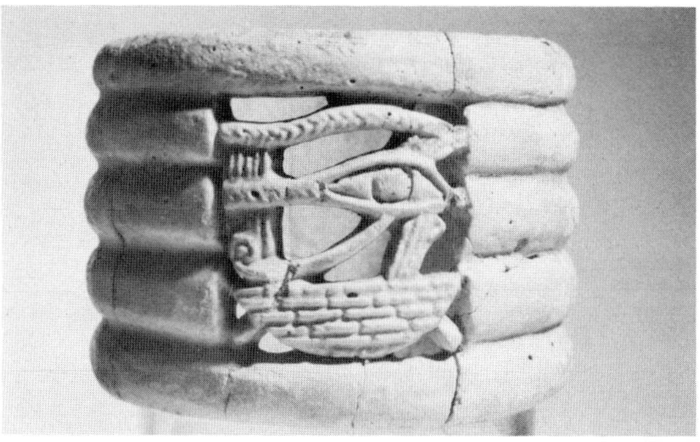

109
Wide Bracelet

Late seventh to sixth century B.C.
MATERIAL: Faience.
COLLECTION: *Oxford, Ashmolean Museum 1914.462a.*

DESCRIPTION: A wide bracelet, flat on the inside, is made to look like five separate hoops. An *udjat*-eye is inserted in openwork above a *neb*-sign.

COLOR: Green.
CONDITION: Broken into many pieces and repaired, with small defects; numerous small holes.
MEASUREMENTS: Height 6.1 cm. Outer diameter 9.8 cm. Inner diameter 7.2-7.3 cm. Thickness 0.8 cm.
PROVENANCE: Sanam, Grave 1516 (Griffith 1912-13, Object no. N 1/1516/6).
BIBLIOGRAPHY: Griffith 1923,122, pl. XXVI, no. 38.

The bracelet was found on the right forearm of a skeleton that the excavator regarded as female. Like Cat. 110, from the same grave, it is probably an inexpensive substitute for an ornament in precious metal. The custom of wearing hoops on the upper arms, forearms, and ankles arose quite early in Egypt and Nubia (A-group and C-group) and continued popular in Napatan and Meroitic times.

The woman was interred lying full length, face down, which was originally the Egyptian, not the Nubian, mode of burial. Since there were no *shawabtis*, which are found in this period in the south only in the tombs of rulers (who adopted the Egyptian fashion), the deceased was probably not an Egyptian, despite the many Egyptian offerings in the grave. She wore a similar bracelet on her left arm, together with bangles, chains of amulets, and other jewelry. Her grave was the most opulently furnished in the Sanam cemetery. Dating comes from a scarab bearing the name of Anlamani (623-593 B.C.) Ankh-ka-[ra], which was found in the grave (Oxford 1914.524: Griffith 1923,114, pl. XLIII,3).

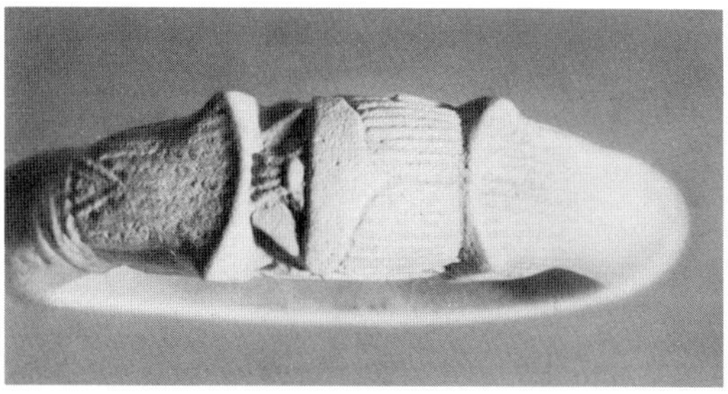

110
Decorated Bracelet

Late seventh to sixth century B.C.
MATERIAL: Faience.
COLLECTION: *Oxford, Ashmolean Museum 1914.461.*

DESCRIPTION: A hoop, flattened inside, has an imitation clasp shaped like a scarab between two papyrus umbels.

COLOR: Light green.
CONDITION: Repeatedly broken and cemented; pieces missing in one break and near "clasp"; badly discolored.
MEASUREMENTS: Height 2.2 cm. Outer diameter 11.8 cm. Inner diameter 8.6-8.8 cm.
PROVENANCE: Sanam, Grave 1516 (Griffith 1912-13, Object no. N 1/1516/7).
BIBLIOGRAPHY: Griffith 1923,122, pl. XXVI, no. 36.

The hoop was found with Cat. 109 on the right forearm of a female skeleton. The imitation clasp reveals that a metal bangle was here copied in a less expensive material. Such ornaments, worn even by wealthy people, reveal that objects of precious metal were in fact restricted to royalty and persons of high rank. Bronze bangles, however, which were common in the Meroitic Period particularly, were worn by members of many classes of society.

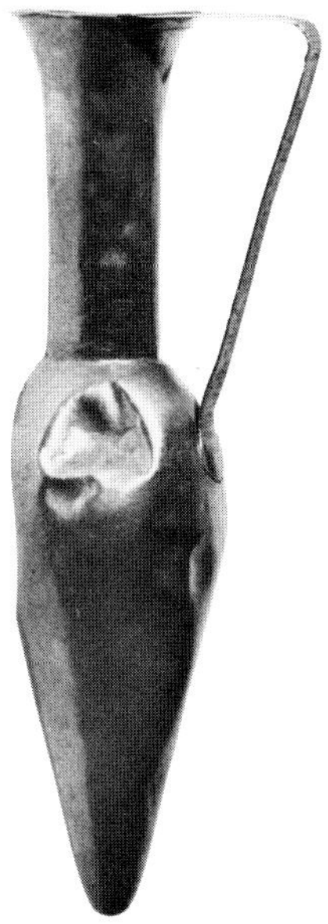

111
Gold Vase of King Aspelta

593-568 B.C. (Gen. 10).
MATERIAL: Gold.
COLLECTION: *Boston (Massachusetts), Museum of Fine Arts 20.341.*

DESCRIPTION: A long-necked vessel, tapering to a point, is distinguished by its slender, elegant form. The handle is riveted to the lip and soldered to the body; on its vertical face is a hieroglyphic inscription: "Osiris King Aspelta, justified before the Great God, the Lord of the Necropolis Anubis on his mountain."

CONDITION: Complete; dented in several places.
MEASUREMENTS: Height 31.3 cm. Diameter 8.3 cm.
PROVENANCE: Nuri, Pyramid Nu. 8, Chamber B (Reisner 1918, Object no. S 18-3-321).
BIBLIOGRAPHY: Reisner 1918b,75-76 (figs.); Reisner 1923c,131; Smith 1946,150,152 (fig. 95); P—M VII 1951,227; Dunham 1955,81,84 (fig. 55), pls. LXXXIX A, XXXIV D; Smith 1965a, pl. 179(B).

The vase was made for the funerary equipment of King Aspelta, since the inscription on the handle addresses him as Osiris. As this king's coffin is pronouncedly Egyptianizing and the vase, too, follows Egyptian prototypes, it is almost certain that close relations were maintained with Egypt despite belligerent entanglements with that country. Cats. 112-114 come from the same tomb.

112
Vase of King Aspelta

593-568 B.C. (Gen. 10).
MATERIAL: Calcite; cap gold with glass inlays and carnelian, turquoise, and steatite beads.
COLLECTION: *Boston (Massachusetts), Museum of Fine Arts 20.1070.*

DESCRIPTION: A tall, slender vessel has two knobs placed high on the body. On the shoulder, on both sides of the vessel, are double cartouches, surmounted by *shu*-feathers, containing the names "Son of Ra Aspelta" (right cartouche) and "King of Upper and Lower Egypt Meri-ka-ra" (left cartouche). Flanking the double cartouches are standing goddesses spreading their wings protectively. Within the triangle between upward- and downward-pointing wings are *udjat*-eyes. A flat-topped cap of gold with glass inlays and beads of carnelian, turquoise, and steatite suspended from woven gold wire chains fits over the rim and shoulder of the vessel.

COLOR: Creamy white; beads dark red, light and dark blue.
CONDITION: Multiple breaks, repaired; portion of top of vessel missing; cap decoration restored; ten of approximately thirty beads preserved.
MEASUREMENTS: Height 25.2 cm. Diameter (at level of knobs) 7.2 cm.
PROVENANCE: Nuri, Pyramid Nu. 8, Chamber A (Reisner 1916, Object no. S 16-4-75).
BIBLIOGRAPHY: Reisner 1917b,33 (fig. 14); Dunham 1955,80,82 (fig. 53), pls. LXXIX, LXXX A; Dunham 1958,113,117 (fig. 88).

The vessel is an alabastron, a common form in Egypt during the Late Period; the knobs on the body are vestigial handles. The cap, with its flat, projecting rim, is quite unusual; the decoration consists of registers of fused-glass inlays in cloisonné. Cats. 111, 113, and 114 come from the same tomb.

Illustrated in color, Volume I, page 88.

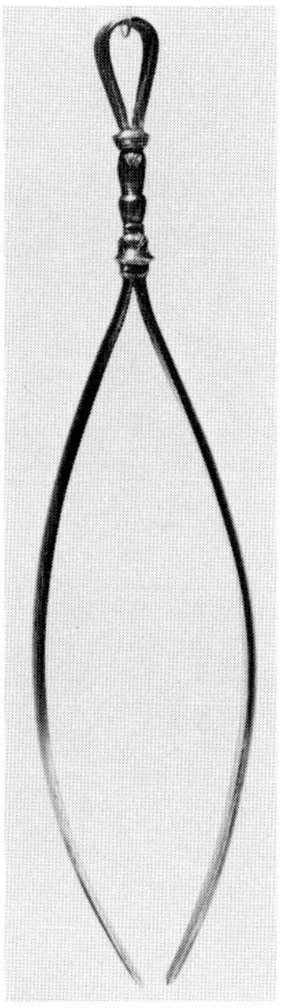

113
Tweezers of King Aspelta

593-568 B.C. (Gen. 10).
MATERIAL: Gold.
COLLECTION: *Boston (Massachusetts), Museum of Fine Arts 20.342.*

DESCRIPTION: The tweezers are concave strips of gold tapering at the ends. The loop is incised with longitudinal lines and attached to a handle in the form of a column shaped like a tied papyrus bundle on a stepped base. Over the capital is an abacus, another capital in the form of a lotus flower, and a second abacus.

CONDITION: Complete.
MEASUREMENTS: Length 18.0 cm. Width 4.3 cm. Thickness 1.3 cm.
PROVENANCE: Nuri, Pyramid Nu. 8, Chamber B (Reisner 1918, Object no. S 18-3-301).
BIBLIOGRAPHY: Reisner 1918b,79 (fig.); Appel 1946,24, (fig. 3r); Dunham 1955,80,84 (fig. 55), pl. CXVIII C.

Several gold and silver tweezers were found in Aspelta's tomb; the handles of the three gold tweezers are all slightly different. It is inexplicable why so many of these implements should have belonged to his tomb equipment, since they are rarely found elsewhere. Cats. 111, 112, and 114 come from the same tomb.

114
Cylinder of King Aspelta

593-568 B.C. (Gen. 10).
MATERIAL: Gold.
COLLECTION: *Boston (Massachusetts), Museum of Fine Arts 21.339a-b.*

DESCRIPTION: A gold cylinder is made in two parts, the upper nesting into the lower. The upper cylinder, which is open at top and bottom, is decorated with three chased ornamental friezes: uraei with sun disks, ram's heads with sun disks, and papyrus umbels. On the lower cylinder is engraved the goddess Mut wearing a Double Crown, her extended wings touching the ground. In front of and behind her are tall papyrus and lily stems on which are a serpent with the crown of Lower Egypt and a vulture, each resting on a *neb*-sign. The accompanying inscription, in good Egyptian, includes the names of King Aspelta. A rosette is engraved on the closed base of the lower cylinder.

CONDITION: Top part found crushed; electrolytically cleaned and restored.
MEASUREMENTS: Height 11.0 cm. Diameter 3.2 cm.
PROVENANCE: Nuri, Pyramid Nu. 8, Chamber A (Reisner 1916, Object no. S 16-3-70h).
BIBLIOGRAPHY: Reisner 1917b,32,33 (fig. 13); Reisner 1918b,80 (fig.); Reisner 1923c,130; Smith 1946,150; P—M VII 1951,227; Dunham 1955,79, pls. XCIII A, CII B-C; Smith 1960,171,172 (fig. 109 left).

Two-piece cylinders of this type have been found in several tombs of Napatan kings, but their function is not known; there are no Egyptian parallels. It is possible that they were handles for fans, the ostrich feathers being inserted into the top. Cats. 111-113 also come from Aspelta's tomb.

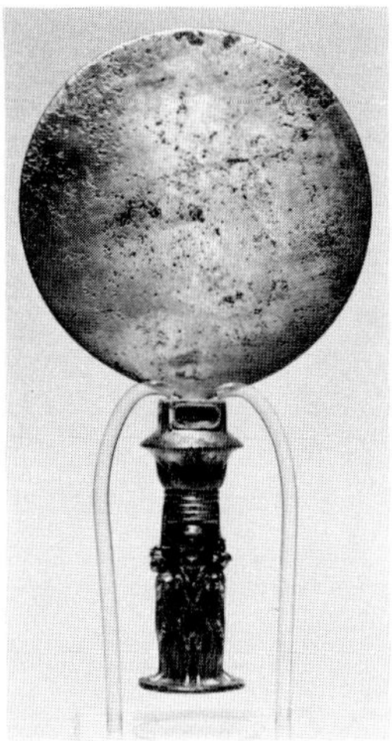

115
Mirror of King Amani-natake-lebte

538-519 B.C. (Gen. 14).
MATERIAL: Silver; gold wire cartouches.
COLLECTION: *Boston (Massachusetts), Museum of Fine Arts 21.338.*

DESCRIPTION: The mirror is attached to a handle shaped like a papyrus column with a square abacus, on two sides of which are horizontal cartouches of applied gold wire in which the king's name was once inlaid. Four frontal male figures, modeled almost in the round, are spaced around the column. The king is represented wearing a four-feather crown, a necklace with three ram's-head pendants, and a chin strap (but no beard). To his right is Amun, wearing two tall feathers, followed by the two hawk-headed gods Ra-Harakhte and Horus, both wearing sun disks.

CONDITION: Complete; mirror plaque slightly corroded; slightly chipped.
MEASUREMENTS: Height 31.5 cm. Height of handle 14.0 cm., diameter 5.3 cm. Width of mirror plaque 17.8 cm.
PROVENANCE: Nuri, Pyramid Nu. 10, Chamber B (Reisner 1917, Object no. S 17-1-11).
BIBLIOGRAPHY: Reisner 1921b,38 (fig.); Reisner 1923c,131; P—M VII 1951,227; Dunham 1955,155,156 (fig. 117), pl. XCI A-E; Smith 1960,173 (fig. 112),174; Wenig 1975a, 417, pl. 416b.

A mirror found in King Shabaqo's tomb has a handle in the form of a palm column with four goddesses standing around it (Boston 21.318). On the handle of King Nastasen's mirror (Khartoum 1374), the third of these magnificent objects, appears the Theban triad—Amun, Mut, and Khonsu—together with a goddess (Isis or Hathor). Only on the present piece is the king represented in the company of the gods. The mirror is an outstanding example of Napatan craftsmanship and demonstrates the high quality of Kushite metalwork.

116
Stamp Seal

First century A.D.
MATERIAL: Faience.
COLLECTION: *Khartoum, Sudan National Museum 518.*

DESCRIPTION: The stamp seal consists of a rectangular ornamented plaque surmounted by an arrangement of three pairs of feathers. A stout ring is joined to the smooth back.

COLOR: Blue green.
CONDITION: Complete when discovered; now cracked and slightly chipped; top broken off in modern times and replaced; discolored on back and in grooves.
MEASUREMENTS: Height 9.3 cm. Width 6.8 cm. Thickness 1.0 cm., with handle 3.7 cm.
PROVENANCE: Meroe, Apedemak Temple (Garstang 1909-10).
BIBLIOGRAPHY: Garstang 1911,22, pl. XXII,4 right. Garstang Photo M. 1056.

Such stamp seals were found in fairly large numbers in Temple T at Kawa (Macadam 1955,186-87, pl. XCVc) and in the city of Meroe. They frequently show vertical cartouches crowned by two tall *shu*-feathers, although numerous examples with purely ornamental decoration are known. Many of the stamp seals found at Meroe come from buildings in which vessels formerly regarded as urns were found (Buildings 909, 924, 929; Garstang 1914b,5).

W. George, one of Garstang's associates, speculated that these seals had some connection with the so-called urns. This interpretation is extremely improbable because many similar stamp seals have been found in temples. Their purpose remains unclear. Seals were often made of durable materials. Whether these objects made in faience were worn or carried on special occasions or fastened somewhere or other as ornamentation or were perhaps set into walls cannot yet be determined. Since we have no precise details on the circumstances of the find, these interesting pieces must for the time being remain undated. Such objects have not been found in the pyramids of Napata or Meroe.

For the dating of this piece to the first century A.D., reference may be made to a wooden chest from Pyramid Beg. N. 18 of Queen Amanikhatashan in the North Cemetery at Meroe, which shows the same ornament as the one on the seal (I owe this reference to K.-H. Priese).

117
Scaraboid in the Form of a Squatting Frog

After 700 B.C.
MATERIAL: Steatite.
COLLECTION: *Khartoum, Sudan National Museum 1670.*

DESCRIPTION: A wide-eyed frog squats on an oblong base with rounded corners and grooved sides. The piece is drilled through lengthwise. Beneath the frog's head is a ram's head with curved horns and a uraeus at the forehead. The underside is incised with hieroglyphs (including the name of Amun) and representations of the bark of the sun, a jackal with its head turned round, and a uraeus.

COLOR: Light brown.
CONDITION: Frog's head partly broken off and restored; right front end of base broken off and replaced, with small chip on underside; worn and discolored.
MEASUREMENTS: Height 2.1 cm. Width 1.9 cm. Length 2.9 cm.
PROVENANCE: Sanam, Grave 58 (Griffith 1913, Object no. N 1/58/2).
BIBLIOGRAPHY: Griffith 1923,132,143, pl. XLVIII,15.

With the deceased were found numerous scarabs and frog figurines. The association of a frog with a ram's head is unique. Possibly, the frog appears here as a protector of Amun. As in Egypt, this animal played an important role in the Kingdom of Kush, since it was frequently represented as an amulet, in temple reliefs, and in sculpture. Probably, it was also a fertility symbol; see p. 90.

118
Funerary Stela of Tedeqen

Second century B.C.
MATERIAL: Granite.
COLLECTION: *Boston (Massachusetts), Museum of Fine Arts 23.870.*

DESCRIPTION: The round top of a rather narrow stela is framed by a polished band. From a sun disk whose wings occupy the whole width of the stela and rest on two columns with papyrus capitals hangs a legend flanked by uraei wearing the crowns of Upper and Lower Egypt. In the central zone, the deceased is represented, facing left; in one hand he holds a small censer in the shape of a horned altar and in the other a libation vessel, from which he pours water onto a sacrificial altar laden with offerings. He wears a long robe, sandals, and a headband with streamers and an ornament at the forehead that resembles a double uraeus. He has a broad collar, armlets, and bracelets. Opposite him, the god Osiris sits on a throne decorated with a stylized representation of the Egyptian symbols of the United Two Lands, the lotus and papyrus stems wound around the ancient hieroglyph for "unification." The god wears an *atef*-crown and a long, close-fitting robe and carries a crook and flail. Behind him stands the goddess Isis, one hand raised and the other holding an *ankh*-sign. On her head is her Egyptian hieroglyph. The scene has an unpolished background. Underneath is an incised four-line inscription in Meroitic cursive containing an offering formula.

COLOR: Grayish black.
CONDITION: Complete; slightly chipped at edges.
MEASUREMENTS: Height 44.8 cm. Width 28.5 cm. Thickness ca. 12.7 cm.
PROVENANCE: Meroe, West Cemetery, Pyramid Beg. W. 19 (Reisner 1923, Object no. S 23-3-871).
BIBLIOGRAPHY: P—M VII,1951,260; Monneret de Villard 1959,96-98, pl. XXIII; Hintze 1961,278; Dunham 1963,80, fig. 60b-c,82.

The scene in which the deceased stands before the deities Osiris and Isis had been transmitted through the Napatan Period (Cats. 73, 74) from much earlier times. Originally, three gods were represented, then only two. The style here, however, is pure Meroitic. This is evident not only in the man's costume, which is that of a prince, but in several details, as in the faces. Osiris and Isis were frequently represented in Meroe as funerary deities; we do not know, however, whether they were worshipped by the whole people or only by the Egyptianized upper class. No Osiris temples are known from the Meroitic Period, although they are repeatedly mentioned in Napatan Period texts. There was a Meroitic Isis sanctuary at Wad Ban Naqa and others probably at Meroe and Naqa. The same scene is shown on a second stela of a prince from the West Cemetery of Meroe (Cat. 120), which is, however, incised only, and the position of the figures is reversed. The goddess has wings and wears horns with a sun disk instead of the Isis sign.

The inscription that hangs from the sun disk contains the Egyptian *sa-ra*, meaning "Son of the Sun," which was the king's title in Egypt, followed by the name of Osiris in Meroitic hieroglyphs. The cursive inscription below the scene is a standard text. After the invocation, or appeal to the gods of the dead (Isis alone being mentioned, presumably because Osiris has already been named in the inscription above), comes the name of the deceased, or nomination, and the prayer with the plea for water and bread, or benediction. The identification of the elements of the inscription comes from Griffith (1911b) and was modified by Hintze (1959).

This benediction formula is known only for private persons, which allows us to wonder whether the deceased represented here was indeed a prince; this is true, too, of Tedeqen's offering table (Cat. 120), where the representation and the offering formula contradict each other. Tedeqen's position in society thus remains uncertain.

119
Offering Table of Tedeqen

Second century B.C.
MATERIAL: Granite.
COLLECTION: *Boston (Massachusetts), Museum of Fine Arts 23.873.*

DESCRIPTION: An offering formula in Meroitic cursive is incised on the polished border of a rectangular offering table with a spout in the underside; the inscription is continued on an unpolished strip under the scene that fills most of the table. In the polished central zone are two deities standing in an attitude of semi-obeisance around an offering table supported by a base shaped like a lotus flower. From libation vessels they pour water which runs along the edge of the food-laden table into a hollowed-out basin from whose sides emerge lotus buds. The figure on the left wears a long garment with a vulture headdress and, on her head, the transformed sign of the goddess Nephthys. On the right is a jackal-headed god, also clad in a long robe. Above the scene is a frieze of round offering loaves.

COLOR: Gray black.
CONDITION: Complete; slightly chipped at edges.
MEASUREMENTS: Height 37.5 cm. Width 38.0 cm. Thickness ca. 8.4 cm.
PROVENANCE: Meroe, West Cemetery, Pyramid Beg. W. 19 (Reisner 1923, not registered).
BIBLIOGRAPHY: P—M VII 1951,260; Dunham 1958,139, fig. 112; Monneret de Villard 1959,94-96, pl. XXII; Dunham 1963,81 (fig. 61c-d),82; Hintze 1961,278.

The inscription contains the customary Meroitic offering formula; see commentary to Cat. 118, which belonged to the same man.

Despite the sign she wears on her head, there are reasons to think it is Isis, not Nephthys, who is represented here. Probably, the sign had no more exact meaning in the south than it did in Egypt. Osiris, Isis, and Anubis were all represented on the earliest Napatan royal grave stelae, but Anubis was omitted as the stelae became smaller (see p. 61). It is possible that he migrated to offering tables, together with Isis, who was firmly established in the cult of the dead. From offering tables, the representation of these two deities making libations was transferred to the walls of royal pyramid chapels (as in Pyramid Beg. N. 17 of King Amanitenmemide, now Berlin/DDR 2260).

The dating into the second century B.C. is based on the epigraphy and on archaeological evidence from the pyramid.

120
Funerary Stela of Taktidamani

About 100 B.C.
MATERIAL: Granite.
COLLECTION: *Berlin/DDR, Ägyptisches Museum 2253.*

DESCRIPTION: On a round-topped stela, beneath a winged sun disk, is a scene in which the deceased appears before Osiris and Isis. He stands on the left, holding a lotus blossom and a long palm frond and raising one arm in supplication. He wears a garment knotted over one shoulder, a headband, and a narrow collar. Seated in front of him, on a throne decorated with the stylized symbols of the United Two Lands, is Osiris, wearing an *atef*-crown and a tight-fitting garment with a circular opening from which emerge his hands, holding crook and flail. Behind the god stands Isis, spreading her wings protectively and holding a *shu*-feather and a vessel from which she pours water. Under the scene is a six-line inscription in Meroitic cursive.

COLOR: Gray black.
CONDITION: Complete; chipped at edges.
MEASUREMENTS: Height 47.0 cm. Width 30.6 cm. Thickness 11.1 cm.
PROVENANCE: Meroe, West Cemetery, Pyramid Beg. W. 18 (Lepsius 1844).
BIBLIOGRAPHY: LD V,54e; LD VI,10, no. 45; Berlin 1899,406; Erman 1907,200, fig. 97; Griffith 1911b,73, inscr. no. 49, pl. XXVII; Erman 1934,355, fig. 151; P—M VII 1951,260; Hintze 1966, pl. 124; Hintze 1968a, pl. 122; Hofmann 1971,59-61; Wenig 1975b,423, pl. 428.

The same scene appears on the Napatan stelae, Cats. 73 and 74, as well as on the funerary stela of "Prince" Tedeqen, Cat. 118; see commentary to Cat. 118 for the differences between the two stelae and for the customary Meroitic offering formula, which appears also on the present piece.

The supposition that Taktidamani was a member of the royal family is based only on his costume and headband; his garb is similar to that of "Prince" Tedeqen (Cat. 118) and to the crown prince of the Cairo group statue, Cat. 135. The benediction formula, however, corresponds to a type reserved solely for private persons (Hintze 1959,12,34). Thus, the social status of Taktidamani—as of Tedeqen—remains uncertain.

121
Votive Tablet of King Tanyidamani

About 100 B.C. (Gen. 44).
MATERIAL: Schist.
COLLECTION: *Baltimore (Maryland), Walters Art Gallery 22.258 (WAG 213).*

DESCRIPTION: A small votive tablet is carved in sunk relief on both sides. On the obverse is King Tanyidamani, wearing a ceremonial robe, a sash, and a long tasseled band slung over his right shoulder. On his head is a *hemhem*-crown with two streamers. Around his neck are a broad collar, a cord with three pendant ram's heads (mostly destroyed), and a ball-bead necklace. His earrings are in the form of ram's heads with sun disks. On his arms are wide armlets and bracelets. He holds a scepter in his outstretched hands. In front of and behind him are panels with inscriptions in Meroitic cursive.

On the reverse is the god Apedemak, wearing a short apron, a haltered garment with a scalelike pattern, and a *hemhem*-crown. He has a collar, pectoral, and broad armlets and bracelets. In his right hand he holds a bunch of durra and a long staff on which is represented a seated lion. In the other hand is a rolled-up stem with an *ankh*-sign at the end. A Meroitic cursive inscription is inset into a panel in front of him.

COLOR: Dark red brown.
CONDITION: Split longitudinally down the middle into two slabs; large pieces missing at top and bottom; numerous cracks; repaired and restored in places with plaster.
MEASUREMENTS: Height 17.8 cm. Width 9.1 cm. Thickness 1.7 cm.
PROVENANCE: Meroe, Temple of Apedemak (Garstang 1909-10). Formerly in the MacGregor Collection.
BIBLIOGRAPHY: Garstang 1910b,67, pl. 22; Garstang 1911,21,62-64 (inscr. 5), pls. I (frontis.), LXIII; MacGregor Coll. 1922,59, no. 469; Monneret de Villard 1942, pl. I left; Steindorff 1946,90, no. 293, pl. LI; P—M VII 1951,237; Hintze 1960b,127; Shinnie 1967, pl. 31; Davidson 1972,51.

This unique votive tablet, dedicated by King Tanyidamani in the Apedemak Temple of Meroe, is of exceptional quality and meticulously detailed. Particularly remarkable is the king's face; the prominent cheekbones, characteristic Kushite fold, fleshy nose, and thick lips are paralleled in the likenesses of Kushite rulers of Dynasty XXV (Cats. 75-77, 81) and of the early Napatan Period. It is astonishing that artistic traditions were maintained so clearly into the first century B.C. although connecting links are almost entirely missing. However, that objects could be produced at the same time which give evidence of marked stylistic and qualitative variations is shown by a comparison with the stela of King Tanyidamani from the Great Temple of Amun at Gebel Barkal (Boston 23.736). The rolled-up plant stem, whose blossom is in the form of an *ankh*-sign, is held also by the god Zeus-Amun on the seal ring, Cat. 186.

Illustrated in color, Volume I, page 97.

122 ■
Stela of King Amanikhabale

About 50-40 B.C. (Gen. 48).
MATERIAL: Steatite.
COLLECTION: *Khartoum, Sudan National Museum 522.*

DESCRIPTION: On a fragment of a round-topped stela is a scene in bold raised relief framed by a raised strip. Below a winged sun disk with uraei wearing the crowns of Upper and Lower Egypt are two gods, sitting back to back. On the left is the ram-headed Amun, wearing a feather-patterned kilt, a haltered garment, and a crown with two feathers and a sun disk. He holds a crooked staff in his right hand and an *ankh*-sign in his left. His ornaments are a broad collar, an amulet, armlets, and bracelets. In front of him stands a king who offers him a three-strand necklace. The king wears the same two-feather crown with sun disk, a haltered garment, a collar, armlet, and bracelet. On the right sits the goddess Mut, wearing a wing-patterned dress, a vulture headdress, and a Double Crown encircled by a band to which is attached an extremely long, narrow object. Her ornaments are a collar, armlets, and bracelets. On the side of her throne is a winged sphinx. The goddess reaches for a necklace offered by a king standing in front of her, who wears a haltered garment and a skirt, reaching almost to his sandaled feet, on which appears a bird with outstretched wings, seen in front view. His crown, similar to the one worn by the king on the left, has in addition ram's horns and two small uraei. His ornaments are a collar, armlets, and bracelets. Beneath the scene is the beginning of an inscription in Meroitic cursive. The smooth back of the stela is slightly convex.

COLOR: Black with gray spots; inscription picked out in white.
CONDITION: Lower left portion of scene and most of inscription missing; large piece missing at upper right; edge chipped; surface damages.
MEASUREMENTS: Height 20.3 cm. Width 18.9 cm. Thickness 3.1 cm.
PROVENANCE: Meroe, Temple of Amun (Garstang 1911).

BIBLIOGRAPHY: Garstang 1912b,47; Addison 1934,28; P—M VII 1951,236; Monneret de Villard 1959,102-03, pl. XXV; Hintze 1961,278-79; Hintze 1966, pl. 125; Shinnie 1967,220, pl. 32; Hintze 1968a, pl. 123; Hofmann 1971,58, pl. 8c; Davidson 1972,49; Wenig 1975b,423, pl. 427b; REM 1038.

Most of the elements of the scene are borrowed from Egyptian iconography, but the composition as a whole, the style, and certain details are Meroitic, such as the bold raised relief, the faces of the kings and the goddess, and the latter's protruding abdomen. Unique to Meroitic art is the bird decoration on the skirt of the king on the right. The winged female sphinx on the side of the goddess's throne is based on Greek prototypes.

At the beginning of the second line of the inscription is the end of a name, *-ble*, followed by the word *qore*, "king." The name must have been Amanikhabale, and the style of the writing belongs to the period of that king. On stylistic grounds, however, one would be inclined to date the offering scene somewhat later. The beginning of the inscription on this temple ex voto seems to mean, according to Hintze (1961,279) "[For his] wife Kaditede King [Amanikha]bale has . . ."

K.-H. Priese has established that a stela formerly in the Turayev Collection and now in Leningrad (Turayev 1912, 11-13; Monneret de Villard 1960,113-17, pl. XXVIII; REM 1001) belongs with this fragment. The Leningrad stela measures as follows, according to Turayev 1912: height 30.0 cm., width at top 17.3 cm., at bottom 12.0 cm. The material is described as greenish-black stone. Twenty-one lines are still preserved; however, according to Priese, about twelve lines are missing between the present piece and that in Leningrad.

123
Wall Inlay with Royal Profile

Late first century B.C.
MATERIAL: Sandstone.
COLLECTION: *Khartoum, Sudan National Museum 62/10/129.*

DESCRIPTION: A royal personage faces left on a fragment of a thin-walled tile. The profile is dominated by the large, stylized eye with its plastic lids, the upper lid being elongated to a cosmetic line. The fleshy nose is slightly hooked, and the lips are thick. The hair is rendered schematically. The vulture headdress has a uraeus beside the vulture's head.

COLOR: Grayish white; traces of pigment (yellow on face, blue and red on background) and of gilding.
CONDITION: Left edge only is original; surface damages, especially in lower portion.
MEASUREMENTS: Height 6.0 cm. Width 4.0 cm. Thickness 1.7 cm.
PROVENANCE: Wad Ban Naqa, Palace (Vercoutter 1959-60).
BIBLIOGRAPHY: Vercoutter 1962,283-84, fig. 13.

This impressive relief was painted and then gilded. Large portions of gold leaf from other fragments of this kind have been preserved (Khartoum 62/10/130), and many gold appliqués were found sticking to the hardened mud that filled the rooms after the abandonment and ruin of the palace of Wad Ban Naqa (unpublished finds in Khartoum). They originally decorated the walls of sun-dried mud-brick. Through these finds, wall tiles were identified in the Meroitic region for the first time, although they would have been, as in Egypt, customary for royal buildings. The preserved gold leaf appliqués include ornaments and inscriptions; Vercoutter (1962,282-83, fig. 12) has published a sample, but most of the material has not yet been evaluated. What is certain is only that Queen Amanishakheto is named, from whose pyramid (Beg. N. 6) comes the Ferlini treasure (Cats. 162-171, 173-175, 181-189). For that reason, it must be assumed that she is the personage here represented.

124
Relief with Royal Profile

Probably early first century A.D.
MATERIAL: Sandstone.
COLLECTION: *Bolton (Lancashire), Bolton Museum and Art Gallery (on permanent loan from Lady Lever Art Gallery, Port Sunlight, Cheshire) A 245.1968.*

DESCRIPTION: A royal head wears a wide circlet; there is no trace of a uraeus. The hair is echeloned at the temples and rendered schematically at the forehead and the back of the head. The plastic eyelids are extended to cosmetic lines. In the straight neck are incised furrows. The loop of a collar and the bead of a necklace are visible behind the neck.

COLOR: Dark yellow to yellowish brown.
CONDITION: Original edges of stone preserved at top and both sides; block worked off to a slant in back; surface abrasions, some modern, in addition to find number scratched in by excavator.
MEASUREMENTS: Height 23.0 cm. Width 26.0 cm. Thickness ca. 19.5 cm.
PROVENANCE: Meroe (Garstang 1911, Find no. M 740/11).
BIBLIOGRAPHY: None. Garstang Photo M. 598.

The soft mouth and chin suggest that this is a queen, but the absence of a uraeus indicates that it must be a prince or princess. The furrowed neck is seen also in a representation of Prince Arikankharer (Cat. 125), to which there are other stylistic connections. For this reason, the present relief should be dated to the early first century A.D. No temple reliefs with comparable representations have been found.

The technique of working off the back of the block to a slant on both sides is typical of Meroitic reliefs, particularly those of the Great Enclosure at Musawwarat es-Sufra. This made the work of fitting them together quicker and easier, since the stonemason, when he lined up the blocks, which were smooth at top and bottom, had to worry only about fitting the edges. The cavities between the blocks and the inner wall were filled with rubble and stone chips.

125
Prince Arikankharer Smiting Enemies

Beginning of first century A.D. (Gen. 53).
MATERIAL: Sandstone.
COLLECTION: *Worcester (Massachusetts), Worcester Art Museum 1922.145.*

DESCRIPTION: In bold raised relief on a rectangular tablet is a scene of triumph similar to those found in Egyptian art from the Old Kingdom on. In the center stands a prince with left leg advanced who holds a group of conquered enemies by their topknots and wields a sword in the same hand. The enemies are represented in three registers, the central figure in each row being full face and the others seen in profile. The prince brandishes a battle-axe above his head. He wears a long-sleeved, knee-length robe and a cape tied around his waist by a double-looped belt that terminates in animal heads. A sword in an ornamental scabbard is secured under the belt. An elaborate diadem holds his schematically rendered hair, and a lion's head crowned with a *hemhem*-crown rests on his forehead. His greaves are in the shape of winged sun disks, and his feet are sandaled. On his neck are three furrows, front and back. Above his upraised sword is an inscription panel that is not completely filled in; beside it is a cartouche with the prince's name in Meroitic hieroglyphs. Behind the prince hovers a goddess with wings on her back and at her ankles; on her head, above a circlet with uraeus, rises a long headdress. With one hand, she holds a long fan over the prince's head; the other grasps a kind of cudgel with leaves (?) attached to it. Her name, Talakh, is incised in Meroitic hieroglyphs in front of her head. Between the prince's legs, a fallen enemy is attacked by a dog, its head shown in front view. To the left of the triumphant scene, at the broken edge, is a hand grasping a long staff and the ropes by which prisoners—three are visible—are bound. Three rows of small incised *ankh*-signs point toward the prince's face; among them are several Meroitic hieroglyphs. The entire scene is framed by a raised edge.

COLOR: Light gray.

CONDITION: Left part of tablet broken off along irregular plane; edges slightly chipped; reddish discoloration in places.
MEASUREMENTS: Height 21.4 cm. Width 25.4 cm. Thickness 4.5 cm.
PROVENANCE: Allegedly from Meroe. Formerly in the Cargill Collection.
BIBLIOGRAPHY: Griffith 1917,21ff., pl. V; Schäfer—Andrae 1925,440 left; Griffith 1929,28; Schäfer—Andrae 1936,456 left; Scharff 1939, pl. 105,4; Schäfer—Andrae 1942,456 left; P—M VII 1951,261(with further older biblio.); Donadoni 1961,1037-38, fig. 1230; Milkovich 1963,156; Rühlmann 1964,654, pl. Vf; Smith 1965b, pl. 371; Shinnie 1967,220, pl. 33; Hofmann 1971,57-58, pl. 8b; Worcester 1973,19; Wenig 1975b,422, pl. 426; Leclant 1976,126, fig. 127; REM 1005.

Prince Arikankharer is represented with King Natakamani and Kandake Amanitore on the walls of the Apedemak Temple at Naqa; his pyramid (Beg. N. 5) is in the North Cemetery of Meroe. Although he apparently never succeeded to the throne, he is here represented in a triumphal scene otherwise reserved for reigning monarchs. The motif—the conqueror holding enemies by their topknots and brandishing a battle-axe—is rendered in classical Egyptian fashion, but the style and many details are purely Meroitic. The prince's robe and his forehead ornament, as well as the goddess's headdress, which is worn only by royal or noble ladies, are encountered for the first time on monuments of Dynasty XXV at Kawa and Sanam, among other places, and later in reliefs of King Senkamanisken in Temple B 700 at Gebel Barkal. There are no parallels for the objects the goddess holds in her hands. That she is here actually using her wings for flying is unprecedented; the only parallel is a graffito on the wall of the temple of Kalabsha, attributed to the Nobadae King Silko of the fifth century A.D. (Curto 1966, fig. 95; Castiglione 1970,98, fig. 7). Graeco-Roman themes must have played a role here, since she is clearly conceived as a victory goddess and is influenced by representations of Nike or Victoria. Her name, Talakh, appears nowhere else; it exists only within the royal name Talakhamani.

The shape of the prince's head, his large eye, and, in particular, his furrowed neck are Meroitic in style; the personage in the Bolton relief, Cat. 124, also has a furrowed neck, in addition to other stylistic connections between the two reliefs. The frontal head of the dog is unparalleled in Meroitic art. Normally it is a lion who accompanies the conqueror and tears an enemy to pieces. Griffith (1917,23) assumed here the influence of Roman art of the early second century A.D., but the prince's name proves that the relief must be dated a century earlier.

We cannot say how much of the relief is missing. Opposite the prince there must have been a god bringing up the group of prisoners, since the *ankh*-signs that approach the prince's face can have emanated only from a deity. The three rows of *ankh*-signs suggested to Griffith (1917,22) that three gods were represented, but this is questionable.

The provenance of the relief is a matter of conjecture. It was perhaps inserted into a temple or palace wall, but nothing similar has thus far been discovered. Its small size, and the difficulty of accommodating it on a wall, suggest that it might have been a sculptor's model, but it appears too meticulously detailed for that function.

Illustrated in color, Volume I, page 15.

126
Libating Goddess

Probably second century A.D.
MATERIAL: Sandstone.
COLLECTION: *Philadelphia (Pennsylvania), University Museum 66.11.42.*

DESCRIPTION: On a narrow rectangular pillar, a goddess standing on a baseline pours water from a jug. She wears a checkered garment that leaves her breasts bare. On her head is a vulture headdress with a vulture head at the forehead and a crown in the form of a shrine.

COLOR: Pale pinkish tan; traces of pigment (green on garment, red on body, yellow on baseline).
CONDITION: Complete; slightly chipped at edges.
MEASUREMENTS: Height 93.0 cm. Width 19.5 cm. Thickness 9.6 cm. Height of figure 49.2 cm.
PROVENANCE: Arminna West, Cemetery B, Grave 23 (Simpson 1963, Location no. 23.6, Object no. 504).
BIBLIOGRAPHY: Simpson 1964,18, fig. 2, pl. XI,6; Simpson 1967b,190,191 (fig. 12), pl. III; Trigger 1974,16 (fig.).

The pillar, which is Meroitic, was discovered reused in a tomb of the Ballana culture; it must have come from one of the local Meroitic tombs, which might have been pyramidal in form (Simpson 1967,189). An architrave (Cairo JE 90020) was also found; it, too, is Meroitic and possibly comes originally from the same structure.

The goddess represented here is certainly the same one who often appears with Anubis in scenes of libation for the deceased on offering tables (Cat. 119) and on the walls of pyramid chapels. Simpson (1967,190 and caption to pl. III) suggests that it is Nephthys who is shown here; the unusual head ornament in the form of a shrine is also the sign for the word "Nephthys." There are reasons, however, to think that in this case it is Isis who is represented with the now missing Anubis; see commentary to Cat. 119.

127
Funerary Stela of a Woman and a Man

Second to third century A.D.
MATERIAL: Sandstone.
COLLECTION: *Cairo, Egyptian Museum JE 40229.*

DESCRIPTION: A reddish-white undercoat was applied to a round-topped, roughly trimmed stela with a smooth, slightly concave surface. Beneath a winged sun disk resting on two papyrus columns stand a woman and a man facing left. She wears a long white skirt; he is naked. They both hold fans (?). In front of each figure is a text of several lines in Meroitic cursive with an offering formula.

COLOR: Light brown; undercoat reddish white; contours, inscriptions, woman's hair, outer wings of sun disk, ornaments on woman's dress black; skin, inner wings of sun disk red; columns, sun disk, and man's hair yellow.
CONDITION: Edges chipped; surface slightly damaged; colors partly obliterated.
MEASUREMENTS: Height 29.0 cm. Width 26.2 cm. Thickness 5.7 cm.
PROVENANCE: Karanog, Grave 275 (Woolley—Randall-MacIver 1908).
BIBLIOGRAPHY: Woolley—Randall-MacIver 1910,48,162, pl. 11; Griffith 1911a,54-55 (Kar. 2),129; P—M VII 1951,77.

The skeleton in the grave (Woolley—Randall-MacIver 1910,162) indicates that the stela belonged to a woman, but since the benediction in the offering formula (see commentary to Cat. 118) appears separately for each figure, it must be surmised that the stela was meant for both of them.

The piece is only roughly finished, but the painting, one of the rare Meroitic examples (see also Cat. 128), is not unskilled and reflects a certain talent on the part of the artist.

The woman's coiffure, with a small braided topknot and hair indicated by short strokes, is seen also on the woman on the bronze vessel, Cat. 196, as well as on the girl on the stela, Cat. 128. The woman's garment is common (Cat. 129). The swastika, a textile ornament repeatedly confirmed by unpublished finds of cloth in a Czechoslovakian excavation in Lower Nubia, is noteworthy, as are the man's earplug and the placement of the two figures side by side. The woman has pointed breasts, such as are present only in representations of young women; see Cat. 196. She is tall and slender, whereas the man is short and squat. Furthermore, the man's curly flaxen hair is unusual. The *ba*-statue, Cat. 156, also has flaxen hair; see the commentary to that piece.

Illustrated in color on page 206.

Funerary Stela of a Woman and a Man (Cat. 127).

128
Funerary Stela of a Girl

Second to third century A.D.
MATERIAL: Sandstone.
COLLECTION: *Philadelphia (Pennsylvania), University Museum E 7079.*

DESCRIPTION: A girl is painted on a round-topped stela beneath a winged sun disk. She is naked, but wears armlets and bracelets, earrings, two short necklaces, and a long necklace falling almost to her navel. She has a topknot, and a headband encircles her curly black hair. Two furrows are indicated on the neck, front and nape. The back of the stela is only roughly finished.

COLOR: Pinkish; hair black; girl's skin and wings of sun disk red; sun disk, uraei, and baseline yellow; headband and object in left hand green; beads on long necklace alternately green and white.
CONDITION: Complete; colors partly obliterated.
MEASUREMENTS: Height 37.0 cm. Width 33.0 cm. Depth 7.7 cm.
PROVENANCE: Karanog, about one meter from northwest corner of Grave 146 (Woolley—Randall-MacIver 1908).
BIBLIOGRAPHY: Woolley—Randall-MacIver 1910,28-29,49, 240, pl. 13; Shinnie 1967,151 (fig. 53); Wenig 1975b,422-23, pl. 427a.

From the Woolley—Randall-MacIver description, it follows that the girl was holding a green object in her left hand, although this is no longer visible (the color description given above was also taken from the excavation report). The form of the stela was adopted from Egypt and is also characteristic for Napata and Meroe (See Cats. 72-74, 118, 120, 127). The representation is, however, Meroitic. The girl is quite young, for a grown woman would have been clothed, but the steatopygia common in this region is already visible. The profile and level shoulders are Meroitic. The furrowed neck appears also in representations of men; see Cats. 124 and 125. All in all, this painted funerary stela presents us with an extraordinarily fine work, which gains in significance because so few Meroitic paintings are preserved.

129
Funerary Stela of Lapakhidaye

Second to third century A.D.
MATERIAL: Sandstone.
COLLECTION: *Khartoum, Sudan National Museum 5261.*

DESCRIPTION: A woman standing on a baseline is represented on a tapering round-topped stela. She wears a long, wide skirt that leaves her breasts bare but covers her feet, and holds an emblematic stave in her clenched left hand. Her shoulders are level and her waist slender, with a skin fold indicated. The incised inscription is in Meroitic cursive. Traces of painted decoration are visible at the top of the stela.

COLOR: Gray brown; traces of reddish pigment on skin and black on hair; traces of red and black above head, probably from a winged sun disk.
CONDITION: Complete; roughly trimmed and surface only coarsely dressed; chip broken from left edge and replaced, with small damaged spot.
MEASUREMENTS: Height 46.4 cm. Width 32.3 cm. Thickness 13.2 cm. Height of figure 36.0 cm.
PROVENANCE: Serra West (Aksha); sent to Sudan Antiquities Service in 1947 by Omda of Serra West through District Commissioner of Wadi Halfa.
BIBLIOGRAPHY: Macadam 1950,44-46, pl. XI,2; Arkell 1950b,25; REM 1031.

The inscription, in a late period style, is only partially decipherable. The woman, whose name Macadam reads as Lapakhidaye, belonged to an influential family, for she was related to a prince of Meroe and to other high officials, who are named in the inscription. She was married to a high priest of Amun.

The curving contour of the hair on the forehead appears also on the head from a *ba*-statue from Faras, Cat. 156.

130
Memorial Stela

First to third century A.D.
MATERIAL: Sandstone.
COLLECTION: *Brooklyn (New York), The Brooklyn Museum, Charles Edwin Wilbour Fund 76.8.*

DESCRIPTION: Shown in raised relief on a rectangular stela with a rounded top are two large figures beneath the horizontal sign for "heaven." They wear short skirts, haltered garments, armlets and bracelets, and broad collars. Their short wigs are encircled by ribbons. Their eyes were inlaid. Each holds an *ankh*-sign and a bow and arrows and has a small doglike animal at heel. In front of the man on the right is the small figure of a king wearing the Double Crown and offering two spherical vessels. In front of the man on the left are four deities on separate baselines. At the top is Osiris with an *atef*-crown. Below him is an unidentified deity, and then either Isis or Hathor wearing the Hathor horns seated in front of a god with a *hemhem*-crown.

COLOR: Gray to yellowish.
CONDITION: Slant break running from upper right to left central edge, repaired; chips at top right, repaired; chips at top left edge, right side, and bottom edge; surface chipped and abraded; inlays missing.
MEASUREMENTS: Height 87.2 cm. Width 79.9 cm. Thickness 10.9 cm. Height of large figures 71.5 and 71.3 cm. Height of deities 15.8-24.2 cm.
PROVENANCE: Not known.
BIBLIOGRAPHY: Sotheby Parke Bernet 1975, 394.

The *ankh*-signs they hold indicate that the two principal figures are divine. Since an offering is being made to them by a king, they may represent drowned persons, who often received divine veneration in Egypt.

The material as well as the style point to a Nubian origin for the stela, and Lower Nubia is the only possible provenance. Several works in Nubian sandstone are preserved that show distant stylistic and thematic connections to the present piece, although none has a precise provenance. Among them are a number of stelae in veneration to drowned persons, e.g., Cairo JE 52809 and temp. no. 9/1/21/2 (Rowe 1940, 1ff., pls. II-III), which are worked in raised relief. The individual represented always carries a bunch of flowers in one hand. Unpublished reliefs are in Leiden (F. 1927/1.2; F. 1938/1.1-.3) and in Munich (Gl. 85-86). They show kings sacrificing to gods and must come from temples. On the basis of style, they are attributed to the first to third century A.D. The Brooklyn stela does not correspond thematically either to the stelae of the drowned or to the temple reliefs, although it is made of the same Nubian sandstone. Furthermore, the style of all of these works differs from that of Roman Egypt as well as from that of Meroe. Consequently, they must have originated in a region where various influences were at work, and this can only have been Lower Nubia.

The juxtaposition of small figures, including animals, with large ones occurs on one other relief, acquired before World War I in Cairo and formerly in a German private collection, which probably shows a Meroitic ruler (Wenig 1969b, 18ff.).

131
Naos

Possibly second century A.D.
MATERIAL: Sandstone.
COLLECTION: *Boston (Massachusetts), Museum of Fine Arts 21.3234.*

DESCRIPTION: A dome-shaped structure, with a rectangular opening into an irregular cavity hollowed out in one side, rises from a flat base. On the floor of the cavity is a trapezoidal depression that probably served to hold a small image of a deity. Three registers of raised relief decorate the outside. Above the base is a frieze of papyrus stems with alternately buds and spreading umbels. In the main register, four figures approach the opening from both sides. The king walks in front, on both sides, his hands raised. He wears the pointed royal kilt that was rarely worn in Meroe, with an animal tail hanging from the back of his belt, a diadem with uraei and streamers, earrings, and a necklace (?). Behind him, on the left, is a winged, human-headed goddess with a sun disk on her head, another figure of the king, and a winged, lion-headed goddess. Behind him, on the right, is a winged, lion-headed goddess, another figure of the king, and a winged, human-headed goddess. At the back of the frieze are two cartouches crowned with *shu*-feathers. The top of the structure is decorated with six bands of various patterns: drops, diamonds, and balls.

COLOR: Gray brown.
CONDITION: Finial broken off from top; damaged around opening, inside cavity, and on lower edge of base; badly chipped, abraded, and discolored in places.
MEASUREMENTS: Height 62.8 cm. Diameter ca. 59.2 cm. Height of royal figures 22.6 cm. Height of goddesses 25.5 cm. Height of opening 23.0 cm., width 18.3 cm.
PROVENANCE: Gebel Barkal, Great Temple of Amun (B 503), in debris (Reisner 1916, Object no. S 16-4-543).
BIBLIOGRAPHY: Griffith 1916,221,255; Wainwright 1928, 184; Reisner 1931,83, no. 60; Steindorff et al. 1933,23, fig. 11; Wainwright 1934,147; Steindorff 1938,147ff., pl. VII; P—M VII 1951,222-23; Dunham 1970,34, no. 24, pls. XXXV-XXXVI; Hofmann 1970,187ff.; Wenig 1973a,42ff.; Hofmann 1975b,21; REM 1004.

When this shrine for a divine image was discovered by Reisner in 1916, Griffith (1916,221,255) compared it both to the omphalos shrine of the god Ammon in the Siwa Oasis that had been described by the Classical author Quintus Curtius and to the omphalos of the Oracle of Delphi. Steindorff, who initially (1933,23) went along with this idea, later (1938,147ff.) offered the more plausible interpretation that the object was an imitation of a beehive hut, such as occur, for example, in Punt (reliefs of the Egyptian Queen Hatshepsut) and widely in Meroe; see the representation of a round hut on the bronze vessel, Cat. 196, and another on a relief found by Garstang (1911, pl. XXI,6). This idea is more enlightening: Our shrine might represent a primeval sanctuary of the god that was an imitation of a secular dwelling. Involved here is the idea, found in Egypt as well as in Meroe, that the temple is the abode of the god. This explanation for the unique Meroitic naos is further supported by the fact (pointed out by K.-H. Priese) that in the Nastasen inscription, Cat. 72, the determinative for the word *k3(r)*, "chapel" or "house of gods," as well as, in two instances, for the word "Napata" has the form of a round hut crowned by a uraeus. The pictograph might well be an indication that an important cult place in Napata, of which we know nothing, had the form of a round hut, since otherwise surely the word for "Napata" would not have been determined with such a sign. Our shrine can therefore be considered as an imitation of that cult place. These transcriptions make it quite clear that it is unnecessary to follow Hofmann's (1970,187ff.) idea that the so-called omphalos might be a copy of an Indian shrine, or stupa, and might indicate relations between Meroe and India. (Hofmann [1975b,21] has recently retracted that view.)

The left cartouche has a throne-name, "Neb-maat-ra," which was borne by three Meroitic rulers. The personal name is extremely difficult to read. Macadam (1955,51, no. 2) thought it might be interpreted as Amanikhabale. Steindorff (1938,150) gives Dunham's transliteration as *Mnkhnqerem* or *Mnkhtqerem*. If the doubtful sign is an *r*, and the name *Mnkhrqerem*, then it resembles that of [—] *reqerem* (beginning destroyed), which appears in Meroitic hieroglyphs on a ram found at Soba (Khartoum, museum garden). If the two names are identical, the naos could be dated into the second half of the second century A.D. F. Hintze has informed me that he has already arrived at the same conclusion with regard to this inscription.

132
Copy of a Meroitic Wall Painting

Original probably second to third century A.D.
MATERIAL: Watercolor.
COLLECTION: *Liverpool, University SAOS 8524.*

DESCRIPTION: A naked, thickset youth carries a yoke over his shoulder, from each end of which is slung an elephant. He holds a long, dark object in his left hand. He has curly hair, and his upper eyelashes are indicated by short strokes. A small creature, holding one hand in front of its face, squats on the yoke.

COLOR: Man's skin, elephants' tusks, and squatting creature on yoke red; contours, elephants, man's hair, and top border stripe dark; background ochre.
CONDITION: Drawing indicates damaged places in original.
MEASUREMENTS: Height 93.0 cm. Width 89.0 cm.
PROVENANCE: Meroe (Garstang excavation).
BIBLIOGRAPHY: None.

This watercolor, which to all appearances reproduces a wall painting, was found among the effects of J. Garstang, the first excavator of Meroe. Since he had been working in the royal quarter, this is likely a palace painting. The motif is unknown in Egyptian or Meroitic art. The closest thing to it is a representation of a man carrying an elephant on his back on a stone window grill found at Qasr Ibrim (Plumley 1970a,16, pl. XXIII,4), which reflects the motif of the ram-bearer that was well known in Egypt and Greece. Perhaps the representations from Meroe and Qasr Ibrim render a folk tale. In that case, this would be our first indication that elephant tales, so popular in Africa, were favored as far back as the Meroitic Period.

Illustrated in color, Volume I, page 104.

133
Head of a Goddess with Broad Collar

About 225 B.C. (Gen. 36).
MATERIAL: Bronze, hollow cast.
COLLECTION: *London, British Museum 63585.*

DESCRIPTION: A female head once had eyes and eyebrows inlaid in another material, and on the forehead the inlaid head of a vulture, whose wings are extended over the wig. Around the furrowed neck is a ball-bead necklace and a broad collar with an inscription panel in the center incised with the cartouches of King Arnekhamani. On the shoulder terminals are falcon heads, behind which are attached thick horizontal suspension loops. The ears are represented as pierced.

COLOR: Dark brown; green patination in places.
CONDITION: Inlays missing as well as crown, which fit into a square hole in the head; cracks and blemishes above right eye and above and behind right ear; crack behind left ear reaching to top of head; small round hole in back of head.
MEASUREMENTS: Height 17.8 cm. Width 15.6 cm. Depth 10.0 cm.
PROVENANCE: Kawa, Temple A, Pronaos, two meters above floor in southwest corner, leaning against wall (Griffith 1930-31, Object no. 0020/1).
BIBLIOGRAPHY: Glanville 1932-33,47, pl. 19a; Macadam 1949,90, pl. 38; Arkell 1950a,39-40; P—M VII 1951,183; Macadam 1955,20,38,173, pls. XCI-XCIIa; Plenderleith 1962, pl. 35; Shinnie 1967, pl. 36; Brunner-Traut 1971,24, fig. 8.

The head probably comes from a ceremonial bark on which a divine image was carried in procession, but a stylistic classification is difficult. Macadam (1955,20) thought the head was Ptolemaic. We can be certain, however, only that the piece is not typically Meroitic, although the king's name indicates that it dates to the early Meroitic Period and may have been made in Kush. Macadam's attribution was based on the forms of the hieroglyphs in the name of King Arnekhamani, who was at that time still unknown; nevertheless, his suggested dating to 308-225 B.C. is very close. F. Hintze's excavations at Musawwarat es-Sufra have shown that the Apedemak Temple there was built by the same ruler, who can now be dated to 235-218 B.C.

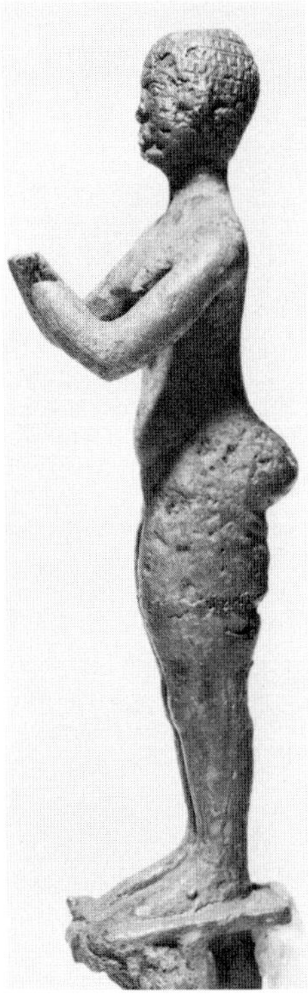

134
Handle in the Form of a Girl

Fifth to third century B.C.
MATERIAL: Bronze, hollow cast.
COLLECTION: *London, British Museum 63597.*

DESCRIPTION: A naked steatopygous girl with schematically rendered hair and small pointed breasts extends her arms in front of her, bent at the elbows. The base on which she stands rests on a semicircular support at the back and an irregular lump of metal at the front, whose concave shape indicates that the piece was fastened to a round metallic object.

COLOR: Dark brown; green patination in places.
CONDITION: Both hands missing; fault in casting at thigh level inadequately patched in ancient times; heavily corroded in places, especially on face.
MEASUREMENTS: Height 16.9 cm. Height of head 2.1 cm. Height of base 4.5 cm., width 3.7 cm., depth 4.0 cm.
PROVENANCE: Kawa, Temple T, Hypostyle Hall, in area of columns 2, 3, 6, and 7 (Griffith 1930-31, Object no. 0702).
BIBLIOGRAPHY: Macadam 1955,148, pl. LXXXIe.

The piece served as the handle of a vessel. That it represents a young girl is suggested by the small pointed breasts, which appear also on the girl standing in front of the circular hut on the Karanog vessel, Cat. 196. Macadam thought the figure might represent a queen or a princess, but it is inconceivable that such personages would be used as handles, or that they would be shown unclothed. An attribution is difficult because of the lack of parallels. The head (especially the hair) seems to be still in the Napatan tradition, but the very naturalistic rendering of the buttocks points to the strong penetration of Meroitic elements.

135
Queen and Prince

First half of second century B.C.
MATERIAL: Basalt.
COLLECTION: *Cairo, Egyptian Museum CG 684.*

DESCRIPTION: Standing to the left of a queen in Meroitic royal costume is a man whose right arm is raised behind her head, the open palm horizontal. The queen wears an ankle-length dress with broad-strapped sandals closed at the heel; a sash is draped over her right shoulder. Her ornaments are a necklace and a cord with three pendant ram's heads. Her left arm is held close to the body, and the right is bent under the breast. Both fists are clenched; the left one is partly drilled and the right is pierced through. She wears a crown base with a diadem and crowned uraeus; two tall feathers with a sun disk and a crowned uraeus rise above her head. Ram's horns curl around her ears.

The prince wears a headband and a long robe that passes over his right shoulder and is tied on the chest, leaving left shoulder and chest bare. His ornaments are a narrow choker, a wide collar, and a narrow ball-bead necklace. His bare feet are slightly splayed. Eyes and eyebrows of both figures were inlaid in another material. They stand on a square base with a tall, round-topped back slab.

COLOR: Dark gray.
CONDITION: Inlays missing as well as objects once held in hands; noses of both figures chipped; surface pitted.
MEASUREMENTS: Height 1.65 m. Width ca. 69.0 cm. Depth ca. 60.0 cm. Height of base 7.0-9.0 cm. Width of base 60.8 cm. Height of queen's head ca. 19.0 cm., of face 11.8 cm. Height of prince's head ca. 18.8 cm., of face 11.3 cm.
PROVENANCE: Meroe, pyramid area (Berghoff 1881).
BIBLIOGRAPHY: Maspero 1907,243 (fig. 225); Bissing 1914, no. 113; Maspero 1921,256 (fig. 492); Maspero 1925,256 (fig. 492); Borchardt 1930,28-29, pl. 125; Scharff 1939,639-40, n. 8; P—M VII 1951,274 (with further older biblio.); Vandier 1961,253, n. 52; Pirenne 1963,443, pl. 109; Wenig 1969a,13ff., fig. 1; Hofmann 1971,59, pl. 12; Wenig 1973a,23 (no. II,2);

Wenig 1975b,424-25, pl. 432; Leclant 1976, 126, fig. 129; Herzog 1977.

Many details of this extremely interesting group are unusual. Inlaid eyes are very rare in Kushite art, but it is, above all, the stylistically divergent treatment of the faces that is surprising. The queen's face is full and roundish, the eyes narrow and the mouth short and straight, with slightly protruding lips. The prince has a pointed face, a wider mouth with more markedly protruding lips, and large eyes—features that remind one of the faces of certain *ba*-statues.

Two similar figures are found in relief in a pyramid chapel of a queen at Meroe (Beg. N. 11); behind the queen stands a prince, recognizable as such by his apparel, who raises his right arm. Because the motif is so similar to this one, and because of the corresponding width of the queen's sash, the owner of that pyramid is certainly to be seen also in this group (Wenig 1969a), and she can be identified, on good grounds, as the sovereign Queen Shanakdakhete (Hintze 1959,35ff.), who reigned in the middle of the second century B.C. (Wenig 1973b,157). Only recently has evidence been produced (Herzog 1977) that the group statue was found near the pyramids of Meroe; it must have come from the North Cemetery, which was the royal necropolis of the period. Because of its size, the statue could hardly have stood in a pyramid chapel. It probably comes from a hitherto unidentified funerary temple, whose existence must be assumed.

Illustrated in color on page 214.

Queen and Prince (Cat. 135).

136 ■
Striding King

Probably late third century B.C.
MATERIAL: Steatite.
COLLECTION: *Khartoum, Sudan National Museum 517.*

DESCRIPTION: A striding male figure wears a knee-length feathered garment under a pleated kilt. On his head is a crown support, slotted across the flat top. Both arms are held at the sides; the point at which the missing right arm was attached can be seen on the belt. The freestanding left arm is preserved as far as the wrist, and a damaged area on the side of the kilt indicates that the hand held an *ankh*-sign. Ornaments consist of a ball-bead necklace, a broad collar, and a pectoral, all worked in bold relief; the armlets are less strongly modeled. The face is longish, smooth, and full-cheeked. The deep-set eyes are small and the nose fleshy, with drilled nostrils. The philtrum is lightly indicated. The mouth is thin but has somewhat thick lips, and the short chin protrudes slightly. Torso and arms are vigorously modeled, and the navel is deeply drilled. A back pillar ending in a truncated pyramid reaches to the nape of the neck and carries a secondary drawing of a male head.

COLOR: Black.
CONDITION: Both legs missing from knees down; right arm broken off at shoulder level; attachment points for arms, hands, and an attribute visible on both sides of body; tip of nose chipped; numerous scratches.
MEASUREMENTS: Height 15.2 cm. Width 5.6 cm. Depth 4.1 cm.
PROVENANCE: Meroe, Temple of Apedemak (Garstang 1909-10).
BIBLIOGRAPHY: Garstang 1911,22, pl. XXII,3; Wenig 1973a,22-23 (no. II,1).

Since the figure is not wearing the divine costume customary in the Meroitic Period, he may be a king, although it is rare for a king to wear an additional garment under his kilt. Furthermore, the *ankh*-sign is usually a divine attribute. It remains unclear, therefore, whether the figure is god or king.

The forceful modeling of the body and the strong plasticity of the ornaments are stylistically striking. Only in the face does one see connections with sculpture in the round of the early Ptolemaic Period; otherwise, the work is purely Meroitic in style, as is clear, among other details, in the straight, cylindrical neck and the markedly level shoulders. An attribution into the late third century B.C. must be understood as a suggestion only; it appears reasonable because this was a period of flourishing artistic activity, whereas only a few works have been preserved from the second century B.C. A later date can hardly be considered, since the two statuettes, Cats. 137 and 138, which most probably belong to the first century B.C., are stylistically quite different.

137 ■
Meroitic Queen

About 70-60 B.C.
MATERIAL: Gold.
COLLECTION: *Khartoum, Sudan National Museum 5457.*

DESCRIPTION: A queen wears the Meroitic ceremonial costume: a long, short-sleeved garment, a broad sash that covers the right shoulder, and a long tasseled ribbon that crosses the right shoulder and falls in front and back to the hem of the robe. The queen's right forearm is raised in front of her breast, while the left arm is extended forward. The clenched hands formerly held objects, now missing. The rich ornaments, partly in relief and partly incised, consist of a wide collar, a cord around the neck with three pendant ram's heads, armlets, and bracelets. Of the crown only two long streamers reaching to the buttocks are preserved. Winged sun disks are incised on the left shoulder of the robe.

CONDITION: Severely damaged due to attempted dismemberment in modern times; head, left leg from shin down, and right foot missing; right shin detached; deep traces of blows on upper left arm, both hands, neck, upper part of body, and legs.
MEASUREMENTS: Height 9.8 cm., including right shin 12.8 cm. Width 5.0 cm. Depth 4.5 cm.
PROVENANCE: Gebel Barkal; found in 1948 in Reisner's excavation debris not far from the Great Temple of Amun by a girl named Amna bint Babikr.
BIBLIOGRAPHY: Shinnie 1959,91f., pls. XX-XXI; Macadam 1966; Shinnie 1967, pls. 29-30; Hofmann 1971,55-56, pl. 10; Wenig 1973a,23-24 (no. II,3).

The statuette is the only preserved Meroitic sculpture in the round in gold. The width of the sash is an important dating criterion; see p. 71. Shinnie (1959,91-92) proposed an attribution to the time of Queen Amanitore, but the width of the sash implies an origin earlier than the period of Amanishakheto and Amanitore (late first century B.C. to early first century A.D.), who are represented with substantially wider sashes. The precious metal suggests that the statuette belonged to the furnishings of a temple.

The curious story of the find—the piece first came to the knowledge of the police and the Sudanese Antiquities Service only after the family of the girl who had found it disagreed on how to share it—suggests that the statuette had already been stolen during Reisner's excavations, hidden, and then rediscovered by chance in 1948. The finder maintained that the figure was already missing head and feet when she came upon it, but the truth of her story is doubtful. In 1966, Macadam published a base for a gold statuette in Oberlin, Ohio, with a cursive inscription naming a ruling queen, Nawidemak, and attempted to prove that it belonged to the present statuette. If that is the case, it refutes the finder's assertion that the piece was incomplete, and it identifies the queen who donated a likeness of herself to a temple. Queen Nawidemak was interred in Pyramid Bar. 6 at Gebel Barkal; she reigned before the middle of the first century B.C. and was one of the Meroitic sovereigns who conducted an active northern policy. Hofmann's (1971,55-56) doubts as to whether this statuette represents a woman, since "the slim physique and missing bosom imply a male figure," can be answered by reference to the queen in the Cairo group statue, Cat. 135, who has similarly slender proportions. In both figures, however, the buttocks are accentuated, which is never true of male figures.

Amanishakheto and Amanitore are the only queens who are represented as very stout. Between Nawidemak and Amanishakheto there was a change in style, which included also the widening of the sash and certain new proportions for the figure.

138 ■
Striding God

First century B.C. or earlier.
MATERIAL: Bronze.
COLLECTION: *Khartoum, Sudan National Museum 2715.*

DESCRIPTION: A striding male figure wears the Double Crown and a royal kilt with a haltered garment; his feet are sandaled. His broad armlets, bracelets, and anklets are incised; a ball-bead necklace and pectoral are modeled partly in bold relief. The right arm extends forward, and the left is at his side, with an *ankh*-sign in the hand. Encircling the crown is a thick hoop above a uraeus frieze. Only one uraeus is at the forehead. Two streamers hanging from the back of the crown widen as they descend to the waist. The long beard is braided and curled at the tip.

COLOR: Dark brown; green patination in places.
CONDITION: Spiral of crown, broken off and replaced with wax in 1953 by Antiquities Service, now missing; surface slightly corroded in places.
MEASUREMENTS: Height 19.9 cm. Width 5.2 cm. Depth 5.9 cm.
PROVENANCE: Kawa, Temple T, Hypostyle Hall (D/E 14) (Griffith 1930-31, Object no. 0607).
BIBLIOGRAPHY: Macadam 1955, 141, pl. LXXVb-c; Hintze 1966, pl. 136 (color); Shinnie 1967, pls. 34-35; Hintze 1968a, pl. 134 (color); Hofmann 1971,47, pl. 5; Wenig 1973a,20-21 (no. I,8); Russmann 1974,71f., app. II, no. 40; Wenig 1974,144-45.

The haltered garment and divine beard are definite indications that a deity is represented (Wenig 1974,137; Russmann 1974,71-72). The *ankh*-sign is another divine attribute (Cat. 136 may be an exception), so that Hofmann's (1971,47) identification of the figure as a likeness of King Taharqo is eliminated for that reason alone as well as being erroneous on stylistic grounds. The statuette must be a Meroitic product, an attribution supported by the facial features and the form of the crown with its encircling hoop.

Hofmann refers to sandals as an attribute of royal likenesses, but gods in Meroitic art also wear them, as, for example, the god Arensnuphis on the south wall of the Temple of Apedemak at Musawwarat es-Sufra. Macadam suggested that the statuette might be a likeness of the god Atum. Although that possibility is not to be excluded, I prefer to assume that the figure represents the god Sebiumeker, who also wears the Double Crown (Wenig 1974,130ff.; Russmann 1974,72). My original view that the piece might be Napatan or Meroitic needs clarification: probably only a date prior to the first century B.C. should be considered. Shinnie (1967,104) had already assumed that the figure could be attributed to that period.
D. Dunham saw it in Khartoum in 1946 and thought the style and details of the garments were Meroitic: he suggested a dating "about the time of Netekaman" (entry on museum card). K.-H. Priese, however, sees stylistic similarities to Cat. 133 and considers the two pieces contemporary (verbal communication).

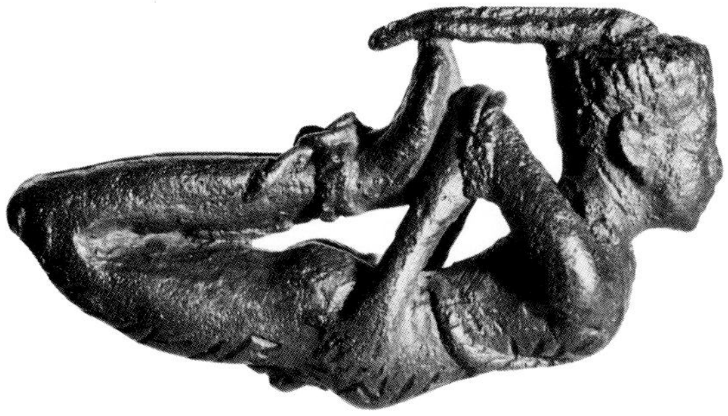

139
Bound Prisoner

Presumably first century B.C. to first century A.D.
MATERIAL: Bronze, solid cast.
COLLECTION: *London, British Museum 65222.*

DESCRIPTION: A naked man is lying on his stomach, his head arched back. His elbows are tied behind his back, and his hands rest on his abdomen. His legs, too, are drawn up and bound, the knot being carefully rendered. A rope slung around his neck is crossed over his chest and runs above his hips to his back. He wears a flat cap with what looks like a feather whose tip rests on his toes. Navel and sexual organs are indicated. On the stomach is an inscription in Meroitic cursive. The remains of a stud are visible on the knees.

COLOR: Dark brown.
CONDITION: Apparently complete; according to an old excavation photograph, there was once a gold chain around the neck.
MEASUREMENTS: Height 4.6 cm. Width 3.0 cm. Length 8.3 cm.
PROVENANCE: Meroe, between Buildings 296 and 292 (Garstang 1911-12); came to British Museum in 1939 from estate of Sir Robert Mond.
BIBLIOGRAPHY: Garstang 1912b,50-51. Garstang Photo M. 476.

It was possible to ascertain the provenance of the figure from an unpublished excavation photograph by J. Garstang, which shows the piece as it was found, heavily corroded and with long chain links around the neck, which were presumably removed during restoration. The figure was found with the bronze parts of a chair or footstool and probably belonged with them. The motif—a prisoner lying on his stomach—is common in Meroitic relief representations; among the wealth of material can be cited the following: three figures cut out of sheet bronze, supposedly decorations for the flagpole of the first pylon of Temple B 500 at Gebel Barkal (B 551, Object no. S 20-3-142a-c: Dunham 1970,59 [fig. 42],60); gray schist relief tablet with three prisoners incised one on top of another, also from Temple B 500 (B 501, Object no. S 20-2-168: Dunham 1970,48, pl. XLVII K); representation in high relief on small hollow bronze socket from Kawa (Object no. 0685, Copenhagen NCG 1702: Macadam 1955, pl. XCVa). The motif is now seen for the first time in sculpture in the round.

The little work is artistically significant in its accuracy of detail; the expression of the face must have been extremely powerful. The inscription on the stomach is to be read as *Qo:qore nobolo*, apparently meaning "Qo, king of the Nubians." If that interpretation is correct, it would provide evidence that Nubians were among the enemies of the Meroitic kingdom. I am indebted to K.-H. Priese for the reading and suggested transliteration.

140
Squatting Bound Prisoner

Presumably first century B.C. to first century A.D.
MATERIAL: Sandstone.
COLLECTION: *Khartoum, Sudan National Museum 24397.*

DESCRIPTION: A man wearing a loincloth squats on his haunches, his head arched back. His elbows are bound behind his back with a double cord whose ends run to his feet, which are also bound. His hands lie at the sides of his chest. There is a deep hole in the chest.

COLOR: Light brown; traces of red pigment on body; eyes outlined in black.
CONDITION: Head and left knee with lower leg broken off and replaced, with damages; head severely abraded; chipped in several places; superficial discoloration in places.
MEASUREMENTS: Height 43.9 cm. Width 20.3 cm. Depth ca. 42.0 cm. Height of head 14.5 cm.
PROVENANCE: Tebo on Island of Argo (Maystre 1965-67).
BIBLIOGRAPHY: Maystre 1973,197, pl. XXXVIIb.

There are a surprising number of prisoner representations in Meroitic art, including a sculpture in the round of very different size (Cat. 139) and reliefs in pyramid chapels and temples, on altar blocks, and on objects of minor art, such as bronze bells. The motif of a prisoner squatting on his haunches, the top of his body arched back, is known from a relief representation on the back of the pylon of the Temple of Apedemak at Naqa (LD V,60b), where a standard of Apedemak with a lion rampant is thrust into the prisoner's chest. Probably, the present figure also had a standard stuck into the hole in the chest. Whether such statues were frequently set up in front of temples is a question that deserves further investigation.

The poor preservation of the head makes it impossible to ascertain whether the statue represented a particular ethnic type.

141
Kneeling Figure with Offering Table

Probably second to third century A.D.
MATERIAL: Bronze.
COLLECTION: *Oxford, Ashmolean Museum 1912.1295.*

DESCRIPTION: A man holding an offering table kneels on a pedestal. He wears a flat-topped cap over his long hair. Winglike forms with upcurving ends extend sideways from his neck, and a tonguelike flange projects from the nape. The details are only lightly modeled.

COLOR: Grayish-black patina with copper-colored spots.
CONDITION: Piece missing from front of pedestal base.
MEASUREMENTS: Height 8.1 cm. Width 6.2 cm. Depth 5.1 cm.
PROVENANCE: Faras, in rubbish near Grave 85 (Griffith 1912, Excavation no. 85/R).
BIBLIOGRAPHY: Griffith 1924,163, pl. LIII,3; Griffith 1925,90.

To judge from the shape of the offering table, the piece must be Meroitic, which one wouldn't expect from the style or from the fact that the figure is winged; an import would seem more likely. Griffith (1924,163) thought the piece might be the leg of a tripod, a plausible interpretation that would explain the tonguelike flange behind the neck. Without dated parallels, one can hardly attempt an accurate attribution. One can only assume an origin in the second or third century A.D. because the Meroitic cemetery of Faras dates to that period; Griffith (1925,90) dated Grave 85 to his Period C (see p. 14). He referred (1924,163) to a similar figure in the British Museum (BM 37642), purchased in Egypt in 1903, 14.2 cm. in height. It represents a king wearing a *nemes*-headdress and also has wings on the back. Thanks are due to T. G. H. James and J. Spencer for information about the piece.

142 ■
Stylized Female Figurine

Third to early fourth century A.D.
MATERIAL: Unfired clay.
COLLECTION: *Khartoum, University 1001.*

DESCRIPTION: Seen in profile, the figure is approximately triangular in form and represents a steatopygous woman. The front of the body is almost flat; nose, breasts, navel, and pubic triangle were made separately and applied, which may also have been the case with the mouth, now missing. There is an incised horizontal line on the forehead. The eyes are represented by punched holes, with a horizontal line above and a curved line below to indicate contours. The nose is crudely formed. The breasts are conical, with punched nipples. Dots are impressed on the abdomen and indicate the pubic hair, which has an incised contour. At each side of the body, near the breasts, are two incised lines with impressed dots between them, and there are more dots on the buttocks.

COLOR: Yellowish brown.
CONDITION: Mouth, made separately, missing; cracked and very soft; surface of buttocks corroded.
MEASUREMENTS: Height 4.9 cm. Width 2.1 cm. Depth 3.7 cm.
PROVENANCE: Meroe, Excavation Area 3, Iron Foundry (Shinnie 1974).
BIBLIOGRAPHY: None.

The figurine, found in the late Meroitic layers of the industrial quarter of Meroe, where the iron-smelting furnaces stood, appears at first sight to belong to an earlier period; on closer examination, however, the piece is stylistically very different from works of the A-group (Cats. 1, 2) and C-group (Cats. 12-18). The female torso, Cat. 143, found in Grave 300 at Karanog, and a small sculpture of a tattooed steatopygous woman from Pyramid Beg. W. 323 (Dunham's Gen. 40-50?: 1963,258-59, fig. 168,9) show that such figures, which had originated more than two thousand years earlier, were still made in the Meroitic Period, a time of flourishing high culture. We can thus conclude that such idols or whatever one likes to call them were made in all periods and by people who had nothing to do with official culture. They indicate not only a continuity of tradition over millennia but also the fact that the Meroitic remains known to us—temples, pyramids, palaces, statues, funerary stelae—are evidence of the upper class only. Very few works of unofficial art, such as this, have been preserved.

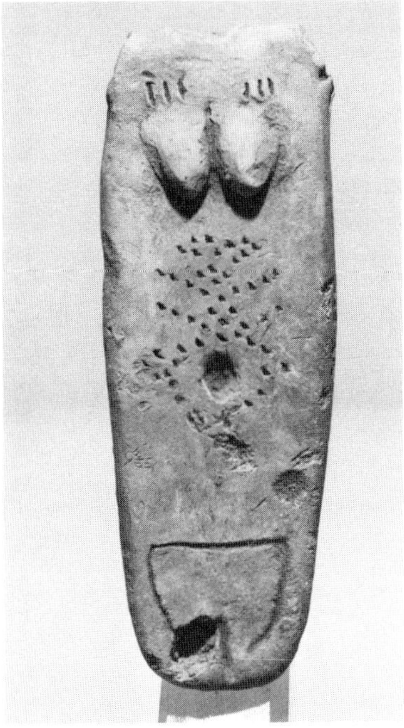

143
Female Torso

First to third century A.D.
MATERIAL: Fired clay.
COLLECTION: *Philadelphia (Pennsylvania), University Museum E 7662.*

DESCRIPTION: Seen from the front, the figure is flat as a board except for the breasts; the bold emphasis of the buttocks is visible in profile only. The breasts are modeled in the round; over each are three vertical incisions. A largish hole represents the navel, which is surrounded by impressed holes. The pubic area has an incised contour. The figure is rounded off below; there are no legs. The division of the buttocks is indicated, and they too are covered with numerous impressed holes.

COLOR: Light brown.
CONDITION: Head missing; arms, which were extended sideways, broken off; holes in front and back; chipped in places.
MEASUREMENTS: Height 12.3 cm. Width 4.5 cm. Depth 2.7 cm.
PROVENANCE: Karanog, Grave 300 (Woolley—Randall-MacIver 1908).
BIBLIOGRAPHY: Woolley—Randall-MacIver 1910,169,247, pl. 96.

Like Cat. 142, this simply made figurine seems at first to date from an earlier period, but the style is basically different from that of the A-group or C-group. The unequivocal context of the find indicates that the work is late Meroitic. On these small sculptures, which belong to unofficial art and are stylistically entirely distinct from official art, see commentary to Cat. 142.

144
Female Torso

Probably first century B.C. to first century A.D.
MATERIAL: Fired clay.
COLLECTION: *Berlin/DDR, Ägyptisches Museum 25951.*

DESCRIPTION: A female torso has emphasized hemispherical breasts and button-like nipples. The rounding of the buttocks indicates that the woman was sitting. The remains of the right arm slant forward. The left arm was held down; the place where it rested on the hip is visible. Thin black lines are discernible on the left arm, the constricted waist, the abdomen, and the back. The shoulder blades are powerfully worked. There is a depression above the collar bone on both shoulders.

COLOR: Light reddish brown.
CONDITION: Head and both arms missing; legs broken off on irregular plane running from beneath middle of abdomen to below buttocks; color abraded.
MEASUREMENTS: Height 4.6 cm. Width 4.4 cm. Depth 2.4 cm.
PROVENANCE: Begrawiya. Formerly in private collection.
BIBLIOGRAPHY: None.

This very fragmentary figure is unparalleled in Meroitic art and is significant for many reasons. There are other representations of naked women (Cat. 161 and Fig. 68), but these come from the Royal Baths of Meroe and show the influence of Alexandrian art.

It is difficult to say who is represented. The emphasis on the breasts implies that the woman is a seated, possibly enthroned, fertility deity, but nothing is known of such deities from Meroe. A glazed relief fragment found at Kawa shows a woman clasping her naked breasts (Oxford 1932,851). Also from Kawa is a statuette with a similar motif (Macadam 1955, pl. LXXXVIIIf), which Ucko 1968,432) says is an attitude of mourning. On the base of a column in front of the Central Temple of the Great

Enclosure of Musawwarat es-Sufra are several deities in bold raised relief, represented in front view, almost fully in the round. Among them is a goddess standing inside a shrine, apparently naked, with hands clasped under the breasts. Whether these few examples can be considered indications of the existence of a mother or fertility deity, which must perhaps be assumed already for the C-group (see commentary to Cat. 12), is very doubtful.

The present piece is unique in its strong naturalism, with the arms being worked freely. It represents the high level of minor art in Meroitic times and suggests an origin during a period of flourishing culture; this implies the first century B.C. as well as the first century A.D.

145
Triple-Protome with Ram and Lions

Late third to second century B.C.
MATERIAL: Sandstone.
COLLECTION: *Berlin/DDR, Ägyptisches Museum 24300 [HU 1]*.

DESCRIPTION: A rectangular plaque with three animal protomes modeled in the round was fashioned from a single block; only the lions' forepaws were made separately and attached. In the center is a ram with curled horns, its muzzle resting on a lotus blossom between the paws. It wears a ring crown with two horizontal corkscrew horns surmounted by two Amun feathers and a decorated sun disk. Two crowned uraei are at the forehead. Flanking the ram are almost identical lions wearing *hemhem*-crowns. The animal at left has a uraeus and the one at right a crescent moon in front of its crown. Anatomical details are highly stylized.

COLOR: Brown to dark brown; traces of white plaster or pigment.
CONDITION: Edges and back only coarsely dressed; right-hand lion's right forepaw broken off and replaced in ancient times; the three other lion forepaws and left-hand lion's crown, found lying in the sand, replaced in modern times; small ancient replacements to ram's muzzle; modern repairs to bridge between muzzle and lotus and to lower left corner of plaque; chipped in places.
MEASUREMENTS: Height 64.3 cm. Width 88.3 cm. Depth 36.6 cm.
PROVENANCE: Musawwarat es-Sufra, Temple of Apedemak, inside, lying front downward at floor level beside an altar (Hintze 1960-61, Excavation no. IIC/24 [no. IIC/28, given in preliminary report, is incorrect]). On indefinite loan from Humboldt University, Berlin/DDR.
BIBLIOGRAPHY: Hintze 1962b,185, pl. LVIIb; Hintze 1962c,451,477 (pl. XIIIb); Hintze 1966, pls. 102-03; Hintze 1968a, pls. 100-101; Hintze 1970, illus. 22; Wenig 1974, 134-35, pl. VIIa; Wenig 1975b,425, pl. 435.

Two such triple-protomes were found in the Temple of Apedemak at Musawwarat es-Sufra (Fig. 41). Similar objects showing a ram between two human-headed gods or goddesses come from the Central Temple of the Great Enclosure. Sculptures of this type fixed over temple portals are not known from Egypt, nor have they been found elsewhere in the Meroitic kingdom. We have here, therefore, a native Meroitic creation unprecedented as an architectural element and possibly restricted to Musawwarat es-Sufra. Hintze (1962b,186; 1962c,451) surmised that the pieces came from a temple in which Amun was worshipped, since the ram sacred to this god appears in the center. One would then have to assume that the two triple-protomes found in the Temple of Apedemak had been brought there from elsewhere, which is not convincing. Amun was the chief deity of the Kingdom of Kush and was certainly displayed in a prominent position in temples other than his own.

Hintze (1962b,185; 1962c,451) thinks the lions are representations of the Egyptian divine couple, Shu (on the left) and Tefnut (on the right), because the crescent moon betokens Tefnut and because both deities appear in Egypt in the form of lions. Lions wearing *hemhem*-crowns, however, are never associated with goddesses. It seems to me that two Meroitic gods are represented here, Sebiumeker (on the left) and Arensnuphis (on the right), for these two deities always appear together. They are usually represented as human-headed (Figs. 40, 42), but their attendant animals are lions, as is shown by the representations on Temple 300 at Musawwarat es-Sufra. The crescent moon might well apply to Arensnuphis; he was related to the Amun of Pnubs, who in his turn was connected with Thoth and thus received a crescent moon as an attribute (cf. Wenig 1974,134f.). Arensnuphis and Sebiumeker were the protective deities of Meroitic temples.

Illustrated in color, Volume I, page 92.

146
Small Seated Lion

Probably first century B.C. to first century A.D.
MATERIAL: Fired clay.
COLLECTION: *Khartoum, Sudan National Museum 62/10/23.*

DESCRIPTION: A lion with pillar-like legs is seated on a flat base, its tail resting on the right flank. It has round eyes, a thick nose, and wide jowls. Around the head is a narrow, collar-like indication of a mane. The chest hair looks as if cut off.

COLOR: Reddish.
CONDITION: Right front corner of base missing; both ears chipped.
MEASUREMENTS: Height 18.0 cm. Width 11.5 cm. Length 17.9 cm.
PROVENANCE: Wad Ban Naqa, Palace, Chamber E (Vercoutter 1959-60).
BIBLIOGRAPHY: Vercoutter 1962,286, figs. 15-16.

The lion figure was found with four others and two falcons, all in fired clay, in a chamber near the columned entrance hall of the palace. It is not certain what purpose such lion figures served. They were not objects of cult observance at the site of the find but had been stored there only. They are extremely stylized and without artistic merit; stylistically, they are completely out of context, although the biblike chest hair is frequently seen in Meroitic lion sculptures, such as those from Basa. An attribution to the middle Meroitic Period is based on the fact that they are later than the triple-protome from Musawwarat es-Sufra, Cat. 145, but earlier than the still more strongly stylized lions of the late Meroitic Period, such as Cat. 147.

147
Couchant Lion

Probably second to early fourth century A.D.
MATERIAL: Sandstone.
COLLECTION: *Berlin/DDR, Ägyptisches Museum 2247.*

DESCRIPTION: A lion with a highly stylized head lies on a flat base that is only large enough to hold it. The attenuated face is dominated by the large nose, which gives an extremely unnatural impression. The cheeks are hollow and the eyes small. Whiskers and mane are schematically rendered. The flanks were only roughly formed.

COLOR: Dark brown.
CONDITION: Forepaws broken off with part of base; nose, right ear, and both sides of base chipped; stucco remains on right ear.
MEASUREMENTS: Height 24.7 cm. Width ca. 23.0 cm. Length 44.9 cm.
PROVENANCE: Meroe (Lepsius 1844).
BIBLIOGRAPHY: Berlin 1899,406; Berlin 1963,34.

The attenuated head is characteristic of late Meroitic lion figures; a comparable piece, of which only the foreparts are preserved, was found in the Polish excavation at Faras (Warsaw 234709: Berlin 1968,119, no. 31, illus.). The precise site of the discovery of the present piece was not recorded by Lepsius; it must have been situated in a temple wall, as the roughly finished flanks indicate. Whether it possessed a purely apotropaic function or projected from a ledge as a dummy water outlet cannot be determined.

148
Lion's Head with Oversized *Hemhem*-Crown

Fourth to third century B.C. (?)
MATERIAL: Bronze, solid cast.
COLLECTION: *Oxford, Ashmolean Museum 1932.830.*

DESCRIPTION: An oversized *hemhem*-crown with a winged sun disk rests on a highly schematized lion's head, which is broken off above the chin. On top of the crown are three sun disks, each decorated with a smaller sun disk between uraei. The lion's whiskers are indicated by small round holes, and the mane is hatched.

COLOR: Brown with areas of green patination.
CONDITION: Pitted by corrosion on both sides; small hole in back of head.
MEASUREMENTS: Height 8.4 cm. Width 5.4 cm. Diameter of head 3.2 cm.
PROVENANCE: Kawa, Temple T, Hypostyle Hall (D/E 14) (Griffith 1930-31, Object no. 0674).
BIBLIOGRAPHY: Macadam 1955,142, pl. LXXVIII,i.

Macadam thought the lion represented "Mandulis or Apedemak" and dated it as late Napatan or perhaps Meroitic. The god Apedemak seems to me more likely. Dating is difficult since there are no comparable pieces, with such an extreme disproportion between head and crown, from either period. The strong schematization of the head might point to an early Meroitic or at best late Napatan period of origin. Lion heads from the Meroitic Period are quite different; see Cats. 145, 147, and Figs. 70, 71.

149
Seated Monkey

Probably second to third century A.D.
MATERIAL: Sandstone.
COLLECTION: *London, British Museum 51740.*

DESCRIPTION: A monkey wearing a ball-bead necklace is seated on a rough, rectangular base, his forepaws clasping his drawn-up knees and his tail resting on the right side of the base. The head is erect, with strongly stylized eyes and jaws. Incised hatchings indicate the fur. The surface is only roughly finished.

COLOR: Dark brown with yellowish-brown spots; traces of red pigment on body and necklace.
CONDITION: Muzzle and left knee with forepaw broken off and replaced, with small gaps; back corners of base missing.
MEASUREMENTS: Height 32.2 cm. Width 11.8 cm. Depth 14.8 cm.
PROVENANCE: Faras, Western Palace, Chamber 34 (Griffith 1912).
BIBLIOGRAPHY: Griffith 1926,29-30, pl. XV,1.

This crudely fashioned monkey was found in a secular building; whether it served as a cult image for some kind of domestic altar cannot be determined. Until recently, the figure was thought to be the only relatively large three-dimensional monkey representation from the Meroitic Period, but during the 1974/75 season P. L. Shinnie found, in Garstang's Temple M 720 in the city of Meroe, an artistically important baboon figure, about 25.0 cm. high (Fig. 72), whose forepaws, now missing, had been stretched forward. Thus, the animal must have played a role in Meroitic religion. In Musawwarat es-Sufra (Temple 300) was found a graffito of a seated monkey holding a writing tablet, which was mistaken for an elephant image (Hofmann 1972). The writing tablet indicates a connection with the monkey of the Egyptian god Thoth, who was worshipped at Meroe. The many small faience monkeys found in the Amun Temple at Meroe suggest that they were also related to the god Amun-Ra, as they were in Egypt. Several monkey figures are preserved from the Napatan Period, e.g., a group of three animals found at Gebel Barkal (Mekhitarian 1961, 134, fig. 40 on 138). Since Dunham (1970) does not mention this piece, it is not known when and by whom it was found; in 1960 it was in the Merowe Museum. Statues of praying apes, donated by Taharqo, were found in Kawa Temple T (Khartoum 2689: Macadam 1955,137, pl. LXX,a-b).

150
Sphinx

Probably second to fourth century A.D.
MATERIAL: Granite.
COLLECTION: *Boston (Massachusetts), Museum of Fine Arts 21.2633.*

DESCRIPTION: A human-headed sphinx lies with extended forepaws on a rectangular base, its tail curled around the left flank. The head is framed by a royal headdress that recedes from a band on the forehead shown by two incised lines. The ribcage and foreleg muscles are indicated. The piece has neither uraeus nor inscription.

COLOR: Gray.
CONDITION: Found broken into four pieces and repaired, with small gaps; left edge of base chipped.
MEASUREMENTS: Height 22.6 cm. Width 12.1 cm. Length 30.8 cm.
PROVENANCE: Gebel Barkal, south of Temple B 502 and north of B 900 (Reisner 1919, Object nos. S 19-12-67a-b, S 19-12-69, S 20-1-98).
BIBLIOGRAPHY: Reisner 1931,83, no. 71; P—M VII 1951,222; Dunham 1970,37, no. 31, pl. XLV.

Iconographically anomalous and stylistically crude, the sphinx cannot be considered among the finest of Meroitic products. The rendering of the leg muscles seems to place it in the Napatan tradition, but the largely misunderstood headdress (which recedes almost directly from the front edge instead of rising, as it ought), the absence of a uraeus, and the odd proportions (the body seems too short) should be considered signs of a very late origin, when the knowledge of many iconographic details had been lost. There are no parallels for the treatment of the protruding, undetailed eyes, which give a very unnatural impression, or for the wide lips.

The position of the tail on the left instead of the customary right flank may indicate that the sphinx was one of two flanking an entrance, as with the two lion figures in front of the Temple of Apedemak at Musawwarat es-Sufra, one of which has its tail over the left flank.

In the absence of stylistically comparable works, the sphinx is difficult to date. Napatan sphinxes (Cats. 77, 86, and the Aspelta sphinx, Khartoum 11777) are too remote, chronologically and stylistically, for comparison. Therefore, an attribution into the late Meroitic Period cannot be more than an assumption, which is based on the statue's stylistic anomalies.

151
Ba-Statue of a Woman

Second to third century A.D.
MATERIAL: Sandstone.
COLLECTION: *Cairo, Egyptian Museum JE 40194.*

DESCRIPTION: On a flat, rectangular pedestal, slipped into a base that is cut only roughly at the sides, stands a woman with long, folded falcon wings on her back. She has full, pendulous breasts with prominent nipples and wide hips covered by a skirt that reaches to her sandaled feet. Her arms are pressed close to her sides, and her right hand holds a fan (?). The hair is indicated as an unarticulated mass bounded by sharp-cut contour lines and echeloned at the temples. The prominent ears have deeply drilled auditory canals. The symmetrical face is distinguished by its strong chin and pointed nose. Three short vertical lines are visible on each cheek, and a curved line crosses the forehead from temple to temple. Finger and toe nails are carefully indicated. A collar is painted around the neck. A socket hole in the top of the head served for the insertion of a sun disk, now missing.

COLOR: Brownish red; traces of reddish brown pigment on body, white on collar.
CONDITION: Head broken off and replaced; minor chips; discolored in places.
MEASUREMENTS: Height 65.8 cm. Height of head 11.6 cm. Height of pedestal 3.6 cm., width 18.5 cm., depth 43.5 cm. Height of base 13.7 cm., width ca. 29.0 cm., depth 44.5 cm.
PROVENANCE: Karanog (Woolley—Randall-MacIver 1908). No tomb number is indicated in excavation publication, but back of base shows no. G 133.
BIBLIOGRAPHY: Woolley—Randall-MacIver 1910,11, pl. 2.

The woman here represented must have had at her disposal workmen who were the equals of those who carved the *ba*-statue of the Viceroy Maloton (Cat. 153), since the faces are very similar. If the statue did come from Tomb 133, it represents a lady named Malitakhide, who was married to Qoqoli, a high priest of Amun at Napata. Qoqoli was closely related to the family of a viceroy, as we are told by an inscription of an offering table in Philadelphia (E 7092: Griffith 1911a,59-60), found in Tomb 133. It is quite conceivable that Malitakhide and Qoqoli were contemporary with Maloton, who may have placed his own workmen at the disposal of his relatives, or perhaps they all commissioned the same sculptor.

The object held in the right hand is not clearly identifiable; it might be a fly swatter, but a kerchief as a badge of rank is not inconceivable. The three vertical strokes on the cheeks are scarifications, which even to this day are found in the same form in the northern Sudan. The line on the forehead might also represent a scarification.

For *ba*-statues, see pp. 88-89.

152
Head from a *Ba*-Statue

First to third century A.D.
MATERIAL: Sandstone.
COLLECTION: *Brooklyn (New York), The Brooklyn Museum, Charles Edwin Wilbour Fund 75.26.*

DESCRIPTION: Lentoid eyes with bulging lids and circular pupils indicated in low relief are set beneath prominent eyebrows in an oval, tapering face with a pointed chin. The mouth is narrow, with slightly pouting lips, and the philtrum is deep. The jutting ears have deeply drilled auditory canals. The hairline is marked by a sharp-cut contour. The sun disk on top of the head is now broken off.

COLOR: Dark grayish brown; traces of reddish brown pigment on skin, black on hair, eyelids, and pupils.
CONDITION: Broken off at base of neck on straight fracture that rises toward back of head; sun disk missing; left eyebrow and upper lid, nose, lower lip, chin, and both ears damaged.
MEASUREMENTS: Height 16.3 cm. Width 12.8 cm. Depth 14.3 cm.
PROVENANCE: Acquired in 1975 from British private collection. No. 1129/2, painted on nape of neck, may have been excavation number.
BIBLIOGRAPHY: None.

As in Cats. 151 and 160, the neck is columnar. The hair is not echeloned at the temples, as in Cats. 151 and 153.

153
Ba-Statue of the Viceroy Maloton

Second to third century A.D.
MATERIAL: Sandstone.
COLLECTION: *Cairo, Egyptian Museum JE 40232.*

DESCRIPTION: A richly adorned man stands on a flat rectangular base, folded falcon wings on his back. His upper arms are held close to the body; the forearms are extended, and the clenched left hand is drilled to hold a staff. He wears a long double coat with a broad apron that extends almost to the sandaled feet and a shorter outer garment draped over the left shoulder and leaving the right shoulder bare. His ornaments consist of armlets, bracelets, and a broad collar of three strands of ball beads with a pendant figurine of Amun, who is shown with a tall feathered crown and splayed feet; the cartouche-shaped links visible on the man's left shoulder probably served as the collar clasp. On the back, a short cape falls in stylized folds from the collar.

The round head, with a symmetrical oval face, rests on a short neck. The eyes protrude, without indications of lids, beneath sharply undercut eyebrows. The nose is pointed, the lips full and drawn slightly upward at the corners. There is a trace of a philtrum. The large ears protrude slightly. A three-band diadem retains the hair, which is echeloned at the temples. A socket hole on top of the head served for attachment of a sun disk.

COLOR: Grayish white; traces of reddish brown pigment on skin, dark purple and yellow brown on collar.
CONDITION: Sun disk and right hand missing; head broken off and replaced; left hand damaged and staff broken; front of base damaged with large piece missing from right corner; face of Amun figurine missing; brownish discolorations and dark spots.
MEASUREMENTS: Height 74.1 cm. Height of head 14.8 cm. Height of base 4.5 cm., width 22.0 cm., depth 56.7 cm.
PROVENANCE: Karanog, Grave 187 (Woolley—Randall-MacIver 1908).

BIBLIOGRAPHY: Woolley—Randall-MacIver 1910,38,47, pls. 1-2; Maspero 1921,256, fig. 493; Griffith 1924,76 top; Maspero 1925,256, fig. 493; P—M VII 1951,73; Dakar—Paris 1966, no. 467; Žabkar 1968, pl. 6; Yoyotte 1966,192 (fig. 7), pl. 193; Wenig 1975b,425,433; Leclant 1976, 128, fig. 135.

Of the staff the man held in his left hand only fragments remain, which were not recorded with the rest of the figure. One may infer from similar statues that a sun disk was originally mounted on the head (Cat. 155).

The work is of high quality and far superior to the general run of *ba*-statues, which are frequently crude and unskilled. From the inscription on the votive tablet (Cairo JE 40234) found in the same grave (Kar. 77: Griffith 1911a,66), we know that the figure represents Maloton, a viceroy of an unidentified place in Lower Nubia called Akin. His tomb yielded unusually valuable objects, particularly bronze receptacles, including a bronze bowl with agricultural scenes (Cat. 196). Cats. 199, 204, and 212 come from the same grave.

154
Head with Scarifications

Second to third century A.D.
MATERIAL: Sandstone.
COLLECTION: *Philadelphia (Pennsylvania), University Museam E 7038.*

DESCRIPTION: The face is a longish oval with plump cheeks. The arched plastic eyebrows springing from the base of the nose serve also to define the upper contours of the bulging eyes and are elongated to cosmetic lines. The philtrum is lightly indicated above a mouth with protruding lips slanting downwards at the sides and a chin with a suggestion of a cleft. Three short vertical strokes are incised on each cheek, and a line curves across the forehead. The ears are carefully but schematically fashioned. The hair is echeloned at the temples and articulated over the forehead by three short vertical incisions. There is a headband and a rectangular hole in the top of the head for a sun disk.

COLOR: Gray brown.
CONDITION: Left eyebrow slightly damaged; minor surface abrasions.
MEASUREMENTS: Height 14.4 cm. Height of face 9.8 cm. Width 10.5 cm. Depth 12.8 cm.
PROVENANCE: Karanog (Woolley—Randall-MacIver 1908).
BIBLIOGRAPHY: Woolley—Randall-MacIver 1910, pl. 9.

The three vertical strokes on each cheek are scarifications and are present also, for example, on the *ba*-statue of a woman, Cat. 151. The line across the forehead, which is present also in Cats. 151, 159, and 160, may also be a scarification.

155
Head with Sun Disk

Second to third century A.D.
MATERIAL: Sandstone.
COLLECTION: *Philadelphia (Pennsylvania), University Museum E 7037.*

DESCRIPTION: The face is sharply tapering with a round chin. The oversized, almond-shaped eyes are highly stylized, with plastic lids. Nostrils are drilled in the long, narrow nose. The philtrum is marked by two incisions, and sharp folds run from the base of the nose to the corners of the wide mouth, whose opening is indicated between a flat upper lip and protruding lower lip. The ears are modeled at the front only, with slanting drilled holes to indicate the auditory canals. The hair is edged by a sharp-cut contour line. On the head is a thick sun disk.

COLOR: Gray brown.
CONDITION: Complete.
MEASUREMENTS: Height 22.4 cm. Height of face 10.4 cm. Width 12.5 cm. Depth 14.5 cm. Diameter of sun disk 10.7 cm., depth 4.6 cm.
PROVENANCE: Karanog (Woolley—Randall-MacIver 1908).
BIBLIOGRAPHY: Woolley—Randall-MacIver 1910, pl. 9.

Only a few of the *ba*-statue heads found at Karanog have eyes contoured with plastic lids, a feature that appears more frequently in the heads from Shablul (Cats. 157, 159). Pointed faces are also found at Karanog, but they are much more common from Shablul. The indication of nasolabial folds is rare in *ba*-heads.

156
Unusual Head of a *Ba*-Statue

First to third century A.D.
MATERIAL: Sandstone.
COLLECTION: *Oxford, Ashmolean Museum 1912.456.*

DESCRIPTION: The face is a longish oval. Beneath the sweeping hairline, the plastic eyebrows arch over plastic-lidded eyes. The nose is broad and fleshy; the nostrils are faintly indicated. The philtrum is emphasized and the mouth protruding, with slightly depressed corners. The ears are prominent. On top of the head is a rectangular hole for a sun disk.

COLOR: Gray brown; on white ground, skin painted reddish brown and hair dark yellow.
CONDITION: Broken along irregular plane from breastbone to nape of neck; back of head and left ear damaged; color badly abraded.
MEASUREMENTS: Height 14.9 cm. Width 10.5 cm. Depth 10.1 cm.
PROVENANCE: Faras, Grave 2502 (Griffith 1912, Excavation no. 1/2502).
BIBLIOGRAPHY: Griffith 1924, 176, pl. LXII, 1; Griffith 1925, 154; Shinnie 1967, pl. 37.

This very unusual head, dated by Griffith to his B-C Period, is one of the most interesting of the series of Lower Nubian *ba*-statues. The fact that the hair is yellow instead of the usual black should not lead us to assume that a foreigner is represented; a light-haired Kushite is meant. A man with light hair is seen on the stela, Cat. 127. It is uncertain whether the head represents a man or a woman; the curving hairline suggests the latter; see Cat. 129, which also has an oval face. The contrasting arcs of the features give this face a particular expression, which is emphasized by the shape of the head.

157
Head of a *Ba*-Statue

Second to third century A.D.
MATERIAL: Sandstone.
COLLECTION: *Philadelphia (Pennsylvania), University Museum E 5035.*

DESCRIPTION: The flat face of this highly stylized head with a very pointed chin is dominated by the huge schematic eyes. The bulging ovoid eyeballs have thick plastic lids and are deep-set under arching orbital ridges and eyebrows that merge into the sides of the large nose. A philtrum is indicated above the small, pouting mouth. The hairline is sharply defined. The large protruding ears are carved in front but only roughly trimmed at the back. On top of the head is a round hole for a sun disk.

COLOR: Gray brown.
CONDITION: Large piece missing from back of head; surface damaged in places.
MEASUREMENTS: Height 13.6 cm. Height of face 12.8 cm. Width 14.9 cm. Depth 12.9 cm.
PROVENANCE: Shablul, near Grave 19 (Randall-MacIver—Woolley 1907).
BIBLIOGRAPHY: Randall-MacIver—Woolley 1909,30.

The form of the eyes, the stark stylization, and the pointed face are found mainly among the *ba*-statues from Shablul, which indicates a local artistic school.

158
Head of a *Ba*-Statue

First to third century A.D.
MATERIAL: Sandstone.
COLLECTION: *Khartoum, Sudan National Museum 759.*

DESCRIPTION: A symmetrical oval face with soft cheeks is dominated by large, almond-shaped eyes set below sharp-cut eyebrows. The eyelids are plastic; the pupils are not indicated. The slightly pouting mouth is highly stylized. The large ears lie close to the head. The hairline is sharply defined and echeloned at the temples. A sharp line running from ear to ear beneath the jaw gives the neck a shaftlike look. On top of the head is a hole for a sun disk.

COLOR: Gray brown.
CONDITION: Broken at base of neck; nose, chin, and edge of neck chipped; small damage in front of left earlobe.
MEASUREMENTS: Height 16.6 cm. Width 11.4 cm. Depth 13.6 cm.
PROVENANCE: Faras, Grave 69 (Griffith 1911, Excavation no. 1/69 R).
BIBLIOGRAPHY: Griffith 1925,89; Mekhitarian 1961,144 (fig. 45).

Further fragments of this *ba*-statue were found by Griffith, but only the feet have been published (Griffith 1924,pl. LXXVII,3). Stylistically, this well-fashioned head is very rare. A comparison with other *ba*-statues in this catalogue emphasizes the stylistic versatility of these sculptures.

159
Head of a *Ba*-Statue

Second to third century A.D.
MATERIAL: Sandstone.
COLLECTION: *Philadelphia (Pennsylvania), University Museum E 5015.*

DESCRIPTION: The head is crudely carved. The pointed face is dominated by oval eyeballs with bulging rims pointed at the outer corners and plastically modeled circular pupils. The orbital ridges are sharply offset from the eye sockets and merge, with the slightly curved eyebrows, into the large nose, which has drilled nostrils. The mouth has a horizontal cleft and a protruding lower lip; the rounded chin juts forward. The large ears are stylized. The hair is echeloned at the temples and sharply contoured. An incised curve runs across the forehead. The base of a sun disk is preserved on the head. A horizontal ridge at the base of the neck may indicate the hem of a garment.

COLOR: Gray brown.
CONDITION: Sun disk broken off; neck damaged on both sides; chipped in places.
MEASUREMENTS: Height 18.4 cm. Height of face 10.4 cm. Width 10.4 cm. Depth 11.5 cm.
PROVENANCE: Shablul, Grave 29 (Randall-MacIver—Woolley 1907).
BIBLIOGRAPHY: Randall-MacIver—Woolley 1909,30,pl.18.

Stylistically, the head is related to another head from Shablul, Cat. 157. On the incised forehead line, which must be regarded as a cicatrice, see Cats. 151, 154, and 160.

160 ■
Reserve Head of a Man

Second to third century A.D.
MATERIAL: Sandstone.
COLLECTION: *Khartoum, Sudan National Museum 13365.*

DESCRIPTION: A head with an oval face rises from a long, cylindrical neck. The eyes lie under sharply receding orbital ridges. Eyebrows and lower lids are marked by incised arched lines. The nose is straight and the mouth somewhat pouting, with a horizontal cleft. The ears are schematic and summarily carved. The hair is indicated by intersecting lines and has a sharp edge, echeloned at the temples. An almost horizontal line is incised on the forehead, and there are traces of a second line beneath it. At the base of the neck (not visible) is a horizontal double line with slanted hatchings.

COLOR: Brown; skin painted red brown; traces of black pigment on hair, white on eyelids, upper forehead line, and base of neck.
CONDITION: Complete.
MEASUREMENTS: Height 26.7 cm. Height of face 15.5 cm. Width 15.2 cm. Depth 18.4 cm.
PROVENANCE: Argin, near the surface between Graves 26 and 27 (Almagro 1963).
BIBLIOGRAPHY: Almagro 1965a,87,pl. 14a-b; Almagro 1965b,62,167, no. 17, pl. 39a-c; Leclant 1976, 128, fig. 138.

Reserve heads did not form part of a statue but were complete in themselves. In Egypt, during Dynasties IV and V, they were placed in the tomb, probably to serve as a substitute for the head in case the mummy should be destroyed. In Lower Nubia, the reserve head was probably set up as a representation of the deceased in the tomb chapel as a substitute for the more customary *ba*-statue.

This head, one of the most unusual Meroitic sculptures, throws a new light on the art of Meroitic Lower Nubia. Its stark stylization and its aesthetic quality render it incomparable to any other sculpture hitherto found in this region; only the cross-hatching of the hair has a parallel, in a head discovered at Gemai (Bates—Dunham 1927, pl. XXXVI,2-3), which is also a reserve head, made separately and not part of a statue, as is shown by the smoothly dressed underside.

Almagro (1965a,87) thinks the incision across the forehead is a diadem. In my opinion, this is out of the question. Still, such forehead lines are found also on a few *ba*-statues (Cats. 151, 154, 159). I suggest that it might be a cicatrice, similar to the three vertical lines on the cheeks that are found on *ba*-heads (Cats. 151, 154) as well as on other types of representation (Cat. 232).

Illustrated in color on page 234.

Reserve Head of a Man (Cat. 160).

161
Venus of Meroe

Second to third century A.D.
MATERIAL: Sandstone and stucco.
COLLECTION: *Munich, Staatliche Sammlung Ägyptischer Kunst ÄS 1334.*

DESCRIPTION: A naked girl, her head turned toward the left, stands with left leg slightly advanced. The left shoulder is higher than the right. The upper arms are held at the sides, and the right hand rests on the abdomen. The eyes are deep-set beneath naturalistic eyebrows. The cheeks are plump and fleshy and the lips protruding, with somewhat depressed corners. The hair, indicated by narrow incisions, is parted in the center, with separate tresses from the brow looped over the ears, and drawn back into a chignon. The breasts are heavy and the thighs powerfully built. The division of the buttocks is indicated; beneath them is a tall rectangular block that served as a support. The shoulder blades are carefully modeled and the curve of the spine suggested.

COLOR: Skin painted red brown.
CONDITION: Head, upper right arm, and right forearm were found broken off and repaired, with restorations; left forearm, right leg from knee and left leg from lower thigh missing; nose and lips abraded; surface damaged in places; color abraded.
MEASUREMENTS: Height 78.9 cm. Height of head 19.8 cm. Width 36.5 cm. Depth ca. 29.0 cm.
PROVENANCE: Meroe, Royal Baths (Garstang 1912-13).
BIBLIOGRAPHY: Garstang 1913b,73ff., pl. IX; P—M VII 1951,241; Munich 1972,135, no. 118; Munich 1976,235, no. 144 (illus.). Garstang Photos M. 114, M. 136, M. 138.

This naked girl, dubbed the Venus of Meroe by the excavator, is perhaps copied from a figure of Aphrodite. The body is softly modeled, but such details as the somewhat raised shoulder, the curved line of the spine, and the powerful thighs indicate that the sculptor was interested in imparting animation to the figure.

Stylistically, the sculpture belongs with a group of statues (Figs. 61,62,67,68) found in the Royal Baths at Meroe; they were erected at the edge of the pool and were intended, like the bathing installation itself, to imitate Roman prototypes. These works were influenced by Alexandrian art. We have no comparable sculptures from other parts of the Meroitic kingdom.

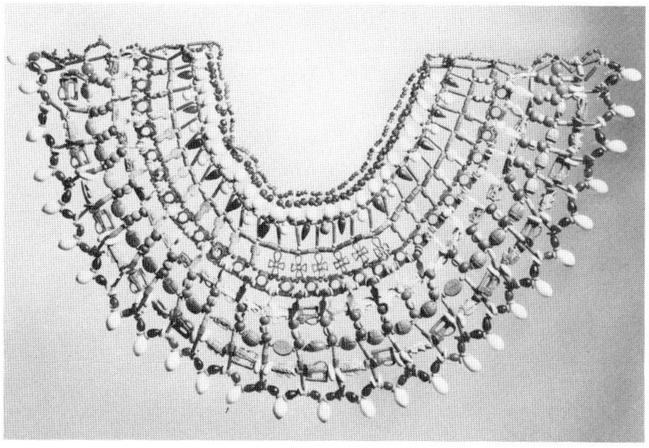

162
Queen's Broad Collar

Late first century B.C. (Gen. 52).
MATERIAL: Semi-precious stones, faience, and glass.
COLLECTION: *Berlin/DDR, Ägyptisches Museum 1755.*

DESCRIPTION: Tubular, discoidal, and circular beads are among the many elements of a broad collar, along with amulets known from Egypt: fish, scarabs, *ankh*-signs, *djed*-pillars, *udjat*-eyes, and uraeus serpents.

COLOR: Stones white, red, green, and dark blue; faience beads and amulets yellow, green, light and dark blue.
CONDITION: Restrung in modern times.
MEASUREMENTS: Length 26.0-65.0 cm. Width ca. 41.0 cm.
PROVENANCE: Meroe, North Cemetery, Pyramid Beg. N. 6. Formerly Ferlini Collection.
BIBLIOGRAPHY: Ferlini 1837,141-45, nos. 129-39; Berlin 1899,407; Ward 1905,155; Schäfer 1910,169ff., no. 284, pl. 34; Breasted—Ranke 1936, pl. 327; Breasted—Ranke 1954, pl. 285.

In 1834, the Italian physician Giuseppe Ferlini, of Bologna, dismantled the pyramid of the Meroitic Queen Amanishakheto and found there, walled up in two hiding places, a cache of objects made of gold, semi-precious stones, and bronze. Among them were many collar elements, which were later reassembled at the Berlin Museum, with the help of relief representations, into two collars (the other is 1757). Although authenticity is impossible, the reconstructed collar gives us a vivid image of these objects of adornment based on Egyptian prototypes. Such broad collars were anchored at the back by a counterpoise, so that the strands would lie flat. Cats. 163-171, 173-175, 181-189 come from the same tomb.

163 ■
Hinged Armlet

Late first century B.C. (Gen. 52).
MATERIAL: Gold with fused-glass inlays.
COLLECTION: *Munich, Staatliche Sammlung Ägyptischer Kunst Ant. 2495b.*

DESCRIPTION: An armlet has two hinged segments decorated with gold wire and fused-glass inlays. A rope-braid border frames the edges. The decoration is in five registers: a frieze of hollow uraei, applied in a single strip; lozenges; frontal deities set in panels (five on each segment), alternating with fields of fish scale pattern; lozenges; and drops.

COLOR: Glass inlays red, light and dark blue.
CONDITION: Twisted out of shape; upper part of one segment crumpled; most of glass inlays missing.
MEASUREMENTS: Height 3.9-4.0 cm. Length (spread open) 24.0 cm.
PROVENANCE: Meroe, North Cemetery, Pyramid Beg. N. 6. Formerly Ferlini Collection, then Berlin 1640. Given to Munich in 1929 by Staatliche Museen zu Berlin in exchange for objects from same find.
BIBLIOGRAPHY: Ferlini 1837, no. 18; LD V,42, no. 1/2; Prisse 1878, pl. 91, no. 32; Berlin 1899,408; Ward 1905,154; Schäfer 1910,104-05, no. 157(b), pls. 1, 21; Munich 1966, no. 72; Munich 1972,141, no. 122; Munich 1976,246, no. 148.

Among the gold ornaments found by Ferlini in the pyramid of Queen Amanishakheto were five pairs of armlets. The counterpart of this one is in West Berlin (1639). It was stolen in April 1945, turned up in England in 1963, and was purchased.

Illustrated in color on page 238.

164
Shield-Ring with Ram's Head and Chapel Facade

Late first century B.C. (Gen. 52).
MATERIAL: Gold with fused-glass inlays and carnelian bead.
COLLECTION: *Munich, Staatliche Sammlung Ägyptischer Kunst Ant. 2446b.*

DESCRIPTION: Hinged to a finger ring is a large shield in the form of a broad collar with a slender ram's head worked in the round. The collar is decorated with gold globules and lozenges surrounded by fused-glass inlay. The horizontal upper edge is a frieze of stylized uraei, applied in a single strip. On the ram's head is a crowned uraeus and a large sun disk with an engraved uraeus frieze; above the crowned uraeus is mounted a carnelian bead. Chains of beads and a necklace with glass inlays are represented beneath the ram's head. Attached to the back of the shield is a rectangular plaque in the form of a richly decorated chapel facade, its entrance almost concealed by the sun disk. On the back of this plaque, level with the ram's head, are five eyelets through which is drawn a gold thread to which the finger ring is fastened. There are seventeen loops behind the lower edge of the collar from which gold shell beads once hung.

COLOR: Glass inlays green and dark blue.
CONDITION: Slightly twisted out of shape; some inlays missing; pendants missing.
MEASUREMENTS: Height 5.5 cm. Width 5.4 cm. Inner ring diameter ca. 1.9 cm.
PROVENANCE: Meroe, North Cemetery, Pyramid Beg. N. 6. Formerly Ferlini Collection.
BIBLIOGRAPHY: Ferlini 1837, no. 30, fig. 7; Hirth 1902, no. 97; Ward 1905,153; Schäfer 1910,117-19, no. 165, pl. 22; Möller 1924, pl. 17; Munich 1966, no. 72 (illus.); Westendorf 1968,232 (color); Kayser 1969, fig. 10; Munich 1972,141, no. 122, pl. 80 lower center; Munich 1976,244, no. 148.

Ferlini found eight shield-rings in Queen Amanishakheto's pyramid (Cats. 166-168, 171); they consist of a finger ring hinged to a plaque, which—with one exception (Cat. 167)—is shaped like a broad collar with an animal or human head worked in the round. Such objects are known only from this find. From the same period (the years around the birth of Christ), we have representations of shield-rings in the temple reliefs of Natakamani (e.g., LD V,62); these, however, are rectangular in shape. The shields in the reliefs are wide enough to cover several fingers. Schäfer (1910,112-13) drew attention to the connections between those representations and the shield-rings of Queen Amanishakheto.

In connection with the pendant from Faras, Cat. 179, the question arose whether the shield-rings were worn on the fingers or were forehead ornaments, such as are still favored by Nubians (Griffith 1925, pl. XXI). But in Cat. 179, the ring is fastened to the top of the pendant, whereas in the shield-rings it is attached behind the plaque, which implies that they were ornaments worn on the fingers. Reference may be made, however, to the relief from the pylon of Queen Amanishakheto's pyramid chapel (Berlin/DDR 2244), in which the forehead ornament has the form of the shield-ring, Cat. 171. Possibly, pieces similar to the pendant, Cat. 179, were worn on the brow. In any case, it is important to note that jewelry of this type is worn even today as it was in Meroitic times.

Chapel facades appear frequently in Meroitic art; they are often represented on the back walls of royal pyramid chapels. The tablet in front of the armlet hinge, Cat. 165, is similarly formed.

E. Kerrn-Lillesø has established that cowrie shells were considered symbols of the vulva and that they are found—either the real thing or an imitation, as on this ring— only on women's ornaments (verbal communication). Similar gold beads in the form of shells are attached to another shield-ring from Queen Amanishakheto's treasure, Cat. 171; Cats. 166 and 167 also had shell beads.

Illustrated in color on page 92.

Hinged Armlet (Cat. 163).

165
Armlet with Rosette Decoration

Late first century B.C. (Gen. 52).
MATERIAL: Gold with fused-glass inlays.
COLLECTION: *Berlin/DDR, Ägyptisches Museum 1644.*

DESCRIPTION: An armlet has two hinged segments decorated with gold wire and fused-glass inlays. A rope-braid border frames the edges. The decoration is in five registers: a frieze of hollow uraei, applied in a single strip; drops; lozenges, alternately inlaid and solid; hollow rosettes, applied in a single strip; two rows of lozenges. Covering the hinge is a plaque with a representation of a chapel facade and a shield in the form of a broad collar with a ram's head. There are sewing holes at the edges.

COLOR: Glass inlays red, light and dark blue.
CONDITION: Slightly twisted out of shape; a few holes; most inlays missing.
MEASUREMENTS: Height 3.2 cm. Length of each segment 9.2 cm.
PROVENANCE: Meroe, North Cemetery, Pyramid Beg. N. 6. Formerly Ferlini Collection.
BIBLIOGRAPHY: Ferlini 1837, no. 21; LD V,42, no. 5/6; Prisse 1878, pl. 91, no. 33; Berlin 1899,408; Schäfer 1908-09, illus. 159 in cols. 271-72; Schäfer 1910,105-07, no. 158(b), pls. 1, 21; Hintze 1966, pl. 132 (color); Hintze 1968a, pl. 130 (color); Wenig 1975b,427, colorpl. LX.

This armlet, too, was found in Queen Amanishakheto's pyramid, with Cats. 163, 169, and 170; see commentary to Cat. 163. Its counterpart (formerly Berlin 1643) was stolen in 1945.

The plaque in the form of a chapel facade that covers the clasp is similar to the one on the shield-ring, Cat. 164. Some of the decoration applied to the lower part of the plaque is apparently missing.

166
Shield-Ring with Lion's Head

Late first century B.C. (Gen. 52).
MATERIAL: Gold with fused-glass inlays.
COLLECTION: *Berlin/DDR, Ägyptisches Museum 22872.*

DESCRIPTION: A finger ring, decorated with a row of gold pellets, is hinged to a semicircular shield in the form of a broad collar ornamented with gold wire and fused-glass inlays; on the shield is a hollow lion's head to which is hinged a *hemhem*-crown. The collar is framed at the top with an applied uraeus strip and around the bottom with gold globules; the decoration consists of rows of lozenges and drops separated by rope-braid strips. Two necklaces, one of gold thread and the other of small gold beads, hang under the lion's head. There are fifteen loops for pendants.

COLOR: Glass inlays blue green.
CONDITION: Partly crushed; most inlays missing; pendants missing.
MEASUREMENTS: Height 4.5 cm. Width 3.7 cm. Inner ring diameter 1.8 cm.
PROVENANCE: Meroe, North Cemetery, Pyramid Beg. N. 6. Formerly Ferlini Collection, then Munich Ant. 704f. Given to Staatliche Museen zu Berlin in 1929 by Staatliche Sammlung Ägyptischer Kunst in exchange for objects from same find.
BIBLIOGRAPHY: Ferlini 1837, no. 24; Schäfer 1910,120-21, no. 167, pl. 23; Scharff 1930,119f., illus. 8 on 120; Breasted—Ranke 1936, pl. 333; Breasted—Ranke 1954, pl. 291; Hintze 1966, pl. 132 (color); Hintze 1968a, pl. 130 (color); Wenig 1975b,427, colorpl. LX.

For shield-rings, and for the shell pendants, see commentary to Cat. 164.

167 ■
Ring with *Udjat*-Eye

Late first century B.C. (Gen. 52).
MATERIAL: Gold with fused-glass inlays.
COLLECTION: *Munich, Staatliche Sammlung Ägyptischer Kunst Ant. 2446d.*

DESCRIPTION: The plaque of a shield-ring is made in two parts connected by loops through which is drawn a gold wire. On the hollow upper part is a sun disk flanked by uraei and bearing an inlaid *udjat*-eye in gold wire. The disk is surmounted by a crowned uraeus and an inlaid *hemhem*-crown. On the lower part, which is framed with strips of rope braid, are six hollow ornaments surrounded by glass inlay. There are loops for shell pendants on the lower edge. The upper portion of the shield is hinged to a finger ring.

COLOR: Glass inlays dark and light blue, black, and white.
CONDITION: Slightly twisted; most inlays missing; pendants and some loops missing.
MEASUREMENTS: Height 5.1 cm. Width 3.0 cm. Inner ring diameter 1.8 cm.
PROVENANCE: Meroe, North Cemetery, Pyramid Beg. N. 6. Formerly Ferlini Collection.
BIBLIOGRAPHY: Ferlini 1837, no. 23; Schäfer 1910,123-24, no. 169, pl. 23; Munich 1966, no. 72 (illus.); Munich 1972,141, no. 122, pl. 80 lower left; Munich 1976,244, no. 148.

The shield-ring is the only one in Queen Amanishakheto's treasure that doesn't have a human or animal head; cf. Cats. 164, 166, 168, 171. Furthermore, the plaque is in two parts. For shield-rings, see the commentary to Cat. 164.

Illustrated in color on page 242.

168
Shield-Ring with Head of the God Sebiumeker

Late first century B.C. (Gen. 52).
MATERIAL: Gold with fused-glass inlays.
COLLECTION: *Munich, Staatliche Sammlung Ägyptischer Kunst Ant. 2446c.*

DESCRIPTION: Hinged to a finger ring is a broad shield surmounted by a man's head worked in the round and two flanking *udjat*-eyes. The shield is ornamented with rope-braid strips and bands of solid lozenges surrounded by fused-glass inlay; a row of gold globules frames the bottom edge. The head wears the Double Crown, which is encircled by a rope-braid strip. There is a uraeus at the brow and a curling beard on the chin; the chin strap is incised. Under the neck are a broad collar and two pectorals suspended from chains of beads made of gold thread and pellets. The *udjat*-eyes are formed of gold wire and inlaid. Ten hollow gold shell beads are suspended from a gold wire drawn through twelve loops around the bottom edge of the shield. The hinge by which the ring is fastened is on the back of the head.

COLOR: Glass inlays dark and light blue, black, and white.
CONDITION: Somewhat twisted; some inlays missing.
MEASUREMENTS: Height 4.7 cm. Width 3.6 cm. Inner ring diameter 1.8 cm.
PROVENANCE: Meroe, North Cemetery, Pyramid Beg. N. 6. Formerly Ferlini Collection.
BIBLIOGRAPHY: Ferlini 1837, no. 28; Hirth 1902, no. 97; Schäfer 1910,119-20, no. 166, pl. 23; Munich 1966, no. 72 (illus.); Munich 1972,141, no. 122 (illus.); Munich 1976, 243-44, no. 148 (color).

The head has been regarded as that of a king, but since it has been proven that there are no representations of bearded kings in Meroitic art (Wenig 1974,137), it must be that of a god, and the Double Crown indicates that it is Sebiumeker, who is frequently represented in Meroe; see Cat. 138, to which, it appears to me, this representation is stylistically related. In the Musawwarat es-Sufra triple-protome (Khartoum 19466) with the heads of Arensnuphis and Sebiumeker (Fig. 42), the heads of both gods appear similarly with shields below.

For the shield-rings found in Queen Amanishakheto's treasure, see commentary to Cat. 164.

169
Armlet with Goddesses

Late first century B.C. (Gen. 52).
MATERIAL: Gold with fused-glass inlays.
COLLECTION: *Munich, Staatliche Sammlung Ägyptischer Kunst Ant. 2495a.*

DESCRIPTION: The armlet consists of two hinged segments. In the center band are four goddesses, their wings made of gold wire with fused-glass inlays, crowned with cow horns and sun disks. Above them is an applied strip of hollow uraei, and below is a band of solid lozenges in an inlaid field. The two pairs of goddesses face each other. Covering the hinge is a winged goddess wearing a Double Crown and standing on a lotus blossom. Holes in the outer corners of the two segments served for sewing.

COLOR: Glass inlays dark blue, green, and red.
CONDITION: Somewhat twisted; small holes in places; some inlays missing; hinge bar modern.
MEASUREMENTS: Width 4.9 cm. Length (spread open) 17.5 cm.
PROVENANCE: Meroe, North Cemetery, Pyramid Beg. N. 6. Formerly Ferlini Collection, then Berlin 1642. Given to Munich in 1929 by Staatliche Museen zu Berlin in exchange for objects from same find.
BIBLIOGRAPHY: Ferlini 1837, no. 20; LD V,42, no. 3/4; Berlin 1899,408; Ward 1905,154; Schäfer 1910,107-08, no. 159(b), pls. 1, 21; Munich 1966, no. 72 (color); Westendorf 1968,232 (color); Munich 1972,141, no. 122 (color); Munich 1976,246, no. 148.

Of the five pairs of armlets found by Ferlini in Queen Amanishakheto's pyramid (see also Cats. 163, 165, 170), three pairs had winged goddesses covering the hinges, as in the present piece and Cat. 170. The Double Crown indicates that the goddess is Mut, the consort of Amun.

Illustrated in color, Volume I, page 92.

Ring with Udjat-*Eye (Cat. 167).*

170
Armlet with Deities

Late first century B.C. (Gen. 52).
MATERIAL: Gold with fused-glass inlays.
COLLECTION: *Munich, Staatliche Sammlung Ägyptischer Kunst Ant. 2455.*

DESCRIPTION: The armlet is made of two hinged segments decorated with gold wire and fused-glass inlays. They are framed with rope braid, thin strips of gold wire, and granulation. At top and bottom are three registers: concentric circles between lozenges. The central band is divided into panels, seven on each segment. In the central panel of each segment is the head of a crowned god, and the heads of crowned goddesses appear on both sides; all are represented in front view and wear shieldlike collars, like those in the shield-rings. These panels are framed with granulation. They alternate with panels filled with a horizontal fishscale pattern. On the hinge is a goddess with four inlaid wings wearing a vulture headdress and a Double Crown and standing on a lotus pad.

COLOR: Glass inlays red, light and dark blue.
CONDITION: Some inlays missing.
MEASUREMENTS: Height 4.6 cm. Length (spread open) 9.0 cm.
PROVENANCE: Meroe, North Cemetery, Pyramid Beg. N. 6. Formerly Ferlini Collection.
BIBLIOGRAPHY: Ferlini 1837, no. 19, fig. 6; Prisse 1878, pl. 91, no. 31; Hirth 1902, no. 63; Ward 1905,153; Schäfer 1910,109-10, no. 160, pl. 21; Möller 1924, pl. 19; Munich 1966, no. 72 (color); Westendorf 1968,232 (color); Munich 1972,141, no. 122 (color); Munich 1976,243, no. 148 (color).

This armlet, too, comes from Queen Amanishakheto's pyramid. The decoration is similar to that of Cat. 163. The goddess figure covering the hinge is like that of Cat. 169; in both cases, it is Mut who is represented. Cat. 165 has a chapel facade over the hinge.

Illustrated in color on page 93.

171
Shield-Ring with Ram's Head Wearing Amun Crown

Late first century B.C. (Gen. 52).
MATERIAL: Gold with fused-glass inlays.
COLLECTION: *Berlin/DDR, Ägyptisches Museum 22870.*

DESCRIPTION: The wide band of the ring is decorated with spirals and was once inlaid. Hinged to it is a semicircular shield in the form of a collar surmounted by a ram's head worked fully in the round. The collar, decorated with applied gold wire and glass inlays, has curving bands of drops, rope braid, lozenges, and granules. Framing the upper edge is an applied strip that probably represents a highly stylized uraeus frieze. The ram's head wears the two-feather crown of Amun and has gold pellets mounted in front of the ears. Below the head are a necklace of gold wire and a chain of gold beads from which hangs a small image of a deity. Six hollow gold shell beads are suspended from a gold wire drawn through ten loops around the bottom of the collar.

COLOR: Glass inlays formerly blue, now faded.
CONDITION: Ring twisted out of shape; three pendant shell beads missing; most inlays missing.
MEASUREMENTS: Height 3.8 cm. Width 3.3 cm. Inner ring diameter ca. 1.9 cm.
PROVENANCE: Meroe, North Cemetery, Pyramid Beg. N. 6. Formerly Ferlini Collection, then Munich Ant. 704a. Given to Staatliche Museen zu Berlin in 1929 by Staatliche Sammlung Ägyptischer Kunst in exchange for objects from same find.
BIBLIOGRAPHY: Ferlini 1837, no. 25; Schäfer 1910,113-15, no. 162, pl. 22; Scharff 1930,119f., illus. 8 on 120; Breasted—Ranke 1936, pl. 333; Breasted—Ranke 1954, pl. 291; Wenig 1975b,427, colorpl. LX.

This shield-ring, too, comes from the gold treasure of Queen Amanishakheto; see Cats. 164, 166-168. Except for Cat. 167, these rings all have heads worked in the round. See commentary to Cat. 164.

172
Armlet with Enthroned Goddess

About 200 B.C.
MATERIAL: Gold with fused-glass inlays.
COLLECTION: *Boston (Massachusetts), Museum of Fine Arts 20.333.*

DESCRIPTION: The armlet consists of three hinged segments decorated with fused-glass inlays and granulation. In the central segment is an enthroned goddess holding in one hand a long staff with *ankh*-signs at top and bottom; the other hand is raised. She is flanked by vertical bands of very flat lozenges. The decoration of the side segments is divided into three registers: diamonds filled with granulation between rows of flat lozenges. On the rounded ends are curving bands of rope braid and uraei. An attachment loop is soldered to each end.

COLOR: Glass inlays green, light and dark blue.
CONDITION: Some inlays missing.
MEASUREMENTS: Height 1.8 cm. Length (spread open) 12.5 cm.
PROVENANCE: Gebel Barkal, Pyramid Bar. 8, in debris of burial chamber (Reisner 1916, Object no. S 16-4-94).
BIBLIOGRAPHY: Reisner 1917b,33, fig. 14; Smith 1942,161,166 (fig. 112); Smith 1946,161,166 (fig. 112); Smith 1952,161-62 (fig. 107); P—M VII 1951,207; Dunham 1957,60 (fig. 32),62, pl. XLII E; Smith 1960,184,187 (fig. 125).

The tomb's owner, who is represented on the walls of the pyramid chapel, was a female member of the royal family, but her name is unknown. After about 270 B.C., the royal cemetery was transferred from Gebel Barkal to Meroe, but a few retainers of the royal house were still buried in the older cemetery; on their connections with the family in Meroe, we know nothing. On the basis of its type, Pyramid Bar. 8 must belong to the period of King Ergamenes II, 218-200 B.C. (Dunham 1957,59ff.; Wenig 1967,9ff.; 1973b,157).

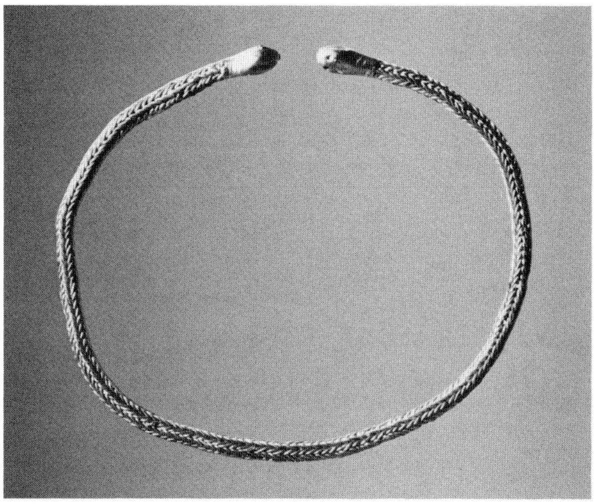

173
Braided Chain

Late first century B.C. (Gen. 52).
MATERIAL: Gold.
COLLECTION: *Berlin/DDR, Ägyptisches Museum 1759.*

DESCRIPTION: Several thin gold wires are braided to form a chain. The hollow terminals are in the form of snake's heads with perforations.

CONDITION: Complete except for clasp device.
MEASUREMENTS: Length 24.4 cm. Diameter 0.3 cm. Length of snake's heads 1.1 cm., diameter 0.5 cm.
PROVENANCE: Meroe, North Cemetery, Pyramid Beg. N. 6. Formerly Ferlini Collection.
BIBLIOGRAPHY: Ferlini 1837, no. 85; LD V,42, no. 42; Berlin 1899,408; Schäfer 1910,168, no. 280, pl. 32; Hintze 1966, pl. 132 (color); Hintze 1968a, pl. 130 (color); Wenig 1975b,427, (colorpl. LX).

A chain from the gold treasure of Queen Amanishakheto is our only evidence for Meroitic workmanship in braided gold wire. It remains uncertain, however, whether this is indeed a Meroitic product or a Greek import. The holes in the terminals were used for the attachment of a clasp.

174
Ornament in the Form of Canine Animal and Uraeus

Late first century B.C. (Gen. 52).
MATERIAL: Gold.
COLLECTION: *Munich, Staatliche Sammlung Ägyptischer Kunst Ant. 2497.*

DESCRIPTION: A tall canine animal stands on a flat rectangular base, a uraeus in front of it. Two thin tubes are attached to the underside of the base.

CONDITION: Complete; left ear bent.
MEASUREMENTS: Height 2.8 cm. Width 0.5 cm. Length 2.3 cm.
PROVENANCE: Meroe, North Cemetery, Pyramid Beg. N. 6. Formerly Ferlini Collection, then Berlin 1659. Given to Munich in 1929 by Staatliche Museen zu Berlin in exchange for objects from same find.
BIBLIOGRAPHY: Ferlini 1837, no. 86, fig. 10; LD V,42, no. 22/23; Berlin 1899,408; Ward 1905,153; Schäfer 1910,153, no. 242(b), pl. 30; Munich 1966, no. 72 (illus.); Munich 1972,142, pl. 79 below; Munich 1976,246, no. 148.

Either threads (Schäfer) or wires (B. V. Bothmer) were drawn through the slender tubes below the base, but it remains difficult to determine how such ornaments from the treasure of Queen Amanishakheto were worn (Berlin former 1658 is a counterpart; former 1657 and 1660 are without uraeus). The animal's proportions are somewhat reminiscent of the Piye reliefs from Gebel Barkal (see p. 56). Schäfer thought the animal was a wolf, and others have called it a jackal, animal of the funerary deity Anubis, but the species remains uncertain. The animal appears in Meroitic art only in ornaments—jackal representations on the walls of pyramid chapels are never so stylized—so no assistance in identification is available from other modes of representation.

Illustrated in color, Volume I, page 91.

175
Bead Pendant

Late first century B.C. (Gen. 52).
MATERIAL: Jasper bead; gold band with fused-glass inlays.
COLLECTION: *Munich, Staatliche Sammlung Ägyptischer Kunst Ant. 2499.*

DESCRIPTION: A flattened jasper bead is banded by a thin gold strip decorated with twisted gold wire and triangular areas of granulation. Attached to the band, in both front and back, are *udjat*-eyes in gold wire with glass inlay.

COLOR: Jasper bead black; glass inlays blue, green, white, and black.
CONDITION: Band slightly flattened in places.
MEASUREMENTS: Height 3.2 cm. Width 3.1 cm. Thickness 2.2 cm. Height of gold band 1.0 cm.
PROVENANCE: Meroe, North Cemetery, Pyramid Beg. N. 6. Formerly Ferlini Collection, then Berlin 1651. Given to Munich in 1929 by Staatliche Museen zu Berlin in exchange for objects from same find.
BIBLIOGRAPHY: Ferlini 1837, no. 2, fig. 4; LD V,42, no. 8/9; Berlin 1899,408; Schäfer 1910,164-65, no. 272(b), figs. 139-40, pl. 32; Munich 1972,143, no. 122, pl. 81 top; Munich 1976,244, no. 148.

This pendant, too, comes from Queen Amanishakheto's pyramid. The gold band around the stone is roughly cut and unframed. An identical piece in Berlin (formerly 1652) was lost in 1945.

Illustrated in color on page 246.

Bead Pendant (Cat. 175).

176
Ornament in the Form of a Canine Animal

Late first century B.C.
MATERIAL: Gold.
COLLECTION: *London, British Museum 68502.*

DESCRIPTION: A slender canine animal, fashioned from two hollow molds, stands on a flat rectangular base. There are four loops on the left side: two on the body and two on the base, near the feet.

CONDITION: Complete; right ear and back of base slightly bent.
MEASUREMENTS: Height 3.1 cm. Width 0.9 cm. Length 2.5 cm. Width of base 0.5 cm.
PROVENANCE: Found near Cyrene, Libya. Bought in 1897 by the Department of Greek and Roman Antiquities and transferred in 1973 to the Department of Egyptian Antiquities.
BIBLIOGRAPHY: Marshall 1911,254-55, no. 2977, pl. LXVIII.

The ornament is very similar to Cat. 174, except that it lacks a uraeus. However, Queen Amanishakheto's treasure also included two of these ornaments without uraei, which are counterparts to this one (formerly Berlin 1657 and 1660: Schäfer 1910,153-54, nos. 243-44, pl. 30). The stylistic resemblance makes it certain that this piece also came from Meroe; how it got to Cyrene remains a question. See the commentary to Cat. 174.

177
Earring in the Form of a Squatting Bird

Third century A.D.
MATERIAL: Gold.
COLLECTION: *Boston (Massachusetts), Museum of Fine Arts 24.549.*

DESCRIPTION: The bird's hollow, bulky figure is made of two gold shells; its plumage is schematically rendered. On top of the body is a cylindrical grooved knob and a loop for the thick ear wire.

CONDITION: Complete.
MEASUREMENTS: Height 3.7 cm. Width 0.7 cm. Length 3.5 cm.
PROVENANCE: Meroe, West Cemetery, Pyramid Beg. W. 179 (Reisner 1922, Object no. S 22-2-607).
BIBLIOGRAPHY: Reisner 1923e,25 (fig.); Dunham 1963,184,187 (fig. 134a, e).

The earring is one of a pair found in an unpillaged tomb that contained numerous objects, including bronze vessels, ivory plaques that had been inlaid into a small casket, different kinds of chains and amulets (many of them gold), rings, and other jewels. The tomb's type dates it to the late Meroitic Period, which is confirmed by other finds.

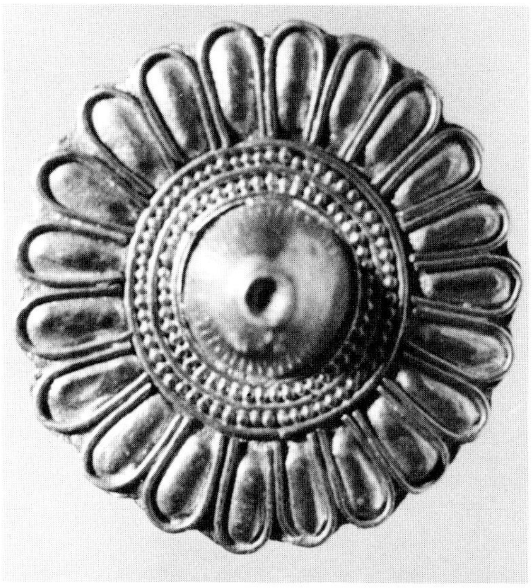

178
Rosette Ear Stud

First to second century A.D.
MATERIAL: Gold.
COLLECTION: *Liverpool, University SAOS 8031.*

DESCRIPTION: The rosette has a hollow projecting cone in the center encircled by two rows of granulation. A long thin hollow tube is soldered inside the cone, at the tip, and projects from the back of the stud. The ornament was secured behind the earlobe by a small disk with a soldered peg that fits into the hollow tube.

CONDITION: Complete; disk of fastener somewhat bent.
MEASUREMENTS: Diameter of rosette 2.2 cm., of tube 0.3 cm., of fastener disk 0.9 cm.
PROVENANCE: Meroe (Garstang 1909-10).
BIBLIOGRAPHY: None.

A similar ear stud (Boston 23.329: Dunham 1963,154-55, fig. 112g) was found in Pyramid Beg. W. 453 of Meroe West Cemetery, which, according to Reisner and Dunham, should be dated in Dunham's Generations 50-60 (?). We must therefore date this ornament, which was probably found in a grave, to the first or second century A.D.

179 ■
Steloform Ornament

Perhaps first century B.C. to first century A.D.
MATERIAL: Gold with fused-glass inlays.
COLLECTION: *Khartoum, Sudan National Museum 762a.*

DESCRIPTION: A steloform pendant with a rounded top and a slightly raised rim is decorated with applied motifs and fused-glass inlays. In the center, flanked by two *udjat*-eyes, is another form borrowed from the Egyptian repertoire of religious symbols. Above, as on stone stelae, is a winged sun disk with two uraei; between the wings is a reversed lotus blossom. Below is a rope-braid band. Five gold shell beads hang from a gold wire drawn through six loops projecting from the bottom edge of the pendant. A hinge with a ring is attached to the top of the back.

COLOR: Glass inlays red and gray black (formerly blue).
CONDITION: Some inlays missing.
MEASUREMENTS: Height of pendant 3.3 cm., width 3.0 cm. Length of shell beads 1.1 cm.
PROVENANCE: Faras, Grave 2782 (Griffith 1912, Excavation no. 1/2782).
BIBLIOGRAPHY: Griffith 1924,166-68, pl. LVIII; Griffith 1925,80-81, pl. XX.

Griffith (1925,80-81) pointed out the similarity between this pendant and several shield-rings from the Ferlini find (Cats. 164, 166-168, 171); the treasure of Queen Amanishakheto did not, however, include steloform rings. Griffith also referred to the triangular gold pendants Nubian women still wear on their foreheads as marriage gifts from their husbands and suggested, correctly, that the custom harked back to Meroitic times, as seen in a relief of Queen Amanishakheto wearing such an ornament (Berlin/DDR 2244). Scharff (1930,121) asked whether shield-rings were worn on the fingers or the forehead; see commentary to Cat. 164. This ornament could have been worn on the forehead since the ring is attached to its top.

Illustrated in color on page 250.

180
Spiral Ring

Probably sixth century B.C.
MATERIAL: Gold.
COLLECTION: *Liverpool, University SAOS 8039.*

DESCRIPTION: A finger ring consists of four and one-half coils of round wire, tapered at the ends.

CONDITION: Complete.
MEASUREMENTS: Height 1.4 cm. Outer diameter 2.5 cm. Inner diameter 2.1 cm. Wire thickness 0.2 cm.
PROVENANCE: Meroe, House 294 (Garstang 1911-12).
BIBLIOGRAPHY: None. Garstang Photo M. 862.

Three spiral finger rings were found by Garstang in a vessel that also contained gold dust and nuggets as well as three gold collar terminals bearing the names of the Napatan rulers Aramatelqo and Malonaqen (Cat. 101). We may therefore attribute the rings to the period of these kings. The second is also in Liverpool (SAOS 8040); the location of the third is not known.

181
Ring with a Queen before Amun

Late first century B.C. (Gen. 52).
MATERIAL: Gold.
COLLECTION: *Berlin/DDR, Ägyptisches Museum 1723.*

DESCRIPTION: The intaglio representation on the bezel of a ring shows a queen standing before the ram-headed god Amun, who is seated on a low throne. Behind her is a goddess wearing a Double Crown who holds an *ankh*-sign in one hand and touches the queen with the other. The queen wears a long robe, an enveloping panther skin, and a tall feathered crown. She holds a scepter ending in a grain stalk (?) and a royal orb.

CONDITION: Complete; minor scratches.
MEASUREMENTS: Bezel 1.6 by 1.7 cm. Inner ring diameter 1.7 cm.
PROVENANCE: Meroe, North Cemetery, Pyramid Beg. N. 6. Formerly Ferlini Collection.
BIBLIOGRAPHY: Ferlini 1837, no. 41; LD V,42, no. 96; Berlin 1899,409; Schäfer 1910,130, no. 173, pl. 24; Wenig 1964,67, pl. IIIc.

Four seal rings from Queen Amanishakheto's pyramid belong to a set on which the legend of the king's divine birth is represented. Here, the queen appears before Amun in the company of the goddess Mut, whose identity we can be sure of because it is always she who accompanies Amun. This is the first scene of the legend; see also Cats. 182-184.

It should be noted that the queen wears a panther skin and is therefore appearing in a priestly role before the god.

Steloform Ornament (Cat. 179).

182
Ring with "Election" Scene

Late first century B.C. (Gen. 52).
MATERIAL: Gold.
COLLECTION: *Berlin/DDR, Ägyptisches Museum 1699.*

DESCRIPTION: The intaglio representation on the bezel of a ring shows a queen raising her arm in supplication before the enthroned Amun. She wears ceremonial dress, a crown with two tall feathers and sun disk, and a uraeus at the forehead. The ram-headed god wears two tall Amun plumes with a sun disk and uraeus. He holds a *was*-scepter topped with an *ankh*-sign in one hand and touches the queen's elbow with the other.

CONDITION: Complete; minor scratches.
MEASUREMENTS: Bezel 2.1 by 1.9 cm. Inner ring diameter 1.8 cm.
PROVENANCE: Meroe, North Cemetery, Pyramid Beg. N. 6. Formerly Ferlini Collection.
BIBLIOGRAPHY: Ferlini 1837, no. 33; LD V,42, no. 97; Berlin 1899,409; Ward 1905,154; Schäfer 1910,130f., no. 174, pl. 24; Wenig 1964,66-67, pl. IIIb; Wenig 1975b,427, colorpl. LX.

This ring, also from Queen Amanishakheto's gold treasure, shows the so-called Election Scene in the legend of the divine birth of the king. It could stand alone, but with Cats. 181, 183, and 184, it is part of a set in which the entire legend is represented. In Cat. 181, the queen appeared before the god. Here, he "elects" her by touching her elbow.

183
Ring with Amun Delivering a Child to the Queen

Late first century B.C. (Gen. 52).
MATERIAL: Gold.
COLLECTION: *Berlin/DDR, Ägyptisches Museum 1711.*

DESCRIPTION: The intaglio representation on the bezel of a ring shows the god Amun giving a child to a queen, who reaches for it. Both god and queen are seated on low thrones, facing each other, the god's leg concealing those of the queen. The god wears the customary feathered crown with sun disk. The queen's headdress is a human-headed scorpion crowned with cow horns and sun disk. All three figures have uraei.

CONDITION: Complete; minor scratches.
MEASUREMENTS: Bezel 1.7 by 2.0 cm. Inner ring diameter 1.7 cm.
PROVENANCE: Meroe, North Cemetery, Pyramid Beg. N. 6. Formerly Ferlini Collection.
BIBLIOGRAPHY: Ferlini 1837, no. 42; LD V,42, no. 99; Berlin 1899,409; Schäfer 1910,131, no. 175, pl. 24; Wenig 1964,58, pl. IIId.

The third scene in the legend of the divine birth of the king is represented on another ring from the treasure of Queen Amanishakheto. The queen has approached Amun (Cat. 181) and been "elected" by him (Cat. 182). Here, he gives her the divine child, heir to the throne, in an indirect representation of procreation. The theme was common in Egyptian art, since the generation of progeny was extremely important and had to be magically assured, but its representation was always veiled. In this case, the meaning is made clear by the handing-over of the child to the queen by Amun, the father. The position of the legs of the two figures is surely not accidental. The child's uraeus indicates that is is the royal heir. The queen's headdress is puzzling; perhaps she is here identified with Selket. The legend is completed on the fourth ring in the set, Cat. 184.

184
Ring with Queen Delivering an Heir to the King

Late first century B.C. (Gen. 52).
MATERIAL: Gold.
COLLECTION: *Berlin/DDR, Ägyptisches Museum 1747.*

DESCRIPTION: The intaglio representation on the bezel of a ring shows a queen presenting the royal heir to the king. The royal couple, both clad in ceremonial robes, are seated on a couch with ornate legs. The queen wears a human-headed crowned scorpion on her head; the king wears only a diadem with two uraei. The child has the customary sidelock.

CONDITION: Complete; minor scratches.
MEASUREMENTS: Bezel 2.2 by 2.5 cm. Inner ring diameter 1.7 cm.
PROVENANCE: Meroe, North Cemetery, Pyramid Beg. N. 6. Formerly Ferlini Collection.
BIBLIOGRAPHY: Ferlini 1837, no. 31; LD V,42, no. 98; Berlin 1899,409; Ward 1905,153; Schäfer 1910,131f., no. 176, pl. 24; Berlin 1963, jacket; Wenig 1964, 58-59, pl. IIIe; Hintze 1966, pls. 132 (color), 133 top; Hintze 1968a, pls. 130 (color), 131 top; Wenig 1975b,427, colorpl. LX.

The scene represented on this ring ends the legend of the divine birth of the king (Cats. 181-183). The heir to the throne, sired by Amun and borne by the queen, is here delivered to the ruling monarch, so that the succession is assured.

The legend of the divine birth of the king was Egyptian in origin. It was represented on temple walls in Egypt from Dynasty XVIII on and continued to play a part in that country, but this set of rings—the latest-known representation of the legend and the only one from Meroitic times—suggests that it had even greater significance in Meroe. It would seem to be associated with the Amun cult, which had been preserved over centuries, so that such scenes were still part of the artistic repertoire.

185
Ring with Enthroned King

First century B.C.
MATERIAL: Gold.
COLLECTION: *Berlin/DDR, Ägyptisches Museum 1696.*

DESCRIPTION: A king, seated on a low throne, is represented in intaglio on the bezel of a ring. He wears ceremonial robes and a diadem with two uraei and a long streamer. He holds in his right hand a royal orb and a long staff with a boxlike terminal that is encircled, just below his hand, by an ornamental ring. In his left hand is another staff.

CONDITION: Complete; minor damages and scratches.
MEASUREMENTS: Bezel 2.0 by 1.7 cm. Inner ring diameter 1.8 cm.
PROVENANCE: Meroe, North Cemetery, Pyramid Beg. N. 6. Formerly Ferlini Collection.
BIBLIOGRAPHY: Ferlini 1837, no. 36; LD V,42, no. 82; Berlin 1899,409; Ward 1905,154; Schäfer 1908-09, cols. 273-74, illus. 160; Schäfer 1910,129f., no. 172, pl. 24; Wenig 1964,58, pl. IIa; Wenig 1975b,427, pl. 438a.

This ring from Queen Amanishakheto's pyramid must be attributed to a time earlier than her own, since the narrow sash the king wears was current before the middle of the first century B.C. This implies that Amanishakheto's treasure consisted of "crown jewels" handed down from various periods. The ornamental ring on the staff is seen on Dynasty XXV representations; it is similar to objects found in the pyramids of Nuri, one of which is Cat. 202. The royal orb might be a pine cone, which frequently played a part in ancient Eastern symbolism.

186
Ring with Zeus-Amun

Late first century B.C. (Gen. 52).
MATERIAL: Gold.
COLLECTION: *Berlin/DDR, Ägyptisches Museum 1700.*

DESCRIPTION: On the bezel of a ring is an intaglio representation of an enthroned god, seen in front view, his feet resting on a recumbent man. The god is bearded and wears a billowing robe draped around his hips. He has an *atef*-crown and ram's horns and holds a long staff in one hand that terminates in a lily; in the other hand is a looped plant stem that ends in an *ankh*-sign.

CONDITION: Complete; slightly scratched.
MEASUREMENTS: Bezel 1.8 by 2.0 cm. Inner ring diameter 1.8 cm.
PROVENANCE: Meroe, North Cemetery, Pyramid Beg. N. 6. Formerly Ferlini Collection.
BIBLIOGRAPHY: Ferlini 1837, no. 34; LD V,42, no. 65; Berlin 1899, 409; Schäfer 1910,134f., no. 184, pl. 25; Wenig 1975b,427, pl. 438b.

The god on this ring from Queen Amanishakheto's pyramid has been identified as Zeus-Amun (Schafer 1910,134f.). Bearded divinities in front view are seen also in the slightly later Apedemak Temple of Natakamani at Naqa. The deity may have arisen in Ptolemaic Egypt from Hellenistic and Egyptian sources, reflecting the symbiosis of the two civilizations. Such deities probably enjoyed a large cult in Meroe as well. The looped plant stem ending in an *ankh*-sign is seen also in the hand of Apedemak (Cat. 121), which proves that the ring originated in Meroe and that the motif was thoroughly assimilated.

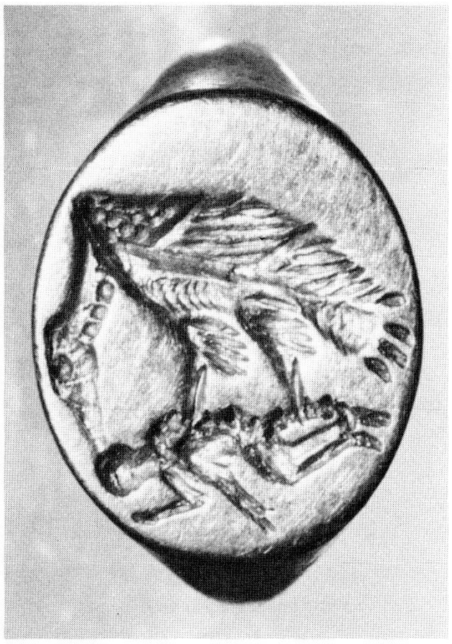

187
Ring with Vulture

Late first century B.C. (Gen. 52).
MATERIAL: Gold.
COLLECTION: *Berlin/DDR, Ägyptisches Museum 1720.*

DESCRIPTION: Represented in intaglio on the bezel of a ring, a huge vulture plucks out the eyes of a man fallen in battle.

CONDITION: Complete; slightly scratched.
MEASUREMENTS: Bezel 1.2 by 1.4 cm. Inner ring diameter 1.5 cm.
PROVENANCE: Meroe, North Cemetery, Pyramid Beg. N. 6. Formerly Ferlini Collection.
BIBLIOGRAPHY: Ferlini 1837, no. 64; LD V,42, no. 69; Berlin 1899,410; Schäfer 1910,145, no. 216, pl. 28; Rühlmann 1965,460, pl. VIc; Hermann 1966,81 (illus. 4),83.

This ring, too, is from Queen Amanishakheto's pyramid. The vulture on the battlefield (Rühlmann 1965,455ff.) is an ancient Eastern symbol of power that was revived in Meroitic art. Representations of bound prisoners (Cats. 139, 140), victory figures (Cat. 125), and battle scenes were very significant in Meroe. The vulture, which—next to the lion—represented royal power, is found in this or similar forms on the walls of temples and especially on bells, usually pouncing on foes or plucking the eyes from slain enemies.

188
Ring with Lion-Headed Bee

Late first century B.C. (Gen. 52).
MATERIAL: Gold.
COLLECTION: *Berlin/DDR, Ägyptisches Museum 1741.*

DESCRIPTION: In intaglio on the bezel of a ring is a bee, represented in the Egyptian style except that it is provided with a lion's head.

CONDITION: Complete; minor scratches.
MEASUREMENTS: Bezel 0.9 by 1.1 cm. Inner ring diameter 1.4 cm.
PROVENANCE: Meroe, North Cemetery, Pyramid Beg. N. 6. Formerly Ferlini Collection.
BIBLIOGRAPHY: Ferlini 1837, no. 71; LD V,42, no. 71; Berlin 1899,409; Schäfer 1910,148, no. 228, pl. 29; Hintze 1966, pl. 132 (color); Hintze 1968a, pl. 130 (color).

This ring, too, comes from Queen Amanishakheto's gold treasure. It is unclear what ideas underlie the representation of a bee with a lion's head. Presumably the Egyptian word for "king," which was written with a bee, was connected with the head of a lion, a royal animal. The symbols were familiar in Egypt at least until the Late Period, but they were often confused in Meroe, possibly because their ancient meanings had been forgotten. The ring's small diameter implies that it was worn by a child.

189
Ring with Woman Nursing a Child

First century B.C.
MATERIAL: Silver.
COLLECTION: *Berlin/DDR, Ägyptisches Museum 1671.*

DESCRIPTION: On the bezel of a ring is an intaglio representation of an enthroned woman suckling a child. She wears a long, close-fitting skirt and a diadem with uraeus. Her ornaments consist of a necklace of globular beads, armlets, bracelets, and anklets. A bird is perched on her head. Around the edge of the bezel is a pattern consisting of rows of large and small circles and a line of curves.

CONDITION: Complete; scratched.
MEASUREMENTS: Bezel 2.2 by 2.5 cm. Inner ring diameter 1.7 cm.
PROVENANCE: Meroe, North Cemetery, Pyramid Beg. N. 6. Formerly Ferlini Collection.
BIBLIOGRAPHY: Ferlini 1837, no. 89; LD V,42, no. 47; Berlin 1899,409; Schäfer 1910,142f., no. 209, pl. 27.

This is the only ring from Queen Amanishakheto's pyramid in which the scene on the bezel is encircled by a decorative pattern. It is generally assumed that Isis is represented with the infant Horus (Schäfer 1910,142f.), but the identification is by no means certain. The figure may be a queen, although nursing women occur very rarely in Egyptian art; it is usually goddesses who are so depicted. The scene might very well be associated with the legend of the divine birth of the king, except that the ring is of a different metal than Cats. 181-184.

190
Offering Basin

Probably first century B.C. to second century A.D.
MATERIAL: Sandstone.
COLLECTION: *Brussels, Musées Royaux d'Art et d'Histoire E. 3981.*

DESCRIPTION: An *ankh*-sign is sunk into the central panel of a basin with a raised edge.

COLOR: Grayish brown.
CONDITION: Complete; edges slightly damaged; discolored in places.
MEASUREMENTS: Height 40.5 cm. Width 33.9 cm. Thickness 14.8 cm.
PROVENANCE: Meroe, Temple of Amun (Garstang 1909-10).
BIBLIOGRAPHY: Garstang 1911, pl. X,4 right. Garstang Photo M. 26.

Several rectangular offering basins have been found at Meroe and elsewhere with *ankh*-signs sunk into the center; Lepsius found a few at Wad Ban Naqa (formerly Berlin 2257). Most are of fired clay and some have spouts, but stone examples are also recorded. Garstang found some at Meroe, but they are unpublished (Berlin/DDR 20617). During the 1974-75 season, P. L. Shinnie recovered, east of the Great Temple of Amun at Meroe, a building (Garstang's M 720) whose ground plan seemed to match that of the Amun Temple at Naqa. An offering basin was sunk into the floor of one of the front chambers. It must accordingly be assumed that these stone offering basins in the form of *ankh*-signs were sunk into the temple floor and served to collect offerings of water.

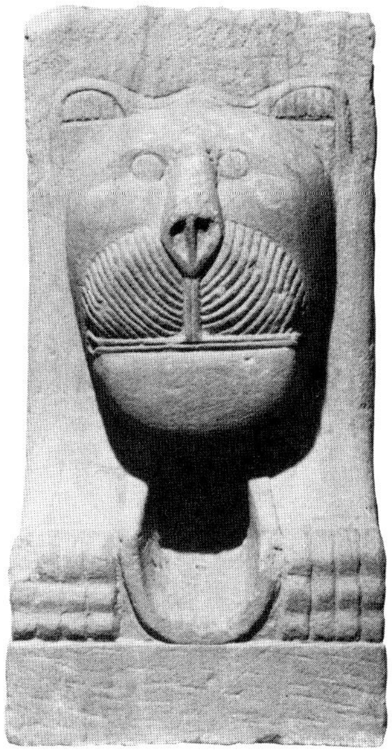

191
Spout for a Wine Press

Beginning of fourth century A.D.
MATERIAL: Sandstone.
COLLECTION: *Khartoum, Sudan National Museum 18101.*

DESCRIPTION: A spout for a basin is made in the form of a highly stylized lion protome. The semicircular spout is between the forepaws. The face is very schematically rendered, with small circular eyes, a long nose, a horizontal mouth, and whiskers indicated by symmetrical close-set upcurving lines.

COLOR: Dark brown.
CONDITION: Complete; right paw and left rim of gutter slightly chipped.
MEASUREMENTS: Height 51.0 cm. Width 26.0 cm. Depth 44.0 cm. Height of head ca. 20.0 cm.
PROVENANCE: Meinarti, Level 18, Detached House (Adams 1964, Excavation no. 6-K-3/1220).
BIBLIOGRAPHY: Adams 1965b,163, pl. XXXIVb; Adams 1966,262, pl. XXXVIIa, c; Hinkel 1966, pl. 102.

In a house standing apart near the Meinarti storehouse was a wine press consisting of three basins made of brick lined with a thick coat of stucco. The lion spout formed the outlet from the topmost basin to a smaller one set lower down with an overflow gutter in its rim. The third basin lay beneath.

Adams (1965b,164) thought the installation was a public bath, possibly intended for ritualistic purposes, but after comparison with eleven similar installations in Lower Nubia between Faras and Ikhmindi, he recognized that it was a wine press and should be dated entirely or chiefly to the later Meroitic Period. The Meroites had imported their wine from Egypt for a long time, and Adams (1966,277-78) thinks that the present winery must have developed when the country was temporarily cut off from Egyptian supplies after the abandonment of the Twelve-Mile Strip (Dodekashoinos) by the Romans in A.D. 297, which made the conveyance of wine from Egypt into the Meroitic territory of Lower Nubia difficult. However, viticulture had been practiced, at least in Upper Nubia, in Dynasty XXV, as evidenced by the resettlement of vintners from Dakhla to Kawa under Taharqo (Stela Kawa VI).

192
Plaque with Leopard

Probably first century A.D.
MATERIAL: Faience, glazed.
COLLECTION: *Khartoum, Sudan National Museum 23159.*

DESCRIPTION: A leopard lies on a fluted plaque that is perforated at both ends. The animal's head is turned backward and the tail is disposed in an ornamental loop.

COLOR: Plaque glazed bluish green; leopard yellow with brown spots.
CONDITION: Found broken into three pieces and repaired; corners of plaque chipped; animal's head and upper right foreleg restored.
MEASUREMENTS: Length 16.5 cm. Width 8.8 cm. Height ca. 6.5 cm. Height of plaque 1.2 cm.
PROVENANCE: Kumbur, north of Akasha (Maystre 1970-71, Excavation no. 21.N.15/98).
BIBLIOGRAPHY: Maystre 1975,91, fig. 35.

The object was probably the lid of a casket. In one hole was a pivot by which the lid could be swung sideways, and there was probably a knob in the other hole. Since no similar objects have been found, dating depends entirely on the basis of the high quality of the workmanship; the first century A.D. is considered to be the artistic prime of Meroe. Meroitic art is rich in animal representations, and this leopard is extremely naturalistic, although the motif of an animal looking backward is ancient. Comparable is a faience plaque in very fragmentary condition, showing a lion, however, instead of a leopard. It was a votive offering found in the Temple of Apedemak at Musawwarat es-Sufra (Hintze 1962a,451, pl. XIb center; 1962b,185, pl. 55b center).

Illustrated in color on page 258.

193
Ram's-Head Inlay

Sixth to third century B.C.
MATERIAL: Bronze.
COLLECTION: *Oxford, Ashmolean Museum 1932.831.*

DESCRIPTION: A ram's head with powerful, carefully incised horns wears a large sun disk decorated with a uraeus frieze. In front of the disk are three crowned uraei, the center one wearing the Amun plumes and the outer ones wearing the crowns of Upper and Lower Egypt. The back of the amulet is flat.

COLOR: Gray green with rusty red discolorations.
CONDITION: Complete.
MEASUREMENTS: Height 9.3 cm. Width 6.1 cm. Thickness 2.1 cm.
PROVENANCE: Kawa, Temple T, Hypostyle Hall (D/E 14) (Griffith 1930-31, Object no. 0633).
BIBLIOGRAPHY: Macadam 1955,176, pl. XCIIIe.

The ram's head, which doubtless served as an inlay, presents us with one of the rare Kushite examples of a triple uraeus; it appears also on faience inlays found in the temples at Gebel Barkal. In Kushite art, the double uraeus represents the union of Egypt and Kush under a single monarch. The addition of the third uraeus, wearing the Amun crown, may attest to the god's domination over the kingdom, which may be inferred from an episode recorded by Diodorus (*Bibliotheca Historica* 3.6), who tells us that Ergamenes (I) had ended the rule of the priests in a coup d'état.

The inlay might well be Napatan or early Meroitic; no precise dating is possible until comparable objects from controlled excavations are published. The Gebel Barkal finds are stylistically not comparable. However, reference may be made to the ram's-head earring, Cat. 98, which must be dated to the late sixth century B.C. and shows a remote stylistic connection to the present piece.

194
Lion Protome

Probably first century B.C.
MATERIAL: Sandstone.
COLLECTION: *Liverpool, Merseyside County Museums 47.48.212.*

DESCRIPTION: A lion's head and forepaws are carved on a small curving plaque with rounded corners. There are perforations at both ends and a square hole between the forepaws, which rest on a small base.

COLOR: Corroded to brown.
CONDITION: Lion's left forepaw missing; lion's head, top edge and both ends of plaque damaged.
MEASUREMENTS: Height 3.0 cm. Width 8.0 cm. Thickness ca. 5.0 cm.
PROVENANCE: Meroe, Temple of Apedemak (Garstang 1909-10).
BIBLIOGRAPHY: Garstang 1911,22, pl. XXII,2 left.

Garstang described the piece as a "lion emblem." Since the edges of the plaque are smoothly finished, it cannot be regarded as a fragment. The curve of the plaque indicates that the piece was mounted onto a round basin with pins drawn through the circular perforations. Because the piece is drilled through, it must have been a spout. We can say nothing about the basin to which it belonged, since there are no parallels from Meroe or Egypt. A dating into the first century B.C. is suggested on the basis of the stylization of the lion's head. The piece is certainly later than the triple-protome from Musawwarat es-Sufra (Cat. 145) but earlier than the wall inlay from the Royal Baths at Meroe (Cat. 214). There are some stylistic connections to the top part of a lion-headed statuette of Apedemak in the Louvre (E. 11157b) inscribed for King Tanyidamani.

Plaque with Leopard (Cat. 192).

195
Model of a Sundial

Probably first century B.C. to second century A.D.
MATERIAL: Wood.
COLLECTION: *Liverpool, University SAOS 8501.*

DESCRIPTION: The top of a sundial is in the form of a temple facade with two pylons, whose side walls are also developed in relief. Above the portal is a sun disk flanked by two uraei. The dial consists of a semicircle divided into eleven sectors by twelve radiating inlaid strips of a different wood. A rod is inserted into a hole at the point from which the dividers radiate.

COLOR: Dark brown.
CONDITION: Front slightly damaged and splintered; modern damage to top right corner; numerous wormholes and some cracks in the back; original rod missing.
MEASUREMENTS: Height 9.8 cm. Width 7.9 cm. Thickness 2.1 cm.
PROVENANCE: Meroe, Temple of Apedemak (Garstang 1909-10). Formerly J. Smith Collection, Liverpool (no. 6242/131).
BIBLIOGRAPHY: Garstang 1911,22, pl. XXII,1.

Chronometry was known in Meroe as it was in Egypt, where several methods for measuring time existed. The Meroe sundial uses the system whereby the shadow of a rod standing at the point from which lines radiate over a flat surface indicates the hour. The oldest example of this type of portable sundial comes from the time of King Merneptah (about 1200 B.C.). Others from the Ptolemaic Period (formerly Berlin 20322 and Petrie 1886, pl. 18,5-6) have twelve sectors. Since the present piece has only eleven, it must be regarded as a model. It is impossible to say what its function was, whether it was a temple votive offering, or why the top is in the form of a temple facade. Stationary sundials from the Roman Period are known from Kertassi and Debod in Lower Nubia. A genuine Meroitic sundial was found in fragments at Basa (now Khartoum: Crowfoot 1911,17, pl. X); in this example, hour lines are cut on a conoidal surface in the upper part of a block. Sundials based on this principle were well known in Egypt during the Ptolemaic Period.

J. Smith, one of Garstang's patrons, was presented with some of his finds from Meroe. They were given to Liverpool University in 1928.

196
Bowl with Agricultural Scenes

Second to third century A.D.
MATERIAL: Bronze.
COLLECTION: *Cairo, Egyptian Museum JE 41017.*

DESCRIPTION: The surface of a large, high-walled bronze bowl is incised with agricultural scenes. A naked girl stands in front of a circular straw hut with a disk-shaped object on the roof and trees around it. In front of her, a kneeling woman, holding a fan (?) in her right hand, reaches with her left for a milk pail held out to her by a bearded man who wears an apron and has a rope slung over his right elbow. The woman wears a skirt and has armlets, bracelets, earrings, and a necklace. She has a topknot and a fancy ribbon around her hair. Near her, behind five large bowls on the ground, stands another woman, who points with her left hand. She wears a skirt and a ribbon in her hair, which is similarly arranged. Behind the man are five pairs of cattle with artificially twisted horns; near the second pair, a man milks a hobbled cow wearing a bell on a fancy ribbon around its neck, which turns its head toward him. Behind the fourth pair of cattle, both steers, a naked man walks with a milk pail under his arm. Several cows face the hut, next to which are calves tethered to a tree. The figures stand on an incised baseline, and above them is a band of braided pattern.

COLOR: Dark reddish brown.
CONDITION: Somewhat bent; bottom damaged; several black spots and purplish discolorations on lower exterior surface.
MEASUREMENTS: Height 17.5 cm. Width 26.6 cm. Inner diameter 24.4-25.8 cm.
PROVENANCE: Karanog, Grave 187 (Woolley—Randall-MacIver 1908).
BIBLIOGRAPHY: Woolley—Randall-MacIver 1910, 59, pls. 26-27; Bissing 1939a, cols. 570-71 (illus. 1); Smith 1965b, pl. 371; Dakar—Paris 1966, no. 466; Yoyotte 1966, 190, illus. 5-6; Shinnie 1967, 18-19 (fig. 3).

The tomb of Viceroy Maloton, of whom a very good *ba*-statue is preserved (Cat. 153), was particularly well furnished with artistically noteworthy objects. Among them were a bronze bowl with cattle representations (Philadelphia E 7155) and many other attractive bronze vessels, including this bowl whose unique decoration supplies us with an abundance of information about agricultural life. Cattle breeding played a significant role in the Meroitic kingdom, as is witnessed by many representations of cattle on the walls of temple and pyramid chapels. The circular hut, which appears also in the Napatan Period (relief from Meroe and hieroglyphs on King Nastasen's stela, Cat. 72), was the usual type of dwelling; stone and brick buildings were rare and were reserved for the upper class. The naos, Cat. 131, found in the Great Temple of Amun (B 500) at Gebel Barkal, also has the form of a round hut, which is still customary in large parts of Africa; see the commentary on that object.

Her opulent jewelry indicates that the seated woman must be a lady of the upper class. The custom of artificially twisting the horns of cattle was already in vogue in Egypt during the New Kingdom and is evidenced in Nubian rock drawings belonging probably to the C-group period.

197
Three-Footed Bowl

Late third to early fourth century A.D.
MATERIAL: Bronze.
COLLECTION: *Philadelphia (Pennsylvania), University Museum E 7145.*

DESCRIPTION: A basin-like vessel, approximately cylindrical in shape, has a straight-walled neck and a broad, flat lip. A tendril pattern is engraved on the body, and a zigzag line encircles the shoulder. Around the neck is a row of dots. Notches are incised into the edge of the lip. The three feet are bent slightly inward.

COLOR: Dark brown.
CONDITION: Complete; discolored in places.
MEASUREMENTS: Height 4.1 cm. Maximum diameter 5.4 cm.
PROVENANCE: Karanog, Grave 293 (Woolley—Randall-MacIver 1908).
BIBLIOGRAPHY: Woolley—Randall-MacIver 1910,62,166, 243, pl. 31; Bissing [1939-41],28; Bissing 1941,12, n. 17.

Bronze vessels of this type with very short, thin legs have been found occasionally in Lower Nubia: e.g., Grave 45 at Karanog (Philadelphia E 7137), from which also comes Cat. 203; Grave 2454 at Faras (Griffith 1924, pl. 32); and Grave E 99 at Gemai (Bates—Dunham 1927, pl. 32,5). However, such vessels appeared not only in Meroitic graves but also in those of the Ballana culture: e.g., Grave 37 at Ballana (Emery—Kirwan 1938, pl. 74, which certainly belongs in the fourth century A.D.); Graves 47 and 121 at the same site (ibid. pl. 74); Grave 12 at Ferka (Kirwan 1935, pl. XVIII,1; Bissing 1941,13, illus. 5), from which Cat. 277 also comes. We should not assume that their dissemination extended over a long period of time; Bissing (1941,12) rightly regards them as one of the most important links between the older finds from Karanog and Faras and those of the Ballana culture; he suggests the late fourth century A.D. for the dating of the pieces from Ferka and Ballana. The Meroitic vessels of this type can come only from the late phase of the Kingdom of Kush, namely, the late third to early fourth century. Bissing (1941,12, n. 17) points in this connection to Grave 2454 at Faras, initially dated by Griffith (1924,154) to his Period B, which was much too early for these metal vessels. Later, Griffith (1925,152) attributed this grave to his Period C, that is, into the last phase of the Meroitic empire.

How far these vessels from Ballana, which are decorated with what Bissing ([1939-41],28) calls typical Greek tendrils and other motifs and represent, he says, a special Alexandrine form, are actually connected with similar ceramic forms (ibid. 28; 1939a, col. 570; 1941,12) needs further investigation.

Cat. 205 comes from the same grave.

198
Bowl with Garlands and Rosettes

Late third century A.D.
MATERIAL: Bronze.
COLLECTION: *Philadelphia (Pennsylvania), University Museum E 7129.*

DESCRIPTION: A straight-walled bowl with a ring base was decorated with a sharp-edged graver. Below the rim, three ridges and two rows of incised motifs encircle the vessel. On the body are double garlands with rosettes and suspended plant (?) ornaments. The same pattern is repeated around the bottom of the vessel. Two bands of decorative motifs run round the base.

COLOR: Reddish.
CONDITION: Complete.
MEASUREMENTS: Height 6.2 cm. Diameter 9.6 cm.
PROVENANCE: Karanog, Grave 331 (Woolley—Randall-MacIver 1908).
BIBLIOGRAPHY: Woolley—Randall-MacIver 1910, 62,174,242, pl. 31.

Two quite similar bowls with garland decoration were found in the grave; the other (Philadelphia E 7131) has a flat bottom. A similarly decorated bowl (Cairo JE 40226) comes from Grave 271. The design was hammered into the bronze with a triangular-section burin that left sharp edges, which reinforce the effect of the design.

199
Large Pitcher

Second to third century A.D.
MATERIAL: Bronze.
COLLECTION: *Philadelphia (Pennsylvania), University Museum E 7512.*

DESCRIPTION: An ovoid pitcher has a trefoil mouth, a wide neck, a short cylindrical stem, and a flaring foot. A handle attached to the lip and curving to the shoulder has, at the top, the form of a head that looks over the mouth of the vessel and arms that are outstretched on the lip. Below, on the flat surface of the handle, are an ornamental motif, a profile head in raised relief, and another ornamental motif. The base of the handle is concealed by an attached frontal face in high relief surrounded by wavy locks. The eyes are sunk, but there are no traces of inlay.

COLOR: Dark to light brown.
CONDITION: Complete; discolored in places as a result of modern treatment.
MEASUREMENTS: Height 15.3 cm. Diameter 9.1 cm., at foot 4.6 cm. Height of topmost head 1.1 cm., of frontal face 2.1 cm.
PROVENANCE: Karanog, Grave 187 (Woolley—Randall-MacIver 1908).
BIBLIOGRAPHY: Woolley—Randall-MacIver 1910, 61,146,245, pl. 29.

In the tomb of Viceroy Maloton, which also yielded Cats. 153, 196, 204, and 212, were found two identical pitchers that the excavators (1910,61) considered to be Alexandrian imports. The form is definitely late antique, which could indicate a place of manufacture outside Nubia. But there is frequent evidence of Meroitic imitation of late antique objects and motifs (Cat. 200), which might be the case with this pitcher. Furthermore, bronze working was for a long time on a substantial footing in Nubia and still more so in southern Meroe.

200
Hanging Lamp

Middle of second century A.D. (Gen. 63).
MATERIAL: Bronze and iron.
COLLECTION: *Boston (Massachusetts), Museum of Fine Arts 24.959.*

DESCRIPTION: The lamp has an almost spherical body and a snoutlike nozzle curving upward to a wide oil hole. The circular burner has a hinged lid with a rosette decoration and a knob in the center. The lamp was suspended by an iron shaft that terminates in a capital and a hook shaped like a griffin's head. The ring handle was shielded from the heat by an acanthus-leaf flame guard. The lamp is connected by a cylindrical rod to a base in the form of an inverted bell. A Meroitic emblem in relief is affixed to the body beneath the oil hole, and on the back of the acanthus leaf is an inscription in Meroitic cursive.

COLOR: Dark brown with areas of corrosion.
CONDITION: Iron rod replaced in modern times.
MEASUREMENTS: Height 57.5 cm. Height of lamp 18.7 cm. Width 12.5 cm. Length 39.7 cm.
PROVENANCE: Meroe, North Cemetery, Pyramid Beg. N. 29 (Reisner 1921, Object no. S 21-3-160).
BIBLIOGRAPHY: Dunham 1957,168 (fig. 109),170, pls. XXXV E, LI B-D; Dunham 1958,132,fig. 103; Dunham 1965, 135 (Group IV, no. 30),139, no. 30; Shinnie 1967,128, fig. 49, pl. 69; Török 1972,35-36.

Two parallels have been found to this lamp from King Takideamani's pyramid: one in Pyramid Beg. W. 122 from Meroe West Cemetery (Boston 24.966), the second by Garstang in the city of Meroe (Garstang 1914b, pl. V,2; Dunham 1957,170). The style of the lamp, especially the acanthus leaf, clearly reveals the influence of late antiquity, but the Meroitic emblem and inscription indicate that this lamp at least—and consequently other similar objects as well—was made in Meroe. The emblem frequently appears in Meroe and has a history there of several centuries. Dunham (1965,131ff.) emphasizes that it cannot be a manufacturer's or an owner's mark. His suggestion that it is the mark of a particular royal workshop is extremely plausible. Török (1972,35ff.), who has also given detailed attention to these emblems, thinks they are owner's marks. In the case of the king, of course, they would be objects from the treasury stock, pieces that were passed on either to his successors or to other individuals. This is conceivable, but Dunham's interpretation is preferable.

201
Lid of a Mirror Case

First century B.C.
MATERIAL: Bronze.
COLLECTION: *Oxford, Ashmolean Museum 1912.460.*

DESCRIPTION: The round lid of a mirror case has a small handle to which is attached a suspension loop. On the outside of the lid is the appliquéd profile bust of a woman, in high relief, her braided hair gathered into a chignon and a thin chain around her neck. The pupil of the eye was inlaid. Two grooves are engraved around the edge. On the inside of the lid, which has a raised rim, is a naked child seated on a lotus blossom and surrounded by lotus leaves. One finger of his left hand touches his mouth, and in his right hand he carries an *ankh*-sign. His figure is encircled by a narrow band with a spiral pattern enclosed in pairs of grooves and a frieze of animals framed by grooves.

COLOR: Outside brown with areas of green patination and discoloration; inside brown.
CONDITION: Complete; inside cleaned in modern times.
MEASUREMENTS: Diameter 19.4 cm., with handle 21.6 cm. Height of bust 8.8 cm. Thickness with appliqué 3.3 cm.
PROVENANCE: Faras, Grave 2589 (Griffith 1912, Excavation no. 1/2589/4).
BIBLIOGRAPHY: Griffith 1924,166, pl. LVI; Griffith 1925,156; Shinnie 1967, pls. 75-76; Oxford 1970,74, pl. 38.

It is interesting that the object was found in a man's grave since in Egypt mirrors were typical funerary gifts for women. The motif on the outside of the case is clearly influenced by Hellenistic art and probably reached Lower Nubia by way of Alexandria. The motifs on the inside, however, are based largely on Egyptian prototypes, such as the youthful god Harpocrates in the center. The animals are all no doubt fabulous creatures, only some of which have prototypes in Egyptian art. Griffith dated the grave to his Period A, that is, the early period of the resettlement of Lower Nubia.

202
Perforated Ring

Probably second to third century A.D.
MATERIAL: Electrum.
COLLECTION: *Boston (Massachusetts), Museum of Fine Arts 42.125.*

DESCRIPTION: A perforated object has concave walls and a belled top.

CONDITION: Complete; scratched; blackish discoloration in places.
MEASUREMENTS: Height 3.1 cm. Outer diameter at top 4.4 cm., at bottom 3.2 cm. Inner diameter 1.8 cm.
PROVENANCE: Gemai, Grave E 3 (Bates 1915, Excavation no. R53, Object no. S 16-1-7).
BIBLIOGRAPHY: Bates—Dunham 1927,79, pls. XXXIII, 6 (L), LXVIII, fig. 1.

This object, like Cats. 217 and 273, has been called an archer's thumb-guard, but Hayes (1973,114f.) has suggested that such shorter rings with belled tops, which are mostly of small diameter, were used as ornamental rings on staffs, a view earlier expressed by Bates—Dunham (1927,79). Such decorative rings on staffs are known from Egypt. They are seen also in representations in the Taharqo temple at Kawa (Macadam 1955, pls. XIIc, XVIc-d, XIXa), always near the king. Another appears on the Meroitic seal ring, Cat. 185. The wider portion of the ring is always the top.

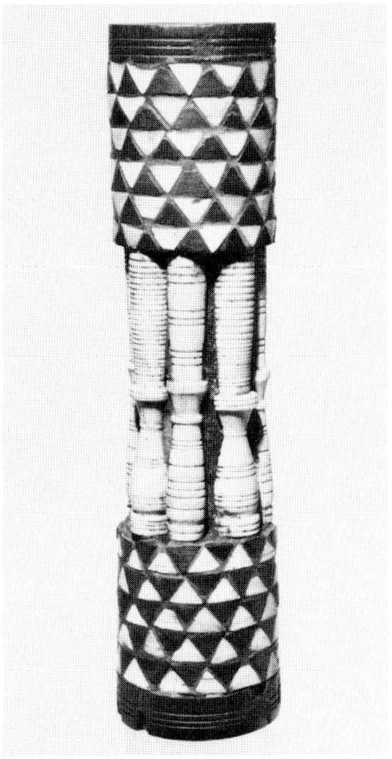

203
Inlaid Cosmetic Container

Late third to early fourth century A.D.
MATERIAL: Wood and ivory.
COLLECTION: *Philadelphia (Pennsylvania), University Museum E 7514.*

DESCRIPTION: A cylindrical cosmetic container is decorated with triangles inlaid in ivory and black wood, laid out in a checkerboard pattern; there are six rows at the top and five at the bottom. Between them is a row of ivory pilasters, fluted transversely and ringed by ornaments that look like stylized capitals. At top and bottom of the container are three narrow incised grooves.

COLOR: Wood dark brown; ivory whitish yellow.
CONDITION: Some inlays missing.
MEASUREMENTS: Height 17.7 cm. Diameter 4.4 cm. Height of half-columns 7.1 cm.
PROVENANCE: Karanog, Grave 45 (Woolley—Randall-MacIver 1908).
BIBLIOGRAPHY: Woolley—Randall-MacIver 1910,31, 32,70,122,245, pl. 25.

A small wooden casket with figurative inlays was found in the unpillaged, richly furnished grave of a young woman; inside it lay this cosmetic container, whose decoration is unique. The triangles arranged in checkerboard pattern remind one remotely of similar decorations on some C-group incised-pattern vessels. This is perhaps a typical African element of decoration, but the complex problem of possible African influence on Meroitic art has been too little investigated for more to be said. The dating of the container is based on a bronze vessel found in the grave, which is similar to Cat. 197; see the commentary to that piece. Cats. 205 and 206 are similar cosmetic containers.

Illustrated in color on page 266.

204
Inlaid Cylinder

Second to third century A.D.
MATERIAL: Wood and ivory.
COLLECTION: *Philadelphia (Pennsylvania), University Museum E 7570.*

DESCRIPTION: A hollow cylinder is decorated with ivory inlays. Two rows of trefoil blossoms alternating with circles are bordered by inlaid bands.

COLOR: Wood dark brown; ivory whitish yellow; traces of red pigment.
CONDITION: Slightly damaged; some inlays missing.
MEASUREMENTS: Height 2.4 cm. Outer diameter 4.6 cm. Inner diameter 2.0 cm.
PROVENANCE: Karanog, Grave 187 (Woolley—Randall-MacIver 1908).
BIBLIOGRAPHY: Woolley—Randall-MacIver 1910,146,246.

The excavators thought that the ring, which was found in the tomb of Viceroy Maloton, was part of a box but concluded that its purpose was uncertain. It may be a knob or an ornament for the head of a staff. Cats. 153, 196, 199, and 212 come from the same tomb.

Inlaid Cosmetic Container (Cat. 203).

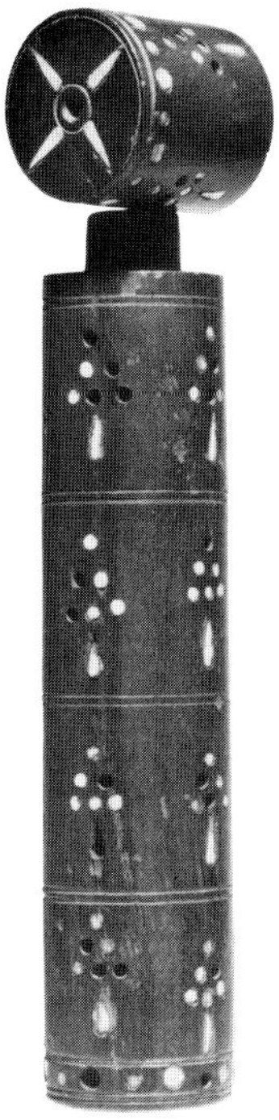

205
Slender Cosmetic Container

Late third to early fourth century A.D.
MATERIAL: Wood and ivory.
COLLECTION: *Philadelphia (Pennsylvania), University Museum E 7515a-b.*

DESCRIPTION: The lid of this cosmetic container was hollowed out as well as the cylinder. The design, in inlaid ivory, consists of rows of stylized "trees" with disk "foliage" and slender "trunks." Between the rows are two narrow grooves. At the base of the cylinder and on the upper edge of the lid are bands of circles. On top of the lid is a hole encircled by a groove and a four-pointed star.

COLOR: Wood dark brown; ivory whitish.
CONDITION: Some inlays missing.
MEASUREMENTS: Height of container 20.9 cm., of lid 5.4 cm. Outer diameter 4.9 cm. Inner diameter 1.6 cm.
PROVENANCE: Karanog, Grave 293 (Woolley—Randall-MacIver 1908).
BIBLIOGRAPHY: Woolley—Randall-MacIver 1910,42, 166,245, pl. 23 (with incorrect grave number).

A few objects had been deposited outside the superstructure of the tomb and were overlooked by grave robbers. They suggest that the tomb was well furnished with offerings. There was probably a knob on the lid of this cosmetic container that fit into the hole. Similar objects are Cats. 203, 206, and 207. On the stylized "trees," see the commentary to Cat. 207. Cat. 197 comes from the same tomb.

206
Elaborate Cosmetic Container

Probably third century A.D.
MATERIAL: Wood.
COLLECTION: *Philadelphia (Pennsylvania), University Museum E 7602a-b.*

DESCRIPTION: The tall slender container is carved in the form of six flattened spheres standing on a flaring base; there is a grooved cylinder above the topmost sphere. The knobbed lid is also hollowed out.

COLOR: Brown.
CONDITION: Complete; slightly chipped and cracked.
MEASUREMENTS: Height with lid 20.2 cm. Diameter of body 3.7 cm., of base 5.7 cm. Inner diameter of container ca. 1.6 cm.
PROVENANCE: Karanog, Grave 521 (Woolley—Randall-MacIver 1908).
BIBLIOGRAPHY: Woolley—Randall-MacIver 1910,200,246, pl. 23 (with incorrect grave number).

The cosmetic container came from a man's grave, which also yielded Cat. 209. See also the cosmetic containers, Cats. 203, 205, and 207.

207
Lid from a Cosmetic Container

Second to third century A.D.
MATERIAL: Wood and ivory.
COLLECTION: *Philadelphia (Pennsylvania), University Museum E 7525.*

DESCRIPTION: The hollow lid is decorated with a design in inlaid ivory. The side of the cylinder is divided into panels by bands of large and small ivory disks; in the panels are, alternately, *ankh*-signs and inverted stylized "trees." On the top of the lid is a hole encircled by a groove and an eight-pointed star whose radials are drop-shaped ivory inlays pointing outward. A circular hole was drilled above the lower edge of the lid.

COLOR: Wood dark brown; ivory yellowish brown.
CONDITION: Complete; slightly chipped; cracked.
MEASUREMENTS: Height 5.9 cm. Outer diameter 5.4 cm. Inner diameter 2.7 cm.
PROVENANCE: Karanog, Grave 116 (Woolley—Randall-MacIver 1908).
BIBLIOGRAPHY: Woolley—Randall-MacIver 1910,132,246.

The lid was one of a few objects found in the pillaged grave of a woman. The excavators called the stylized design, which appears also on Cat. 205, a "Noah's ark tree"; it is perhaps a stylized blossom. It is striking, however, that the pattern is here apparently inverted. There was probably a knob at one time that fit into the hole in the top of the lid. See also the cosmetic containers, Cats. 203, 205, and 206.

208
Inlaid Box

Third century A.D.
MATERIAL: Wood, ivory, and bronze.
COLLECTION: *Philadelphia (Pennsylvania), University Museum E 7517.*

DESCRIPTION: A rectangular wooden box is constructed of four corner uprights joined by battens, the uprights serving also as legs. The side panels are fastened to the insides of the battens and are thus recessed. A sliding lid with a flat projecting handle fits into a slot just below the rim. All four sides of the box are decorated with inlaid ivory. On the frame are large and small circles, and on the wall panels are framed motifs similar to Maltese crosses. A later owner added bronze strips, fastened with nails, to one top corner and three lower corners. A lock plate was mounted with large-headed nails, and two cracks in the lid were patched with bronze rivets. The ring handles on the upper corners of the long sides may be original.

COLOR: Wood dark brownish black; ivory whitish yellow; bronze dark brown with areas of green patination.
CONDITION: Some inlays missing.
MEASUREMENTS: Height 16.5 cm. Width 11.7 cm. Length 23.7 cm.
PROVENANCE: Karanog, Grave 445 (Woolley—Randall-MacIver 1908).
BIBLIOGRAPHY: Woolley—Randall-MacIver 1910,44, 71,245, pl. 22.

The box, used for storing jewelry or cosmetic articles, is substantially better made than Cat. 209. It became brittle after long use and was repaired, carelessly, with bronze. A lock plate was added at the same time. An attribution to the third century A.D. is based on the style of the inlays and on the fact that nothing comparable has been found in securely dated older Meroitic graves.

Gordon Salter, of the Henry Francis DuPont Winterthur Museum, in Winterthur, Delaware, kindly examined the wood and determined that it belongs to the species *Dalbergia melanoxylon*, known as African Blackwood or Senegal ebony.

Illustrated in color on page 270.

209
Small Inlaid Box

Third century A.D.
MATERIAL: Wood and ivory.
COLLECTION: *Cairo, Egyptian Museum JE 40221.*

DESCRIPTION: A simple rectangular wooden box has a slot for a sliding lid with a pediment-shaped handle. The sides and bottom of the box are dovetailed. On all four sides are inlaid ivory disks, a band of small ones at top and bottom and a central row of alternating large and small ones. The lid is similarly adorned. A row of small disks runs round the top edge and appears also on top of the handle.

COLOR: Wood brown; ivory white.
CONDITION: Pieces missing from one side of box and from lid; damaged and cracked; some inlays missing.
MEASUREMENTS: Height of box 7.3 cm., of lid 1.4 cm. Width of box 8.4 cm., of lid 5.4 cm. Length of box 17.1 cm., of lid 16.3 cm.
PROVENANCE: Karanog, Grave 521 (Woolley—Randall-MacIver 1908).
BIBLIOGRAPHY: Woolley—Randall-MacIver 1910,71,200, pl. 22.

In contrast to Cat. 208, this box is very simply decorated. Several boxes of this and similar type, used for the storage of jewelry or cosmetic articles, were found at Karanog. They must all belong to the third or perhaps even the early fourth century A.D. Cat. 206 comes from the same tomb.

Inlaid Box (Cat. 208).

210
Painted Casket

Second to third century A.D.
MATERIAL: Fired clay.
COLLECTION: *Khartoum, Sudan National Museum 728.*

DESCRIPTION: The rim of a rectangular casket is bent inward on three sides, and beneath the border thus formed is a slot for the sliding lid, which has a semicircular handle. On top of the lid are painted two stylized serpents holding plant stems; a face is painted on the handle. The ends of the casket have projecting wings and are decorated with *sa*-symbols, a horizontal one beneath the handle and a standing one on the opposite end. The long sides are painted in checkerboard pattern. There are small holes in the long sides slightly below the rim.

COLOR: Decoration red brown and violet brown on light orange to whitish slip.
CONDITION: Piece missing from upper rim; chipped and abraded.
MEASUREMENTS: Height of box 10.4 cm. Width of box 13.9 cm., of lid 8.4 cm. Length of box 15.9 cm., of lid 15.1 cm.
PROVENANCE: Faras, Grave 2805 (Griffith 1911, Excavation no. 1/2805).
BIBLIOGRAPHY: Griffith 1924,162-63, pl. LI,21; Griffith 1925,164.

Boxes made of fired clay were frequently substituted for more costly wooden ones; like the latter, they are more or less uniform in style. The handle decoration is similar to Cat. 211 from Karanog. The holes were used evidently to thread a cord through by which the box could be carried.

211
Lid from a Casket

Second to third century A.D.
MATERIAL: Fired clay.
COLLECTION: *Philadelphia (Pennsylvania), University Museum E 8737.*

DESCRIPTION: At one end of a flat casket lid is an upright gable-shaped handle with a stylized face, consisting of a nose and two eyes, painted on the front. The top of the lid is decorated with a crocodile, facing right, on a baseline.

COLOR: Face black and white on dark red slip; crocodile red and black on light orange to whitish slip.
CONDITION: Left side of handle and left edge of lid chipped.
MEASUREMENTS: Length 17.1 cm. Width 9.6 cm. Height 4.0 cm. Thickness 1.2 cm.
PROVENANCE: Karanog, Grave 735 (Woolley—Randall-MacIver 1908).
BIBLIOGRAPHY: Woolley—Randall-MacIver 1910,233,274, pl. 98.

Both face and crocodile were common Meroitic ceramic motifs. Cat. 210 also has a stylized face painted on the handle.

Illustrated in color on page 273.

212
Carved Spoon

Second to third century A.D.
MATERIAL: Wood.
COLLECTION: *Philadelphia (Pennsylvania), University Museum E 7422.*

DESCRIPTION: A spoon, made in one piece, has a handle in the form of a rearing uraeus wearing a Double Crown. The serpent's platform base joins the handle to the bowl of the spoon, in which is carved an *ankh*-sign.

COLOR: Brown.
CONDITION: Face of uraeus missing; slightly chipped and cracked.
MEASUREMENTS: Length 18.8 cm. Width of bowl 2.4 cm. Height of uraeus 9.8 cm.
PROVENANCE: Karanog, Grave 187 (Woolley—Randall-MacIver 1908).
BIBLIOGRAPHY: Woolley—Randall-MacIver 1910,146,244, pl. 109.

Several wood and bronze spoons were found in the tomb of Viceroy Maloton; the workmanship of this one is outstanding. The excavators (1910,244) thought the handle might represent a crocodile, but it is certainly a rearing uraeus. Other objects from the same tomb are Cats. 153, 196, 199, and 204.

213
Pendant with Geometric Decoration

Pre-Christian.
MATERIAL: Serpentine.
COLLECTION: *Oxford, Ashmolean Museum 1932.808.*

DESCRIPTION: A geometric pattern is carved in bold raised relief on the front of a rather long object that tapers to a rounded end. The top and sides are grooved. The back is convex and has a transverse perforation.

COLOR: Grayish green to blackish.
CONDITION: Complete.
MEASUREMENTS: Height 10.7 cm. Width 5.0 cm. Thickness 1.9 cm.
PROVENANCE: Kawa, Settlement Area (Griffith 1930-31, Object no. 0845).
BIBLIOGRAPHY: Macadam 1955,188, pl. XCVIc.

The hole in the back indicates that the object was suspended, perhaps from a necklace, in which case it might have served as an amulet. Since there are no parallels, it is impossible to say precisely what were its function and date. Macadam (1955,188) called it post-Meroitic, with a question mark. We can be certain, however, only that it is pre-Christian. Macadam illustrated the object with its narrow end upward and consequently referred to it as a "round-topped stela," but it appears questionable that it is really intended as an imitation of a stela.

Lid from a Casket (Cat. 211).

214
Lion on Crescent Moon

Second to third century A.D.
MATERIAL: Fired clay, glazed.
COLLECTION: *Liverpool, Merseyside County Museums 49.47.847.*

DESCRIPTION: On a boldly curving crescent moon are the head and forepaws of a highly stylized lion wearing a *hemhem*-crown. The back of the object is crudely slipped.

COLOR: Formerly pale green; now partly discolored dark to red brown.
CONDITION: Smashed into several pieces and repaired, with restorations; glaze spalled in places.
MEASUREMENTS: Height 24.2 cm. Width 23.1 cm. Thickness 5.3 cm.
PROVENANCE: Meroe, Royal Baths, South Wall (Garstang 1912-13, Excavation no. GN 147).
BIBLIOGRAPHY: Garstang 1913b,79. Garstang Photo M. 123.

On the south side of the pool in the Royal Baths at Meroe was a narrow platform behind which rose a stuccoed and decorated wall. On the platform, near the edge of the pool, sculptures had been erected; see Cat. 161 and Figs. 61, 62, 67. The lower course of the wall was decorated with plaques with lions, cattle, *ankh*-signs, and amulets; medallions with female heads in late Hellenistic style (Cat. 215); and lions on crescent moons, such as the present piece. This motif is found in Meroitic art only on vessels (e.g., globular vessel from Grave 731 at Faras: Griffith 1924,259, pl. XLV,4). The crescent moon alone, however, is a common decorative element on vessels from Faras and Karanog and is sometimes combined with *ankh*-signs, blossoms, and other motifs. Lion's heads in front view are also common Meroitic decorative elements (Cat. 241).

215
Wall Inlay

Second to third century A.D.
MATERIAL: Fired clay, glazed.
COLLECTION: *Brussels, Musées Royaux d'Art et d'Histoire E. 3709.*

DESCRIPTION: A female bust with upturned face, long hair reaching to the shoulders, and indications of a garment is represented in high relief on a circular plaque.

COLOR: Greenish with light to red-brown areas.
CONDITION: Badly cracked and abraded; restored in places.
MEASUREMENTS: Height 26.5 cm. Width 25.5 cm. Thickness 2.2 cm.
PROVENANCE: Meroe, Royal Baths, South Wall (Garstang 1912-13).
BIBLIOGRAPHY: None. Garstang Photo M. 179.

This medallion, with its late Hellenistic head, comes from the same wall as Cat. 214, and Cat. 161 was found very nearby; see the commentaries to those objects. Several medallions such as this were found inlaid into the wall along with other motifs, arranged without noticeable regularity.

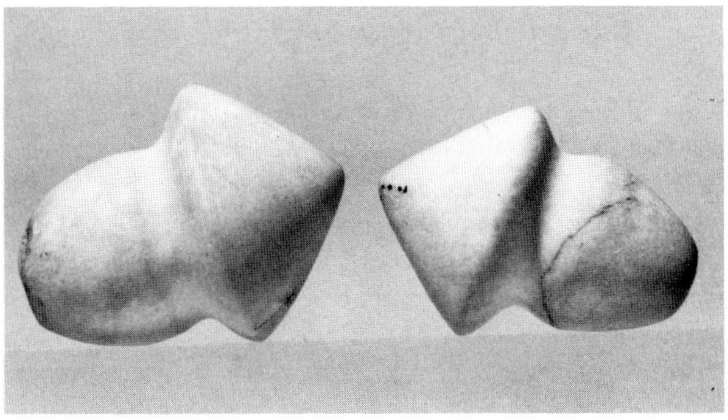

216
Earplugs

Probably first to fourth century A.D.
MATERIAL: Calcite (?).
COLLECTION: *Khartoum, University 101-102.*

DESCRIPTION: The earplugs are mushroom-shaped, with pointed, beveled "umbels." The stems are grooved beneath the "umbel" and taper to a flattened end.

COLOR: White.
CONDITION: Complete.
MEASUREMENTS: Height 3.3 and 3.5 cm. Width 2.4 and 2.6 cm. "Stem" thickness 1.8 and 1.9 cm.
PROVENANCE: Sururab (West Bank, north of Khartoum), Grave 14, on skeleton (Ahmed Ali Hakem 1974, Excavation no. 74.B.14/4a-b).
BIBLIOGRAPHY: None.

Earplugs, like nose and lip plugs, were known in the Sudan during the Neolithic Period but were seldom worn by Meroites. The present piece may indicate the influence of a surrounding, non-Meroitic culture; one might consider the Gebel Moya culture (Addison 1949), which is contemporary with the late Napatan and Meroitic Periods. However, since the grave from which the earplugs came cannot be definitely dated into the Meroitic Period, some other influence may be in evidence.

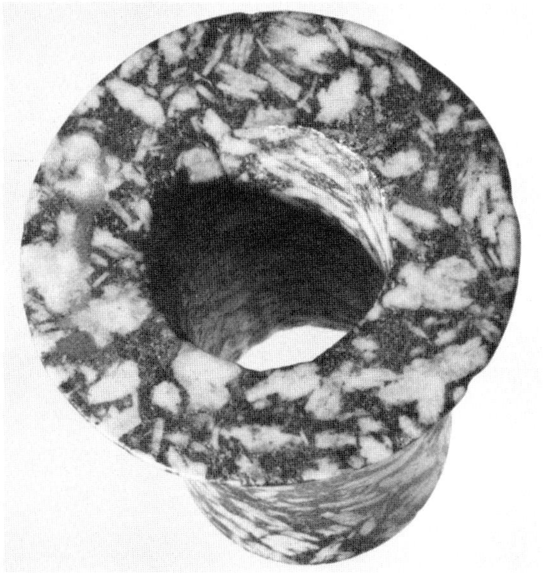

217
Archer's Thumb-Guard

Probably fourth to fifth century A.D.
MATERIAL: Stone.
COLLECTION: *Liverpool, Merseyside County Museums 49.47.819.*

DESCRIPTION: The polished thumb-guard is shaped like a horn and has a wide perforation. Top and bottom are smooth.

COLOR: Black and white.
CONDITION: Complete.
MEASUREMENTS: Height 4.8 cm. Outer diameter at top 5.0 cm., at bottom 3.5 cm. Inner diameter at top 2.7 cm., at bottom 2.1 cm.
PROVENANCE: Meroe (Garstang 1910-14).
BIBLIOGRAPHY: None.

It must be assumed that this object from Garstang's excavations at Meroe came from a tomb. It can then be dated to the post-Meroitic Period, since the cemetery uncovered by Garstang belongs to that era. Similar pieces found by the same excavator are illustrated in Garstang 1911 (pl. XXXVI,2). Emery and Kirwan (1938,233) were the first to suggest that these stone rings were worn by archers to protect the thumb while stretching the bowstring. In three cases, they found such rings on the thumbs of skeletons, as later did Arkell (1949a,122). The number of these objects found has steadily risen, and they have been discovered also in some royal pyramids at Meroe (Beg. N. 29, N. 28, N. 51). Their identification as thumb-guards is now secure. A relief in the Temple of Apedemak at Musawwarat es-Sufra shows both the god Apedemak and King Natakamani wearing such rings (Fig. 54); the wider side of the ring rests on the base of the thumb (Hintze 1971a, pls. 21, 25).

It is not possible to date the thumb-guards precisely unless one can do so from the context of the find. They were in use from the Meroitic Period well into the post-Meroitic Period and changed very slightly in form.

The present piece matches Hayes' type IC (1973,114, fig. 3).

218
Decorated Beaker

Probably first to second century A.D.
MATERIAL: Faience, glazed.
COLLECTION: *Khartoum, Sudan National Museum 13965.*

DESCRIPTION: The upper part of the beaker has an almost vertical wall; the lower part is conoidal, and the base is flat. Under the rim is a frieze of impressed, highly stylized uraei with sun disks on their heads.

COLOR: Blue; frieze yellow.
CONDITION: Complete.
MEASUREMENTS: Height 7.7 cm. Diameter at mouth 10.4 cm., at base 3.6 cm. Wall thickness 1.1 cm.
PROVENANCE: Argin (Almagro 1960-61, Excavation no. 24-V-9 MAN 90).
BIBLIOGRAPHY: Catalan 1963,35,90 (fig. 19, no. 4), pl. VIII,2B.

The beaker is rare in form and extraordinarily fine in quality. The impressed decoration is found elsewhere; see Cats. 249 and 250. Its quality, and the impressed decoration, date the piece probably to the first or perhaps the early second century A.D.

Illustrated in color on page 277.

219
Fragments from a Large Vessel

Fourth to third century B.C.
MATERIAL: Fired clay.
COLLECTION: *Berlin/DDR, Ägyptisches Museum 29039* [*HU 41*].

DESCRIPTION: Five fragments of a large vessel are painted with a vineyard scene. An archer is preparing to shoot a bird which is pecking at a grape.

COLOR: Light red brown; decoration purple.
CONDITION: Five partially fitting fragments.
MEASUREMENTS: Height ca. 23.0 cm. Width ca. 15.0 cm. Wall thickness 0.9 cm.
PROVENANCE: Musawwarat es-Sufra, Great Enclosure, landfill of central terrace (Hintze 1967, 1968, Excavation no. GA/117). On permanent loan from Humboldt University, Berlin.
BIBLIOGRAPHY: None.

In the landfill of the central terrace of the Great Enclosure at Musawwarat es-Sufra, which supported a colonnaded temple, were found numerous scattered fragments of a large vessel of unusual form. It had a round bottom with a conoidal ring base and tapered toward the top; the two handles were braided. In the middle of the vessel was a broad cross-hatched band. On the lower part of the body were painted four stylized trees, probably palms; on its upper part, to which the present fragments belonged, were vine branches.

The location of the find allows only one conclusion: the vessel was ritually destroyed during the foundation ceremonies for the building and then "interred" underneath it. Since the temple was built not later than the third century B.C., a date prior to that is logical for the vase. The find is thus extremely important, since painted Meroitic ceramics have hitherto not been attested before the first century B.C. How far stylistic connections existed between the decoration of the vessel and early Hellenistic vine-branch patterns has not yet been investigated.

Decorated Beaker (Cat. 218).

220
Vessel Fragment with Naked Couple

Probably second century A.D.
MATERIAL: Fired clay.
COLLECTION: *Liverpool, Merseyside County Museums 49.47.840.*

DESCRIPTION: Fragments of the edge of a beaker that had a straight wall, thickening slightly at the rim, are decorated with a scene painted in brick red. On the left stands a naked man with a full beard, seen from behind, who turns to the right and bends slightly forward. His left arm is extended behind his body; his right arm hangs down in front of him. A naked woman, in front view, is turned toward him. She holds in front of her abdomen a large rectangular patterned object. Lotus flowers on slender stems appear between and behind the two figures. A damaged area to the right indicates the place where the handle was attached, and beyond it is preserved a painted arm with an object in the hand, part of another scene.

COLOR: Light brown; decoration brick red and purple.
CONDITION: Two fitting fragments.
MEASUREMENTS: Height 4.7 cm. Width 10.3 cm. Wall thickness 0.4 cm.
PROVENANCE: Meroe, presumably Building 289 (Garstang 1910-14, object designated GN 140; the number 289 is written in pencil on the back of the sherd, possibly indicating the building from which it came).
BIBLIOGRAPHY: None.

Meroitic ceramic vessels decorated with narrative scenes are very rare, and this one is our only example of Alexandrian influence in pottery decoration; it appears more frequently in sculpture (Cats. 161, 215; Figs. 61,62,67,68). The content of the scene is puzzling, but, since both figures are naked, it is probably erotic. The use of a concealing fabric is present in two other examples of Meroitic art: on the inside wall of the Temple of Apedemak at Musawwarat es-Sufra (Hintze 1971a, pls. 66a, 67), three men hold a cloth which almost completely conceals a cow; and on the wall of the Great Enclosure is an incised scene that is clearly erotic in nature; see p. 81 and Fig. 59. Scenes of this kind are unknown in Egypt and represent, therefore, a distinctly Meroitic artistic contribution, which found entry into both official and unofficial art.

221
Wine Vessel with Spotted Antelope

Second to third century A.D.
MATERIAL: Fired clay.
COLLECTION: *Brooklyn (New York), The Brooklyn Museum, Charles Edwin Wilbour Fund 71.84.*

DESCRIPTION: A somewhat elongated globular pot has a low concave neck and a flat lip. Black-white-black bands encircle the vessel just below the neck, at the shoulder, and near the bottom. On the shoulder are vine branches with white-daubed leaves. On the body, a spotted antelope runs toward the right. There are also vine branches with leaves, a fruit-laden tree, and, drawn in outline, a bird facing right.

COLOR: Red brown; decoration black and white.
CONDITION: Two small restorations to lip; discolored in places.
MEASUREMENTS: Height 27.6 cm. Diameter 26.9 cm., at lip 8.7 cm.
PROVENANCE: Not known. Vessel bears old numbers: D. W./35/6 and N. 76a/s.nss./1200.
BIBLIOGRAPHY: Collection David-Weill 1971, no. 20; Brooklyn 1974,96-97.

Numerous vessels found at Karanog and Faras are similar in shape to this one, have the same red-brown slip and black-white-black bands, and are decorated with vine branches. Cat. 222 also belongs to this group. It is probably safe to assume that they all come from the same workshop. Cat. 230 has the red-brown slip and the black-white-black bands but cannot be included in this group because its shoulder decoration is of a different type.

The present pot and Cat. 222 are so similar that they must have been painted by the same artist, whom we shall call the "Antelope Painter." The shape of the animal's body, the curving line of the back, and the manner in which the bird is rendered are too similar to be coincidental. Still, there are differences. The animal here is spotted, and its horns are almost parallel. Only one of its legs is stretched out at full length from the body. The shoulder painting is also different; the leaves here are daubed with white. These divergencies show that the painter did not work according to a pattern. In the attempt to distinguish specific hands in ceramic decoration, we must pay attention not only to individual motifs but to overall composition and stylistic characteristics. Certainly other pots can be attributed to the Antelope Painter once the long overdue examination of Meroitic ceramic decoration is undertaken in earnest. Cat. 223 possibly comes from the same artist; see the commentary thereto.

Illustrated in color on page 96.

222
Vessel with Running Antelope

Second to third century A.D.
MATERIAL: Fired clay.
COLLECTION: *Philadelphia (Pennsylvania), University Museum E 8162.*

DESCRIPTION: The pot is similar in form to Cat. 221 and has the same dark-light-dark bands below the neck, at the shoulder, and near the bottom. Leafless tendrils decorate the shoulder. On the body is a running antelope with unusual horns. In front of and behind him are vine branches. On the other side is a bird, very sketchily rendered.

COLOR: Red brown; decoration blackish brown and whitish buff.
CONDITION: Complete; lip chipped; colors abraded in places.
MEASUREMENTS: Height 28.4 cm., of central register 10.5 cm. Diameter 28.1 cm., at lip 9.0 cm.
PROVENANCE: Karanog, Grave 542 (Woolley—Randall-MacIver 1908).
BIBLIOGRAPHY: Woolley—Randall-MacIver 1910,56,58(g), 205,261, pl. 54; Curto 1965, fig. 276 second from left, above; Curto 1966, fig. 276 second from left, above.

Although there are stylistic differences between the present vessel and Cat. 221, this pot, too, can be attributed to the Antelope Painter; see the commentary to Cat. 221. Cat. 223 may have been painted by the same artist; see the commentary thereto. The stylistic differences may be attributable to different periods of production.

223
Two-Handled Vessel with Antelopes and Birds

Second to third century A.D.
MATERIAL: Fired clay.
COLLECTION: *Cairo, Egyptian Museum JE 40086.*

DESCRIPTION: A somewhat flattened globular vessel has a ring base and a wide, collared neck that tapers gently to a slightly flaring lip. Two longitudinally grooved handles are attached to the neck, just below the collar, and arch to the shoulder, which is encircled by stylized leafy vine branches. The body is set off by two broad dark bands at the shoulder and again below the bulge. In the central register are two antelopes running right, upright vine branches, a fruit-laden tree, two birds, another fruit-laden tree, a clump of stylized lotus plants, a trellis (?) with tendrils, two clusters of vine leaves, a horned altar, and three birds.

COLOR: Red brown; decoration black and white.
CONDITION: Small chips missing from lip and foot; colors abraded and discolored in places.
MEASUREMENTS: Height 29.0 cm., of neck 6.4 cm. Diameter 28.5 cm., at lip 10.2 cm.
PROVENANCE: Karanog, Grave 315 (?) (Woolley—Randall-MacIver 1908).
BIBLIOGRAPHY: Woolley—Randall-MacIver 1910,58(g).

Although there are many vessels with handles, this particular form of pot is uncommon. The painted decoration is stylistically closely related to that of two vessels found in Karanog Grave 712: Cat. 224 and Philadelphia E 8156 (Woolley—Randall-MacIver 1910, pl. 45). Another vessel from the same grave (Philadelphia E 8182: ibid. pl. 56) may also be related to this group.

Running antelopes, so far as I know, appear on only two other vessels, Cats. 221 and 222. Those two were painted by the same artist. Considering its stylistic connections to Cat. 222, I would attribute this vessel also to the Antelope Painter.

224
Pot with Geese and Altars

Second to third century A.D.
MATERIAL: Fired clay.
COLLECTION: *Philadelphia (Pennsylvania), University Museum E 8157.*

DESCRIPTION: A large globular vessel has a short neck, a flaring lip, and a round bottom. On the neck is a dark-light-dark-light-dark band, and on the shoulder are vine branches with light and dark leaves above a much more stylized vine pattern bounded above and below by dark-light-dark bands. On the body of the vessel are two low tables, one laden with fruit and the other with large almond-shaped offerings; a vine garland trails over both. Next comes a horned altar and beside it three geese turned to the right. Behind them is a large, dark inverted triangle, fringed at the top, and two very large insects flying toward each other. Another garland surrounds this group.

COLOR: Red brown; decoration blackish brown and whitish.
CONDITION: Complete; colors abraded in places.
MEASUREMENTS: Height 28.3 cm. Diameter 31.5 cm.
PROVENANCE: Karanog, Grave 712 (Woolley—Randall-MacIver 1908).
BIBLIOGRAPHY: Woolley—Randall-MacIver 1910,56-57, 229,261, pl. 45.

The vessel is very similar in form to Cats. 221 and 222 and, like them, has a red-brown slip, bands of color, and vine decoration on the shoulder. The pot is a product of the "vine-leaf school"; see pp. 95, 98. With another vessel from the same grave (Philadelphia E 8156: Woolley—Randall-MacIver 1910, pl. 45), attributable to the same school, it is one of the most interesting of Meroitic ceramics. Only on this vessel do we see a clear depiction of geese, although the meaning of their activity, pecking at a horned altar, remains puzzling. It is perhaps a caricature, which may also be true of the pitcher Philadelphia E 8156, where an antelope(?) lies beside an altar and eats from it.

Woolley—Randall-MacIver (1910,56-57) thought the present vessel carried a representation of the "Table of the Sun," as described in Herodotus 3. 17 (see pp. 59-60). In my view, that interpretation is farfetched. I think the excavators are closer to the mark (ibid. 57) when they suggest that an African motif may be represented here, but until the influence of African motifs on Meroitic art has been investigated, nothing more can be said on this point.

Illustrated in color, Volume I, page 130.

225
Ring-Flask

First to second century A.D.
MATERIAL: Fired clay.
COLLECTION: *London, British Museum 51477.*

DESCRIPTION: A ring-shaped flask has a long cylindrical neck collared below the flaring flat lip and two slender handles curving from below the collar to the base of the neck. On front and back of the ring is a guilloche pattern. On the outside is a design of tendrils, branches, and leaves. The decoration is filled in with red in places.

COLOR: Light orange brown; decoration red and black.
CONDITION: Piece missing from lip; one handle broken off and replaced; one side of ring badly corroded; hole drilled in one side of ring; discolored in places.
MEASUREMENTS: Height 23.2 cm. Diameter 15.7 cm., of ring 5.7 cm.
PROVENANCE: Faras, in rubble of Grave 1092 (Griffith 1912, Excavation no. 1/1092).
BIBLIOGRAPHY: Griffith 1924,151, pl. XXVII (type LIX); Griffith 1925,131.

Ring vases existed in Egypt during the New Kingdom, but this is our only example from the Meroitic Period. The neck was turned on a wheel, but the body was shaped by hand. It is impossible to say with certainty whether the vessel is an import or a native product. Griffith attributed the flask to his Period B-C.

Illustrated in color, Volume I, page 128.

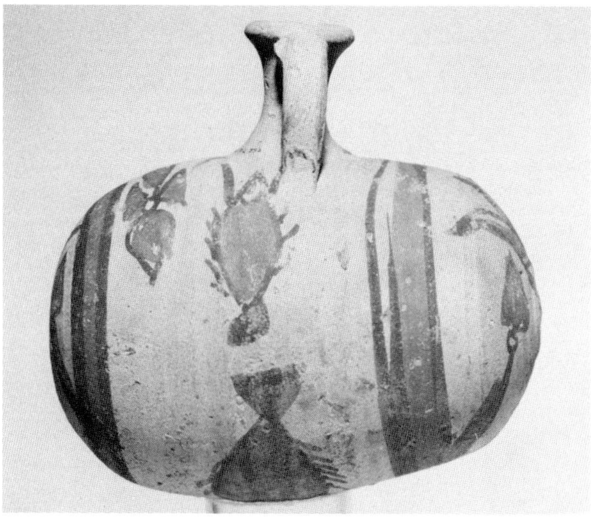

226
Barrel-Shaped Vessel

Second to third century A.D.
MATERIAL: Fired clay.
COLLECTION: *Oxford, Ashmolean Museum 1912.392.*

DESCRIPTION: The vessel is shaped like a barrel with rounded ends. It has a slender neck, a slightly flaring lip, and two handles that curve from below the lip to the shoulder. On each side of the pot, running axially, are red bands bounded by erratically drawn lines. On each rounded end is a stylized lotus plant with blossom and two stems with buds. Two *ankh*-signs and three fish, painted red, appear on the body. Parts of the lotus plants are also filled in with red.

COLOR: Yellowish light brown; decoration red and black.
CONDITION: Complete; colors abraded in places.
MEASUREMENTS: Height 14.3 cm. Width 10.6 cm. Length 14.5 cm.
PROVENANCE: Faras, Grave 1021 (Griffith 1912, Excavation no. 1/1021/3).
BIBLIOGRAPHY: Griffith 1924,151, pl. XXVII (type LX); Griffith 1925,120.

Griffith (1924,151) designated this unique vessel a pilgrim's barrel, and, in fact, in side view it is indeed reminiscent of a pilgrim's bottle. The fish motif is found infrequently on Meroitic ceramics; another example is Cat. 254. The lotus, however, is quite common, and must have been a resurrection symbol in Meroe as in Egypt; it would otherwise be unintelligible on pots that served as funerary offerings. Griffith attributed this vessel to his Period C.

227
Vessel with Winged Cobras

Second to third century A.D.
MATERIAL: Fired clay.
COLLECTION: *Brooklyn (New York), The Brooklyn Museum, Charles Edwin Wilbour Fund 67.177.*

DESCRIPTION: A large globular vessel, bulging toward the bottom, has a short, narrow concave neck. The decoration consists of bands of alternating light and dark stripes below the neck, below the shoulder, and at the broadest point of the bulge. On the body are four rearing cobras wearing sun disks and uraei, who rest on the lowest striped band. Two of the serpents are winged, the wings being extended sideways and very carefully detailed.

COLOR: Red brown; decoration white, black, and red.
CONDITION: Complete; discolored in places.
MEASUREMENTS: Height 29.4 cm. Diameter 25.2 cm., at neck 4.3 cm.
PROVENANCE: Not known.
BIBLIOGRAPHY: None.

Vessels of this form are very common in the Meroitic Period. It has certain connections with Cats. 221, 222, 224, and 232, except that the neck terminates without a lip. Crowned serpents were seldom represented on ceramics; they belonged to the repertoire of decorative motifs used in official art. In general, ceramic decoration had its own motifs, which arose from other areas of belief. A winged serpent appears also on Cat. 228, although there the wings extend in front of the body. Closely related to the present vessel is Philadelphia E 8170 from Karanog (Woolley—Randall-MacIver 1910, pl. 48), where the spread wings belong to a vulture, not a serpent. The similarity of motif, color, and striped bands suggests that the vessels came from the same workshop and were possibly painted by the same artist.

228
Handled Jar with Winged Serpent

Second to third century A.D.
MATERIAL: Fired clay.
COLLECTION: *Philadelphia (Pennsylvania), University Museum E 8168.*

DESCRIPTION: A tall jar has a slightly rounded bottom, a short neck tapering to a flaring flat lip, and a handle curving from below the lip to the base of the shoulder. On the lip are colored bands. A vine tendril with small leaves encircles the shoulder. Black-red-black bands frame the body at top and bottom, and between them are three rearing horned cobras from whose mouths issue streams of *ankh*-signs. One of them is winged, the wings extending in front of the body.

COLOR: Buff; decoration red and black.
CONDITION: Complete; discolored in places.
MEASUREMENTS: Height 33.8 cm. Diameter 17.4 cm., at lip 9.8 cm.
PROVENANCE: Karanog, Grave 301 (Woolley—Randall-MacIver 1908).
BIBLIOGRAPHY: Woolley—Randall-MacIver 1910, 169, 261, pl. 49.

The form of the vessel is common, but the winged cobra is extremely rare in Meroitic ceramics; see the commentary to Cat. 227. The motif of a cobra with wings extended forward is unparalleled.

229
Vase with Giraffes

Second to third century A.D.
MATERIAL: Fired clay.
COLLECTION: *Philadelphia (Pennsylvania), University Museum E 8154.*

DESCRIPTION: An ovoid vessel with a rounded bottom, tall cylindrical neck, and modeled lip has a band of alternating large and small circles on the shoulder and, on the body, four highly stylized giraffes filled in with cross-hatching and dots. The body design has no boundary lines. The large circles and the animals' bodies are filled in with white.

COLOR: Dark red brown; decoration black and white.
CONDITION: Complete; body cracked; colors abraded in places.
MEASUREMENTS: Height 37.9 cm. Diameter 22.8 cm.
PROVENANCE: Karanog, Grave 528 (Woolley—Randall-MacIver 1908).
BIBLIOGRAPHY: Woolley—Randall-MacIver 1910,56, 201,261, pl. 53.

Giraffes are represented on four vessels from Karanog; Cat. 230 is another. The motif is also found on vessels from Faras, e.g., Cat. 236, which is closely related to this one by reason of its identical shape. Here, however, the design is painted, not drawn. The circle-chain motif is found frequently on painted Meroitic vessels (Cats. 239 and 245), but the lack of boundary lines is very unusual.

230
Vessel with Giraffes and Serpent

Second to third century A.D.
MATERIAL: Fired clay.
COLLECTION: *Philadelphia (Pennsylvania), University Museum E 8183.*

DESCRIPTION: A large vessel with a short neck is encircled by dark-light-dark bands at the base of the neck, on the shoulder, and near the bottom. On the shoulder is an undulating serpent, filled in with light paint, with three curving stemlike *ankh*-signs in its mouth. The body is spotted, except for a small portion near the head, which is decorated with transverse zigzags. On the body of the vessel is a frieze of five giraffes, four of them browsing from trees standing in front of them. The animals' bodies have dark and light patches, and their necks are cross-hatched.

COLOR: Red brown; decoration deep brown and whitish.
CONDITION: Complete: discolored and colors abraded in places.
MEASUREMENTS: Height 34.2 cm. Diameter 27.4 cm.
PROVENANCE: Karanog, Grave 566 (Woolley—Randall-MacIver 1908).
BIBLIOGRAPHY: Woolley—Randall-MacIver 1910,57,209, 262, pl. 41; Curto 1965, fig. 276 left; Curto 1966, fig. 276 left.

Its excellent state of preservation and above all the quality of its decoration render this vessel, probably used for wine storage, outstanding among the huge quantity of similar pots. The light-colored snake contrasts strikingly with the red-brown slip. Serpents are frequently painted on the shoulder of vessels such as this and sometimes also on beakers. The three *ankh*-signs in the mouth are often found also with frogs. Giraffes are depicted on several, mostly tall, jars of distinct shape from Karanog and Faras (Cats. 229 and 236); see the commentary to Cat. 229.

231
Wine Vessel with Dancing Fauns

Second to third century A.D.
MATERIAL: Fired clay.
COLLECTION: *Philadelphia (Pennsylvania), University Museum E 8216.*

DESCRIPTION: The vessel is the same shape as Cat. 227. There are light bands at the base of the neck, the shoulder, and the broadest point of the bulge. The shoulder is undecorated. On the body are four squat, muscular, naked figures with brutish tufts of hair and manes, short horns, and animal ears and tails. They wear hoops around their upper arms, wrists, and ankles. Three of them dance with right leg in the air and arms held out from the body. The fourth stands with both feet on the ground and plays a double flute held in both hands. Between the figures are large amphorae on stands. The round bottom of the vessel is light-colored.

COLOR: Red brown; decoration gray and white.
CONDITION: Complete; colors badly abraded in places.
MEASUREMENTS: Height 30.9 cm. Diameter 25.6 cm.
PROVENANCE: Karanog, Grave 112 (Woolley—Randall-MacIver 1908).
BIBLIOGRAPHY: Woolley—Randall-MacIver 1910,54, 133,262, pl. 45.

The figures somewhat resemble Egyptian representations of the god Bes, but it looks rather as if they were intended to be dancing fauns, a motif adopted from the Hellenistic repertoire. The scene is apparently a bacchanalian revel celebrating and honoring the god Dionysos, at which wine would have been lavishly dispensed. The motif thus points to the function of the vessel; it was used for wine storage.

232
Vessel with Lions

Second to third century A.D.
MATERIAL: Fired clay.
COLLECTION: *Oxford, Ashmolean Museum 1912.321.*

DESCRIPTION: A large spherical storage vessel has a short, narrow neck curving to a slightly flaring lip. The slip is yellow brown on the shoulder, red brown on the body. There are dark-light-dark bands around the neck, at the shoulder, and on the lower body. The shoulder is decorated with two lions attacking fallen men. One victim, by his features and hair a black-skinned African, has three short vertical strokes on his cheek. The lions are red brown; the men are gray-tinged black. One wears a checkered and the other a striped loincloth. There is a depression on the shoulder of the vessel and wheel grooves on the body.

COLOR: Yellow brown and red brown; decoration reddish brown, black, violet, grayish black, and white.
CONDITION: Fragments from top of vessel reassembled, with restorations; lower vessel extensively restored.
MEASUREMENTS: Height now 28.0 cm. Diameter ca. 30.7 cm., at mouth 4.9 cm.
PROVENANCE: Faras, Grave 675 (Griffith 1912, Excavation no. 1/675).
BIBLIOGRAPHY: Griffith 1924,163, pl. LII,4; Griffith 1925,102; Shinnie 1967, pl. 46.

The motif of lions attacking fallen men belongs to the repertoire of official art, e.g., the pylon of the Temple of Apedemak at Naqa and a sandstone sculpture from the Apedemak Temple at Basa, now in Khartoum (Fig. 70). This is the only ceramic vessel on which it appears. The men are dark-skinned enemies of the Meroites. The three vertical strokes on the cheek of one of them are seen elsewhere, on the faces of Meroites as well as their enemies (Cats. 151 and 154); on this subject, see p. 88.

Illustrated in color on page 288.

233
Beaker with Pastoral Scene

Probably second century A.D.
MATERIAL: Fired clay.
COLLECTION: *Philadelphia (Pennsylvania), University Museum E 8451.*

DESCRIPTION: The beaker has a conical lower body and a large base. A scene with several figures is bounded above and below by thin, irregular double lines. A naked man with curly dark hair holds a stick in his upraised hand and two in the other. Walking before him is an immense, long-tailed dog wearing a fancy collar. In front of it are two quadrupeds, a shrub between them. The figures are all painted red.

COLOR: Buff; decoration red and purplish brown.
CONDITION: Several large fragments missing.
MEASUREMENTS: Height 8.0 cm. Diameter 9.8 cm.
PROVENANCE: Karanog, Grave 189 (Woolley—Randall-MacIver 1908).
BIBLIOGRAPHY: Woolley—Randall-MacIver 1910,55, 147,268, pl. 43; Curto 1965, fig. 274 top right; Curto 1966, fig. 274 top right.

Narrative scenes with several figures are rare in Meroitic ceramic decoration. The excavators (1910,55) thought this was a hunting scene, with the man carrying a spear in his hand. The interpretation is questionable, since the quadrupeds are not in flight but walking. Perhaps they are cattle being driven. The dog is strikingly large.

Illustrated in color, Volume I, page 131.

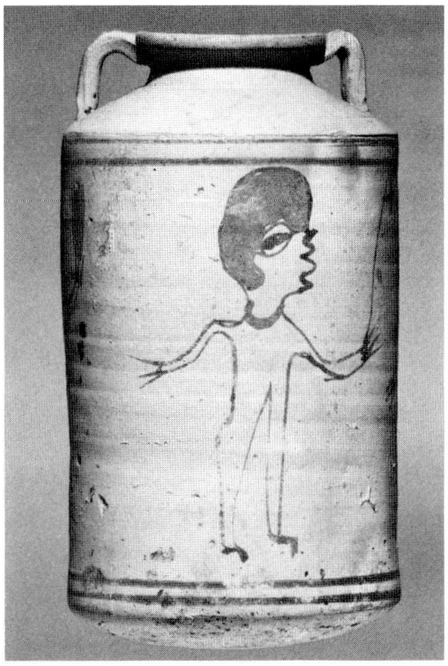

234
Double-Handled Jar

First century A.D.
MATERIAL: Fired clay.
COLLECTION: *Oxford, Ashmolean Museum 1912.322.*

DESCRIPTION: The jar has a rounded base and a conical shoulder tapering to a very short neck with a wide mouth and flat lip. Two handles rise almost vertically from the shoulder and curve to the lip. On the body, bounded at top and bottom by narrow double lines, are a lotus plant with flower and three men facing right, the third one holding a kind of fan and the other two with sticks in their left hands. All have their right arms extended back from the body. The first and third men wear necklaces.

COLOR: Bright yellow; decoration red and grayish black.
CONDITION: Complete; lip chipped; discolored and colors abraded in places.
MEASUREMENTS: Height 26.4 cm. Diameter 15.4 cm., at lip 8.8 cm.
PROVENANCE: Faras, Grave 701 (Griffith 1912, Excavation no. 1/701 A/2).
BIBLIOGRAPHY: Griffith 1924,151, pl. XXVI (type LIVb); Griffith 1925,103.

The meaning of the scene is unclear. The motif resembles that of Cat. 235 from Karanog, and the style is identical, so we may assume that the vessels were painted by the same artist; see the commentary to Cat. 235. Griffith dated the jar to his Period B.

Vessel with Lions (Cat. 232).

235
Jar with Men and Lotus Plants

First century A.D.
MATERIAL: Fired clay.
COLLECTION: *Philadelphia (Pennsylvania), University Museum E 8193.*

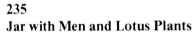

DESCRIPTION: A tall, wide-mouthed jar with a rounded base has a conical shoulder that angles sharply inward to a low cylindrical neck. On the shoulder are eight slender inverted triangles, probably stylized petals. Double lines encircle the body at the top, slightly below the halfway point, and just above the inflection to the base. In the top zone are two men with sticks facing right, each standing before a tall, stylized lotus plant, which in one case has another plant beside it. One of the men leads by a cord an animal that sits on the ground behind him. The petals on the shoulder, one of the men, and the two lotus plants are painted red.

COLOR: Yellowish brown; decoration red and purplish brown.
CONDITION: Complete; minor chips; discolored in places.
MEASUREMENTS: Height 37.0 cm. Diameter at shoulder 19.4 cm., at base 18.1 cm. Height of zone of decoration 15.5 cm.
PROVENANCE: Karanog, Grave 535 (Woolley—Randall-MacIver 1908).
BIBLIOGRAPHY: Woolley—Randall-MacIver 1910,203,262, pl. 43.

The vessel is taller than most jars of this type (Cats. 234, 237, and 255). The decoration covers only about half of the body, which suggests that the height of such scenes remained the same, no matter how tall the vessel. The motif is a variant of Cat. 234. The animal is probably a dog, and the rendering suggests a caricature, although its meaning is unclear. The figures are stylistically related to those of Cat. 234, and the painting technique is also similar. The two vessels must have been painted by the same artist. Since Cat. 234 was found at Faras, we may assume that products from many workshops were widely distributed.

236
Vase with Prisoner Scene

First century A. D.
MATERIAL: Fired clay.
COLLECTION: *Oxford, Ashmolean Museum 1912.412.*

DESCRIPTION: The tall, ovoid vessel has a long, almost cylindrical neck and an offset rim. On the body are two giraffes, each standing before a tall, stylized leafless tree. One giraffe is followed by a prisoner, his hands tied behind his back, wearing a flat-topped headdress. The other is followed by a man holding a long staff.

COLOR: Yellowish white to light brown; decoration black.
CONDITION: Complete; minor chips; discolored in places.
MEASUREMENTS: Height 37.4 cm. Diameter 23.3 cm., at mouth 7.9 cm.
PROVENANCE: Faras, Grave 1090 (Griffith 1912, Excavation no. 1/1090/6).
BIBLIOGRAPHY: Griffith 1925,129.

In style and in some of its motifs, the vessel greatly resembles Cat. 237; it is clear that they were painted by the same artist. A characteristic feature of his style is the way the line of the lower eyelid is carried over to delineate the ear in a single stroke. Such idiosyncrasies are not the product of a "school" or of accident but the marks of a "signature." Griffith attributes the vessel to his Period B. Cat. 241 comes from the same tomb.

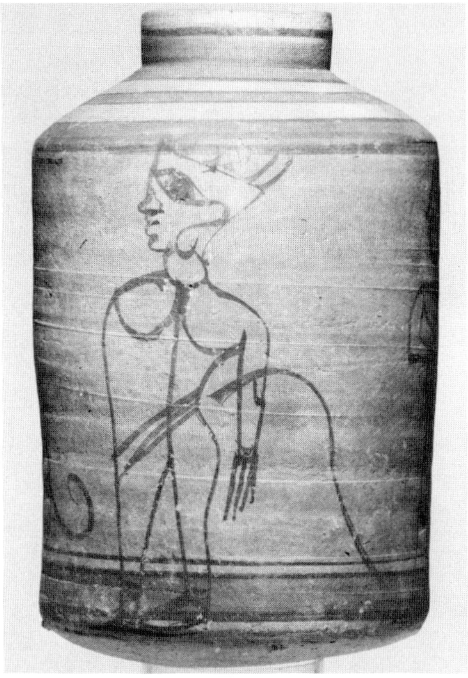

237
Jar with Prisoner Scene

First century A. D.
MATERIAL: Fired clay.
COLLECTION: *Oxford, Ashmolean Museum 1912.475.*

DESCRIPTION: A wide-mouthed jar with a rounded base has a conical shoulder and a low cylindrical neck. Red bands bounded by dark lines encircle the neck, shoulder, and lower body. Drawn in outline on the body is a prisoner wearing a flat headdress, hands tied behind his back. He is followed by two men, each of whom holds a plant stem in his hands, and a dog sitting erect on its hindquarters and holding something in its forepaws.

COLOR: Yellow brown; decoration red brown and grayish black.
CONDITION: Complete; discolored in places.
MEASUREMENTS: Height 25.6 cm. Diameter 16.9 cm., at mouth 8.0 cm.
PROVENANCE: Faras, Grave 2698 (Griffith 1912, Excavation no. 1/2698/14).
BIBLIOGRAPHY: Griffith 1924,154, pl. XXXIII,1; Griffith 1925,159; Charleston 1955,37, pl. 80.

In the richly furnished Grave 2698, Griffith found, among other objects, a black-ware beaker similar to Cat. 260 and a great many decorated ceramics, including this vessel. The shape is not unusual (see Cats. 235, 255, and 234 with handles), but the motif has only one parallel, Cat. 236, a pot of a different form. The two vessels were certainly decorated by the same artist; see commentary to Cat. 236. Griffith attributes this vessel to his Period B.

238
Pot with Human Faces

Second to third century A.D.
MATERIAL: Fired clay.
COLLECTION: *Philadelphia (Pennsylvania), University Museum E 8275.*

DESCRIPTION: The spherical pot has a low cylindrical neck. The body decoration is bounded at the top by a line and below by two irregular lines. Four leafy lotus stems ending in flowers rise from the baseline to the neck of the vessel. Between them are four frontal faces with large stylized eyes and crescents painted on the forehead. Flanking the faces are cruciform motifs or *ankh*-signs. The lotus leaves and two of the faces are painted red; the other two are dark in color.

COLOR: Buff; decoration red and purplish brown.
CONDITION: Complete.
MEASUREMENTS: Height 20.7 cm. Diameter 18.0 cm.
PROVENANCE: Karanog, Grave 530 (Woolley—Randall-MacIver 1908).
BIBLIOGRAPHY: Woolley—Randall-MacIver 1910,203,264, pl. 49.

Several vessels from Karanog are decorated with frontal faces (Adams 1964a,150, nos. 60-61). The motif appears on the inside of a dish from Grave 304 (Philadelphia E 8478: Woolley—Randall-MacIver 1910, pl. 51); on a spherical vessel from Grave 626 (Philadelphia E 8272: ibid. pl. 70); and on a beaker from Grave 655 (Philadelphia E 8784: ibid. pl. 93). It also appears on ceramics from Faras (Griffith 1924, pls. L,1, LI,6). The faces are not stylistically uniform, although they all lack mouths and have protruding ears. On the present pot, each face has a crescent-shaped ornament on the forehead, which resembles the curves that sometimes appear on the faces of sculptures (Cats. 151, 159, and 160). For the question of scarification, see p. 88.

239
Pot with Panel Decoration

Probably first century A.D.
MATERIAL: Fired clay.
COLLECTION: *Philadelphia (Pennsylvania), University Museum E 8291.*

DESCRIPTION: The spherical vessel has a low neck that widens very slightly to the mouth. A narrow stripe encircles the base of the neck. On the upper shoulder is a band of slant-striped large circles connected by narrow, cross-striped bars. The upper body is divided into uniform panels, containing alternately *ankh*-signs and geometric motifs. The *ankh*-signs and parts of the other motifs are filled in with red.

COLOR: Buff; decoration red and purplish brown.
CONDITION: Complete; rim slightly chipped; discolored in places.
MEASUREMENTS: Height 16.9 cm. Diameter 16.5 cm.
PROVENANCE: Karanog, Grave 316 (Woolley—Randall-MacIver 1908).
BIBLIOGRAPHY: Woolley—Randall-MacIver 1910,173,264, pl. 72.

The regularity of the decoration represents an artistic concept that was the product of a particular school or workshop; because of the precision with which the designs are applied, I have called this the "academic" style; see p. 95. Many ceramics from Lower Nubia belong to this group (Cats. 240 and 241). The band of large circles around the shoulder is a representation of the ball-bead necklaces worn by royalty and deities in relief and sculpture; it appears frequently in ceramic decoration, especially on globular vessels. Examples come from Karanog (Philadelphia E 8278 from Grave 753: Woolley—Randall-MacIver 1910, pl. 71) and from Faras (London BM 51446 from Grave 2636: Griffith 1924, pl. XLV,13). These pots are all, perhaps, the work of a single painter. His products, beakers as well as spherical vessels, must have been very popular.

240
Pot with Star Decoration

First century A.D.
MATERIAL: Fired clay.
COLLECTION: *Philadelphia (Pennsylvania), University Museum E 8310.*

DESCRIPTION: The pot is similar in form to Cats. 239 and 241, except that its neck is higher and narrower. On the shoulder is a band of circles above a frieze of frontal uraei. The body decoration, bounded above and below by double lines, consists of two rows of ten eight-pointed stars. On the bottom of the vessel are three lotus stems, the middle one ending in a flower and the other two with buds.

COLOR: Buff; decoration red and purplish brown.
CONDITION: Complete; gray metal residue on neck; discolored in places.
MEASUREMENTS: Height 13.4 cm. Diameter 13.7 cm., at mouth 4.5 cm.
PROVENANCE: Karanog, Grave 543 (Woolley—Randall-MacIver 1908).
BIBLIOGRAPHY: Woolley—Randall-MacIver 1910,205,265, pl. 43 (with incorrect grave no.).

The uraei are similar to those decorating another spherical vessel, Cat. 241 from Faras. The row of circles on the upper shoulder also appears on Cat. 239; there, however, they are filled in with slant stripes. In style as well as motifs, there are connections among these vessels, which can all be attributed to the "academic" school because of the careful execution of the designs; see p. 95.

241
Pot with Lion Masks

First century A.D.
MATERIAL: Fired clay.
COLLECTION: *Oxford, Ashmolean Museum 1912.410.*

DESCRIPTION: The vessel is similar in form to Cat. 239. The decoration is bounded by thin black double lines encircling the neck and the lower body. Six lotus flowers rest on the lower lines, each surmounted by three frontal uraei crowned with sun disks and, above them, a lion mask. The lotus and uraei composition is again repeated above the lion mask. Between these motifs are pairs of *ankh*-signs, one above the other, each formed like a fan with seven upright "ribs." The sun disks and the fan shapes are painted red.

COLOR: Pale yellow; decoration red and purplish brown.
CONDITION: Complete; neck broken and repaired; chipped and discolored in places.
MEASUREMENTS: Height 18.9 cm. Diameter 18.6 cm., at mouth 7.5 cm.
PROVENANCE: Faras, Grave 1090 (Griffith 1912, Excavation no. 1/1090/4).
BIBLIOGRAPHY: Griffith 1924,159, pl. XLV,12; Griffith 1925,129; Shinnie 1967, pl. 47; Oxford 1970,75 (fig. 39).

To some extent, the vessel is stylistically related to Cats. 239 and 240. The outlines of the motifs are very carefully drawn in a style I have labeled "academic." Griffith (1924,159) thinks "jewelers' designs" may be represented; he takes the transformed *ankh*-signs for feather fans. I cannot follow this explanation, since I can find no interpretation for that motif.

Griffith classified the vessel in his Period B. Cat. 236 comes from the same tomb.

242
Openwork Bowl

First century A.D.
MATERIAL: Fired clay.
COLLECTION: *Oxford, Ashmolean Museum 1912.449.*

DESCRIPTION: A tall, goblet-shaped bowl has a profiled ring base. The wall is perforated by a row of tall narrow rectangles, a band of trefoils, and another row of rectangles. Between the rectangles, in both top and bottom rows, are painted *ankh*-signs. The trefoils are outlined in a dark color, and dark lines define the boundaries of each row of cutouts. The base of the vessel is open.

COLOR: Light brown; decoration black.
CONDITION: Found in fragments and repaired, with restorations; chipped and colors abraded in places.
MEASUREMENTS: Height 9.0 cm. Diameter 10.0 cm., at foot 4.5 cm.
PROVENANCE: Faras, Grave 2081 (Griffith 1912, Excavation no. 1/2081/R).
BIBLIOGRAPHY: Griffith 1924,162, pl. LI,16; Griffith 1925,145.

This vessel and Cat. 243 are the only Meroitic examples of openwork ceramics. Griffith (1924,162) suggested that it might be an incense burner, which seems questionable. Perhaps it served as a container for another, closed vessel and had a purely ornamental function.

The opulent finds from this grave included several black-ware vessels, including Cat. 260. Griffith dated the grave to his Period B.

243
Openwork Jug

First century A.D.
MATERIAL: Fired clay.
COLLECTION: *Khartoum, University 502.*

DESCRIPTION: An almost spherical jug has a ring base and a narrow neck widening toward the modeled lip. Two small handles curve from below the lip to the shoulder, which is decorated with four-pointed stars resting on crescent moons. Below them is a rich ornamental plant pattern with red leaves. On the lower body are four openwork *ankh*-signs, outlined in red and dark color, and between them are vertical rows of geometric pattern. Inside the jug is another vessel, attached at shoulder level.

COLOR: Light brown; decoration red and purplish.
CONDITION: Piece missing from rim; chipped and colors abraded in places.
MEASUREMENTS: Height 13.6 cm. Diameter 9.3 cm., at mouth 2.8 cm., at foot 5.3 cm.
PROVENANCE: Nawa (island near Dongola), 1966.
BIBLIOGRAPHY: None.

This vessel and the preceding one are the only examples of Meroitic openwork ceramics. This pot is unique in that there is a second one, with a closed body, inside it. It must have been intended for the storage of liquids.

The suggested dating is based on its relationship with Cat. 242, which originated very probably in the first century A.D.

244
Handled Jug

Second to third century A.D.
MATERIAL: Fired clay.
COLLECTION: *Philadelphia (Pennsylvania), University Museum E 8313.*

DESCRIPTION: The jug's cylindrical body is inflected sharply at the shoulder, which curves to a very tall, thin neck that broadens, like a funnel, to the lip. The conical lower body tapers to a ring base. The neck is collared, and a single handle attached below the collar curves vertically to the shoulder. A vine branch encircles the flat top of the lip, and three leafy vine branches, all drawn differently, decorate the shoulder. The cylindrical body is bounded by dark-light-dark bands at top and bottom and divided into five panels separated by areas of hatched pattern. Identical decoration in the five panels consists of a large stylized plant with two spread leaves on which birds are perched, looking outward. Under the leaves are stylized upright branches and *ankh*-signs. The vine leaves and *ankh*-signs are daubed with white.

COLOR: Red brown; decoration black and whitish.
CONDITION: Large chip missing from body.
MEASUREMENTS: Height 22.1 cm., of neck 8.7 cm. Diameter 15.6 cm., at lip 5.6 cm.
PROVENANCE: Karanog, Grave 614 (Woolley—Randall-MacIver 1908).
BIBLIOGRAPHY: Woolley—Randall-MacIver 1910,215,265, pl. 48.

Adams (1964a,145) thinks the vessel is an Egyptian import. If he is right, most of the red-brown vessels with vine-leaf decoration would have to be regarded as imports, since there are very close stylistic connections between them and the present piece. The theory, however, has not been proved. But it is certain that the form of the vessel and the vine-leaf decoration are due to influences from Hellenized Egypt.

245
Long-Necked Bottle

Third century A.D.
MATERIAL: Fired clay.
COLLECTION: *Khartoum, Sudan National Museum 18886.*

DESCRIPTION: The flask has a spherical body and a very long neck that expands to the rim. The decoration is painted in grayish black in white bands on a dark red slip. Trefoils encircle the neck, just below the rim, and a row of connected circles, alternately large and small, runs round the upper shoulder. Below them are eight-pointed rosettes in panels separated by cross-striped bars, a band of striped triangles, and another row of rosettes in panels. A striped band frames the decoration at the bottom.

COLOR: Dark red; decoration white and grayish black.
CONDITION: Complete; colors abraded in places.
MEASUREMENTS: Height 33.6 cm., of neck 16.0 cm. Diameter 18.8 cm., at mouth 8.4 cm.
PROVENANCE: Semna South, Meroitic Cemetery, Grave N-432 (Žabkar 1968, Excavation no. N-432,03).
BIBLIOGRAPHY: None.

The excavator found three such long-necked vessels in the intact Grave N-432 at Semna South. The very elegant form is common in Meroitic ceramics and has been found in diverse places all over Lower Nubia. The decoration was very carefully executed, the motifs being outlined and the circles painted. Stylistically, no other vessel in this catalogue can match the present one. The dating comes from a suggestion made by the excavator (letter of August 30, 1976).

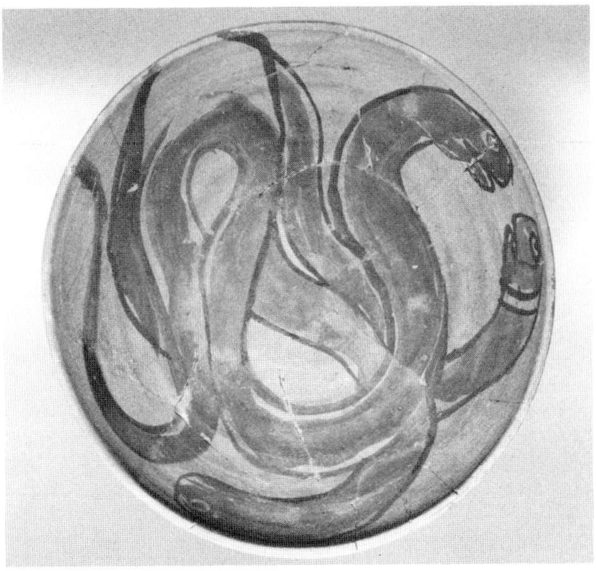

246
Bowl with Serpent Decoration

Second to third century A.D.
MATERIAL: Fired clay.
COLLECTION: *Oxford, Ashmolean Museum 1912.397.*

DESCRIPTION: The outside of the bowl is decorated with two dark bands beneath the rim. On the inside are three entwined red serpents.

COLOR: Outside yellowish brown with purplish-brown decoration; inside orange brown with black and red-brown decoration.
CONDITION: Found smashed to pieces and reassembled, with restorations.
MEASUREMENTS: Height 5.4 cm. Diameter 5.7 cm.
PROVENANCE: Faras, Grave 1034, in rubble (Griffith 1912, Excavation no. 1/1034/5).
BIBLIOGRAPHY: Griffith 1924,162, pl. LI,7; Griffith 1925,122.

In form and exterior decoration, the bowl belongs to a common type; Cat. 247 is another example. However, I know of no parallels for the serpents on the inside. Serpents appear already on incised vessels of the C-group, and are frequently found on Meroitic ceramics (Cat. 230), but the style of this representation is quite untypical.

247
Bowl with Bird Decoration

Second to third century A.D.
MATERIAL: Fired clay.
COLLECTION: *Philadelphia (Pennsylvania), University Museum E 8731.*

DESCRIPTION: Two dark bands encircle the bowl beneath the rim. On the inside is a bird with its head turned backward, its red body outlined in dark brown.

COLOR: Light brown inside and out; decoration dark brown and red.
CONDITION: Complete; bottom discolored.
MEASUREMENTS: Height 4.0 cm. Diameter 10.9 cm.
PROVENANCE: Karanog, Grave 3 (Woolley—Randall-MacIver 1908).
BIBLIOGRAPHY: Woolley—Randall-MacIver 1910,58, 117,274, pl. 93.

The only find from the disturbed Grave 3 at Karanog was this decorated bowl, which is similar in form to Cat. 246 and belongs to a common type. For the motif, a bird looking backward, there are no Meroitic parallels. Woolley—Randall-MacIver (1910,58) thought it was an ibis or flamingo. I rather think it a vulture because of the shape of the beak.

248
Round Box with Lid

First century B.C. to first century A.D.
MATERIAL: Fired clay.
COLLECTION: *Oxford, Ashmolean Museum 1912.339.*

DESCRIPTION: The cylindrical box has an almost flat base, a collar, and a recessed lip on which the slightly vaulted lid fits. The lid has a knob with a hole through the center. Both box and lid are decorated with a pattern that is probably an imitation of basketwork. The narrow side of the lid is painted red brown, as are the collar and a band above the base. There are six holes beneath the flange.

COLOR: Outside creamy white; inside light brown; decoration red brown and purple.
CONDITION: Broken into several pieces and repaired, with gaps. Chipped and discolored in places.
MEASUREMENTS: Height 14.8 cm., of box 10.8 cm., of lid 5.5 cm. Diameter 16.4 cm.
PROVENANCE: Faras, Grave 937 A (Griffith 1912, Excavation no. 1/937A/7).
BIBLIOGRAPHY: Griffith 1924,162, pl. LI,19; Griffith 1925,113; Shinnie 1967, pl. 43 right.

Among the objects found in the richly furnished Grave 937 A was a black polished pot with a Ptolemaic coin inside (further details are unavailable). In his excavation report, Griffith dated the grave to his Period A-B, that is, the early period of the resettlement of Lower Nubia, from the first century B.C. to the first century A.D.

249
Beaker with Impressed Design

Second to third century A.D.
MATERIAL: Fired clay.
COLLECTION: *Boston (Massachusetts), Museum of Fine Arts 23.1467.*

DESCRIPTION: A tall, polished beaker has a straight wall, tapering to a flat base. The body is decorated with eleven rows of close-set impressed motifs.

COLOR: Brick red.
CONDITION: Complete.
MEASUREMENTS: Height 9.7 cm. Diameter 8.4 cm.
PROVENANCE: Meroe, West Cemetery, Pyramid Beg. W. 308 (Reisner 1923, Object. no. S 23-1-290).
BIBLIOGRAPHY: Dunham 1963,143,343 (fig. G, no. 28).

Red polished ware is a typical Meroitic ceramic product, although it is by no means so common as the painted vessels, which are usually unpolished. There are relatively few ceramic vessels with impressed design. In this case, a uniform pattern was produced by close-set small motifs impressed into the soft clay with a die. Cat. 250 also has impressed pattern. Cat. 251 comes from the same tomb.

250
Goblet with Impressed *Ankh*-Signs

Second to third century A.D.
MATERIAL: Fired clay.
COLLECTION: *Boston (Massachusetts), Museum of Fine Arts 23.1466.*

DESCRIPTION: A tall, red polished goblet has a small ribbed stem and a flaring foot. The impressed decoration consists of four rows of *ankh*-signs, bounded above and below by incised lines.

COLOR: Dull red.
CONDITION: Complete; chipped and discolored in places.
MEASUREMENTS: Height 8.3 cm. Diameter 8.4 cm.
PROVENANCE: Meroe, West Cemetery, Pyramid Beg. W. 306 (Reisner 1923, Object no. S 23-2-190).
BIBLIOGRAPHY: Dunham 1963,143,343 (fig. G, no. 38).

Goblets such as this are rare in Meroitic ceramics. The form was based on Roman prototypes. The impressed-design technique was known throughout the Meroitic kingdom, although painted ceramics are much more common. Cat. 249 is also impressed.

251
Beaker with Floral Stars

Second to third century A.D.
MATERIAL: Fired clay.
COLLECTION: *Boston (Massachusetts), Museum of Fine Arts 23.1469.*

DESCRIPTION: The beaker has a two-stage cylindrical profile. The upper part widens slightly to the rim, and the lower part, which is sharply offset, has a rounded bottom. On the upper part is a scalelike pattern, and below are six-pointed floral stars. Both design fields are bounded above and below by lines. On the bottom of the vessel is an eight-pointed floral star, the points joined by faint double curving lines to form an octagon.

COLOR: Yellowish brown; decoration dark brown.
CONDITION: Complete.
MEASUREMENTS: Height 8.4 cm. Diameter 8.9 cm., at mouth 8.6 cm.
PROVENANCE: Meroe, West Cemetery, Pyramid Beg. W. 308 (Reisner 1923, Object no. S 23-1-293).
BIBLIOGRAPHY: Dunham 1963,143,343 (fig. G, no. 19).

This beaker is one of the most attractive of Meroitic ceramics. The decoration is very carefully painted but without the "academic" precision of the spherical vessels, Cats. 239-241. Vessels of this form have been found in the West Cemetery at Meroe in pyramids which must be dated between Dunham's Generations 50 and 60.

A vessel of this form was found in Karanog Grave 738 (Philadelphia E 8457: Woolley—Randall-MacIver 1910, pl. 78). It, too, has a scalelike pattern on the upper part, although the rest of the decoration is different. We may assume, therefore, that both vessels came from the same workshop, and we may infer from the high quality of the eggshell ware that the workshop belonged to the royal palace. The Karanog vessel suggests, however, that it also supplied ceramics to private individuals in Lower Nubia.

Illustrated in color on page 97.

252
Beaker with Crescents and *Ankh*-Signs

Second to third century A.D.
MATERIAL: Fired clay.
COLLECTION: *Boston (Massachusetts), Museum of Fine Arts 13.4031.*

DESCRIPTION: A beaker with a large base widens slightly to the mouth. The decoration is in two registers, separated by a line and bounded above and below by double lines. In both registers are *ankh*-signs resting on crescents. The designs are carefully executed and picked out in red. On the base of the vessel are four radiating petals within a circle.

COLOR: Yellowish white; decoration red and purple.
CONDITION: Broken and repaired, with gaps.
MEASUREMENTS: Height 7.7 cm. Diameter 9.1 cm.
PROVENANCE: Kerma, Meroitic Cemetery, Grave 22:3 (Reisner 1913, Location no. K 22:x3, Object no. SU 577).
BIBLIOGRAPHY: Reisner 1914,13, fig. 7; Reisner 1923a, 42 (fig. 12,4),55.

The motif is found frequently on beakers and spherical vessels, e.g., London BM 51446 from Faras (Griffith 1924, pl. XLV,13) and Philadelphia E 8235 from Karanog (Woolley—Randall-MacIver 1910, pl. 65), as well as on wine jars, e.g., Philadelphia E 8161 from Karanog (Woolley—Randall-MacIver 1910, pl. 54). Stylistically, the present piece is close to the academic school by reason of its meticulous execution, but it is not a product of that workshop, since the red fillings are applied without precision.

253
Beaker with Mythical Creature

First century A.D.
MATERIAL: Fired clay.
COLLECTION: *London, British Museum 51615.*

DESCRIPTION: The beaker is similar in form to Cats. 233, 252, and 254, but the wall in this case is slightly indrawn. A red band encircles the rim. On the body, bounded above and below by irregular double lines, are a seated monster, winged and antennaed, and five trefoils. The creature's body and parts of the trefoils are painted red.

COLOR: Orange brown; decoration red and black.
CONDITION: Broken and repaired, with restorations.
MEASUREMENTS: Height 8.8 cm. Diameter 9.1 cm.
PROVENANCE: Faras, Grave 786 (Griffith 1912, Excavation no. 1/786 R).
BIBLIOGRAPHY: Griffith 1924,161, pl. L,9; Griffith 1925,106.

The winged monster has parallels in Meroitic ceramics. A sherd from Faras Grave 2692 shows a monster with the body of a lion and the head and feet of a bird (Griffith 1924, pl. LII,3). A lion-bodied monster, winged and antennaed, also appears on the inside of the mirror case, Cat. 201. Griffith attributed this beaker to his Period B.

Illustrated in color on page 300.

254
Beaker with Two Crocodiles

Probably second to third century A.D.
MATERIAL: Fired clay.
COLLECTION: *Cairo, Egyptian Museum JE 89983.*

DESCRIPTION: The beaker is similar in form to Cats. 233, 252, and 253. On the body, between top and bottom boundary lines, are two strongly stylized crocodiles with birds perched on their tails; one of the birds has its wings spread, as if in flight. Above and below the head of one of the crocodiles are fish, painted in dark color. The crocodiles' scales are rendered in checkerboard pattern, and red dots are placed randomly in some of the squares.

COLOR: Light pink; decoration red and black.
CONDITION: Complete; chipped and abraded.
MEASUREMENTS: Height 8.4 cm. Diameter 9.9 cm.
PROVENANCE: Adindan (Seele 1963-64, Field no. B-80).
BIBLIOGRAPHY: None.

Crocodiles and birds appear frequently on Meroitic ceramics. The former animals seem to turn up primarily on beakers; Cairo JE 40084/26 from Karanog (Woolley—Randall-MacIver 1910, pl. 80) is a close stylistic parallel to the present piece.

255 ■
Pot with Frog Decoration

First century A.D.
MATERIAL: Fired clay.
COLLECTION: *Edinburgh, Royal Scottish Museum 1912.315.*

DESCRIPTION: The jar has a conical shoulder, a low cylindrical neck, and a wide mouth. Broad red bands encircle the neck, shoulder, and upper and lower body. There are four *udjat*-eyes on the shoulder and three frogs facing right on the body, each crowned with a sun disk and holding a long branch with leaves and buds.

COLOR: Light yellow; decoration red and black.
CONDITION: Broken and repaired, with small gaps; color abraded in places.
MEASUREMENTS: Height 20.6 cm. Diameter 15.4 cm., at mouth 6.6 cm.
PROVENANCE: Faras, Grave 731 (Griffith 1912, Excavation no. 1/731/5).
BIBLIOGRAPHY: Griffith 1924,159, pl. XLVI,10; Griffith 1925,104.

The vessel has a common form; Cats. 235 and 237 are other examples. The frog appears frequently on Meroitic ceramics of diverse form, but it turns up mostly on beakers and almost always holds a branch or a grain stalk; sometimes it also holds a stalk shaped like an *ankh*-sign in the mouth. For the frog as a fertility symbol, see p. 90. Griffith classifies the vessel in his Period B.

Beaker with Mythical Creature (Cat. 253).

256
Vase with Vine Decoration

Probably third century A.D.
MATERIAL: Fired clay.
COLLECTION: *Philadelphia (Pennsylvania), University Museum E 8208.*

DESCRIPTION: A broad-shouldered vessel has a low cylindrical neck and a large base. Dark lines encircle the neck and the body. On the shoulder is a simple vine-branch pattern with grape clusters.

COLOR: Reddish; decoration black.
CONDITION: Complete; colors abraded and discolored in places.
MEASUREMENTS: Height 19.5 cm. Diameter 15.6 cm., at mouth 6.6 cm.
PROVENANCE: Karanog, grave no. not recorded (Woolley—Randall-MacIver 1908).
BIBLIOGRAPHY: Woolley—Randall-MacIver 1910,262, pl. 60.

The form of this vessel is quite rare, but the vine-branch motif is very frequently found on Meroitic ceramics. It is present already on Cat. 219, from the third century B.C., and was undoubtedly adopted from Hellenistic iconography. No stylistic connections exist between the decoration of this pot and that of any others with this motif.

257
Pot with Branches and Circular Patterns

Most probably third century A.D.
MATERIAL: Fired clay.
COLLECTION: *Washington, D.C., National Museum of Natural History, Smithsonian Institution 448,235.*

DESCRIPTION: An elongated globular vessel has a low neck and a wide mouth with a thick, flat lip. Two very small handles are attached to the shoulder, which is decorated with a grapevine pattern, banded above and below. The two registers of decoration on the body are separated by broad double stripes. In the top register, simple stylized branches alternate with circular patterns. Below, upright branches alternate with long horizontal ones. Two broad bands close the field of decoration.

COLOR: Red brown; decoration black.
CONDITION: Complete; bottom corroded.
MEASUREMENTS: Height 35.7 cm. Diameter 31.7 cm.
PROVENANCE: Qustul, Grave Q 475, in front of unfired clay brick masonry of entrance (Seele 1963-64, Field no. Q-1689). Formerly Chicago, Oriental Institute Museum 21476. Presented by excavators to Mrs. Lyndon B. Johnson, who gave it to Smithsonian Institution in 1966.
BIBLIOGRAPHY: Seele 1974,9-11, fig. 6.

The vessel was found outside an intact grave that contained the skeletons of an adult couple. The funerary offerings included pottery jars, metal utensils, cosmetic articles, and two lead pots, on one of which the Greek words AMMŌNIT AGORAUS were pecked out on the surface. Stylistically, the decoration of the present pot reflects a late phase of development and points toward the very schematic decoration of the Ballana culture.

258
Footed Beaker with Grapevine Pattern

Possibly first to second century A.D.
MATERIAL: Fired clay.
COLLECTION: *Brussels, Musées Royaux d'Art et d'Histoire E. 3571.*

DESCRIPTION: The beaker has a gently indrawn wall and a two-step foot. The decoration, an encircling grapevine pattern, is unbounded by lines above or below.

COLOR: Red brown; decoration black.
CONDITION: Slightly chipped, with small restorations on rim; color abraded in places.
MEASUREMENTS: Height 10.8 cm. Diameter at mouth 13.0 cm., at foot 6.3 cm.
PROVENANCE: Faras, Grave 720 B (Griffith 1912, Excavation no. 1/720 B/R).
BIBLIOGRAPHY: Griffith 1925,104.

Griffith attributed the beaker, which was thrown on a wheel, to his Period A-B. For both the form and the decoration, there are numerous parallels from Karanog (Philadelphia E 8897: Woolley—Randall-MacIver 1910, pl. 52; E 8698 and E 8699: ibid. pl. 90) as well as Faras (Griffith 1924, pl. XXXVIII, type LXIVi) and other sites (Steindorff 1935, pl. 66). From this type of beaker, which was in use throughout the Meroitic Period, a new form evolved in the Ballana culture, of which Cat. 285 is a typical example.

259
Beaker with Barbotine Decoration

First to second century A.D.
MATERIAL: Fired clay.
COLLECTION: *Philadelphia (Pennsylvania), University Museum E 8704.*

DESCRIPTION: A tall hemispherical bowl with an offset lip tapers to a ring base. The decoration consists of lumps of clay, applied in bands and festoons.

COLOR: Dark and light brown; applied lumps of clay gray.
CONDITION: Broken into eight pieces and repaired, with gaps.
MEASUREMENTS: Height 7.2 cm. Diameter 10.1 cm.
PROVENANCE: Karanog, Grave 579 (Woolley—Randall-MacIver 1908).
BIBLIOGRAPHY: Woolley—Randall-MacIver 1910,211,273, pl. 90.

The Roman technique of decorating vessels with applied lumps of clay spread over large areas of Europe in the first and second centuries A.D. Imitations of this "barbotine" ware (named after a patissier of King Louis XIV of France) have been found not only in Egypt (e.g., Coptos) but in Meroitic graves as well, especially in Lower Nubia. Woolley—Randall-MacIver (1910,53) thought the Nubian examples were Roman imports, but Adams (1964a,146,160) believes they are Egyptian imitations of the Roman product, an opinion shared by Shinnie (1967,120) and Eggebrecht (Munich 1972,149). G. Grimm believes the barbotine vessels found in Nubia may be native products (verbal communication). Griffith attributed most of the barbotine beakers he found at Faras to his Period B, that is, roughly the first century A.D., a date with which Shinnie concurs.

If one agrees with Adams that all the vessels that came to Nubia from Egypt served simply as containers, it is difficult to imagine what commodity the barbotine vessels contained. It is more likely that they are Nubian imitations of the Roman ware and are similar to Egyptian imitations.

260
Beaker with Impressed Lotus Plants

First century A.D.
MATERIAL: Fired clay.
COLLECTION: *Khartoum, Sudan National Museum 726.*

DESCRIPTION: The beaker is indrawn slightly at the mouth and has an impressed pattern of tall lotus stems with, alternately, buds and flowers. The design is bounded above and below by double lines of impressed dots.

COLOR: Dark brownish black.
CONDITION: Piece missing from top; mouth slightly chipped.
MEASUREMENTS: Height 11.1 cm. Diameter at mouth 7.7 cm., at base 6.1 cm.
PROVENANCE: Faras, Grave 2081 (Griffith 1912, Excavation no. 1/2081/R).
BIBLIOGRAPHY: Griffith 1924,157, pls. XV (type Ia), XLI,20; Griffith 1925,145.

This kind of handmade black-ware beaker with incised or punched decoration was used throughout the Meroitic Period, but the decoration is more often impressed (Cats. 261 and 264), a technique that goes back to the Neolithic Era. In general, however, Meroitic black ware is much rarer than painted ware.

261
Black Bowl with Ostriches

Second to third century A.D.
MATERIAL: Fired clay.
COLLECTION: *Philadelphia (Pennsylvania), University Museum E 8735.*

DESCRIPTION: A polished, straight-walled bowl with a round bottom is decorated with a frieze of stylized ostriches, rendered with close-set impressed dots. There are six suspension holes under the rim.

COLOR: Black; traces of white pigment in impressions.
CONDITION: Complete; broken into two pieces and repaired.
MEASUREMENTS: Height 5.4 cm. Diameter 8.5 cm.
PROVENANCE: Karanog, Grave 743 (Woolley—Randall-MacIver 1908).
BIBLIOGRAPHY: Woolley—Randall-MacIver 1910,45, 52,233,274, pl. 102.

This handmade bowl was found with painted Meroitic ceramics in an undisturbed grave. Stylistically, it recalls older Nubian products. The forms and designs of hand-shaped ceramics, which were made by women, lasted much longer than those of wheel-turned vessels, which were made by men.

Neither the form nor the decorative motif is unique; a fragment of a similar vessel was also found at Karanog (Philadelphia E 9011: Woolley—Randall-MacIver 1910, pl. 100).

262
Dish on Openwork Base

Early third century B.C.
MATERIAL: Fired clay.
COLLECTION: *Boston (Massachusetts), Museum of Fine Arts 24.1003.*

DESCRIPTION: A shallow dish with impressed decoration has three wide legs, spaced asymmetrically, that meet to form a stand. On the rim is a band of chevrons and a smooth stripe. The inside is divided by smooth bands into four panels, which are filled with designs that imitate basketwork, alternate panels having the same design. On the curving feet are parallel lines of short oblique dashes.

COLOR: Gray to dark brown.
CONDITION: Fragment missing from rim.
MEASUREMENTS: Height 10.3 cm. Diameter 24.5 cm.
PROVENANCE: Gebel Barkal, Pyramid Bar. 15 (Reisner 1916, Object no. S 16-2-8).
BIBLIOGRAPHY: Dunham 1957,43-44, fig. 20.

Dunham (1957,44) called this vessel a "dish on open-work base," an interpretation we favor for this unique object. In Faras Grave 194, which Griffith dates to his Period A, was found a red-brown bowl with an openwork base (Griffith 1924, pls. XXXI [type LXXXVIb], XL,12). These imaginative vessels were undoubtedly influenced by the African sensibility, which is reflected much more strongly in black and brown wares than in painted ceramics.

263
Beaker with Zigzag Design

First century A.D.
MATERIAL: Fired clay.
COLLECTION: *Oxford, Ashmolean Museum 1912.366.*

DESCRIPTION: A tall beaker widening toward the mouth is decorated with closely spaced impressed dots. There are broad plain stripes at top and bottom and double zigzag bands, also left plain, on the body. The impressed dots are filled with red pigment.

COLOR: Black; red pigment in impressions.
CONDITION: Complete; slightly chipped.
MEASUREMENTS: Height 10.6 cm. Diameter at mouth 9.3 cm.
PROVENANCE: Faras, Grave 972 (Griffith 1912, Excavation no. 1/972/4).
BIBLIOGRAPHY: Griffith 1924,157, pl. XLI,21; Griffith 1925,115; Shinnie 1967, pl. 55 right.

In Faras Grave 972, which Griffith (1924,157) dated to his Period B, were found two handmade black-ware beakers with red pigment rubbed into their designs. In a Meroitic house in Faras, Griffith found sherds with impressed decoration, a pattern picked out in both red and white (Oxford 1912.899). Normally, only white pigment was rubbed into the designs, as it had been in the C-group.

The decoration of this vessel shows connections to the incised-pattern C-group wares, and the beaker shape is remotely reminiscent of beakers from the Kerma culture. Here, too, as with all the black-ware vessels from the Meroitic Period, which were shaped by hand, there is a clear reflection of the cultural continuity of Nubia over millennia.

264
Pot with Zigzag Decoration

Probably third century A.D.
MATERIAL: Fired clay.
COLLECTION: *Boston (Massachusetts), Museum of Fine Arts 24.385.*

DESCRIPTION: A spherical pot has a wide neck narrowing somewhat toward the lip. There are impressed dots on the lip and a broad ornamental band on the shoulder. On the body, framed above and below by incised double lines, are interlocking chevrons, alternately smooth and dotted. The bottom of the vessel is divided by two smooth stripes into panels, which are filled with alternately smooth and dotted bands.

COLOR: Brownish black.
CONDITION: Complete; surface corroded in places.
MEASUREMENTS: Height 17.2 cm. Diameter 15.6 cm., at mouth 7.2 cm.
PROVENANCE: Gemai, in debris of Mound T (Bates 1916, Excavation no. S 16-1-25/TR).
BIBLIOGRAPHY: Bates—Dunham 1927,86, pl. XXIV,1,A.

One can see in this Meroitic vessel a particularly close connection to the decoration of C-group ceramics, especially in the alternating smooth and decorated stripes. Many pots of this form have been found in Meroitic graves of both Nubia and the northern Sudan (Griffith 1924, pl. XV below), although it is not absolutely typical for the period. Another close parallel was found at Gebel Moya (Addison 1949, 91,222-23, pl. 111,3-4). The settlement and cemetery remains there exposed belong to a very simple culture contemporary with late Napatan and Meroitic civilization, and interchanges between the two are repeatedly manifest. See commentary to Cat. 216.

265
Gourd-Shaped Vessel with Lid

Second to third century A.D.
MATERIAL: Fired clay.
COLLECTION: *Philadelphia (Pennsylvania), University Museum E 8967.*

DESCRIPTION: A black, gourd-shaped pot with lid is decorated with close-set punched dots arranged in linear patterns, primarily evenly spaced zigzags running in various directions. There are two holes in each side of the rim and another in the center of the lid.

COLOR: Black; white pigment in incisions.
CONDITION: Complete.
MEASUREMENTS: Height 11.7 cm., with lid 15.7 cm. Diameter 15.1 cm.
PROVENANCE: Karanog, Grave 549 (Woolley—Randall-MacIver 1908).
BIBLIOGRAPHY: Woolley—Randall-MacIver 1910,52,280, pl. 101.

This handmade pot imitates a basket in the shape of a gourd. The holes in the rim served for fastening the lid and for carrying the vessel or hanging it up. Woolley—Randall-MacIver (1910,52) mentions an almost identical vessel found in Egypt by Flinders Petrie, which belonged to the late Predynastic Period (Petrie 1901, pl. VI).

266 ■
Queen's Crown

Fourth to fifth century A.D.
MATERIAL: Silver with semi-precious stones and glass inlays.
COLLECTION: *Cairo, Egyptian Museum JE 70455.*

DESCRIPTION: The broad circlet is framed with applied silver roll-rims and ornamented with semi-precious stones mounted in beaded silver settings between heavily embossed panels incised with *udjat*-eyes, the pupils inset with glass and carnelian. Five winged uraei crowned with sun disks, all cut out of silver and incised, are fastened to the rim of the circlet.

COLOR: Stones and inlays red.
CONDITION: Found badly crushed; restored and consolidated with wax; minor gaps and damages; some inlays missing.
MEASUREMENTS: Height 12.6 cm., with uraei 19.6 cm. Diameter ca. 15.0 cm. (now 12.7 by 25.6 cm.). Thickness of circlet 0.4 cm., of uraei 0.1 cm.
PROVENANCE: Ballana, Tomb B 118, Room 1, on the bier (Emery—Kirwan 1932-34, Object no. B. 118-29).
BIBLIOGRAPHY: Emery 1933, unnumbered pl.,3; ILN 1933b,923 (illus.); Emery—Kirwan 1938,153 (no. 29),186 (cat. no. 10, with incorrect room no.), pl. 36 A-B; Bissing 1939a,cols. 573-74 (fig. 5),579f.; Bissing 1941, 19 (fig. 11),21; Emery 1948, pl. 13A; Kirwan 1963,62-63 (pl. 16),77; Emery 1965,81 (fig. 7b top left), pl. X top; Curto 1965,362 (fig. 291 center); Curto 1966,362 (fig. 291 center).

The excavation in 1932-34 of the post-Meroitic tombs at Ballana and Qustul provided a sensation in the archaeological world. This was the first discovery of royal crowns from Nubia and the northern Sudan. Moreover, the royal dead were accompanied by women, possibly concubines, and servants, as well as by animals, which included cattle, camels, and dogs, some of which had been killed by strangulation or the breaking of their necks. The custom of human sacrifice had been widespread in the Kerma culture (see p. 31) and was perhaps sporadically practiced even during the Napatan and Meroitic Periods (see pp. 72-73). The tombs also contained objects that reflect the apex of development of the Ballana culture.

According to the excavators' observations, based on skeletal remains, the body that had fallen off the bier in Tomb B 118 when the burial chamber roof collapsed was that of a woman. The offerings directly around this individual, however, were spearheads and archer's thumb-guards. Until the skeleton is reexamined, it remains doubtful, therefore, whether the occupant of the tomb was a king or a queen. If it was indeed a woman, the offerings evoke Meroitic representations of warrior queens. Five other people, including a woman and a child, were interred in the burial chamber, as well as a cow.

The *udjat*-eyes on this royal crown are very painstakingly wrought and almost classical Egyptian in style; the winged serpents are less meticulously fashioned. Both motifs had appeared frequently in Kushite art since the early Napatan Period (Cats. 103, 104, and 114), and their presence here indicates a cultural continuity up to the time of the Lower Nubian kings of Ballana and Qustul (as is true also of Cat. 267). The semi-precious stones, however, suggest the influence of some other culture, possibly that of late antique Byzantium. This crown may be seen as an example of a Meroitic prototype transformed to conform to contemporary taste. See the commentary to Cat. 267.

267
King's Crown

Fourth century A.D.
MATERIAL: Silver and semi-precious stones.
COLLECTION: *Cairo, Egyptian Museum JE 88885.*

DESCRIPTION: Applied silver strips give the broad circlet a roll-rim at top and bottom, and a vertical band riveted to the outside holds the two ends firmly together. In the central register is a frieze of embossed Horus hawks perched on bases and wearing Double Crowns. Behind each hawk is a lotus blossom. Above and below are bands of bead pattern. Mounted at the top of the circlet is a ram's head worked in the round, its horns curving around the ears and onto the cheeks. The animal's crown consists of a broad crescent moon and a set of horizontal ram's horns surmounted by four tall feathers flanked by uraei. An oval garnet is mounted on top of the ram's head, and carnelians decorate its crown. On each side of the ram's head are fastened six large uraei followed by one small one, all cut out of silver and crowned with sun disks and all facing the ram's crown.

COLOR: Stones red.
CONDITION: Found crushed but complete; large pieces now missing (see commentary); restored in places.
MEASUREMENTS: Height 30.6 cm., of circlet 9.3 cm., of uraei 5.8 and 2.3 cm. Diameter 23.5 cm. Thickness 0.7 cm.
PROVENANCE: Ballana, Tomb B 80, Room 3, on head of Burial C (Emery—Kirwan 1932-34, Object. no. B. 80-48).
BIBLIOGRAPHY: Emery 1933, unnumbered pl.,9; ILN 1933b,920-21 (figs. 6, 8); Emery—Kirwan 1938,127 (no. 48),184 (cat. no. 3), pls. 24 C, 33 A; Bissing 1941,19 (fig. 13),21-22; Emery 1948, pl. 12; Kirwan 1963, 63 (pl. 17),75; Emery 1965,80 (fig. 7a), pl. XI; Curto 1965,362 (fig. 291 left); Curto 1966,362 (fig. 291 left).

Eight servants and several animals were interred with the king buried in Tomb B 80, and the numerous offerings included many weapons; see commentary to Cat. 276, an incense burner from the same tomb. The crown, like two quite similar examples from Tombs B 95 and 114 as well as the queen's crown, Cat. 266, is decorated with Meroitic—originally Egyptian—motifs, e.g., the ram's head, the plumed crown derived from the *atef*-crown, the uraei, and the Horus hawks.

Other elements, however, such as the crescent and the semi-precious stones mounted *en cabochon,* support the theory of a later and to a certain extent a foreign influence. Bissing (1939a, col. 580) pointed out that objects with inlaid semi-precious stones had been found in Spain in Gothic sites of the migration period. The technique probably spread from the Black Sea region to Egypt (Alexandria) and from there reached Lower Nubia. As the sole pre-medieval analogy to such gem-studded crowns as this one, Bissing cites the Novocherkassk crown, dated to the fourth century A.D.; earlier Byzantine crowns are not comparable. Thus, according to Bissing, the Nubian silver crowns point to the influence of highly developed Alexandrian goldsmithery techniques which had in turn absorbed influences from the Black Sea region.

The crown was almost complete when discovered and was illustrated in that condition by the excavators. The crescent rested on a rod that projected above the ram's head. During restoration, the rod was lost and the crown was fastened directly to the head with a wide strip of metal applied at the back. The top of the uraeus mounted to the right of the crescent and large portions of the circlet were also lost.

The rod and crescent are important, because a similar ornament appears on the head of a Nobadae king in a fresco in the Christian church of Abd el-Gadir (Arkell 1961,193, fig. 24) as well as in several representations of eparchs from the Great Cathedral at Faras, such as Cat. 293, in which the rod and crescent surmount a helmet-like crown. Michałowski (1974,49-50) has studied such head ornaments, but only insofar as they were worn by eparchs of Christian Nubia.

Illustrated in color on page 308.

King's Crown (Cat. 267).

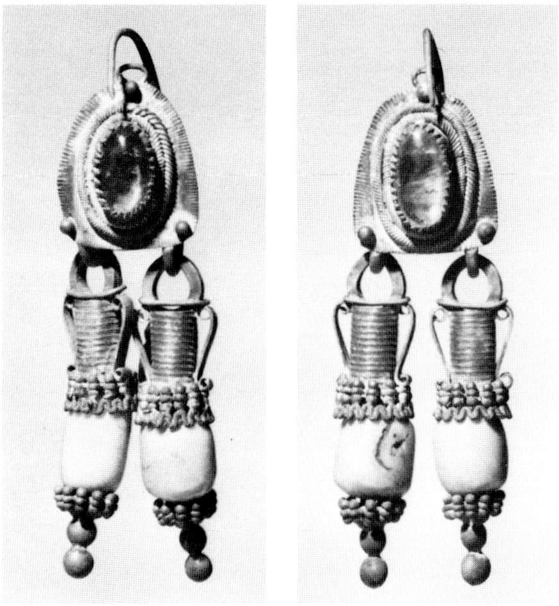

268
Pendant Earrings

Second half of fourth century A.D.
MATERIAL: Silver with amethyst and coral beads.
COLLECTION: *Cairo, Egyptian Museum JE 70357a-b.*

DESCRIPTION: An oval cabochon amethyst is mounted in a claw setting on a silver plaque. At the top of the plaque and in the lower corners are beadlike appliqués that conceal wire loops extending from the back of the earring. Suspended from the two bottom loops are filigreed pendants set with coral beads. A large wire hook is soldered to the back of the plaque and was secured in the top loop when the earring was worn.

COLOR: Amethysts violet; corals orange red.
CONDITION: Complete.
MEASUREMENTS: Length 9.5 cm. Width 2.9 cm.
PROVENANCE: Qustul, Tomb Q 14, in a linen bundle lying on surface above pit (Emery—Kirwan 1932-34, Object no. Q. 14-65).
BIBLIOGRAPHY: Emery 1932a,85; Emery—Kirwan 1938,47 (no. 65),193-94 (cat. no. 45), pl. 41 B; Emery 1948, pl. 21 B; Kirwan 1963,63 (pl. 20), 71-72; Emery 1965, pl. XV.

The earrings were found in a linen bundle lying near the skeleton of a woman whose throat had been cut. They are clearly late Roman in form. According to Török (1974,368), the grave, on the basis of other finds, should most probably be dated from the middle to the end of the fourth century and is contemporary with Tomb B 47 (see p. 103).

269
Bead Armlet

Fourth century A.D.
MATERIAL: Carnelian.
COLLECTION: *Cairo, Egyptian Museum JE 70347.*

DESCRIPTION: Fifteen large lenticular beads from an armlet were found on a man's left arm.

COLOR: Bright to dark violet.
CONDITION: Complete; beads slightly chipped.
MEASUREMENTS: Diameter of beads ca. 1.4 cm. Thickness 1.3 to 1.5 cm.
PROVENANCE: Ballana, Tomb B 9, on Burial C in burial pit (Emery—Kirwan 1932-34, Object no. B. 9-2).
BIBLIOGRAPHY: Emery—Kirwan 1938,89 (no. 2),188 (cat. no. 18), pl. 38 B (with incorrect object no. B. 9-3).

The man on whose skeleton the armlet was found was apparently a warrior, judging from the weapons buried with him. Cat. 274 comes from the same tomb; see the commentary thereto.

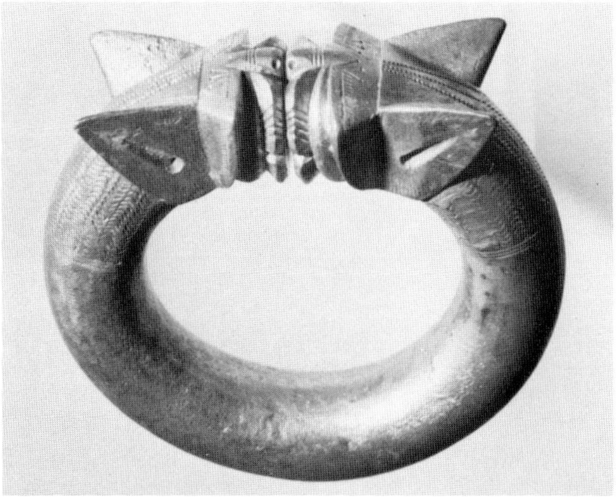

270
King's Massive Bracelet

Fourth century A.D.
MATERIAL: Silver.
COLLECTION: *Cairo, Egyptian Museum JE 70296.*

DESCRIPTION: A massive silver rod was curved to form a bracelet. The terminals are in the form of highly stylized lion's heads.

CONDITION: Complete.
MEASUREMENTS: Outer diameter 8.9 cm. Diameter of rod 2.7 cm.
PROVENANCE: Ballana, Tomb B 6, on Burial C (Emery—Kirwan 1932-34, Object no. B. 6-23).
BIBLIOGRAPHY: Emery 1933, unnumbered pl.,5 left; Emery—Kirwan 1938, 87 (no. 23), 187 (cat. no. 16), pl. 39 A bottom left; Emery 1948, pl. 17 B; Kirwan 1963,62 (pl. 19); Emery 1965, pl. XV.

The bracelet was found on the left wrist of the skeleton of a king, who was buried with his crown, jewelry, and weapons, including an iron spear. The lion's-head terminals are here merely decorative; they do not serve as clasps, as decorative terminals did in earlier bracelets.

271
Queen's Anklet

Second half of fourth century A.D.
MATERIAL: Silver.
COLLECTION: *Cairo, Egyptian Museum JE 70354.*

DESCRIPTION: The anklet is a thick silver rod curved almost into a circle. The terminals are in the form of highly stylized lion's heads.

CONDITION: Complete.
MEASUREMENTS: Outer diameter 8.5 to 10.0 cm. Diameter of rod 1.7 cm.
PROVENANCE: Ballana, Tomb B 47, on Burial C in Room 3 (Emery—Kirwan 1932-34, Object no. B. 47-40).
BIBLIOGRAPHY: Emery—Kirwan 1938,110 (no. 40),190 (cat. no. 29), pl. 39 B; Kirwan 1963,74f.

The unpillaged tomb of a queen was one of the richest in the cemetery. At the entrance lay the skeleton of a horse, and two men and a woman were found in the anterooms; they had probably been compelled to accompany their royal mistress in death as servants. The treasure in jewelry bestowed on the queen for her use in the hereafter is astonishing: twenty silver armlets, nine pairs of earrings, fourteen necklaces, eleven silver rings, and a great deal more, including a crown set with semi-precious stones. The anklet was found on her left ankle (Emery—Kirwan 1938,190 erroneously says "right ankle"). Stylistically, the lion's heads are very similar to those of the royal armlets from Ballana Tomb 6 (Cat. 270); the pieces must be fairly contemporary.

For the dating of the tomb, see Török 1974,365ff. (esp. 368). Cats. 275 and 278 come from the same tomb.

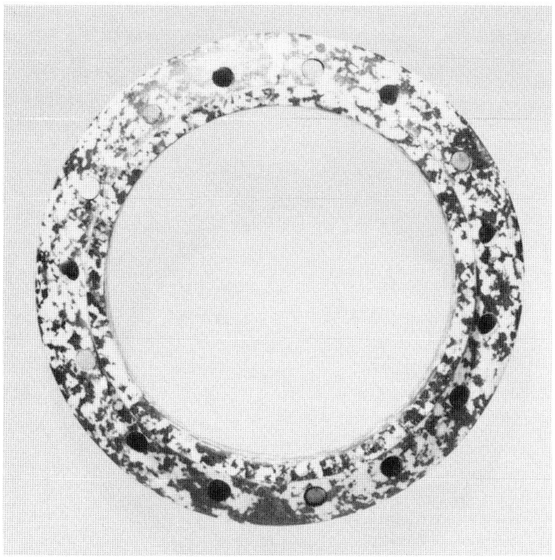

272
Armlet with Colored Inlays

Fourth to fifth century A.D.
MATERIAL: Breccia with paste inlays.
COLLECTION: *Cairo, Egyptian Museum JE 70351.*

DESCRIPTION: A hoop, fashioned from a single piece of stone, is flat on the inside and has a stepped profile. On both sides of the projecting ledge are fifteen colored paste inlays.

COLOR: Speckled gray and white; inlays orange, dark brown, and green.
CONDITION: Some inlays missing on one side.
MEASUREMENTS: Outer diameter 9.9 cm. Inner diameter 7.0 cm. Width 2.0 cm.
PROVENANCE: Ballana, Tomb B 80, on Burial H in Room 3 (Emery—Kirwan 1932-34, Object no. B. 80-33).
BIBLIOGRAPHY: Emery—Kirwan 1938,126 (no. 33),192 (cat. no. 36), pl. 38 C.

Three armlets, two of stone and one of silver, were found on the right arm of a servant dispatched with his king. Cats. 267 and 276 come from the same tomb.

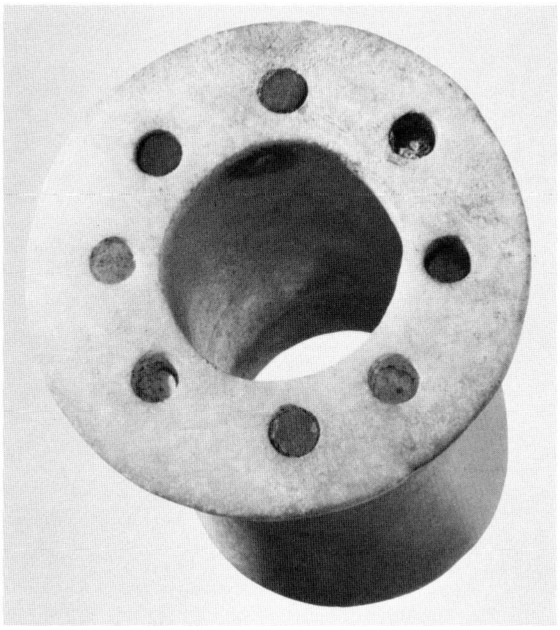

273
Archer's Ornamented Thumb-Guard

Fourth to fifth century A.D.
MATERIAL: Alabaster with glass and stone inlays.
COLLECTION: *London, British Museum 64043.*

DESCRIPTION: The thumb-guard is polished and comparatively thin-walled. Colored stone and glass inlays are set into eight depressions drilled into the flat edge of the wide end.

COLOR: Whitish; inlays dark green and brown.
CONDITION: Five inlays missing; somewhat abraded and slightly chipped; brownish discoloration in places.
MEASUREMENTS: Height 5.0 cm. Outer diameter 4.3 (top) to 3.1 cm. Inner diameter 2.0 (top) to 2.1 cm.
PROVENANCE: Sesebi, Grave 201, northwest of the city (Blackman 1936-37, Excavation no. 36.37.329).
BIBLIOGRAPHY: None.

The object was found on the floor of the brick-vaulted burial chamber, among the remains of a bed; for its identification as a thumb-guard, see the commentary to Cat. 217. Thumb-guards were in use in the Sudan over a long period and changed very little, so their dating depends on the context of the find. It is certain that thumb-guards decorated with inlays on one edge belong to the Ballana culture; the inlays recall those of the stone armlet, Cat. 272. Hayes (1973,114, fig. 3) classifies guards of this shape in her type 1C. I am indebted to H. W. Fairman for information about this piece.

274
Archer's Bracer

Fourth century A.D.
MATERIAL: Silver.
COLLECTION: *Cairo, Egyptian Museum JE 70758.*

DESCRIPTION: The bracer is shaped like a pair of wings, with a tablike extension in the center. It is decorated with engraved geometric designs.

CONDITION: Complete; broken and repaired with wax.
MEASUREMENTS: Length 10.9 cm. Width 6.1 cm., at top 4.1 cm.
PROVENANCE: Ballana, Tomb B 9, near Burial C in burial pit (Emery—Kirwan 1932-34, Object no. B. 9-28).
BIBLIOGRAPHY: Emery—Kirwan 1938,90 (no. 28),233 (cat. no. 277), pl. 52 B, fig. 86 B opposite 233.

The object was found on the left wrist of a warrior who had been buried with his sword, spears, thumb-guards, and many other valuable possessions. That bracers such as this were generally used by archers is suggested by several examples found at Ballana. The tablike extension was secured over the thumb with a chain and protected it from the released bowstring. The wings were held in place probably by a leather thong around the wrist.

275
Incense Burner in the Form of a Pine Cone

Second half of fourth century A.D.
MATERIAL: Bronze.
COLLECTION: *Cairo, Egyptian Museum JE 70924.*

DESCRIPTION: An incense burner shaped like a pine cone rests on an openwork column supported by a pedestal with four feet in the form of lion's paws. The top of the cone is a hinged lid that can be swung open. The meticulously engraved scales of the lid are almost closed, while those of the lower part are opened out. A leaf and tendril pattern decorates the column, and a beaded band makes the transition from the shaft to its tall base. The openwork walls of the pedestal are also decorated with leaves and tendrils, and *ankh*-signs are incised in the top corners. The incense fumes escaped through a large hole in the center of the lid and two rows of smaller holes.

COLOR: Golden brown.
CONDITION: Complete; small areas of corrosion.
MEASUREMENTS: Height 25.7 cm. Width of pedestal 11.4 cm.
PROVENANCE: Ballana, Tomb B 47, Room 2 (Emery—Kirwan 1932-34, Object no. B. 47-10).
BIBLIOGRAPHY: Emery—Kirwan 1938,108 (no. 10),362-63 (cat. no. 804), pl. 97 A.

A similar incense burner was found in Tomb B 121. The forms, e.g., the base of the shaft and the leaf and tendril pattern, come from the late antique repertoire. Based on the meticulous fashioning of the scales and the plasticity of those on the lower part of the cone, the incised details of the scales and the leaves in the tendril patterns, and the plasticity of the feet, A. Effenberger suggests a date in the second half of the fourth century A.D., when very probably the object was indigenous (verbal communication). Török (1974,365ff., esp. 368) arrived at the same date for the tomb, which he placed in the middle or late fourth century. Cats. 271 and 278 come from the same tomb.

276
Incense Burner in the Form of a Lion

Fourth to fifth century A.D.
MATERIAL: Bronze.
COLLECTION: *Cairo, Egyptian Museum JE 70925.*

DESCRIPTION: The incense burner is in the form of a highly stylized standing lion with a detachable head. In the wide open jaws one can see not only the teeth but a tiny tongue. The mane is very schematically rendered, and the long thin tail is tucked under the right hind leg to end in a curl on the right flank. There are loops at the back of the head and the base of the tail, from which chain links still hang. The fumes escaped from openings in the jaws, nose, and ears, as well as in the sides of the body.

COLOR: Golden brown.
CONDITION: Large piece missing from left side of body; small areas of corrosion.
MEASUREMENTS: Height 18.0 cm. Length 18.7 cm. Width 8.7 cm.
PROVENANCE: Ballana, Tomb B 80, Room 4 (Emery—Kirwan 1932-34, Object no. B. 80-59).
BIBLIOGRAPHY: ILN 1933b,922 (illus.); Zippert 1933-34,154 (fig. 10); Emery—Kirwan 1938,128 (no. 59),363 (cat. no. 805), pl. 96 A; Bissing 1941,14-15, fig. 8; Bissing[1939-41],25 (fig. 3),27; Emery 1948, pl. 42 B; Kirwan 1963,68 (pl. 34), 76; Emery 1965, pl. XVII; Dakar—Paris 1966, no. 471.

Tomb B 80 of a king was the most opulently furnished in the Ballana cemetery. The ruler was accompanied in death by several servants, including a woman, and by a camel and a dog. The offerings included a variety of weapons, such as swords, spears, and arrowheads, as well as thumb-guards, tools, and bronze objects of diverse kinds.

This incense burner has achieved considerable renown in the scientific literature on account of its style. Bissing (1941,14,n. 29) stated that the excavators thought it might have an East Asian provenance, which Kirwan (1963,76) confirmed. Kirwan still thought that Persian influence was very likely and referred to a similar vessel, though of a later date, that was seen in an exhibition of Iranian art held in London in 1962 (ibid. pl. 35). Bissing, however, stated long ago (1941,14-15) that similar Coptic objects existed; in his opinion, the present piece is Egyptian and cannot be dated later than the fifth century A.D., based on a comparison with a related piece in Karlsruhe. Bissing states (1941,15) that there are similar East Asiatic objects, which he thinks are based on the same prototypes as the present piece, but he does not specify what these prototypes might be. A. Effenberger rejects both an Alexandrian and a Coptic provenance for the incense burner; he believes it is Nubian but says that the possibility of East Asiatic influence is not to be excluded (verbal communication). Cats. 267 and 272 come from the same tomb.

277
Hanging Lamp in the Form of a Dove

Late fourth century A.D.
MATERIAL: Bronze.
COLLECTION: *Oxford, Ashmolean Museum 1935.488.*

DESCRIPTION: The lamp is in the form of a dove with a long beak, its head turned slightly to the right. The wings are plastically formed, and the plumage is incised, individual feathers being carefully rendered. The tail terminates in a burner, and a curving spur underneath it serves for support. The oil hole on the back has a hinged triangular lid. Three loops for chains are attached to the back of the neck and the sides of the tail, the chains being gathered into a large metal loop from which a single chain leads to a double suspension hook.

COLOR: Brown.
CONDITION: Complete; upper beak broken off and repaired; discolored in places.
MEASUREMENTS: Height 11.2 cm. Length 15.7 cm. Width 6.5 cm. Length of chain ca. 54.0 cm.
PROVENANCE: Ferka, Cemetery A, on mound above Tomb 12 (Kirwan 1934-35, Excavation no. A/12/1).
BIBLIOGRAPHY: Kirwan 1935,194, pl. XXI,3; Zippert 1936-37,183; Emery—Kirwan 1938,168; Kirwan 1939,7,31, pl. VII; Bissing 1939a, col. 578; Bissing 1941,11 (fig. 3),12; Bissing [1939-41],22; Arkell 1950a, 38,39 pl. 1, fig. 1; Arkell 1961,183 (fig. 23a).

Bissing (1941,12) has demonstrated that lamps of avian form (they were not all doves) were developed in Christian Egypt in the fourth to seventh century A.D. and spread from there, even reaching Germany with the Romans (Grimm 1969, 52-53).

Closely related to the present piece is a lamp found in Altrip Citadel and now in the Speyer Museum (Bissing 1941,11, fig. 4). According to Volbach (1921, pl. 8,42; cited by Bissing (1941, 12,n. 15), it should be dated to the third or fourth century. G. Bersu, the excavator of Altrip, dated it to the second half of the fourth century (Bissing 1941,12, no. 14). Bissing also stated (1939a, col. 579) that it could be dated fairly accurately to A.D. 380. The date given here for the present piece is based on its resemblance to the Altrip lamp. Kirwan dated it to the fifth or sixth century.

Similar lamps have been found at Qustul (Cairo JE 71131 from Tomb Q 14) and at Sheikh Abade (Antinoopolis) in Upper Egypt (Recklinghausen 515: Wessel 1963,29, pl. I; Effenberger 1975, pl. 88). These lamps all have double burners instead of a single one. Volbach dated the Recklinghausen lamp to the fifth century (Essen 1963,278, no. 189). Effenberger (1975,197) suggested the fifth to sixth century, which is certainly too late.

Also found in Tomb A 12 at Ferka was a coin dating from the reign of the Emperor Commodus (A.D. 180-92). Taking this find, too, into consideration, Bissing repeatedly asserted that the grave—and therefore the lamp as well—could not be dated later than the fourth century.

278
Lamp in the Form of a Male Head

Second half of fourth century A.D.
MATERIAL: Bronze with silver and garnet inlays.
COLLECTION: *Cairo, Egyptian Museum JE 71124.*

DESCRIPTION: The lamp is in the form of a male head, flattened in back and resting on a ring base. The eyes are inlaid, with garnet pupils and silver eyeballs. The stylized hair is arranged in incised waves reaching to the ears. The oil hole is on the crown of the head, and a handle hinged to the top loops round to serve as a lid as well. The burner is in the base of the flattened neck.

COLOR: Golden brown; garnet inlays red.
CONDITION: Complete.
MEASUREMENTS: Height 5.1 cm., with lid 5.9 cm. Length 12.0 cm., of face 6.1 cm. Width 6.1 cm.
PROVENANCE: Ballana, Tomb B 47, Room 3 (Emery—Kirwan 1932-34, Object no. B. 47-67).
BIBLIOGRAPHY: Emery—Kirwan 1938,111 (no. 67),371 (cat. no. 831), pl. 102 C; Emery 1948, pl. 40 A; Essen 1963,381, no. 466 (illus.).

Three lamps of this type have been found. The second came from Qustul Tomb 3 (Cairo JE 71125: Emery—Kirwan 1938, pl. 102 E), and the third was found at Qasr Ibrim by Emery (Bacon 1971,227, fig. 80). Volbach (Essen 1963,381) has stated that they would be inconceivable without the influence of early Byzantine heads. When he says that these early Byzantine influences were transmuted into a characteristic and expressive style, he means that he thinks the lamps are Nubian products, an opinion with which I concur. A. Effenberger, however, believes this lamp is an import from Alexandria or the Fayum and dates it to the middle of the fourth century (verbal communication); he thinks it reflects certain stylistic peculiarities of Alexandrian art of the early fourth century and refers to the tetrarch groups in Venice (Effenberger 1975, fig. 3) for the form of the ears.

If we consider the lamp along with other objects from the royal tombs at Ballana, e.g., Cat. 279, it becomes clear that there was indeed a strong Alexandrian influence, which had appeared in Lower Nubia as early as the second and third centuries A.D. (Cats. 161 and 215; Figs. 61, 62, 67, 68).

Bissing (1939b, col. 509) thinks the lamps may be provincial products, without the archaistic features of, for example, the standard lamps (Cat. 279) or the crudity of the fifth- and sixth-century terracottas from the city of Menas (Kaufmann 1910, pls. 73-76).

Illustrated in color, Volume I, page 114.

279
Standard Lamp

Fourth to fifth century A.D.
MATERIAL: Bronze.
COLLECTION: *Cairo, Egyptian Museum JE 71151.*

DESCRIPTION: A naked youth holds two poles in the form of plant stems, each with a capital surmounted by a large circular plate and a detachable lamp in the form of a dolphin, one of which has an *ankh*-sign mounted on its tail. The youth's hair is parted in the middle and edged with two rows of curls worked in the round; he wears a thick fillet. The eyebrows are rendered as closely spaced incised vertical dashes, and the nose and chin are sharply pointed. The body is more summarily modeled. Around the youth's neck is a ribbon, indicated by two incised lines, from which hangs a cross incised on his chest.

COLOR: Dark brown.
CONDITION: One plate and *ankh*-sign missing; corrosion damage in places.
MEASUREMENTS: Height (excluding modern base) 48.0 cm. Height of youth 31.0 cm. Width across hands 15.4 cm.
PROVENANCE: Ballana, Tomb B 3, Room 2 (Emery—Kirwan 1932-34, Object no. B. 3-37).
BIBLIOGRAPHY: ILN 1932,956-57 (fig. 8); Emery—Kirwan 1938,80 (no. 37), 366 (cat. no. 811), pl. 98 C; Bissing [1939-41],24; Emery 1948, pl. 37 B.

Two other standard lamps of this type were found in the royal tombs of Ballana (B 2 and B 80). In these two examples, Maltese crosses rather than *ankh*-signs are mounted on the dolphins' tails. Like the cross the youth wears in the present piece, they indicate Christian influence. It is not certain, however, that they were made by Christians, and they certainly cannot be regarded as evidence that the rulers of Ballana had adopted Christianity, for the barbaric custom of sacrificing retainers and dependents was still practiced here.

Bissing discussed these lamps in detail (1939a, cols. 577-78; 1939b, col. 509; 1941,15-16). He believes them to be pagan household articles that were taken over by an Egyptian cloister and then stolen, and he refers here to the reports of the Coptic *apa,* or abbott, Shenute, regarding the pillaging of the monasteries about A.D. 400 by the invading Nobadae from Lower Nubia (1939a, col. 578). Stylistically, according to Bissing, these figures of youths are non-Egyptian and archaistic, reflecting provincial archaism based on a "good Greek foundation" (1939b, col. 509). Bissing refers to human figures used as lamp bearers discovered in Etruria and Pompeii, which are, however, earlier in date than the Ballana pieces and hold only one lamp (1941, 15,n. 35). Youths holding two lamps appear, sporadically, only in the Romanesque age (Erfurt Cathedral: ibid. 16).

Bissing thinks these lamps can have originated only in a center of Greek culture, not in distant southern Nubia, and he therefore regards the present piece as an import from one of the Roman cities of Egypt: Ptolemais, Antinoopolis, or Alexandria itself (1941,16). A. Effenberger is in partial agreement. On stylistic grounds, he thinks the lamps may be early Coptic (Antinoopolis, latter half of the fourth century), and suggests that they were possibly manufactured in a Christianized workshop, although he does not believe they came to Nubia until the fifth or sixth century (verbal communication). This dating, however, is too late, since Tomb B 3 must be dated to the fourth or fifth century.

G. Grimm knows of no related pieces in Egyptian or Alexandrian art and therefore thinks the lamp bearers are clearly Nubian in origin (verbal communication to B. V. Bothmer).

280
Horse-Head Lamp

Probably second to third century A.D.
MATERIAL: Bronze.
COLLECTION: *London, British Museum 66576.*

DESCRIPTION: The lamp has a tublike body with an elongation for the burner, a raised rim, and a ring base. The heart-shaped oil hole and round burner are worked into the depressed top, and a curving ornament is engraved above the oil hole. The handle arches back over the lamp and ends in a horse's head with open jaws and upright ears; the features of the head and neck, including the musculature and the stylized mane, are carefully worked.

COLOR: Light brown to black.
CONDITION: Tip of horse's right ear missing; handle broken and repaired.
MEASUREMENTS: Height 10.1 cm., of lamp 4.8 cm. Length 19.7 cm. Width 8.2 cm. Diameter of base 5.6 cm.
PROVENANCE: Qasr Ibrim, Cemetery 192, Tomb 23 (Emery 1961-62, Excavation no. 192-23-32).
BIBLIOGRAPHY: Emery 1962, 607, fig. 17; Bacon 1971, 226, 227 (fig. 79).

This lamp, found in a tomb of the Ballana culture, reflects the stylistic influence of late Hellenistic art. A similar object, in which the handle ends in a horse's forequarters, was found in Pyramid Beg. N. 18 of Queen Amanikhatashan of the late first to early second century A.D. (Boston 24.967: Dunham 1957, pl. LI A). Thus, these lamps must have been fairly common in Meroe. Although they were influenced by late Hellenistic art, it must be assumed that they were indigenous products; see commentary to Cat. 200.

A. J. Mills dates the lamp to the first to second century A.D. (letter of August 24, 1976, to A. J. Spencer of the British Museum) and refers to Pompeian parallels. To him I owe the information that Grave 23 was one of the most opulent in Cemetery 192.

281
Bowl with Loop Handles

Probably fifth century A.D.
MATERIAL: Bronze.
COLLECTION: *Cairo, Egyptian Museum JE 89674.*

DESCRIPTION: A shallow, straight-walled bowl has a wide, flat lip encircled by a beaded band and rests on a separately made stem with a flaring foot, decorated with another beaded band. Two elaborate loop handles soldered to the sides of the vessel are adorned with lion's heads. Double lines are incised on the lip, on the bowl, and on the foot, and there are concentric circles inside the vessel.

COLOR: Brown; small areas of discoloration.
CONDITION: Complete.
MEASUREMENTS: Height 15.4 cm., of bowl 12.4 cm. Width 22.0 cm. Diameter at lip 18.1 cm., at foot 9.6 cm.
PROVENANCE: Qasr Ibrim, Cemetery 192, Tomb 2 (Emery 1961, Excavation no. 192-2-129).
BIBLIOGRAPHY: Emery 1967, pl. II.

From Emery's description (1967, 57, fig. 1), the bowl must have come from Tomb 2 in Cemetery 192. The plunderers who had ransacked most of the tombs failed to note that this one contained a magazine next to the burial chamber. The discoveries made in this undisturbed room were astonishingly abundant and included numerous bronze objects. Bowls such as the present one are, in form and workmanship, typical products of post-Meroitic culture in Lower Nubia. Similar or almost identical examples were found in, among other places, the royal Tomb B 4 at Ballana (Emery — Kirwan 1938, pl. 72) and in more recent excavations at the same place (Farid 1963b, 91, pl. V) as well as at Gemai (Khartoum 1505: Shinnie 1967, pl. 66). The relatively wide distribution of these vessels in Lower Nubia indicates that they are indigenous Nubian products.

A lamp in the form of a man's head, similar to Cat. 278, was also found in the tomb.

282
Kohl Pot in the Form of a Sphinx

Second half of fourth century A.D.
MATERIAL: Wood and ivory.
COLLECTION: *Cairo, Egyptian Museum JE 70422.*

DESCRIPTION: A sphinx wearing a long wig with a fillet and a small uraeus sits on a pedestal in the form of an Egyptian cavetto cornice. The eyes are inlaid. The pointed beard reaches to the ears. A deep tubular cavity is bored into the top of the head.

COLOR: Dark brown; inlays black and white.
CONDITION: Nose and beard partly missing; small hole in back of head and wormholes in back of figure; corners of base chipped.
MEASUREMENTS: Height 11.0 cm. Width 3.2 cm. Depth 3.8 cm.
PROVENANCE: Qustul, Tomb Q 14, in leather bag above pit opening (Emery—Kirwan 1932-34, Object no. Q. 14-58).
BIBLIOGRAPHY: Emery — Kirwan 1938,47 (no. 58), 343 (cat. no. 736), pl. 86 B-C; Emery 1948, pl. 36 A; Emery 1965, pl. XIV.

Judging by the weapons in the grave, Tomb Q 14 certainly belonged to a man. On the surface lay the skeleton of a woman whose throat had been slit (see commentary to Cat. 268). She was probably the widow of the deceased; whether she willingly accompanied her husband in death or was violently dispatched is impossible to say. In a leather bag and a linen bundle were found numerous objects, principally cosmetic articles and jewelry, including the earrings, Cat. 268, as well as the present piece, which still had a residue of kohl paste inside. The tomb also contained a hanging lamp stylistically quite similar to Cat. 277.

The motif of the seated sphinx is Egyptian and was preserved through Meroitic art into the Ballana Period. Stylistically, however, this sphinx is clearly post-Meroitic.

283
Small Block with Relief Carving

Probably second half of fourth century A.D.
MATERIAL: Sandstone.
COLLECTION: *London, British Museum 67158.*

DESCRIPTION: A small block, slightly larger at the top, has approximately square depressions in both top and bottom surfaces. All four sides are carved with relief representations of naked human figures, two men alternating with two steatopygous women. The figures all extend their arms sideways and hold stylized trees or bunches of plants, which frame the corners of the block. The men are shown in frontal view, squatting with their legs outspread and genitalia clearly exposed. They have pointed faces and curved double lines running across the forehead. The women are crouched on the left leg, the right knee raised and head turned to the left. Both men and women wear double hoops on the upper arms, bracelets, and anklets; the women have necklaces as well. The sides of the block are framed at the top by three parallel ridges in bold relief.

COLOR: Brownish yellow.
CONDITION: Large piece missing from top of block; numerous chips; blackish discoloration in places.
MEASUREMENTS: Height 10.6 cm. Width ca. 10.4 cm.
PROVENANCE: Qasr Ibrim, House X-1, Room 2, floor of second stratum (Plumley 1964, Excavation no. 64/52).
BIBLIOGRAPHY: None.

The excavator regarded the block as a capital for a timber pillar (British Museum inventory entry), a plausible interpretation considering the depressions in its top and bottom surfaces. On the other hand, one can't entirely exclude the possibility of its having been a bed pedestal. The representations are of no help in determining the block's function. Very few examples of relief work are known from the Ballana Period, and they cannot be dated with any precision; this absence of parallels makes it difficult to say anything about the function of the present piece.

284
Inlay in the Form of a Naked Woman

Fourth to fifth century A.D.
MATERIAL: Ivory.
COLLECTION: *Brooklyn (New York), The Brooklyn Museum, Charles Edwin Wilbour Fund 60.66.2.*

DESCRIPTION: An ivory inlay from a casket is in the form of a naked woman who clutches her long wig in both hands. Her breasts and navel are indicated by concentric circles. She wears a mantle visible on both sides of her body, a ball-bead necklace, armlets, and bracelets.

COLOR: Light brown; black substance in incisions.
CONDITION: Complete.
MEASUREMENTS: Height 7.9 cm. Width 3.4 cm. Thickness 0.2 cm.
PROVENANCE: Not known; probably Gebel Adda.
BIBLIOGRAPHY: None.

The inlay comes from a casket, such as those which have been found in tombs of the Ballana culture. An almost identical inlay (Cairo JE 90041) was found in Grave 848 of Gebel Adda Cemetery 3. We may infer, therefore, that Gebel Adda was also the provenance of the present piece.

The outstanding example of casket inlay is the end of a large wooden chest found in the royal Tomb Q 14 at Qustul and dated to the second half of the fourth century (Fig. 80). Its numerous and varied ivory inlays include figurative motifs as well as ornamental ones. A similar chest in a good state of preservation found at Gebel Adda has inlaid representations of the deities Venus, Hathor, and Harpocrates (Millet 1964, pl. IV, figs. 9-10). Millet (ibid. 9) believes that such chests came to Lower Nubia from Byzantine Egypt as trade or booty. It is true that similar objects of the same period have been found in Egypt, e.g., a fragment of a chest from Hawara with representations of nymphs, winged boys, and birds (Petrie 1889, 12, pl. XVIII).

Bissing (1941,24,n. 76) also thought such chests were Egyptian imports. But he refers to the Karanog chests (ibid. 24,nn. 76-77; 1939a, col. 579), such as Cats. 208 and 209. These chests, which must be dated to the late Meroitic Period, are similar in form to the Ballana Period chests, and they have ivory inlays. Although these inlays do not include figurative motifs, such as those which appear in some of the later finds from Egypt and Lower Nubia, they do prove that Nubia had an earlier tradition of inlaid chests. The ball-bead necklace worn by the Brooklyn figure is reminiscent of a type of ornament worn in Nubia since much earlier times and may be a sign of a Nubian origin.

That human figures, mainly deities of the Egyptian and Greek pantheons, as well as animals and sphinxes appear as inlaid motifs does not preclude the possibility that the chests originated in Nubia. Relations with Egypt were very close during this period, and many influences flowed from north to south.

285
Ovoid Beaker

Fourth to sixth century A.D.
MATERIAL: Fired clay.
COLLECTION: *Cambridge, Fitzwilliam Museum E.2.1962.*

DESCRIPTION: The wall of a wide-mouthed ovoid beaker is drawn in and then expands again to the flat base. On two sides of the vessel are painted vertical rows of horizontal dashes from the rim almost to the middle of the body. On the other two sides are three horizontal strokes beginning at the rim and diverging slightly as they swoop down the body. Two irregular lines are incised around the widest point of the vessel.

COLOR: Dark red brown; decoration whitish yellow.
CONDITION: Complete; foot slightly chipped.
MEASUREMENTS: Height 13.6 cm. Diameter 11.2 cm., at mouth 8.9 cm., at foot 5.5 cm.
PROVENANCE: Qasr Ibrim, Cemetery 193, Tomb 151 (Emery 1962, Excavation no. 193-151-1).
BIBLIOGRAPHY: None.

The vessel form evolved from such frequently found Meroitic beakers as Cat. 258. It reflects, therefore, the cultural continuity between the Meroitic and Ballana Periods. The decoration, however, belongs to the Ballana Period only; it is not found on Meroitic ceramics.

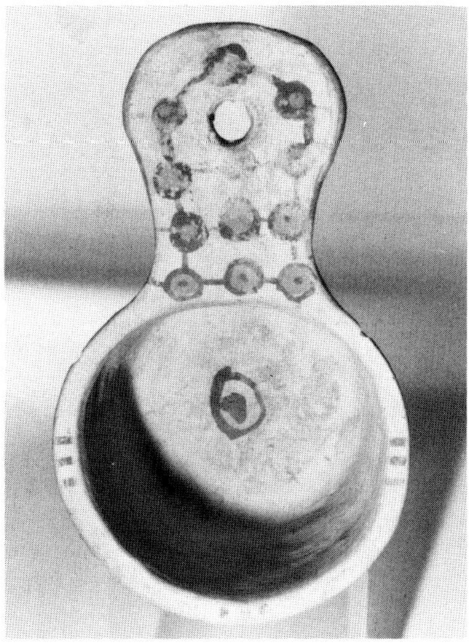

286
Long-Handled Beaker

Fourth century A.D.
MATERIAL: Fired clay.
COLLECTION: *Cairo, Egyptian Museum JE 89935.*

DESCRIPTION: A painted cylindrical beaker has a flat, narrow projecting lip and a wide flat handle with incurved sides and a rounded end. On the lip are three groups of three short black strokes, and on the handle are circles connected by rods. Below the rim is a band of concentric circles joined by horizontal lines and, below, several encircling stripes. A circle with a dot inside it is painted on the floor of the vessel.

COLOR: Buff; decoration black, red, and pink.
CONDITION: Complete; chipped and colors badly abraded.
MEASUREMENTS: Height 9.2 cm. Width 15.3 cm. Diameter 9.2 cm.
PROVENANCE: Qustul (Seele 1963-64, Excavation no. Q-2288).
BIBLIOGRAPHY: None.

The beaker is undoubtedly an imitation of a bronze vessel, since examples of the latter have been found repeatedly in Nubia. The date is based on the very schematic decoration, which reflects the transition to the Ballana culture, and on the fact that beakers with handles were used in the fourth century.

287
Black Pot with Cruciform Ornament

Probably third to fourth century A.D.
MATERIAL: Fired clay.
COLLECTION: *Oxford, Ashmolean Museum 1912.897.*

DESCRIPTION: A polished spherical pot has a low neck and a wide mouth. Below the slightly flaring lip is a band of closely spaced short vertical grooves. A cruciform design is incised on all four sides of the body.

COLOR: Black; incisions filled with white.
CONDITION: Broken and repaired, with restorations; chipped in places.
MEASUREMENTS: Height 8.0 cm. Diameter 8.8 cm., at lip 6.5 cm.
PROVENANCE: Faras, Western Palace (Griffith 1912).
BIBLIOGRAPHY: Griffith 1926,22,31, pl. XVIII,9.

Several black pots (including Cat. 260) were found in the Meroitic cemetery at Faras; some have very similar cruciform designs (Griffith 1924, pl. XLI,9,18). They bear out Griffith's contention (ibid. 157, pl. XLI,9) that the design represents a stylized lotus blossom. The present example is even more stylized than the ones Griffith illustrated. The ornament has no relation to the Christian symbol.

The form of the pot is common for black ware. Another example comes from Faras Grave 2335 (ibid. pl. XV, type IIj).

288
Stand for a Large Bowl

Fourth to sixth century A.D.
MATERIAL: Fired clay.
COLLECTION: *Brussels, Musées Royaux d'Art et d'Histoire E. 3106.*

DESCRIPTION: A stand intended to support a large dish or other vessel has a shallow bowl, a fluted stem, and a tall base. The stand is hollow throughout. It is decorated in white with cross-hatched stripes and dotted triangles.

COLOR: Red brown; decoration white.
CONDITION: Broken and repaired; minor chips; discolored in places.
MEASUREMENTS: Height 29.4 cm. Diameter at rim 15.6 cm., at foot 11.0 cm.
PROVENANCE: Meroe, Grave 309 (Garstang 1910).
BIBLIOGRAPHY: Garstang 1911, pl. XLV, no. 23; Werbrouck 1945,2 (fig. 2),5.

Garstang found a large quantity of such objects in a cemetery lying directly east of the city of Meroe. From photographs preserved in Liverpool, it follows that fairly large vessels or dishes were placed in the cavities of these stands. Nothing comparable is known from the Meroitic Period or the post-Meroitic Ballana culture of Lower Nubia. These stands are the products of a population that made its home in the northern Sudan after the fall of the Meroitic empire, since the context of the finds results in a post-Meroitic dating. These new inhabitants of Meroe and its environs must have been the Noba, who are mentioned in the inscription of the Axumite King Ezana (see Vol. I, p. 105).

289
Christian Relief

Early seventh century A.D.
MATERIAL: Sandstone.
COLLECTION: *Warsaw, Muzeum Narodowe 234081.*

DESCRIPTION: A bird with stylized upraised wings, its body turned to the left and its head to the right, is represented in bold raised relief on a rectangular block that comes from a frieze. A bulla hangs from a ribbon around its neck, and above its head is a Maltese cross. Below the left wing is a columnar altar. The bird is flanked by two tall columns with rectangular bases and capitals with leafy volutes and stylized oval fruit. The capitals are surmounted by decorated abaci and architrave blocks. On the right is visible the wing of another bird with an altar beneath it. The relief was once whitewashed.

COLOR: Red; traces of whitewash.
CONDITION: Damaged around edges and in middle of left wing.
MEASUREMENTS: Height 25.6 cm. Width 42.8 cm. Thickness 16.5 cm.
PROVENANCE: Faras, found reused in the pedestal for a monumental cross (Michałowski 1963-64, Excavation no. 86/63-4).
BIBLIOGRAPHY: Michałowski 1966,1; Michałowski 1967,64,pl. 14; Iwaszkiewicz 1974,381f., fig. 2 on 407.

The 1960-64 Polish excavations at Faras turned up several very similar architectural blocks that had originally formed part of a frieze around the apse of the first cathedral on the site (Warsaw 234082 and 234083: Iwaszkiewicz 1974,377ff.). This was a triple-naved structure with an apse at the north end, erected at the beginning of the seventh century on the ruins of a more ancient building from the pagan era. It was destroyed toward the middle of the seventh century during the Arab invasion from Egypt, and later another church was built close by the south gate to the fortress of Faras. In front of this church was erected a large stone pedestal for a monumental wooden cross. The present block was found embedded in this pedestal, and others from the same frieze were reused in the walls and apse of the second cathedral (Michałowski 1965,184).

The bird with its head turned was adopted from Egypt, where it was a frequent motif in early Christian iconography. It has been found in several places in Lower Nubia, e.g., a fragment of a stela from Qasr Ibrim (Plumley 1970b, fig. 109; Dinkler 1975, fig. 11). The species of the bird remains uncertain. Michałowski (Berlin 1968, no. 34) and Plumley (1970b,132) think it is a dove, which is plausible in view of the importance of the dove in Christian iconography. E. Lucchesi Palli (1972, cited by Dinkler 1975,27) believes it to be an eagle, another bird that had an important place in early Christian art. Dinkler (1975,28) is undecided on this question. The birds almost always wear a bulla, a small case serving as an amulet, suspended from a ribbon around the neck.

A very similar block entered the collection of the British Museum (BM 606) before 1840, its provenance unknown. Considering its resemblances to the recently discovered reliefs, there can be no further doubt that it, too, comes from Faras (Iwaszkiewicz 1974,384f.).

For the decoration of early Christian churches in Nubia, see pp. 109-11.

290 ■
Relief Fragment with Warrior Saint

Late eleventh or twelfth century A.D.
MATERIAL: Wood.
COLLECTION: *Khartoum, Sudan National Museum 20719.*

DESCRIPTION: A warrior saint and a horse are represented in a fragment cut out of a wooden relief. The saint is standing on the body of a fallen man whose head is raised. He wears a long robe, secured at the breast with a cruciform clasp, and a cape, and holds a long sword in his left hand. The bridled horse is turned to the right, its forequarters being visible in side view next to the saint. The back of the relief is covered with a Greek inscription starting with the name of Saint Epimachus. A vertical strip of wood projecting from the back is perforated at the top.

COLOR: Dark brown with bright patches.
CONDITION: Left side broken off; front and back abraded and contours worn smooth.
MEASUREMENTS: Height 21.6 cm. Width 8.4 cm. Thickness ca. 1.0 cm.
PROVENANCE: Attiri, Church, southeast room (Mills 1966-67, Excavation no. 16-J-6/45).
BIBLIOGRAPHY: None.

Attiri, a rocky island at the southern end of the Second Cataract, was the home of a Christian community in the fourteenth century. This wooden relief was found with four similar pieces in a church; all show traces of long use. According to A. J. Mills, who provided information about the object, these are fairly ancient pieces worn on the breast by priests during the divine service. A similar relief was found by Plumley at Qasr Ibrim in a tomb dated to the eleventh or twelfth century, where it lay on the body of the deceased (Plumley 1966,11, pl. VI,4; Plumley 1970b, 133, fig. 81). Whether these objects were originally intended as pectorals is doubtful, however, since the projecting strip of wood on the back indicates that it was meant to be inlaid into some sort of background. The inscription is secondary, in Mills' opinion, and was incised only after the left side of the piece was broken off. The identification to Saint Epimachus, who is named in the inscription, may accordingly be secondary as well; the image might be that of a crusader.

Mills believes the relief to be an import, and others have suggested Syria as its place of origin. Plumley, however, is convinced that the piece he found is a product of Christian Nubian art, about which we know very little. I believe that this object, with its scene of Christian triumph, originated in Nubia, although a stylistic influence from elsewhere is by no means denied.

291 ■
Saint Menas on Horseback

About A.D. 1000.
MATERIAL: Parchment.
COLLECTION: *London, British Museum OR 6805.*

DESCRIPTION: At the end of a manuscript consisting of eighteen sheets of parchment is the drawing of a man on horseback who, according to the legend written above his head, is Saint Menas. The saint, whose face is shown in profile, wears a tunic and a Roman military uniform. He has two bracelets on his right wrist. He holds a javelin pointing downward, and a circular shield is visible behind his left shoulder. Three crowns are painted above him. A naked man with a long pointed beard is kneeling in front of the horse, his head and torso turned toward the viewer and his right hand reaching out to touch the horse's hoof. A cloth is folded over his left arm. Between his legs can be seen the head of a cock.

COLOR: Brown, yellowed; drawing black.
CONDITION: Damaged at top, bottom, and right edges.
MEASUREMENTS: Page size 14.9 by 9.0 cm.
PROVENANCE: Found by nomadic Arabs in the hills near Edfu. Given to the British Museum in 1907 by R. de Rustafjaell.
BIBLIOGRAPHY: Budge 1909,13ff.; Griffith 1909; Griffith 1913,4, 6-15; Zyhlarz 1928,132-44; Müller 1975,93ff., esp. 94.

The parchment manuscript consists of two parts; the first is paginated and contains a text in Old Nubian. It was found together with some Coptic manuscripts, all of which had originally been stored in the Makarios monastery near Edfu. During the persecutions of the Christians by al-Hakim between 1007 and 1012, they were removed for safekeeping to Serra, near Faras (Griffith 1913,4). Since the language is Old Nubian, the manuscript must have originated in Nubia.

The text is a sermon in simple language relating a miracle wrought by Saint Menas on a pagan woman who lived in a village near Alexandria and was barren, like all the creatures living in her house. Hearing of the miracles the saint was performing in a church in Mareotis, she vowed to dedicate to him the first egg her hens laid. When this event took place, she set out to find the saint and, along the way, engaged in conversation with a boatman on a riverbank. He promised to take the egg to Saint Menas, and she undertook to turn Christian if fruitfulness were granted to her. The boatman forgot to keep his promise, however, and ate the egg.

Months later, when the boatman was praying in church, the saint appeared to him, mounted on a white horse, and struck him on the head, at which instance a cock appeared beneath him. The saint seized it and took it to the woman's house, ordering her to call her first son Menas and predicting that her whole house would become fruitful. After the woman had borne a son, as had been predicted for her, and her servant maids had given birth to children, they were all baptized and converted to Christianity. The drawing shows the moment when the saint appears to the boatman in the church; the cock is already visible between the man's legs. The three crowns above the saint symbolize his innocence, patience, and martyrdom.

Griffith (1913,15) pointed out that saints are always depicted frontally in Christian Nubian art, which we know chiefly through church frescoes; see Cats. 292 and 293. The saint is here shown in profile. Since no other Nubian manuscript illustrations are known, it is impossible to say to what extent this is a deviation from the usual practice.

292 ■
Bishop Petros under the Protection of the Apostle Peter

About A.D. 975.
MATERIAL: Paint on plaster.
COLLECTION: *Warsaw, Muzeum Narodowe 234031.*

DESCRIPTION: The Apostle Peter stands behind Bishop Petros, his hands placed protectively on the bishop's shoulders. Peter wears a long white robe with yellow, red, and blue stripes. Around his head is a red-bordered halo, and he has a crown on which are mounted three small crosses. His face is dominated by large, stylized eyes, the lower lids edged in green and red. He has a long white beard and a drooping mustache. The bishop's skin is dark brown. His face is oval, his eyes large, and his ears prominent. He has a drooping black mustache and a tuft of hair on the chin. He wears a long white robe concealed by an overgarment decorated with a red mesh pattern with spots of red and green. The bishop holds a book in his left hand bound in red and yellow and adorned with gems; two fingers of his right hand reach out to touch it. A maniple is wound around his index finger. On each side of Peter's head and above it are legends in Coptic.

COLOR: Background gray white; red, dark brown, light brown, yellow, green, white, and black.
CONDITION: Large gaps on right side; colors abraded in places.
MEASUREMENTS: Height 2.43 m. Width 1.16 m. Height of Apostle's figure 2.25 m. Height of bishop's figure 1.87 m.
PROVENANCE: Faras, Great Cathedral, Episcopal Hall, west wall, 2.80 m. above floor level (Michałowski 1962, Excavation no. 62-60).
BIBLIOGRAPHY: Michałowski 1974, 180-84, no. 33 (with complete biblio.).

Although the paintings on the walls of the Great Cathedral of Faras are always described as frescoes, they are in fact secco paintings, the paint having been applied to dry, not wet, plaster.

Petros, a Monophysite, was bishop of Faras (the ancient Pachoras) from 974 to 999; he served as bishop of the cathedral until 997. He died in 999 at the age of ninety-three and was buried near the church, on the southern slope of Mount Faras.

The painting is important for several reasons. It marks the transition from the yellow to the red style, which reached its zenith in the second half of the tenth century (see pp. 110-11). And since it is known that Petros took over the diocese of Faras in 973 or 975, the painting must have been executed about that time. It thus represents a fixed point for the dating of Nubian Christian murals.

That the bishop was a dark-skinned African is clear not only from this painting but from his remains (Dzierżykray-Rogalski 1966,83ff.).

ΑΠΟCΤΟΛΟΙ

293
Christ Protecting an Eparch

First half of the twelfth century A.D.
MATERIAL: Paint on plaster.
COLLECTION: *Warsaw, Muzeum Narodowe 234033.*

DESCRIPTION: Christ stands behind the much smaller figure of an eparch, raising his right hand in benediction and holding a book in his left hand whose cover is adorned with gems. His head is framed by a halo. He wears a long red tunic under a brown cowled cloak; his feet are sandaled. His glance is directed upward, and his lips are painted in the shape of the Greek chi. He has a mustache, a beard, and a tuft of hair on his chin. The eparch raises both hands in supplication. He wears a long dark gray tunic, a bell-shaped skirt, and a sash draped over his left shoulder; his feet are sandaled. Around his neck is an orange necklace from which hangs a golden cross. He wears a golden helmet-like crown surmounted by a rod ending in a horizontal crescent. There is lettering in Christ's halo and a legend in Graeco-Nubian at top left.

COLOR: Background light brown to reddish; red, black, yellow, white, dark brown, and dark gray.
CONDITION: Numerous defects.
MEASUREMENTS: Height 2.14 m. Width 0.71 m. Height of Christ 1.83 m. Height of eparch 1.15 m.
PROVENANCE: Faras, Great Cathedral, south nave, north side of first east pilaster (Michałowski 1962, Excavation no. 62-63).
BIBLIOGRAPHY: Michałowski 1974,264-67, no. 58 (illus. and biblio.).

This huge painting in the late style comes from the final epoch of Faras Cathedral, which was destroyed probably in 1175 during an invasion by the Egyptians under Ibrahim al-Kurdi. The late style was characterized by a broad range of colors (see p. 110).

The eparch was a secular official who functioned as metropolitan of a province. His most important attribute was a helmet-like crown adorned with a crescent mounted on a rod together with two or four horns. The crescent on a rod was adopted from the pagan era; it must have possessed great significance in the Ballana culture since it appears on a Ballana crown, Cat. 264.

Detail illustrated here and in color on page 112.

294
Pilgrim's Bottle with Entwined Serpents

Eleventh to twelfth century A.D.
MATERIAL: Fired clay.
COLLECTION: *Khartoum, Sudan National Museum 15309.*

DESCRIPTION: A pilgrim's bottle has a thick body and a short neck with a flat projecting lip. Two loop handles are attached at the base of the neck and the shoulder. On the front and back of the vessel are identical paintings of entwined horned serpents, their tongues extended. Their bodies are divided longitudinally, half being patterned and the other half plain. The narrow side of the bottle is decorated with a wide red-brown band framed on each side by three faint lines and ornamented underneath the handles with geometric patterns.

COLOR: Yellow brown and dark red; decoration dark brown and reddish brown.
CONDITION: Pieces missing from lip; one handle broken off and repaired; fairly large areas of corrosion on one side; numerous small chips; colors badly abraded and discolorations from outflowing liquid.
MEASUREMENTS: Height 21.9 cm. Width 16.9 cm. Depth 13.5 cm.
PROVENANCE: Meinarti (Adams 1963, Excavation no. 6.K.3/151).
BIBLIOGRAPHY: Adams 1970,128 (fig. 62); Plumley 1975,12.

This type of pilgrim's bottle was popular in Egypt from Dynasty XVIII on. According to Adams (1970,118), the painting must be attributed to the late Christian Period.

The motif of entwined serpents is by no means typical for Christian iconography; it is, in fact, adapted from much earlier prototypes, as is Cat. 295. Plumley in 1974 found similar decoration on the fragments of a large storage jar in a Ballana Period house in Qasr Ibrim (Plumley 1975,12, pl. VII, 1). It is astonishing that this very rare motif should come to light again after so long a time — more than five hundred years. There must have been intermediate links in its transmission, but none have yet been discovered.

Illustrated in color on page 330.

Pilgrim's Bottle with Entwined Serpents (Cat. 294).

295
Fragments of a Pilgrim's Bottle

Ninth century A.D.
MATERIAL: Fired clay.
COLLECTION: *Warsaw, Muzeum Narodowe 234566.*

DESCRIPTION: A highly stylized dove is painted on fragments from the face of a large pilgrim's bottle. There is a small cross on the bird's head, and a censer is suspended from three chains held in its beak. The head and parts of the plumage are painted red. Above the bird is a much smaller and very simplified giraffe browsing from a tall tree. The animal's head and body are red, and its long neck is striped with red. Framing the face of the vessel is a wide ornamental band of concentric circles connected by irregular lines. The narrow side of the bottle is decorated with geometric patterns.

COLOR: Reddish brown; decoration black and red.
CONDITION: Thirteen fragments reassembled, with gaps; numerous small chips; bright and dark discolorations.
MEASUREMENTS: Height 24.4 cm. Width ca. 36.5 cm.
PROVENANCE: Faras, second cathedral, northwest room, at floor level (Michałowski 1962-63, Excavation no. 54/62-3).
BIBLIOGRPAHY: Michałowski 1967,68 (fig.); Berlin 1968,127, no. 67 (illus.); Essen 1969, no. 70 (illus.); Kołodziejczyk 1969,191ff. (illus.); Zurich 1970, no. 70.

This pilgrim's bottle from the classical period of Christian Nubia reflects a long tradition of painted ceramics; quite similar motifs are present on late Meroitic vessels.

The dove is an important Christian symbol. The browsing giraffe appears on only one other vessel of the Christian Period (Shinnie—Chittick 1961, 56, fig. 25,2), but giraffes were frequent on late Meroitic ceramics (Cats. 229, 230, 236). The circles are also based on ancient prototypes. Thus, this unique vessel testifies to the fact that Nubian craftsmen returned, after centuries, to ancient forms and designs, amalgamating pagan with Christian. Links from the Ballana Period are lacking but must have existed.

BMFA	*Bulletin of the Museum of Fine Arts, Boston*
JARCE	*Journal of the American Research Center in Egypt*
JEA	*Journal of Egyptian Archaeology*
JNES	*Journal of Near Eastern Studies*
LAAA	*University of Liverpool Annals of Archaeology and Anthropology*
ZÄS	*Zeitschrift für ägyptische Sprache und Altertumskunde*

Adams 1962a Adams, W., "An Introductory Classification of Christian Nubian Pottery." *Kush* 10 (1962), pp. 245-88.

Adams 1962b Adams, W. "Pottery Kiln Excavations." *Kush* 10 (1962), pp. 62-75.

Adams 1964a Adams, W. "An Introductory Classification of Meroitic Pottery." *Kush* 12 (1964), pp. 126-73.

Adams 1964b Adams, W. "Post-Pharaonic Nubia in Light of Archaeology, I." *JEA* 50 (1964), pp. 102-20.

Adams 1965a Adams, W. "Post-Pharaonic Nubia in Light of Archaeology, II." *JEA* 51 (1965), pp. 160-78.

Adams 1965b Adams, W. "Sudan Antiquities Service Excavations at Meinarti 1963-1964." *Kush* 13 (1965), pp. 148-76.

Adams 1965c Adams, W. "Architectural Evolution of the Nubian Church, 500-1400 A.D." *JARCE* 4 (1965), pp. 87-139.

Adams 1966 Adams, W. "The Vintage of Nubia." *Kush* 14 (1966), pp. 262-83.

Adams 1968 Adams, W. "Settlement Patterns in Microcosm: The Changing Aspect of a Nubian Village during Twelve Centuries." In: Chang, K., ed., *Settlement Archaeology*, pp. 174-207. Palo Alto, 1968.

Adams 1970 Adams, W. "The Evolution of Christian Nubian Pottery." In: Dinkler, E., ed., *Kunst und Geschichte Nubiens in christlicher Zeit*, pp. 111-28. Recklinghausen, 1970.

Adams 1973 Adams, W. "Progress Report on Nubian Pottery: 1. The Native Wares." *Kush* 15 (1967-68 [1973]), pp. 1-50.

Adams 1974 Adams, W. "Sacred and Secular Polities in Ancient Nubia." *World Archaeology* 6 (1974), pp. 39-51.

Adams 1976 Adams, W. "Meroitic North and South, A Study in Cultural Contrasts." In: *Meroitica: Schriften zur altsudanesischen Geschichte und Archäologie*, vol. 2, pp. 11-25, 119-75. Berlin/DDR, 1976.

Adams 1977 Adams, W. *Nubia: Corridor to Africa*. London, 1977.

Adams—Nordström 1963 Adams, W., and Nordström, H.-Å. "The Archaeological Survey on the West Bank of the Nile: Third Season, 1961-1962." *Kush* 11 (1963), pp. 10-46.

Addison 1934 Khartoum, Gordon Memorial College, Museum of Antiquities. *A Short Guide to the Museum of Antiquities*. By F. Addison. 2d ed. Khartoum, 1934.

Addison 1949 Addison, F. *Jebel Moya*. The Wellcome Excavations in the Sudan, 1-2. London, 1949.

Addison 1950 Addison, F. "Archaeological Discoveries on the Blue Nile." *Antiquity* 24 (1950), pp. 12-24.

Aldred 1961 Aldred, C. *The Egyptians*. Ancient Peoples and Places, 18. London, 1961.

Allen 1950 Allen, T. *Occurrences of Pyramid Texts with Cross Indexes of These and Other Egyptian Mortuary Texts*. Chicago, University, Oriental Institute. Studies in Ancient Oriental Civilization, 27. Chicago, 1950.

Almagro 1965a Almagro, M., et al. "Excavations by the Spanish Archaeological Mission in the Sudan, 1962-63 and 1963-64." *Kush* 13 (1965), pp. 78-95.

Almagro 1965b Almagro, M. *La necrópolis meroítica de Nag Gamus (Masmas. Nubia Egipcia).* Comité español de la UNESCO para Nubia. Memorias de la misión arqueológica, 8. Madrid, 1965.

Almagro 1975 Almagro Basch, M.; Almagro Gorbea, J.; and del Carmen Pérez Die, M. *Arte faraónico.* Exhibition catalogue: Madrid, Zaragoza, Barcelona; October 1975-May 1976. Madrid, 1975.

Anderson 1968 Anderson, J. "Late Paleolithic Skeletal Remains from Nubia." In: Wendorf, F., ed., *The Prehistory of Nubia*, vol. 2, pp. 996-1040. Dallas, 1968.

Appel 1946 Appel, B. *Skin Beauty and Health.* Westfield, Massachusetts, 1946.

Arkell 1947 Arkell, A. "Discoveries Which Suggest the Existence of a Hidden Rock Temple: Colossal Statues Identified in the Sudan. A Sudanese Abu Simbel: Colossal Statues Created by a Kushite King to Emulate the Memorial of Rameses II." *The Illustrated London News* 210 (1947), pp. 214-15.

Arkell 1949a Arkell, A. *Early Khartoum. An Account of the Excavation of an Early Occupation Site Carried Out by the Sudanese Government Antiquities Service in 1944-5.* London, 1949.

Arkell 1949b Arkell, A. *The Old Stone Age in the Anglo-Egyptian Sudan.* Sudan Antiquities Service. Occasional Papers, no. 1. Khartoum, 1949.

Arkell 1950a Arkell, A. "Gold Coast Copies of 5th-7th Century Bronze Lamps." *Antiquity* 24 (1950), pp. 38-40.

Arkell 1950b Arkell, A. "Varia Sudanica." *JEA* 36 (1950), pp. 24-40.

Arkell 1951 Arkell, A. "Meroë and India." In: *Aspects of Archaeology in Britain and Beyond. Essays Presented to O.G.S. Crawford*, pp. 32-38. London, 1951.

Arkell 1953 Arkell, A. *Shaheinab. An Account of the Excavation of a Neolithic Occupation Site Carried Out for the Sudan Antiquities Service in 1949-50.* London, 1953.

Arkell 1955a Arkell, A. "An Early Predynastic Sudanese Bowl from Upper Egypt." *Kush* 3 (1955), pp. 95-96.

Arkell 1955b Arkell, A. *A History of the Sudan from the Earliest Times to 1821.* London, 1955.

Arkell 1961 Arkell, A. *A History of the Sudan from the Earliest Times to 1821.* 2d ed., rev. London, 1961.

Arkell 1975 Arkell, A. *The Prehistory of the Nile Valley.* Handbuch der Orientalistik, Abt. 7, vol. 1. Leiden and Cologne, 1975.

Arkell 1977 Arkell, A. "Dating 'Early Khartoum.' " In: *Ägypten und Kusch* [Festschrift Hintze], pp. 53-55. Schriften zur Geschichte und Kultur des Alten Orients, 13. Berlin/DDR, 1977.

Arnold 1962 Arnold, D. *Wandrelief und Raumfunktion in ägyptischen Tempeln des neuen Reiches.* Münchner ägyptologische Studien, 2. Berlin/West, 1962.

Bacon 1971 Bacon, E. *Archaeology: Discoveries in the 1960's.* New York, 1971.

Badawy 1964 Badawy, A. "An Egyptian Fortress in the 'Belly of Rock': Further Excavations and Discoveries in the Sudanese Island of Askut." *The Illustrated London News* 245 (1964), pp. 86-88.

Badawy 1965 Badawy, A. "Askut: A Middle Kingdom Fortress in Nubia." *Archaeology* 18, no. 2 (1965), pp. 124-31.

Badawy 1966 Badawy, A. "Archaeological Problems Relating to the Egyptian Fortress at Askut." *JARCE* 5 (1966), pp. 23-27.

Badawy ms. Badawy, A. "Askut: An Egyptian Island Fortress of the Middle Kingdom in Upper Nubia." *Mitteilungen aus der Ägyptischen Sammlung* 10 (forthcoming).

Bakry 1967 Bakry, H. "Psammētichus II and His Newly-found Stela at Shellâl." *Oriens Antiquus* 6 (1967), pp. 225-44.

Bates—Dunham 1927 Bates, O., and Dunham, D. "Excavations at Gammai." In: *Harvard African Studies.* Vol. 8, *Varia Africana IV*, pp. 1-121. Harvard University, Peabody Museum, African Department. Cambridge, Massachusetts, 1927.

Batrawi 1935 Batrawi, A. *Report on the Human Remains.* Service des Antiquités de l'Égypte. Mission archéologique de Nubie, 1929-1934. Cairo, 1935.

Batrawi 1945-46 Batrawi, A. "The Racial History of Egypt and Nubia." *Journal of the Royal Anthropological Institute* 75 (1945), pp. 81-101; 76 (1946), pp. 131-56.

Baumgartel 1960 Baumgartel, E. *The Cultures of Prehistoric Egypt, II.* London, 1960.

Baumgartel 1970 Baumgartel, E. Review of Ucko, P., *Anthropomorphic Figurines of Predynastic Egypt and Neolithic Crete with Comparative Material from the Prehistoric Near East and Mainland Greece,* London, 1968. *JEA* 43 (1970), pp. 198-201.

Beckerath 1971 Beckerath, J. *Abriss der Geschichte des alten Ägypten.* Munich and Vienna, 1971.

Beckett 1910 Beckett, H. "A Summary of the Literature Relating to the History of Nubia." In: Reisner, G., ed., *The Archaeological Survey of Nubia. Report for 1907-1908,* vol. 2, pp. 343-67. Egypt, Survey Department. Cairo, 1910.

Bentley—Crowfoot 1924 Bentley, O., and Crowfoot, J. "Nuba Pots in the Gordon College." *Sudan Notes and Records* 7, no. 2 (1924), pp. 18-28.

Berlin 1899 Berlin, Museen. *Ausführliches Verzeichnis der ägyptischen Altertümer und Gipsabgüsse.* 2d ed. Berlin, 1899.

Berlin 1963 Berlin, Museen. *Nubien und Sudan im Altertum. Führer durch die Sonderausstellung des Berliner Aegyptischen Museums.* Berlin/DDR, 1963.

Berlin 1968 Berlin, Museen. *Faras.* Exhibition catalogue: Staatliche Museen zu Berlin. Berlin/DDR, [1968].

Berlin 1976 Berlin, Museen. *Ägyptische Kunst aus dem Brooklyn Museum.* Exhibition catalogue: Ägyptisches Museum, Berlin/West. Berlin/West, 1976.

Bibliography 1939 Hill, R., ed. *A Bibliography of the Anglo-Egyptian Sudan from the Earliest Times to 1937.* Oxford and London, 1939.

Bibliography 1962 Nasri, A., ed. *A Bibliography of the Sudan, 1938-1958.* London, 1962.

Bibliography 1975 Hainsworth, M. "Bibliography on Nubia and Meroe." Computer printout. Paris, 1975.

Bietak 1968 Bietak, M. *Studien zur Chronologie der nubischen C-Gruppe: Ein Beitrag zur Frühgeschichte Unternubiens zwischen 2200 und 1550 vor Chr.* Berichte des Österreichischen Nationalkomitees der UNESCO-Aktion für die Rettung der Nubischen Altertümer, 5. Österreichische Akademie der Wissenschaften, Philosophisch-historische Klasse. Denkschriften, 97. Vienna, 1968.

Bissing 1914 Bissing, F. von. *Denkmäler ägyptischer Skulptur.* Munich, 1914.

Bissing 1928 Bissing, F. von. "Die älteste Darstellung des Doppeladlers." *Forschungen und Fortschritte* 4 (1928), p. 54.

Bissing 1939a Bissing, F. von. "Die Funde in den Nekropolen von Kostol, Ballana und Firka am II. Nilkatarakt und ihre zeitliche und kunstgeschichtliche Stellung." *Jahrbuch des Deutschen Archäologischen Instituts* 54 (1939), pp. 569-81.

Bissing 1939b Bissing, F. von. Review of Emery, W., and Kirwan, L., *The Royal Tombs of Ballana and Qustul,* Cairo, 1938. *Orientalistische Literaturzeitung* 42, no. 8/9 (1939), pp. 506-12.

Bissing [1939-41] Bissing, F. von. "Lieber Freund!" In: *F. Baloža Skolotāja Velte* [Festschrift for F. Ballod], pp. 21-32. n.p., [1939-41].

Bissing 1941 Bissing, F. von. "Die kunstgeschichtliche Bedeutung der neuentdeckten Nekropolen im Gebiet des II. Nilkataraktes." In: *Miscellanea Gregoriana, racolta di scritti pubblicati nel I centenario dalla fondazione del Pont. Museo Egizio (1839-1939),* pp. 9-28. Vatican, 1941.

Boardman 1964 Boardman, J. *The Greeks Overseas.* Baltimore, 1964.

Borchardt 1911 Borchardt, L. *Statuen und Statuetten von Königen und Privatleuten im Museum von Kairo, Nr. 1-1294.* Part 1, *Text und Tafeln zu Nr. 1-380.* Catalogue général des antiquités égyptiennes du Musée du Caire, nos. 1-1294. Berlin, 1911.

Borchardt 1925 Borchardt, L. *Statuen und Statuetten von Königen und Privatleuten im Museum von Kairo, Nr. 1-1294.* Part 2, *Text und Tafeln zu Nr. 381-653.* Catalogue général des antiquités égyptiennes du Musée du Caire, nos. 1-1294. Berlin, 1925.

Borchardt 1930 Borchardt, L. *Statuen und Statuetten von Königen und Privatleuten im Museum von Kairo, Nr. 1-1294.* Part 3, *Text und Tafeln zu Nr. 654-950.* Catalogue général des antiquités égyptiennes du Musée du Caire, nos. 1-1294. Berlin, 1930.

Bosanquet 1912 Bosanquet, R. "Second Interim Report on the Excavations at Meroë in Ethiopia. Part III—On the Bronze Portrait Head." *LAAA* 4 (1912), pp. 66-71.

Bosse 1936 Bosse, K. *Die menschliche Figur in der Rundplastik der ägyptischen Spätzeit von der XXII. bis zur XXX. Dynastie.* Ägyptologische Forschungen, 1. Glückstadt, Hamburg, and New York, 1936.

Bothmer 1960 The Brooklyn Museum. *Egyptian Sculpture of the Late Period, 700* B.C. *to* A.D. *100.* By B. V. Bothmer. Brooklyn, 1960. Reprinted 1969.

Bothmer 1970 The Brooklyn Museum. *Brief Guide to the Department of Ancient Art.* By B. V. Bothmer and J. Keith. Brooklyn, 1970.

Bothmer 1978 Bothmer, B. V. "On Photographing Egyptian Art." *Studien zur Altägyptischen Kultur* 6 (1978), forthcoming.

Boufides 1970 Boufides, N. "Shabaka and Amenirdis." *Athens Annals of Archaeology* 3, no. 2 (1970), pp. 275-85.

Brace 1969 Brace, C. "A Nonracial Approach towards the Understanding of Human Diversity." In: Montagu, M., ed., *The Concept of Race,* pp. 103-52. New York, 1969.

Breasted 1908 Breasted, J. "Oriental Exploration Fund of the University of Chicago: Second Preliminary Report of the Egyptian Expedition." *The American Journal of Semitic Languages and Literatures* 25 (1908-1909), pp. 1-110.

Breasted 1943 Breasted, C. *Pioneer to the Past: The Story of James Henry Breasted, Archaeologist, Told by His Son.* New York, 1943.

Breasted—Ranke 1936 Breasted, J. *Geschichte Ägyptens.* Translated by H. Ranke. 2d ed. Vienna, 1936.

Breasted—Ranke 1954 Breasted, J. *Geschichte Ägyptens.* Translated by H. Ranke. 2d ed., repr. [Zurich, 1954].

Brentjes 1962 Brentjes, B. *Wildtier und Haustier im Alten Orient.* Lebendiges Altertum, Populäre Schriftenreihe für Altertumswissenschaft, 11. Berlin/DDR, 1962.

Brooklyn 1956 The Brooklyn Museum. *Five Years of Collecting Egyptian Art, 1951-1956. Catalogue of an Exhibition Held at The Brooklyn Museum, 11 December, 1956 to 17 March, 1957.* Brooklyn, 1956. Reprinted 1969.

Brooklyn 1974 The Brooklyn Museum. *Brief Guide to the Department of Egyptian and Classical Art.* By B. V. Bothmer and J. Keith. Rev. ed. Brooklyn, 1974.

Brunner-Traut 1971 Brunner-Traut, E. "Ein Königskopf der Spätzeit mit dem 'Blauen Helm' in Tübingen." *ZÄS* 97 (1971), pp. 18-30.

Budge 1907 Budge, E. *The Egyptian Sûdân, Its History and Monuments.* 2 vols. London, 1907.

Budge 1909 Budge, E. *Texts Relating to Saint Mêna of Egypt and Canons of Nicaea in a Nubian Dialect with Facsimile.* London, 1909.

Budge 1912 Budge, E. *Egyptian Religion.* Vol. 2, *Annals of Nubian Kings with a Sketch of the History of the Nubian Kingdom of Napata.* Books on Egypt and Chaldaea, 33. London, 1912.

Budge 1928 Budge, E. *A History of Ethiopia, Nubia and Abysinnia.* 2 vols. London, 1928.

Buettner-Janusch 1973 Buettner-Janusch, J. *Physical Anthropology: A Perspective.* New York, 1973.

Burckhardt 1819 Burckhardt, J. *Travels in Nubia.* London, 1819.

CAH 1973 *The History of the Middle East and the Aegean Region c. 1800-1380* B.C. Cambridge Ancient History, vol. 2, part 1. Cambridge, 1973.

CAH 1975 *The History of the Middle East and the Aegean Region c. 1380-1000* B.C. Cambridge Ancient History, vol. 2, part 2. Cambridge, 1975.

Cailliaud 1821-62 Cailliaud, F. *Voyage à l'oasis de Thèbes et dans les déserts situés à l'orient et à l'occident de la Thébaïde, fait pendant les années 1815, 1816, 1817 et 1818.* Paris, 1821-62.

Cailliaud 1826 Cailliaud, F. *Voyage à Meroé, au fleuve blanc, au-delà de Fâzoql dans le midi du royaume de Sennâr, à Syouah et dans cinq autres oasis; fait dans les années 1819, 1820, 1821 et 1822.* Paris, 1826.

Cairo 1949 *Encyclopédie photographique de l'art.* [Vol. 4], *Le Musée du Caire.* Photographs by A. Vigneau. Text by E. Drioton. Paris, 1949.

Castiglione 1970 Castiglione, L. "Diocletianus und die Blemmyes." *ZÄS* 96 (1970), pp. 90-103.

Catalan 1963 Pellicer Catalan, M. *La necrópolis meroítica de Nag-Shayeg: Argín (Sudán).* Comité español de la UNESCO para Nubia. Memorias de la misión arqueológica, 2. Madrid, 1963.

Cavvadias 1894 Athens, Mouseion tēs Akropoleōs. *Musée national. Antiquités mycéniennes et égyptiennes, sculptures, vases, terres-cuites, bronzes, Musée de l'Acropole.* By P. Cavvadias. Athens, 1894.

Chamla 1968 Chamla, M. "Les Populations anciennes du Sahara et des régions limitrophes. Études des restes osseux humains néolithiques et protohistoriques." *Mémoires du Centre de Recherches Anthropologiques, Préhistoriques et Ethnographiques* 9 (1968), pp. 1-249.

Chapman—Dunham 1952 Chapman, S., and Dunham, D. *The Royal Cemeteries of Kush.* Vol. 3, *Decorated Chapels of the Meroitic Pyramids at Meroë and Barkal.* Boston, 1952.

Charleston 1955 Charleston, R. *Roman Pottery.* London, 1955.

Chatterji 1968 Chatterji, S. *India and Ethiopia from the Seventh Century* B.C. Asiatic Society Monographs Series, 15. Calcutta, 1968.

Chittick 1957a Chittick, H. "An Inscription on Gebel Barkal." *JEA* 43 (1957), pp. 42-44.

Chittick 1957b Chittick, H. "A New Type of Mound Grave." *Kush* 5 (1957), pp. 73-77.

Clarke 1916 Clarke, S. "Ancient Egyptian Frontier Fortresses." *JEA* 3 (1916), pp. 155-79.

Collection David-Weill 1971 Paris, Hôtel Drouot. *Collection D. David-Weill. Le mercredi 16 juin 1971.* Paris, 1971.

Collins 1968 Collins, R. *Problems in African History.* Englewood Cliffs, New Jersey, 1968.

Coon 1963 Coon, C. *The Origin of Races.* New York, 1963.

Cooney 1939 Cooney, J. "Accessions of the Egyptian Department." *The Brooklyn Museum Quarterly* 26 (1939), pp. 44-45.

Cooney 1963 Cooney, J. "Assorted Errors in Art Collecting." *Expedition* 6, no. 1 (1963), pp. 20-27.

Crawford 1951 Crawford, O. *Fung Kingdom of Sennar.* Gloucester, 1951.

Crawford 1953 Crawford, O. *Castles and Churches in the Middle Nile Region.* Sudan Antiquities Service. Occasional Papers, no. 2. Khartoum, 1953.

Crawford 1955 Crawford, O. *Said and Done: Autobiography of an Archaeologist.* London, 1955.

Crawford—Addison 1951 Crawford, O., and Addison, F. *Abu Geili and Saqadi & Dar el Mek.* The Wellcome Excavations in the Sudan, 3. London, 1951.

Cromer 1906 Cromer, Lord E. *Report of His Majesty's Agent and Consul-General on the Finances, Administration, and Condition of Egypt and the Sudan in 1905.* London, 1906.

Crowfoot 1911 Crowfoot, J. *The Island of Meroe.* In: Egypt Exploration Society, Archaeological Survey of Egypt. Memoirs, 19. London, 1911.

Curto 1965 Curto, S. *Nubia: Storia di una civiltà favolosa.* Novara, [1965].

Curto 1966 Curto, S. *Nubien: Geschichte einer rätselhaften Kultur.* Munich, [1966].

Dakar—Paris 1966 *L'art nègre: Sources, évolution, expansion. Exposition organisée au Musée Dynamique à Dakar par le Commissariat du Festival Mondial des Arts Nègres et au Grand Palais à Paris par la Réunion des Musées Nationaux.* Dakar-Paris, 1966.

David 1975 David, A. *The Egyptian Kingdoms.* Oxford, 1975.

Davidson 1972 Davidson, B. *Africa: History of a Continent.* Photographs by W. Forman. Rev. ed. London, 1972.

Davies 1962 Davies, N. *Tutankhamun's Painted Box. Reproduced in Colour from the Original in the Cairo Museum.* Explanatory text by A. Gardiner. Oxford, 1962.

Desanges 1968 Desanges, J. "Vues grecques sur quelques aspects de la monarchie méroïtique." *Bulletin de l'Institut Français d'Archéologie Orientale* 67 (1968), pp. 89-104.

Desroches-Noblecourt 1954 Desroches-Noblecourt, C. "La cueillette du raisin dans la tombe d'une musicienne de Neïth à Saïs (un exemple du 'romantisme' égyptien au Musée du Louvre)." *Arts asiatiques* 1 (1954), pp. 40-60.

De Vries 1973-74 De Vries, C. "The Nubian Publication Project." *Chicago, University, Oriental Institute. Report,* 1973/1974, pp. 39-41.

De Vries 1975 De Vries, C. "Communication Concerning the Work of the Oriental Institute Nubian Expedition." In: Michałowski, K., ed., *Nubia: Récentes Recherches,* pp. 18-21. Warsaw, 1975.

De Vries 1976 De Vries, C. "The Oriental Institute Decorated Censer from Nubia." In: *Studies in Honor of George R. Hughes, January 12, 1977,* pp. 55-74. Chicago, University, Oriental Institute. Studies in Ancient Oriental Civilization, 39. Chicago, 1976.

Dinkler 1970 Dinkler, E., ed. *Kunst und Geschichte Nubiens in christlicher Zeit.* Recklinghausen, 1970.

Dinkler 1975 Dinkler, E. "Beobachtungen zur Ikonographie des Kreuzes in der nubischen Kunst." In: Michałowski, K., ed., *Nubia: Récentes Recherches,* pp. 22-30. Warsaw, 1975.

Diop 1962 Diop, C. "Histoire primitive de l'humanité: Évolution du monde noir." *Bulletin de l'Institut Français d'Afrique Noire* (Dakar), series B, *Sciences humaines* 24 (1962), pp. 449-541.

Dixon 1963 Dixon, D. "A Meroitic Cemetery at Sennar (Makwar)." *Kush* 11 (1963), pp. 227-34.

Dixon 1964 Dixon, D. "The Origin of the Kingdom of Kush (Napata-Meroë)." *JEA* 50 (1964), pp. 121-32.

Dixon—Wachsmann 1964 Dixon, D., and Wachsmann, K. "A Sandstone Statue of an Auletes from Meroë." *Kush* 12 (1964), pp. 119-25.

Donadoni 1961 Donadoni, S. "Meroe." In: *Enciclopedia dell'arte antica, classica e orientale,* vol. 4, pp. 1037-38. Rome, 1961.

Donadoni 1969 Donadoni, S. "Les débuts du christianisme en Nubie." *Mémoires de l'Institut d'Égypte* 59 (1969), pp. 25-33.

Drenkhahn 1967 Drenkhahn, R. "Darstellungen von Negern in Ägypten." Dissertation zur Erlangung der Doctorwürde der Philosophischen Fakultät der Universität Hamburg. Hamburg, 1967.

Du Bourguet 1970 Du Bourguet, P. "La Peinture murale copte: Quelques problèmes devant la peinture murale nubienne." In: Dinkler, E., ed., *Kunst und Geschichte Nubiens in christlicher Zeit,* pp. 303-24. Recklinghausen, 1970.

Dunham 1946 Dunham, D. "Notes on the History of Kush, 850 B.C.-A.D. 350." *American Journal of Archaeology* 50 (1946), pp. 378-88.

Dunham 1947 Dunham, D. "Four Kushite Colossi in the Sudan." *JEA* 33 (1947), pp. 63-65.

Dunham 1948 Dunham, D. "Two Pieces of Furniture from the Egyptian Sudan." *BMFA* 46, no. 266 (1948), pp. 98-101.

Dunham 1950 Dunham, D. *The Royal Cemeteries of Kush.* Vol. 1, *El Kurru.* Boston, 1950.

Dunham 1952 Dunham, D. "Notes on a Gold Pectoral from Napata." *JNES* 11 (1952), pp. 111-12.

Dunham 1953 Dunham, D. "From Tumulus to Pyramid—and Back." *Archaeology* 6, no. 2 (1953), pp. 87-94.

Dunham 1955 Dunham, D. *The Royal Cemeteries of Kush.* Vol. 2, *Nuri.* Boston, 1955.

Dunham 1957 Dunham, D. *The Royal Cemeteries of Kush.* Vol. 4, *Royal Tombs at Meroë and Barkal.* Boston, 1957.

Dunham 1958 Dunham, D. *The Egyptian Department and Its Excavations.* Boston, 1958.

Dunham 1963 Dunham, D. *The Royal Cemeteries of Kush.* Vol. 5, *The West and South Cemeteries at Meroë.* Boston, 1963.

Dunham 1965 Dunham, D. "A Collection of 'Pot-Marks' from Kush and Nubia." *Kush* 13 (1965), pp. 131-47.

Dunham 1967 Dunham, D. *The Second Cataract Forts.* Vol. 2, *Uronarti, Shalfak, Mirgissa.* Boston, 1967.

Dunham 1970 Dunham, D. *The Barkal Temples.* Boston, 1970.

Dunham—Janssen 1960 Dunham, D., and Janssen, M. *Second Cataract Forts.* Vol. 1, *Semna, Kumma.* Boston, 1960.

Dunham—Macadam 1949 Dunham, D., and Macadam, M. "Names and Relationships of the Royal Family of Napata." *JEA* 35 (1949), pp. 139-49.

Dzierżykray-Rogalski 1966 Dzierżykray-Rogalski, T. "Remarques sur la typologie anthropologique des fresques de Faras (Pachoras)." In: *Mélanges offerts à Kazimierz Michałowski,* pp. 83-89. Warsaw, 1966.

Edel 1955 Edel, E. "Inschriften des Alten Reiches. V. Die Reiseberichte des *Ḥrw-ḫwjf* (Herchuf)." In: Firchow, O., ed., *Ägyptologische Studien,* pp. 51-75. Deutsche Akademie der Wissenshaften zu Berlin, Institut für Orientforschung. Veröffentlichung Nr. 29 [Festschrift Grapow]. Berlin/DDR, 1955.

Edel 1967 Edel, E. "Die Ländernamen Unternubiens und die Ausbreitung der C-Gruppe nach den Reiseberichten des *Ḥrw-ḫwjf.*" *Orientalia* 36 (1967), pp. 133-58.

Effenberger 1975 Effenberger, A. *Koptische Kunst: Ägypten in spätantiker, byzantinischer und früh-islamischer Zeit.* Leipzig, 1975.

Eggebrecht 1975 Eggebrecht, A. "Keramik." In: Vandersleyen, C., ed., *Das Alte Ägypten,* pp. 348-58. Propyläen Kunstgeschichte, 15. Berlin/West, 1975.

Emery 1931 Emery, W. "Preliminary Report of the Work of the Archaeological Survey of Nubia 1930-1931." *Annales du Service des Antiquités de l'Égypte* 31 (1931), pp. 70-80.

Emery 1932a Emery, W. "Ancient Nubian Art Saved from Submergence: Further Discoveries." *The Illustrated London News* 181 (1932), p. 85.

Emery 1932b Emery, W. "Preliminary Report of the Work of the Archaeological Survey of Nubia 1931-1932." *Annales du Service des Antiquités de l'Égypte* 32 (1932), pp. 38-46.

Emery 1933 Emery, W. "Preliminary Report of the Work of the Archaeological Survey of Nubia 1932-1934." *Annales du Service des Antiquités de l'Égypte* 33 (1933), pp. 201-7.

Emery 1948 Emery, W. *Nubian Treasure: An Account of the Discoveries at Ballana and Qustul.* London, 1948.

Emery 1962 Emery, W. "Excavations at Qasr Ibrim: New Light on the Still Enigmatic X-Group Peoples." *The Illustrated London News* 241 (1962), pp. 605-7.

Emery 1965 Emery, W. *Egypt in Nubia.* London, 1965.

Emery 1967 Emery, W. "Egypt Exploration Society: Preliminary Report on Excavations at Kasr Ibrim, 1961." In: Egypt, Service des Antiquités, *Fouilles en Nubie (1961-1963),* pp. 55-60. Cairo, 1967.

Emery—Kirwan 1935 Emery, W., and Kirwan, L. *The Excavations and Survey between Wadi Es-Sebua and Adindan, 1929-1931.* Service des Antiquités de l'Égypte. Mission archéologique de Nubie, 1929-1934. Cairo, 1935.

Emery—Kirwan 1938 Emery, W., and Kirwan, L. *The Royal Tombs of Ballana and Qustul.* Service des Antiquités de l'Égypte. Mission archéologique de Nubie, 1929-1934. Cairo, 1938.

Erman 1907 Erman, A. *A Handbook of Egyptian Religiön.* Translated by A. S. Griffith. London, 1907.

Erman 1934 Erman, A. *Die Religion der Ägypter.* Berlin and Leipzig, 1934.

Essen 1963 Essen, Villa Hügel. *Koptische Kunst: Christentum am Nil.* Exhibition catalogue. Essen, 1963.

Farid 1963a Farid, S. *Excavations at Ballana, 1958-1959.* Cairo, 1963.

Farid 1963b Farid, S. "Excavations of the Antiquities Department at Ballana, Preliminary Report (Season 1959)." In: Egypt, Service des Antiquités, *Fouilles en Nubie (1959-1961),* pp. 89-93. Cairo, 1963.

Fazzini 1971 Hempstead, New York, Hofstra University, Emily Lowe Gallery. *Art of Ancient Egypt: A Selection from The Brooklyn Museum . . .* By R. Fazzini. Exhibition catalogue. Hempstead, 1971.

Fazzini 1975 Fazzini, R. *Images for Eternity: Egyptian Art from Berkeley and Brooklyn.* Exhibition catalogue. Brooklyn, 1975.

Ferlini 1837 Ferlini, G. *Cenno sugli scavi operati nella Nubia e catalogo degli oggetti ritrovati.* Bologna, 1837.

Firth 1912 Firth, C. *The Archaeological Survey of Nubia. Report for 1908-1909.* Egypt, Survey Department. Cairo, 1912.

Firth 1915 Firth, C. *The Archaeological Survey of Nubia. Report for 1909-1910.* Egypt, Survey Department. Cairo, 1915.

Firth 1927 Firth, C. *The Archaeological Survey of Nubia. Report for 1910-1911.* Egypt, Survey Department. Cairo, 1927.

Fischer 1961 Fischer, H. "The Nubian Mercenaries of Gebelein during the First Intermediate Period." *Kush* 9 (1961), pp. 44-80.

Gadallah 1963 Gadallah, F. "Meroitic Problems and a Comprehensive Meroitic Bibliography." *Kush* 11 (1963), pp. 196-216.

Gardiner 1916a Gardiner, A. "An Ancient List of the Fortresses of Nubia." *JEA* 3 (1916), pp. 184-92.

Gardiner 1916b Gardiner, A. "The Defeat of the Hyksos by Kamōse: The Carnarvon Tablet, No. 1." *JEA* 3 (1916), pp. 95-110.

Garstang 1910a Liverpool, University, Institute of Archaeology. *Excavations at Meroë, Sudan, 1910. Guide to the Ninth Annual Exhibition of Antiquities Discovered.* By J. Garstang. Liverpool, 1910.

Garstang 1910b Garstang, J. "Preliminary Note on an Expedition to Meroë in Ethiopia." *LAAA* 3 (1910), pp. 57-70.

Garstang 1911 Garstang, J. *Meroë, the City of the Ethiopians.* Oxford, 1911.

Garstang 1912a Liverpool, University, Institute of Archaeology. *Excavations at Meroë, Sudan, 1912. Guide to the Eleventh Annual Exhibition of Antiquities Discovered.* By J. Garstang. Liverpool, 1912.

Garstang 1912b Garstang, J. "Second Interim Report on the Excavations at Meroë in Ethiopia. Part I—Excavations." *LAAA* 4 (1912), pp. 45-52.

Garstang 1913a Liverpool, University, Institute of Archaeology. *Excavations at Meroë, Sudan, 1913. Guide to the Twelfth Annual Exhibition of Antiquities Discovered.* By J. Garstang. Liverpool, 1913.

Garstang 1913b Garstang, J. "Third Interim Report on the Excavations at Meroë in Ethiopia." *LAAA* 5 (1913), pp. 73-83.

Garstang 1914a Liverpool, University, Institute of Archaeology. *Excavations at Meroë, Sudan, 1914. Guide to the Thirteenth Annual Exhibition of Antiquities Discovered.* By J. Garstang. Liverpool, 1914.

Garstang 1914b Garstang, J., and George, W. "Fourth Interim Report on the Excavations at Meroë in Ethiopia." *LAAA* 6 (1914), pp. 1-21.

Garstang 1914-16 Garstang, J. "Fifth Interim Report on the Excavations at Meroë in Ethiopia. Part I—General Results." *LAAA* 7 (1914-16), pp. 1-10.

Garstang Photo Photographs taken by J. Garstang at Meroe. In the School of Archaeology and Oriental Studies, University of Liverpool.

Gerster 1964 Gerster, G. *Nubien: Goldland am Nil.* Zurich and Stuttgart, 1964.

Giorgini 1965 Giorgini, M. *Soleb, I, 1813-1963.* Florence, 1965.

Glanville 1932-33 Glanville, S. "A Statue of Tirhaqah (Taharqa) and Other Nubian Antiquities." *The British Museum Quarterly* 7 (1932-33), pp. 45-47.

Gratien 1973 Gratien, B. "Les nécropoles Kerma de l'Ile de Saï. *Études sur l'Égypte et le Soudan Anciens. Cahier de Recherches de l'Institut de Papyrologie et d'Égyptologie de Lille,* no. 1 (1973), pp. 143-84.

Gratien 1974 Gratien, B. "Les nécropoles Kerma de l'Ile de Saï, II." *Études sur l'Égypte et le Soudan Anciens. Cahier de Recherches de l'Institut de Papyrologie et d'Égyptologie de Lille,* no. 2 (1974), pp. 51-74.

Gratien 1975 Gratien, B. "Les nécropoles Kerma de l'Ile de Saï, III." *Études sur l'Égypte et le Soudan Anciens. Cahier de Recherches de l'Institut de Papyrologie et d'Égyptologie de Lille,* no. 3 (1975), pp. 43-66.

Gratien 1978 Gratien, B. *Les Cultures Kerma.* Lille, 1978.

Greenberg 1966 Greenberg, J. *The Languages of Africa.* New York, 1966.

Greene 1972 Greene, D. "Dental Anthropology of Early Egypt and Nubia." *Journal of Human Evolution* 1 (1972), pp. 315-24.

Greene—Armelagos 1972 Greene, D., and Armelagos, G. *The Wadi Halfa Mesolithic Population.* University of Massachusetts. Department of Anthropology Research Report, no. 11. Amherst, Massachusetts, 1972.

Griffith 1909 Griffith, F. "Some Old Nubian Christian Texts." *Journal of Theological Studies* 10, no. 40 (1909), pp. 545-51.

Griffith 1911a Griffith, F. *Karanòg: The Meroitic Inscriptions of Shablûl and Karanòg.* Pennsylvania, University, University Museum, Egyptian Department. Eckley B. Coxe Junior Expedition to Nubia, vol. 6. Philadelphia, 1911.

Griffith 1911b Griffith, F. *Meroitic Inscriptions. Part I, Sôba to Dangêl.* In: Egypt Exploration Society, Archaeological Survey of Egypt. Memoirs, 19. London, 1911.

Griffith 1912 Griffith, F. *Meroitic Inscriptions. Part II, Napata to Philae and Miscellaneous.* Egypt Exploration Society, Archaeological Survey of Egypt. Memoirs, 20. London, 1912.

Griffith 1913 Griffith, F., ed. *The Nubia Texts of the Christian Period.* Preussische Akademie der Wissenschaften, Jahrgang 1913. Philosophisch-historische Classe, no. 8. Berlin, 1913.

Griffith 1916 Griffith, F. "An Omphalos from Napata." *JEA* 3(1916), p. 255 [also p. 221 under "Notes and News"].

Griffith 1917 Griffith, F. "Meroitic Studies III: A Sculptured Panel from Meroë." *JEA* 4 (1917), pp. 21-24.

Griffith 1921 Griffith, F. "Oxford Excavations in Nubia." *LAAA* 8 (1921), pp. 1-18, 65-104.

Griffith 1922 Griffith, F. "Oxford Excavations in Nubia." *LAAA* 9 (1922), pp. 67-124.

Griffith 1923 Griffith, F. "Oxford Excavations in Nubia." *LAAA* 10 (1923), pp. 73-171.

Griffith 1924 Griffith, F. "Oxford Excavations in Nubia." *LAAA* 11 (1924), pp. 115-25, 141-80.

Griffith 1925 Griffith, F. "Oxford Excavations in Nubia." *LAAA* 12 (1925), pp. 57-172.

Griffith 1926 Griffith, F. "Oxford Excavations in Nubia." *LAAA* 13 (1926), pp. 17-37, 49-93.

Griffith 1929 Griffith, F. "Scenes from a Destroyed Temple at Napata." *JEA* 15 (1929), pp. 26-28.

Grimm 1969 Grimm, G. *Die Zeugnisse ägyptischer Religion und Kunstelemente im römischen Deutschland.* Études préliminaires aux religions orientales dans l'Empire Romain, 12. Leiden, 1969.

Grossmann 1971 Grossmann, P. "Zur Datierung der frühen Kirchenanlagen aus Faras." *Byzantinische Zeitschrift* 64 (1971), pp. 330-50.

Habachi 1972 Habachi, L. *The Second Stela of Kamose and His Struggle Against the Hyksos Ruler and His Capital.* Abhandlungen des Deutschen Archäologischen Instituts Kairo, ägyptologische Reihe, vol. 8. Glückstadt, 1972.

Habachi 1977 Habachi, L. "Mentuhotp, the Vizier and Son-in-Law of Taharqa." In: *Ägypten und Kusch* [Festschrift Hintze], pp. 165-70. Schriften zur Geschichte und Kultur des Alten Orients, 13. Berlin/DDR, 1977.

Hakem 1971 Ali [Hakem], A. "The Nature and Development of Meroitic Architecture." Dissertation submitted for the degree of Doctor of Philosophy at University of Cambridge, 1971.

Hakem 1972 Ali [Hakem], A. "Meroitic Settlement of the Butana (Central Sudan)." In: Ucko, P.; Tringham, R.; Dimbleby, G., eds., *Man, Settlement and Urbanism,* pp. 639-46. London, 1972.

Hassan 1967 Hassan, Y. *The Arabs and the Sudan from the 7th to ca. 16th Centuries.* Edinburgh, 1967.

Hassan 1973 Hassan, Y. *Tabagat Wad Deifalla.* Khartoum, 1973.

Hayes 1973 Hayes, R. "The Distribution of Meroitic Archer's Rings: An Outline of Political Borders." In: *Meroitica: Schriften zur altsudanesischen Geschichte und Archäologie,* vol. 1, pp. 113-22. Berlin/DDR, 1973.

Helck 1971 Helck, W. *Betrachtungen zur grossen Göttin und den ihr verbundenden Gottheiten.* Religion und Kultur der alten Mittelmeerwelt in Parallelforschungen, 2. Munich and Vienna, 1971.

Hermann 1966 Hermann, A. "Magische Glocken aus Meroë." *ZÄS* 93 (1966), pp. 79-89.

Herzog 1957 Herzog, R. *Die Nubier.* Deutsche Akademie der Wissenschaften zu Berlin, Völkerkundliche Forschungen. Herausgegeben von der Sektion Völkerkunde und Deutsche Volkeskunde, 2. Berlin/DDR, 1957.

Herzog 1977 Herzog, R. "Die Fundumstände einer meroitischen Statuengruppe." In: *Ägypten und Kusch* [Festschrift Hintze], pp. 171-74. Schriften zur Geschichte und Kultur des Alten Orients, 13. Berlin/DDR, 1977.

Hinkel 1966 Hinkel, F. *Tempel ziehen um.* Leipzig, 1966.

Hinkel 1977 Hinkel, F. "Ein neues Triumphbild des meroitischen Löwen." In: *Ägypten und Kusch* [Festschrift Hintze], pp. 175-82. Schriften zur Geschichte und Kultur des Alten Orients, 13. Berlin/DDR, 1977.

Hintze 1955 Hintze, F. "Die sprachliche Stellung des Meroïtischen." *Institut für Orientforschung, Veröffentlichung* 26 (1955), pp. 355-72.

Hintze 1959 Hintze, F. *Studien zur meroitischen Chronologie und zu den Opfertafeln aus den Pyramiden von Meroe.* Abhandlungen der Deutschen Akademie der Wissenschaften zu Berlin. Klasse für Sprachen, Literatur und Kunst, Jahrgang 1959, Nr. 2. Berlin/DDR, 1959.

Hintze 1960a Hintze, F. "Vorbericht über die Butana-Expedition 1958 des Instituts für Ägyptologie der Humbolt-Universität zu Berlin." In: *Forschen und Wirken,* vol. 3, pp. 361-99. Festschrift zur 150-Jahr-Feier der Humbolt-Universität zu Berlin. Berlin/DDR, 1960.

Hintze 1960b Hintze, F. "Die meroitische Stele des Königs Tañyidamani aus Napata." *Kush* 8 (1960), pp. 125-62.

Hintze 1961 Hintze, F. "Zu den in *Kush* VII, pp. 93ff., veröffentlichten meroitischen Inschriften." *Kush* 9 (1961), pp. 278-82.

Hintze 1962a Hintze, F. *Die Inschriften des Löwentempels von Musawwarat Es Sufra.* Abhandlungen der Deutschen Akademie der Wissenschaften zu Berlin. Klasse für Sprachen, Literatur und Kunst, Jahrgang 1962, Nr. 1. Berlin/DDR, 1962.

Hintze 1962b Hintze, F. "Preliminary Report on the Excavations at Musawwarat Es Sufra, 1960-1 by the Institute of Egyptology, Humbolt University, Berlin." *Kush* 10 (1962), pp. 170-202.

Hintze 1962c Hintze, F. "Vorbericht über die Ausgrabungen des Instituts für Ägyptologie der Humbolt-Universität zu Berlin in Musawwarat es Sufra, 1960-1961." *Wissenschaftliche Zeitschrift der Humbolt-Universität zu Berlin. Gesellschafts- und Sprachwissenschaftliche Reihe* 11 (1962), pp. 441-88.

Hintze 1963a Hintze, F. "Musawwarat es Sufra: Preliminary Report on the Excavations of the Institute of Egyptology, Humbolt University, Berlin, 1961-1962 (Third Season)." *Kush* 11 (1963), pp. 217-26.

Hintze 1963b Hintze, F. "Musawwarat es Sufra: Vorbericht über die Ausgrabungen des Instituts für Ägyptologie der Humbolt-Universität zu Berlin, 1961-1962 (Dritte Kampagne)." *Wissenschaftliche Zeitschrift der Humbolt-Universität zu Berlin. Gesellschafts- und Sprachwissenschaftliche Reihe* 12 (1963), pp. 63-77.

Hintze 1963c Hintze, F. "Preliminary Note on the Epigraphic Expedition to Sudanese Nubia 1962." *Kush* 11 (1963), pp. 93-95.

Hintze 1964 Hintze, F. "Das Kerma-Problem." *ZÄS* 91 (1964), pp. 79-86.

Hintze 1966 Hintze, F., and Hintze, U. *Alte Kulturen im Sudan.* Leipzig, 1966.

Hintze 1967 Hintze, F. "Meroe und die Noba." *ZÄS* 94 (1967), pp. 79-86.

Hintze 1968a Hintze, F., and Hintze, U. *Civilizations of the Old Sudan: Kerma, Kush, Christian Nubia.* Translated by P. Prochnik. Leipzig, 1968.

Hintze 1968b Hintze, F. "Musawwarat es Sufra: Vorbericht über die Ausgrabungen des Instituts für Ägyptologie der Humbolt-Universität zu Berlin, 1963 bis 1966 (Vierte bis sechste Kampagne)." *Wissenschaftliche Zeitschrift der Humbolt-Universität zu Berlin. Gesellschafts- und Sprachwissenschaftliche Reihe* 17 (1968), pp. 667-84.

Hintze 1970 Hintze, F., and Hintze, U. "Einige neue Ergebnisse der Ausgrabungen des Instituts für Ägyptologie der Humbolt-Universität zu Berlin in Musawwarat es Sufra." In: Dinkler, E., ed., *Kunst und Geschichte Nubiens in christlicher Zeit,* pp. 49-70. Recklinghausen, 1970.

Hintze 1971a Hintze, F. *Musawwarat es Sufra.* Vol. I, 2, *Der Löwentempel, Tafelband.* Humbolt-Universität zu Berlin. Archäologische Forschungen im Sudan. Berlin/DDR, 1971.

Hintze 1971b Hintze, F. "Musawwarat es Sufra: Vorbericht über die Ausgrabungen des Instituts für Ägyptologie der Humbolt-Universität zu Berlin 1968 (siebente Kampagne)." *Berliner Beiträge zur Ägyptologie und Sudanarchäologie. Wissenschaftliche Zeitschrift der Humbolt-Universität zu Berlin. Gesellschafts- und Sprachwissenschaftliche Reihe* 20 (1971), pp. 227-45.

Hintze 1973 Hintze, F. "Meroitic Chronology: Problems and Prospects." In: *Meroitica: Schriften zur altsudanesischen Geschichte und Archäologie,* vol. 1, pp. 127-44. Berlin/DDR, 1973.

Hirth 1902 *Georg Hirth's Formenschatz: Eine Quelle der Belehrung und Anregung für Künstler und Gewerbetreibende, wie für alle Freunde stilvoller Schönheit, aus den Werken der besten Meister aller Zeiten und Völker.* Munich and Leipzig, 1902.

Hofmann 1967 Hofmann, I. *Die Kulturen des Niltals von Aswan bis Sennar vom Mesolithikum bis zum Ende der christlichen Epoche.* Hamburg, Museum für Völkerkunde und Vorgeschichte. Monographien zur Völkerkunde, 4. Hamburg, 1967.

Hofmann 1970 Hofmann, I. "Der sogenannte Omphalos von Napata." *JEA* 56 (1970), pp. 187-92.

Hofmann 1971 Hofmann, I. *Studien zum meroitischen Königtum.* Monographies Reine Élisabeth, 2. Brussels, 1971.

Hofmann 1972 Hofmann, I. "Eine neue Elefantengott-Darstellung aus dem Sudan." *JEA* 58 (1972), pp. 245-46.

Hofmann 1975a Hofmann, I. "Notizen zu den Kampfszenen am sogenannten Sonnentempel von Meroe." *Anthropos* 70 (1975), pp. 513-36.

Hofmann 1975b Hofmann, I. *Wege und Möglichkeiten eines indischen Einflusses auf die meroitische Kultur.* Studia Instituti Anthropos, 23. St. Augustin bei Bonn, 1975.

Hoskins 1835 Hoskins, G. *Travels in Ethiopia, Above the Second Cataract of the Nile; Exhibiting the State of That Country, and Its Various Inhabitants under the Dominion of Mohammed Ali; and Illustrating the Antiquities, Arts, and History of the Ancient Kingdom of Meroe.* London, 1835.

Huard 1973 Huard, P. "Influences culturelles transmises au Sahara tchadien par le groupe C de Nubie." *Kush* 15 (1967-68 [1973]), pp. 84-124.

ILN 1932 "Wonderful Discoveries in Nubia: Silver Horse-Harness; Iron Spears. 'The Gemmy Bridle Glittered Free': Nubian Horse Trappings. Steps to a Great Archaeological Discovery: Treasure from a Nubian Region Destined to be Submerged." *The Illustrated London News* 180 (1932), pp. 954-57.

ILN 1933a "A Mysterious Nubian Tribe, Half-Christian, Half-Pagan: New Tomb-Finds near Abu Simbel." *The Illustrated London News* 182 (1933), pp. 264-65.

ILN 1933b "Treasure from Intact Tombs of Mysterious Nubian Kings: Christian Symbolism Associated with Pagan Gods and Slave-Sacrifice. Astonishing Art Forms of the Byzantine-Nubian Period Found in Upper Egypt: Further Examples from the Royal Tombs Discovered Intact Near Abu Simbel." *The Illustrated London News* 182 (1933), pp. 919-23.

ILN 1950 "The Libation Stand of King Piankhy: A Unique Object, Found in the Sudan and Now Restored." *The Illustrated London News* 217 (1950), p. 699.

Iwaszkiewicz 1974 Iwaszkiewicz, B. "La frise de l'abaside de la première Cathédrale de Faras." *Orientalia Christiana Periodica* 40 (1974), pp. 377-407.

Jacquet 1971 Jacquet, J. "Remarques sur l'architecture domestique à l'époque méroïtique; documents recueillis sur les fouilles d'Ash-Shaukan." *Beiträge zur ägyptischen Bauforschung und Altertumskunde* 12 (1971), pp. 121-31.

Jakobielski 1973 Jakobielski, S., and Krzyżaniak, L. "Polish Excavations at Old Dongola, Third Season, December 1966-February 1967." *Kush* 15 (1967-68 [1973]), pp. 143-64.

Junker 1920a Junker, H. *Bericht über die Grabungen der Akademie der Wissenschaften in Wien auf den Friedhöfen von El-Kubanieh-Nord, Winter 1910-1911.* Akademie der Wissenschaften in Wien, Philosophisch-historische Klasse. Denkschriften, 64/3. Vienna, 1920.

Junker 1920b Junker, H. *Das erste Auftreten der Neger in der Geschichte.* Vortrag gehalten in der statutenmässigen Jahressitzung der Akademie der Wissenschaften in Wien am 30. Mai 1920. Vienna, 1920.

Junker 1921 Junker, H. *Der nubische Ursprung der sogenannten Tell el-Jahudiye-Vasen.* Akademie der Wissenschaften in Wien, Philosophisch-historische Klasse. Sitzungsberichte 198/3. Vienna, 1921.

Junker 1922 Junker, H. "The First Appearance of the Negroes in History." *JEA* 7 (1922), pp. 121-32.

Junker 1925 Junker, H. *Ermenne. Bericht über die Grabungen der Akademie der Wissenschaften in Wien auf den Friedhöfen von Ermenne (Nubien) im Winter 1911/12.* Akademie der Wissenschaften in Wien, Philosophisch-historische Klasse. Denkschriften, 67. Vienna and Leipzig, 1925.

Junker 1926 Junker, H. *Toschke. Bericht über die Grabungen der Akademie der Wissenschaften in Wien auf dem Friedhof von Toschke (Nubien) im Winter 1911/12.* Akademie der Wissenschaften in Wien, Philosophisch-historische Klasse. Denkschriften, 68. Vienna and Leipzig, 1926.

Känel — Maystre 1976 Geneva, Musée d'Art et d'Histoire. *Akasha, 3500 ans d'histoire et de civilisation en Nubie soudanaise.* By F. von Känel and C. Maystre. Exhibition catalogue. Geneva, 1976.

Katznelson 1970 Katznelson, I. *Napata i Meroe; drevnie tsarstva Sudana.* Moscow, 1970.

Kaufmann 1910 Kaufmann, K. *Die Menasstadt und das Nationalheiligtum der altchristlichen Ägypter in der westalexandrinischen Wüste; Ausgrabungen der Frankfurter Expedition am Karm Abu Mina, 1905-1907.* Leipzig, 1910.

Kawar 1964 Shahid (Kawar), I. "Byzantino-Arabica: The Conference of Ramla, A.D. 524." *JNES* 23 (1964), pp. 115-31.

Kayser 1969 Kayser, H. *Ägyptisches Kunsthandwerk.* Bibliothek für Kunst- und Antiquitätenfreunde, 26. Braunschweig, 1969.

Keating 1964 Keating, R. "Prodigieuses moissons dans les champs de fouille." *Le Courrier de l'UNESCO* (Paris) 17, no. 10 (1964), pp. 27-32, 34.

Keimer 1951 Keimer, L. "A Gold Pectoral from Napata." *JNES* 10 (1951), pp. 225-27.

Kirwan 1934 Kirwan, L. "A Sudanese of the Saite Period." *Cairo, Institut Français d'Archéologie Orientale. Mémoires* 66 (1934), pp. 373-77.

Kirwan 1935 Kirwan, L. "The Oxford University Excavations in Nubia, 1934-1935." *JEA* 21 (1935), pp. 191-98.

Kirwan 1937 Kirwan, L. "A Contemporary Account of the Conversion of the Sudan to Christianity." *Sudan Notes and Records* 20, no. 2 (1937), pp. 289-95.

Kirwan 1939 Kirwan, L. *The Oxford University Excavations at Firka.* London, 1939.

Kirwan 1953 Kirwan, L. "The Ballana Civilization." *Bulletin de la Société Royale de Géographie d'Égypte* 25 (1953), pp. 103-10.

Kirwan 1960 Kirwan, L. "The Decline and Fall of Meroe." *Kush* 8 (1960), pp. 163-73.

Kirwan 1963 Kirwan, L. "The X-Group Enigma: A Little-Known People of the Nubian Nile." In: Bacon, E., ed., *Vanished Civilizations,* pp. 33-35. London, 1963.

Kitchen 1973 Kitchen, K. *The Third Intermediate Period in Egypt (1100-650 B.C.).* Warminster, 1973.

Kołodziejczyk 1969 Kołodziejczyk, K. "A Pilgrim Bottle from Faras." *Études et travaux* 3 (1969), pp. 191-97.

Kraus 1964 Kraus, T. "Der Kiosk von Naga." *Archäologischer Anzeiger,* 1964, no. 4, pp. 834-67.

Kraus 1969 Kraus, T. "Rom und Meroe." *Mitteilungen des Deutschen Archäologischen Instituts Abteilung Kairo* 25 (1969), pp. 49-56.

Krzyżaniak 1974 Krzyżaniak, L. "Druga i trzecia kampania badán wykopaliskowych w Kadero (Sudan). Second and Third Excavation Campaign at Kudero (Sudan). Zweite und dritte Ausgrabungskampagne in Kadero (Sudan)." *Fontes Archaeologici Posnanienses* 25 (1974), pp. 187-95.

Krzyżaniak 1975 Krzyżaniak, L. "Kadero (First Season, 1972)." *Études et travaux* 8 (1975), pp. 361-66.

Krzyżaniak ms. Krzyżaniak, L. "Preliminary Report for the Sudan Antiquities Service." Unpublished manuscript.

Kuentz 1934 Kuentz, C. "Remarques sur les statues de Harwa." *Bulletin de l'Institut Français d'Archéologie orientale* 34 (1934), pp. 143-63.

Kühnert-Eggebrecht 1969 Kühnert-Eggebrecht, E. *Die Axt als Waffe und Werkzeug im alten Ägypten.* Münchner ägyptologische Studien, 15. Berlin/West, 1969.

Lal 1967 Lal, B. "Indian Archaeological Expedition to Nubia, 1962; A Preliminary Report." In: Egypt, Service des Antiquités, *Fouilles en Nubie (1961-1963),* pp. 95-118. Cairo, 1967.

Landström 1970 Landström, B. *Ships of the Pharaohs: 4000 Years of Egyptian Shipbuilding.* London, 1970.

Lapis 1966 Lapis, I. "Chastnyĭ skul'pturnyĭ portret v fivakh vremeni XXV — nachala XXVI dinastii." *Vestnik drevneĭ istorii,* 1966, no. 3, pp. 105-12.

LD V Lepsius, R. *Denkmaeler aus Aegypten und Aethiopien nach den Zeichnungen der von Seiner Majestät dem Koenige von Preussen Friedrich Wilhelm IV nach diesen Ländern gesendeten und in den Jahren 1842-1845 ausgeführten wissenschaftlichen Expedition . . .* Part 5, *Aethiopische Denkmaeler.* Berlin, [1849-59].

LD VI Lepsius, R. *Denkmaeler aus Aegypten und Aethiopien nach den Zeichnungen der von Seiner Majestät dem Koenige von Preussen Friedrich Wilhelm IV nach diesen Ländern gesendeten und in den Jahren 1842-1845 ausgeführten wissenschaftlichen Expedition . . .* Part 6, *Inschriften mit Ausschluss der Hieroglyphischen.* Berlin, [1849-59].

LD T III Lepsius, R. *Denkmäler aus Aegypten und Aethiopien.* Text. Vol. 3, *Theben.* Edited by E. Naville and K. Sethe. Leipzig, 1900.

Leclant 1963 Leclant, J. "Kshta, Pharaon, en Égypte." *ZÄS* 90 (1963), pp. 74-81.

Leclant 1964 Leclant, J. "Fouilles et travaux en Égypte et au Soudan, 1962-1963." *Orientalia* 33 (1964), pp. 337-404.

Leclant 1965a Leclant, J. "Fouilles et travaux en Égypte et au Soudan, 1963-1964." *Orientalia* 34 (1965), pp. 175-232.

Leclant 1965b Leclant, J. *Recherches sur les monuments thébains de la XXVe dynastie dite éthiopienne.* Cairo, 1965.

Leclant 1966 Leclant, J. "Fouilles et travaux en Égypte et au Soudan, 1964-1965." *Orientalia* 35 (1966), pp. 127-78.

Leclant 1969 Leclant, J. "L'Archéologie méroïtique. Recherches en Nubie et au Sudan. Résultants et perspectives." *Acts du Premier Colloque International d'Archéologie Africaine.* Études et Documents Tchadiens. Mémoires, I. 1969.

Leclant 1970 Leclant, J. "La Religion méroïtique." In: *Histoire des Religions I,* Encyclopédie de la Pléiade, vol. 29, pp. 141-53. Paris, 1970.

Leclant 1973 Leclant, J. "Les Recherches archéologiques dans le domaine méroïtique." *Meroitica: Schriften zur altsudanesischen Geschichte und Archäologie,* vol. 1, pp. 19-59. Berlin/DDR, 1973.

Leclant 1975a Leclant, J. "État présent des études nubiennes." *Bulletin de la Société Française d'Égyptologie,* no. 74 (1975), pp. 7-18.

Leclant 1975b Leclant, J. "Fouilles et travaux en Égypte et au Soudan, 1973-1974." *Orientalia* 44 (1975), pp. 200-244.

Leclant 1976 Leclant, J. "Kushites and Meroites: Iconography of the African Rulers in the Ancient Upper Nile." In: *The Image of the Black in Western Art,* vol. 1, pp. 89-132. Publication of the Menil Foundation, Inc. New York, 1976.

Leipzig 1976 Krauspe, R. *Ägyptisches Museum der Karl-Marx-Universität Leipzig.* Leipzig, 1976.

Linant de Bellefonds 1958 Linant de Bellefonds, M. *Journal d'un voyage à Méroé dans les années 1821 et 1822.* Edited by M. Shinnie. Sudan Antiquities Service. Occasional Papers, no. 4. Khartoum, 1958.

Livingstone 1962 Livingstone, F. "On the Non-existence of Human Races." *Current Anthropology* 3 (1962), pp. 279-81.

Los Angeles 1974 Los Angeles County Museum of Art. *Age of the Pharaohs: Egyptian Art from American Collections.* Exhibition catalogue. Los Angeles, 1974.

Lucas—Harris 1962 Lucas, A. *Ancient Egyptian Materials and Industries.* 4th ed., rev. and enl. by J. R. Harris. London, 1962.

Lucchesi Palli 1972 Lucchesi Palli, E. "Ergebnisse und Probleme auf Grund der jüngsten Ausgrabungen." Review of Dinkler, E., ed., *Kunst und Geschichte Nubiens in christlicher Zeit,* Recklinghausen, 1970. *Römische Quartalschrift für christliche Altertumskunde und Kirchengeschichte* 67, nos. 3/4 (1972), pp. 234-39.

Macadam 1949 Macadam, M. *The Temples of Kawa.* Vol. 1, *The Inscriptions.* 2 vols. Oxford University Excavations in Nubia. London, 1949.

Macadam 1950 Macadam, M. "Four Meroitic Inscriptions." *JEA* 36 (1950), pp. 43-47.

Macadam 1955 Macadam, M. *The Temples of Kawa.* Vol. 2, *History and Archaeology of the Site.* 2 vols. Oxford University Excavations in Nubia. London, 1955.

Macadam 1966 Macadam, M. "Queen Nawidemak." *Bulletin of the Allen Memorial Art Museum, Oberlin College* 23, no. 2 (1966), pp. 42-71.

MacGaffey 1966 MacGaffey, W. "Concepts of Race in the Historiography of Northwest Africa." *Journal of African History* 7 (1966), pp. 1-17.

MacGregor Collection 1922 London, Sotheby, Wilkinson & Hodge. *Catalogue of the MacGregor Collection of Egyptian Antiquities.* June 26 — July 6, 1922. London, 1922.

McHugh 1974 McHugh, W. "Late Prehistoric Cultural Adaptation in Southwest Egypt and the Problem of the Nilotic Origins of Saharan Cattle Pastoralism." *JARCE* 11 (1974), pp. 9-22.

Marks 1970 Marks, A. *Preceramic Sites.* The Scandinavian Joint Expedition to Sudanese Nubia. Publications, 2. Stockholm, 1970.

Marshall 1911 British Museum, Department of Greek and Roman Antiquities. *Catalogue of the Jewellery, Greek, Etruscan, and Roman in the Departments of Antiquities, British Museum.* By F. Marshall. London, 1911.

Maspero 1907 Maspero, G. *L'Archéologie égyptienne.* Paris, 1907.

Maspero 1911 Maspero, G. *Rapports relatifs à la consolidation des temples.* Service des Antiquités de l'Égypte. Les temples immergés de la Nubie. Cairo, 1911.

Maspero 1921 Maspero, G. *Art in Egypt.* London, 1921.

Maspero 1925 Maspero, G. *Geschichte der Kunst in Ägypten.* Stuttgart, 1925.

Maystre 1973 Maystre, C. "Excavations at Tabo, Argo Island, 1965-1968; Preliminary Report." *Kush* 15 (1967-68 [1973]), pp. 193-99.

Maystre 1975 Maystre, C. "Découvertes récentes (1969-1972) près d'Akasha." In: Michałowski, K., ed., *Nubia: Récentes Recherches,* pp. 88-92. Warsaw, 1975.

Mekhitarian 1961 Mekhitarian, A. "Mission au Soudan." *Chronique d'Égypte* 36 (1961), pp. 113-47.

Menil 1976 *The Image of the Black in Western Art.* Vol. 1, *From the Pharaohs to the Fall of the Roman Empire.* Publication of the Menil Foundation, Inc. New York, 1976.

Michałowski 1965 Michałowski, K. "Polish Excavations at Faras—Fourth Season, 1963-1964." *Kush* 13 (1965), pp. 177-89.

Michałowski 1966 Michałowski, K. *Faras: Centre artistique de la Nubie chrétienne.* Scholae Adriani De Buck Memoriae Dicatae, 3. Leiden, 1966.

Michałowski 1967 Michałowski, K. *Faras: Die Katedrale aus dem Wüstensand.* Cologne, 1967.

Michałowski 1974 Michałowski, K. *Faras: Die Wandbilder in den Sammlungen des Nationalmuseums zu Warschau.* Die Inschriften bearbeitete Stefan Jakobielski. Warsaw and Dresden, 1974.

Michałowski 1975 Michałowski, K., ed. *Nubia: Récentes Recherches.* Warsaw, 1975.

Mileham 1910 Mileham, G. *Churches in Lower Nubia.* Edited by D. Randall-MacIver. Pannsylvania, University, University Museum, Egyptian Department. Eckley B. Coxe Junior Expedition to Nubia, vol. 2. Philadelphia, 1910.

Milkovich 1963 Milkovich, M. "Ancient Art in the Worcester Art Museum." *Archaeology* 16, no. 3 (1963), pp. 154-61.

Millet 1963 Millet, N. "Gebel Adda: Preliminary Report for 1963." *JARCE* 2 (1963), pp. 147-65.

Millet 1964 Millet, N. "Gebel Adda Expedition Preliminary Report, 1963-1964." *JARCE* 3 (1964), pp. 7-14.

Millet 1968 Millet, N. *Meroitic Nubia.* Ph.D. dissertation, Yale University, 1968. Ann Arbor, Michigan (University Microfilms), 1968.

Mills — Nordström 1966 Mills, A. J., and Nordström, H.-Å. "The Archaeological Survey from Gemai to Dal; Preliminary Report of the Season 1964-65." *Kush* 14 (1966), pp. 1-15.

Mohammed Wad Dayfallah 1800 Mohammed Wad Dayfallah. *Ṭabaqat Wad Ḍayfallah* [Biography of Worthies of Fung Kingdom of Sennar, c. 1800]. Edited by I. Sadiq and S. Mandil. Cairo, 1930.

Möller 1924 Möller, G. *Die Metallkunst der Alten Ägypter.* Berlin, 1924.

Monneret de Villard 1938 Monneret de Villard, U. *Storia della Nubia cristiana.* Orientalia christiana analecta, 118. Rome, 1938.

Monneret de Villard 1941 Monneret de Villard, U. *La Nubia romana.* Publicazioni dell'Istituto per l'Oriente. Rome, 1941.

Monneret de Villard 1942 Monneret de Villard, U. "Il culto del sole a Meroe." *Rassegna di studi etiopici* 2 (1942), pp. 107-42.

Monneret de Villard 1935-57 Monneret de Villard, U. *La Nubia medioevale.* Service des Antiquités de l'Égypte. Mission archéologique de Nubie, 1929-1934. Cairo, 1935-57.

Monneret de Villard 1959 Monneret de Villard, U. "Inscrizioni della regione di Meroe." *Kush* 7 (1959), pp. 93-114.

Monneret de Villard 1960 Monneret de Villard, U. "Testi meroitici della Nubia settentrionale." *Kush* 8 (1960), pp. 88-124.

Monnet 1952 Monnet, J. "Un vase à libation royal du culte d'Amon-Rē de Gematon." *Revue d'égyptologie* 9 (1952), pp. 91-99.

Morgan 1909 Morgan, H. de. "L'Égypte primitive." *Revue de l'École d'Anthropologie de Paris* 19 (1909), pp. 263-81.

Morgan 1912 Morgan, H. de. "Report on Excavations Made in Upper Egypt during the Winter 1907-1908." *Annales du Service des Antiquités de l'Égypte* 12 (1912), pp. 25-50.

Mukherjee 1955 Mukherjee, R.; Rao, C.; and Trevor, J. *The Ancient Inhabitants of Jebel Moya.* Cambridge, 1955.

Müller 1904 Müller, W. *Äthiopien. Der Alte Orient,* vol. 6, no. 2. 1904.

Müller 1970a Müller, C. "Deutsche Textfunde in Nubien." In: Dinkler, E., ed., *Kunst und Geschichte Nubiens in christlicher Zeit,* pp. 245-58. Recklinghausen, 1970.

Müller 1975 Müller, C. "Die nubische Literatur. Bestand und Eigenart." In: Michałowski, K., ed., *Nubia: Récentes Recherches,* pp. 93-100. Warsaw, 1975.

Müller 1970b Müller, H. *Ägyptische Kunst.* Frankfurt am Main, 1970.

Munich 1966 Munich, Ägyptische Sammlung des bayerischen Staates. *Die ägyptische Sammlung des bayerischen Staates.* Exhibition catalogue. Munich, 1966.

Munich 1972 Munich, Staatliche Sammlung Ägyptischer Kunst. *Staatliche Sammlung Ägyptischer Kunst.* Munich, 1972.

Munich 1976 Munich, Staatliche Sammlung Ägyptischer Kunst. *Staatliche Sammlung Ägyptischer Kunst.* 2d ed., enl. Munich, 1976.

Murdock 1959 Murdock, G. *Africa: Its Peoples and Their Culture History.* New York, 1959.

Myers — Shinnie 1948 Myers, O., and Shinnie, P. "Archaeological Discoveries during the Winter of 1947-48, Excavations in the Second Cataract Area." *Sudan Notes and Records* 29 (1948), pp. 128-29.

Nordström 1962 Nordström, H.-Å. "Excavations and Survey in Faras, Argin and Gezira Dabarosa." *Kush* 10 (1962), pp. 34-58.

Nordström 1972 Nordström, H.-Å. *Neolithic and A-Group Sites.* The Scandinavian Joint Expedition to Sudanese Nubia, 3. Upsalla, 1972.

Nur 1956 Nur, S. "Two Meroitic Pottery Coffins from Argin in Halfa District." *Kush* 4 (1956), pp. 86-87.

Nur 1962 Nur, S. "The Circular Brick Building of Wad Ban Naga." *Chronique d'Égypte* 37 (1962), p. 76.

O'Connor 1969 O'Connor, D. "Nubian Archaeological Material of the First to the Second Intermediate Period: An Analytical Study." Dissertation submitted for the degree of Doctor of Philosophy at University of Cambridge, 1969.

Otto 1963 Otto, K.-H. "Shaqadud, A New Khartoum Neolithic Site outside the Nile Valley." *Kush* 11 (1963), pp. 108-15.

Otto 1964 Otto, K.-H. "Khartoum-Neolithikum am Jebel Shaqadud." In: *Varia Archaeologica Wilhelm Unverzagt zum 70. Geburtstag dargebracht,* pp. 9-13. Deutsche Akademie der Wissenschaften zu Berlin. Schriften der Sektion für Vor- und Frühgeschichte, 16. Berlin/DDR, 1964.

Otto 1967 Otto, K.-H. "Zur Klassifikation der meroïtischen Keramik vom Musawwarat es Sufra (Republik Sudan)." *Zeitschrift für Archäologie* 1 (1967), pp. 1-32.

Otto 1973 Otto, K.-H. "Die Drehscheibenkeramik von Musawwarat es Sufra und die Klassifikation der meroitischen Keramik." In: *Meroitica: Schriften zur altsudanesischen Geschichte und Archäologie,* vol. 1, pp. 221-25. Berlin/DDR, 1973.

Oxford 1914 Oxford, University, Ashmolean Museum. *Report of the Visitors of the Ashmolean Museum of Art and Archaeology.* Oxford, 1914.

Oxford 1951 Oxford, University, Ashmolean Museum, Department of Antiquities. *A Summary Guide to the Collections.* Oxford, 1951.

Oxford 1970 Oxford, University, Ashmolean Museum. *Ancient Egypt.* By P. Moorey. Oxford, 1970.

Palmer 1965 Palmer, L. *Mycenaeans and Minoans: Aegean Prehistory in the Light of Linear B Tablets.* London, 1965.

Petrie 1886 Petrie, W., et al. *Naukratis.* Part 1, *1884-5.* Egypt Exploration Society. Memoirs, 3. London, 1886.

Petrie 1889 Petrie, W. *Hawara, Biahmu, and Arsinoe.* London, 1889.

Petrie 1901 Petrie, W. *Diospolis Parva, The Cemeteries of Abadiyeh and Hu, 1898-9.* With chapters by A. Mace. Egypt Exploration Society. Special Extra Publication [Memoirs, 20]. London, 1901.

Phythian-Adams 1914-16 Phythian-Adams, W. "Fifth Interim Report on the Excavations at Meroë in Ethiopia. Part II--Detailed Examination." *LAAA* 7 (1914-16), pp. 11-22.

Pirenne 1963 Pirenne, J. *Histoire de la civilisation de l'Égypte ancienne.* Vol. 3. Neuchâtel and Paris, 1963.

Plenderleith 1962 Plenderleith, H. *The Conservation of Antiquities and Works of Art; Treatment, Repair and Restoration.* Rev. ed. London, 1962.

Plumley 1964 Plumley, J. "Qasr Ibrîm 1963-1964." *JEA* 50 (1964), pp. 3-5.

Plumley 1966 Plumley, J. "Qasr Ibrîm 1966." *JEA* 52 (1966), pp. 9-12.

Plumley 1967 Plumley, J. "Qasr Ibrîm December 1966." *JEA* 53 (1967), pp. 3-5.

Plumley 1970a Plumley, J. "Qasr Ibrîm 1969." *JEA* 56 (1970), pp. 12-18.

Plumley 1970b Plumley, J. "Some Examples of Christian Nubian Art from the Excavations at Qasr Ibrîm." In: Dinkler, E., ed., *Kunst und Geschichte Nubiens in christlicher Zeit,* pp. 129-40. Recklinghausen, 1970.

Plumley 1971 Plumley, J. "Pre-Christian Nubia (23 B.C.-535 A.D.). Evidence from Qasr Ibrim." *Études et travaux* 11 (1971), pp. 7-24.

Plumley 1975 Plumley, J. "Qasr Ibrîm, 1974." *JEA* 61 (1975), pp. 5-27.

Plumley — Adams 1974 Plumley, J., and Adams, W. "Qasr Ibrîm, 1972." *JEA* 60 (1974), pp. 212-38.

P—M II 1972 Porter, B.; Moss, R.; and Birney, E. *Topographical Bibliography of Ancient Egyptian Hieroglyphic Texts, Reliefs, and Paintings.* Vol. 2, *Theban Temples.* 2d ed., rev. and aug. Oxford, 1972.

P—M VII 1951 Porter, B., and Moss, R. *Topographical Bibliography of Ancient Egyptian Hieroglyphic Texts, Reliefs, and Paintings.* Vol. 7, *Nubia, the Deserts, and Outside Egypt.* Oxford, 1951.

Prague 1975 Prague. Náprstkova Museum. *Průvodce výstavou Náprstkova Muzea. Tajemná Núbie, Čs. archeologické výzkumy v Egyptě 1961-65.* Prague, 1975.

Priese 1968 Priese, K.-H. "Nichtägyptische Namen und Wörter in den ägyptischen Inschriften der Könige von Kusch I." *Mitteilungen des Instituts für Orientforschung der Deutschen Akademie der Wissenschaften zu Berlin* 14 (1968), pp. 165-91.

Priese 1970 Priese, K.-H. "Der Beginn der kuschitischen Herrschaft in Ägypten." *ZÄS* 98 (1970), pp. 16-32.

Priese 1973 Priese, K.-H. "Articula." *Études et travaux* 7 (1973), pp. 156-62.

Priese 1974 Priese, K.-H. "ʾI*rm* und ʾꜣ*m*, das Land Irame. Ein Beitrag zur Topographie des Sudan im Altertum." *Altorientalische Forschungen* 1 (1974), pp. 7-41.

Priese 1977 Priese, K.-H. "Eine verschollene Bauinschrift des frühmeroitischen Königs Aktisanes (?) von Gebel Barkal." In: *Ägypten und Kusch* [Festschrift Hintze], pp. 343-67. Schriften zur Geschichte und Kultur des Alten Orients, 13. Berlin/DDR, 1977.

Prisse 1878 Prisse d'Avennes, A. *Histoire de l'art égyptien d'après les monuments, depuis les temps les plus reculés jusqu'à la domination romaine.* Paris, 1878-79.

Randall-MacIver — Woolley 1909 Randall-MacIver, D., and Woolley, C. *Areika.* Pennsylvania, University, University Museum, Egyptian Department. Eckley B. Coxe Junior Expedition to Nubia, vol. 1. Philadelphia, 1909.

Randall-MacIver — Woolley 1911 Randall-MacIver, D., and Woolley, C. *Buhen.* Pennsylvania, University, University Museum, Egyptian Department. Eckley B. Coxe Junior Expedition to Nubia, vols. 7 and 8. Philadelphia, 1911.

Reisner 1908 Reisner, G. "The Archaeological Survey of Nubia." *Egypt, Survey Department, Archaeological Survey of Nubia. Bulletin* 1 (1908), pp. 9-24.

Reisner 1910 Reisner, G. *The Archaeological Survey of Nubia. Report for 1907-1908.* Vol. 1, *Archaeological Report.* Egypt, Survey Department. Cairo, 1910.

Reisner 1914 Reisner, G. "New Acquisitions of the Egyptian Department. A Garrison Which Held the Northern Sudan in the Hyksos Period, about 1700 B.C." *BMFA* 12, no. 69 (1914), pp. 9-24.

Reisner 1915 Reisner, G. "Accessions to the Egyptian Collections during 1914." *BMFA* 13, nos. 76 and 80 (1915), pp. 29-36, 71-83.

Reisner 1917a Reisner, G. "The Barkal Temples in 1916" [Part 1]. *JEA* 4 (1917), pp. 213-27.

Reisner 1917b Reisner, G. "Excavations at Napata, the Capital of Ethiopia." *BMFA* 15, no. 89 (1917), pp. 25-34.

Reisner 1918a Reisner, G. "The Barkal Temples in 1916" [Part 2]. *JEA* 5 (1918), pp. 99-112.

Reisner 1918b Reisner, G. "Known and Unknown Kings of Ethiopia." *BMFA* 16, no. 97 (1918), pp. 67-82.

Reisner 1920 Reisner, G. "The Barkal Temples in 1916" [Part 3]. *JEA* 6 (1920), pp. 247-64.

Reisner 1921a Reisner, G. "Historical Inscriptions from Gebel Barkal." *Sudan Notes and Records* 4 (1921), pp. 59-75.

Reisner 1921b Reisner, G. "The Royal Family of Ethiopia." *BMFA* 19, nos. 112 and 113 (1921), pp. 21-38.

Reisner 1923a Reisner, G. *Kerma, Parts I-III.* Harvard University, Peabody Museum, African Department. *Harvard African Studies,* vol. 5. Cambridge, Massachusetts, 1923.

Reisner 1923b Reisner, G. *Kerma, Parts IV-V.* Harvard University, Peabody Museum, African Department. *Harvard African Studies,* vol. 6. Cambridge, Massachusetts, 1923.

Reisner 1923c Reisner, G. "The Lost History of Ethiopia: Now for the First Time Revealed." *The Illustrated London News* 162 (1923), pp. 126-31.

Reisner 1923d Reisner, G. "The Meroitic Kingdom of Ethiopia: A Chronological Outline." *JEA* 9 (1923), pp. 34-77.

Reisner 1923e Reisner, G. "The Pyramids of Meroe and the Candaces of Ethiopia." *BMFA* 21, no. 124 (1923), pp. 12-27.

Reisner 1925 Reisner, G. "Excavations in Egypt and Ethiopia 1922-1925." *BMFA* 23, no. 137 (1925), pp. 17-29.

Reisner 1931 Reisner, G. "Inscribed Monuments from Gebel Barkal." *ZÄS* 66 (1931), pp. 76-100.

REM 1004 Repertoire d'Epigraphie meroitique. *Meroitic Newsletter: Bulletin d'informations méroïtiques,* no. 1 (1968), p. 15.

REM 1005 Repertoire d'Epigraphie meroitique. *Meroitic Newsletter: Bulletin d'informations méroïtiques,* no. 1 (1968), p. 15.

REM 1031 Repertoire d'Epigraphie meroitique. *Meroitic Newsletter: Bulletin d'informations méroïtiques,* no. 2 (1969), p. 17.

REM 1038 Repertoire d'Epigraphie meroitique. *Meroitic Newsletter: Bulletin d'informations méroïtiques,* no. 3 (1969), p. 4.

Ricke 1967 Ricke, H. *Ausgrabungen von Khor-Dehmit bis Bet El-Wali.* Chicago, University, Oriental Institute, Nubian Expedition, vol. 2. Chicago, 1967.

Rightmire 1975 Rightmire, G. "Problems in the Study of Later Pleistocene Man in Africa." *American Anthropologist* 77 (1975), pp. 28-52.

Rosellini 1832-44 Rosellini, I. *I monumenti dell'Egitto e della Nubia, disegnati dalla spedizione scientifico—letteraria toscana in Egitto; distribuiti in ordine di materie, interpretati ed illustrati dal dottore Ippolito Rosellini.* Pisa, 1832-44.

Roveri 1963 Roveri, A. "Nubia." In: *Enciclopedia dell'arte antica, classica e orientale,* vol. 5, pp. 570-76. Rome, 1963.

Rowe 1940 Rowe, A. "Newly-identified Monuments in the Egyptian Museum Showing the Deification of the Dead Together With Brief Details of Similar Objects Elsewhere." *Annales du Service des Antiquités de l'Égypte* 40 (1940), pp. 1-68.

Rühlmann 1964 Rühlmann, G. "Der Löwe im altägyptischen Triumphalbild." *Wissenschaftliche Zeitschrift der Martin-Luther Universität Halle-Wittenberg. Gesellschafts- und Sprachwissenschaftliche Reihe, Halle* 13 (1964), pp. 651-58.

Rühlmann 1965 Rühlmann, G. "Der Geier auf dem Schlachtfeld. Bemerkungen zu einem altorientalischen Machtsymbol." *Wissenschaftliche Zeitschrift der Martin-Luther Universität Halle-Wittenberg. Gesellschafts- und Sprachwissenschaftliche Reihe, Halle* 14 (1965), pp. 455-69.

Russmann 1968-69 Russmann, E. "Two Royal Heads of the Late Period in Brooklyn." *The Brooklyn Museum Annual* 10 (1968-69), pp. 87-108.

Russmann 1969-70 Russmann, E. "Further Aspects of Kushite Art in Brooklyn." *The Brooklyn Museum Annual* 11 (1969-70), pp. 144-59.

Russmann 1974 Russmann, E. *The Representation of the King in the XXVth Dynasty.* Monographies Reine Élisabeth, 3. Brussels and Brooklyn, 1974.

Sameh 1975 Sameh, W. "Zur Enstehung der ägyptischen Kunst." *Du: Europäische Kunstzeitschrift* 4 (1975), pp. 57-65.

Sauneron — Yoyotte 1952 Sauneron, S., and Yoyotte, J. "La campagne nubienne de Psammétique II et sa signification historique." *Bulletin de l'Institut Français d'Archéologie Orientale* 50 (1952), pp. 157-207.

Säve-Söderbergh 1941 Säve-Söderbergh, T. *Ägypten und Nubien: Ein Beitrag zur Geschichte altägyptischer Aussenpolitik.* Lund, 1941.

Säve-Söderbergh 1949 Säve-Söderbergh, T. "A Buhen Stela from the Second Intermediate Period (Khartūm no. 18)." *JEA* 35 (1949), pp. 50-58.

Säve-Söderbergh 1960 Säve-Söderbergh, T. "The Paintings in the Tomb of Djehuty-hetep at Debeira." *Kush* 8 (1960), pp. 25-44.

Säve-Söderbergh 1964 Säve-Söderbergh, T. "Preliminary Report of the Scandinavian Joint Expedition: Archaeological Investigations between Faras and Gamai, November 1962-March 1963." *Kush* 12 (1964), pp. 19-30.

Säve-Söderbergh 1965 Stockholm, Museum of National Antiquities. *Nubia. Abu Simbel.* By T. Säve-Söderbergh. Exhibition catalogue. Stockholm, 1965.

Säve-Söderbergh 1969 Säve-Söderbergh, T. "Die Akkulturation der nubischen C-Gruppe im Neuen Reich." In: *XVII. Deutscher Orientalistentag vom 21. bis 27. Juli 1968 in Würzburg. Vorträge,* part 1, pp. 12-20. Wiesbaden, 1969.

Säve-Söderbergh 1973 Säve-Söderbergh, T. "Preliminary Report of the Scandinavian Joint Expedition. Archaeological Investigations between Faras and Gemmai, November 1963 — March 1964." *Kush* 15 (1967-68 [1973]), pp. 211-50.

Sayce 1912 Sayce, A. "Second Interim Report on the Excavations at Meroë in Ethiopia. Part II—The Historical Results." *LAAA* 4 (1912), pp. 53-65.

Sayce 1914-16 Sayce, A. "Fifth Interim Report on the Excavations at Meroë in Ethiopia. Part III—The Great Stela." *LAAA* 7 (1914-16), pp. 23-24.

Sayce 1923 Sayce, A. *Reminiscences.* London, 1923.

Schäfer 1895 Schäfer, H. "Eine Bronzefigur des Taharka." *ZÄS* 33 (1895), pp. 114-16.

Schäfer 1901 Schäfer, H. *Die äthiopische Königsinschrift des Berliner Museums: Regierungsbericht des Königs Nastesen des Gegners des Kambyses.* Leipzig, 1901.

Schäfer 1905 Schäfer, H. *Urkunden der älteren Äthiopenkönige.* Urkunden des ägyptischen Altertums, vol. 3, pts. 1-2. Leipzig, 1905-1908.

Schäfer 1908-09 Schäfer, H. "Ägyptischer Goldschmuck aus dem Ende des II. Jahrtausends vor Chr." *Amtliche Berichte aus den Königlichen Kunstsammlungen* 30 (1908-1909), pp. 269-75.

Schäfer 1910 Schäfer, H. *Ägyptische Goldschmiedearbeiten.* Königliche Museen zu Berlin Mitteilungen aus der Ägyptischen Sammlung, 1. Berlin, 1910.

Schäfer — Andrae 1925 Schäfer, H., and Andrae, W. *Die Kunst des alten Orients.* Propyläen-Kunstgeschichte, 2. Berlin, 1925.

Schäfer — Andrae 1936 Schäfer, H., and Andrae, W. *Die Kunst des alten Orients.* Propyläen-Kunstgeschichte, 2. 2d ed. Berlin, 1936.

Schäfer — Andrae 1942 Schäfer, H., and Andrae, W. *Die Kunst des alten Orients.* Propyläen-Kunstgeschichte, 2. 3d rev. ed. Berlin, 1942.

Scharff 1926 Scharff, A. "Die Ausgrabung von Kerma." *Orientalistische Literaturzeitung* 29 (1926), pp. 89-98.

Scharff 1930 Scharff, A. "Altes und Neues von den Goldschmiedearbeiten der Ägyptischen Abteiling." *Berliner Museen* 51 (1930), pp. 114-21.

Scharff 1939 Scharff, A. "Ägypten." In: *Handbuch der Archäologie*, vol. 1, pp. 433-642. Munich, 1939.

Schiff Giorgini 1965 Giorgini, M. *Soleb, I. 1813-1963*. Florence, 1965.

Scott-Moncrieff 1907 Scott-Moncrieff, P. "Some Notes on the XVIIIth Dynasty Temple at Wady Halfa." *Proceedings of the Society of Biblical Archaeology* 29 (1907), pp. 39-46.

Scott-Moncrieff 1908 Scott-Moncrieff, P. "The Ruined Sites at Musawwarat Es-Sufra and Naga." *Proceedings of the Society of Biblical Archaeology* 30 (1908), pp. 192-203.

Seele 1974 Seele, K. "University of Chicago Oriental Institute Nubian Expedition: Excavations between Abu Simbel and the Sudan Border, Preliminary Report." *JNES* 33 (1974), pp. 1-43.

Shinnie 1953 Shinnie, P. "Two Statues at Naqa." *Kush* 1 (1953), p. 53.

Shinnie 1954 Shinnie, P. "Excavations at Tanqasi, 1953." *Kush* 2 (1954), pp. 66-85.

Shinnie 1959 Shinnie, P. "A Gold Statuette from Jebel Barkal." *Kush* 7 (1959), pp. 91-92.

Shinnie 1967 Shinnie, P. *Meroe: A Civilization of the Sudan*. Ancient Peoples and Places, 55. New York and Washington, 1967.

Shinnie — Chittick 1961 Shinnie, P., and Chittick, H. *Ghazali—A Monastery in the Northern Sudan*. Sudan Antiquities Service. Occasional Papers, no. 5. Khartoum, 1961.

Simpson 1962 Simpson, W. "Nubia: 1962 Excavations at Toshka and Arminna." *Expedition* 4, no. 4 (1962), pp. 37-46.

Simpson 1963 Simpson, W. *Heka-Nefer and the Dynastic Material from Toshka and Arminna*. Publications of the Pennsylvania-Yale Expedition to Egypt, no. 1. New Haven and Philadelphia, 1963.

Simpson 1964 Simpson, W. "The Pennsylvania-Yale Expedition to Egypt Preliminary Report for 1963: Toshka and Arminna (Nubia)." *JARCE* 3 (1964), pp. 15-23.

Simpson 1967a Simpson, W. "The Archaeological Expedition to Egyptian Nubia." *Discovery, Magazine of the Peabody Museum of Natural History, Yale University* 1, no. 1 (1967), pp. 4-11.

Simpson 1967b Simpson, W. "The Pennsylvania-Yale Expedition to Egypt Preliminary Report for 1963: Toshka and Arminna (Nubia)." In: Egypt, Service des Antiquités, *Fouilles en Nubie (1961-1963)*, pp. 185-94. Cairo, 1967.

Smith 1962 Smith, H. S. *Preliminary Reports of the Egypt Exploration Society's Nubian Survey*. Cairo, 1962.

Smith 1966 Smith, H. S. "The Nubian B-Group." *Kush* 14 (1966), pp. 69-124.

Smith 1976 Smith, H. S. *The Fortress of Buhen: The Inscriptions*. Egypt Exploration Society. Memoirs, 48. London, 1976.

Smith 1942 Boston, Museum of Fine Arts. *Ancient Egypt as Represented in the Museum of Fine Arts*. By W. S. Smith. Boston, 1942.

Smith 1946 Boston, Museum of Fine Arts. *Ancient Egypt as Represented in the Museum of Fine Arts*. By W. S. Smith. 2d ed. with index. Boston, 1946.

Smith 1952 Boston, Museum of Fine Arts. *Ancient Egypt as Represented in the Museum of Fine Arts*. By W. S. Smith. 3d ed., rev. Boston, 1952.

Smith 1954 Smith, W. S. *Country Life in Ancient Egypt*. Museum of Fine Arts Picture Book, 2. Boston, [1954].

Smith 1958 Smith, W. S. *The Art and Architecture of Ancient Egypt*. Baltimore, 1958.

Smith 1960 Boston, Museum of Fine Arts. *Ancient Egypt as Represented in the Museum of Fine Arts*. By W. S. Smith. 4th ed., rev. Boston, 1960.

Smith 1965a Smith, W. S. *The Art and Architecture of Ancient Egypt*. Harmondsworth, Middlesex, 1965.

Smith 1965b Smith, W. S. "Nubian Art." In: *Encyclopedia of World Art*, vol. 10, pp. 729-43. New York, 1965.

Snowden 1970 Snowden, F. *Blacks in Antiquity: Ethiopians in the Greco-Roman Experience*. Cambridge, Massachusetts, 1970.

Sotheby Parke Bernet 1975 New York, Sotheby Parke Bernet, Inc. *Greek, Etruscan, Roman, Byzantine, Egyptian, Western Asiatic, Islamic Antiquities... Public Auction, Thursday, November 20 . . .* New York, 1975.

Steindorff 1933 Steindorff, G.; Ricke, H.; and Aubin, H. "Der Orakeltempel in der Ammonsoase." *ZÄS* 69 (1933), pp. 1-24.

Steindorff 1935 Steindorff, G. *Aniba*. Vol. 1. Service des Antiquités de l'Égypte. Mission archéologique de Nubie, 1929-1934. Glückstadt and Hamburg, 1935.

Steindorff 1937 Steindorff, G. *Aniba*. Vol. 2. Service des Antiquités de l'Égypte. Mission archéologique de Nubie, 1929-1934. Glückstadt and Hamburg, 1937.

Steindorff 1938 Steindorff, G. "The So-called Omphalos of Napata." *JEA* 24 (1938), pp. 147-50.

Steindorff 1946 Baltimore, Walters Art Gallery. *Catalogue of the Egyptian Sculpture in the Walters Art Gallery*. By G. Steindorff. Baltimore, 1946.

Strouhal 1971 Strouhal, E. "Evidence of the Early Penetration of Negroes into Prehistoric Egypt." *The Journal of African History* 12 (1971), pp. 1-9.

Terrace 1959 Terrace, E. "Three Egyptian Bronzes." *BMFA* 57, no. 308 (1959), pp. 48-53.

Terrace 1968 Terrace, E. "Urbanity and Verism: The Late Period in Boston." *Connoisseur* 169 (1968), pp. 117-23.

Török 1972 Török, L. "A Special Group of Meroitic Property Marks from the lst to 2nd Centuries A.D." *Meroitic Newsletter: Bulletin d'informations méroïtiques*, no. 10 (1972), pp. 35-44.

Török 1974 Török, L. "An Archaeological Note on the Connections Between the Meroitic and Ballana Cultures." In: *Studia Aegyptiaca I; Recueil d'études dédiées à Vilmos Wessetsky à l'occasion de son 65e anniversaire*, pp. 361-78. Études publiées par les chaires d'histoire ancienne de l'Université Loránd Eötvös de Budapest, 9. Budapest, 1974.

Török 1976 Török, L. "Traces of Alexandrian Architecture in Meroe: A Late Hellenistic Motif in Its History." In: *Studia Aegyptiaca II*, pp. 115-38. Études publiées par les chaires d'histoire ancienne de l'Université Loránd Eötvös de Budapest, 17. Budapest, 1976.

Trigger 1965 Trigger, B. *History and Settlement in Lower Nubia*. Yale University Publications in Anthropology, 69. New Haven, 1965.

Trigger 1966 Trigger, B. "The Languages of the Northern Sudan: An Historical Perspective." *The Journal of African History* 7 (1966), pp. 19-25.

Trigger 1967 Trigger, B. *The Late Nubian Settlement at Arminna West*. Publications of the Pennsylvania-Yale Expedition to Egypt, no. 2. New Haven and Philadelphia, 1967.

Trigger 1968 Trigger, B. *Beyond History: The Methods of Prehistory*. New York, 1968.

Trigger 1969a Trigger, B. "The Royal Tombs at Qustul and Ballana and Their Meroitic Antecedents." *JEA* 55 (1969), pp. 117-28.

Trigger 1969b Trigger, B. "The Social Significance of the Diadems in the Royal Tombs at Ballana." *JNES* 28 (1969), pp. 255-61.

Trigger 1970 Trigger, B. *The Meroitic Funerary Inscriptions from Arminna West*. Publications of the Pennsylvania-Yale Expedition to Egypt, no. 4. New Haven and Philadelphia, 1970.

Trigger 1974 — Trigger, B. "La candace; personnage mystérieux." *Archéologia*, no. 77 (1974), pp. 11-17.

Trigger 1976 — Trigger, B. *Nubia under the Pharaohs.* Boulder, Colorado, 1976.

Turayev 1912 — Turayev, B. "Neskol'ko egipetskikh nadpiseĭ iz moeĭ kollektsii i iz Moskovskavo Rumiantsevskavo Muzeia." *Russkoe Arkheologichskoe Obshchestvo, Klassicheskoe Otdielenie. Zapiski* 7 (1912), pp. 1-19.

Ucko 1968 — Ucko, P. *Anthropomorphic Figurines of Predynastic Egypt and Neolithic Crete with Comparative Material from the Prehistoric Near East and Mainland Greece.* Royal Anthropological Institute Occasional Papers, 24. London, 1968.

Vandier 1958 — Vandier, J. *Manuel d'archéologie égyptienne.* Vol. 3, *Les grandes époques; la statuaire.* Paris, 1958.

Vandier 1961 — Vandier, J. "Trois statues égyptiennes au Musée du Louvre." *Revue du Louvre* 11 (1961), pp. 243-58.

van Gerven 1973 — van Gerven, D.; Carlson, D.; and Armelagos, G. "Racial History and Bio-cultural Adaptation of Nubian Archaeological Populations." *The Journal of African History* 14 (1973), pp. 555-64.

van Moorsel 1970 — van Moorsel, P. "Die Wandmalereien der zentralen Kirche von Abdallah Nirqi." In: Dinkler, E., ed., *Kunst und Geschichte Nubiens in christlicher Zeit,* pp. 103-10. Recklinghausen, 1970.

Vantini 1970 — Vantini, J. *The Excavations at Faras: A Contribution to the History of Christian Nubia.* Bologna, 1970.

Vercoutter 1961 — Vercoutter, J. "Le Sphinx d'Aspelta de Defeia (Khartoum Museum No. 11777)." In: *Mélanges Mariette,* pp. 97-104. Institut Français d'Archéologie Orientale. Bibliothèque d'études, 32. Cairo, 1961.

Vercoutter 1962 — Vercoutter, J. "Un Palais des 'Candaces', contemporain d'Auguste (Fouilles à Wad-ban-Naga 1958-1960)." *Syria* 39 (1962), pp. 263-99.

Vercoutter 1970 — Vercoutter, J. *Mirgissa I.* Paris, 1970.

Vercoutter 1973 — Vercoutter, J. "La XVIIIe dynastie à Saï et en Haute-Nubie." *Études sur l'Égypte et le Soudan anciens. Cahier de recherches de l'Institut de Papyrologie et d'Égyptologie de Lille,* no. 1 (1973), pp. 7-38.

Vercoutter 1974 — Vercoutter, J. "Saï 1972-1973." *Études sur l'Égypte et le Soudan anciens. Cahier de recherches de l'Institut de Papyrologie et d'Égyptologie de Lille,* no. 2 (1974), pp. 11-26.

Vercoutter 1975 — Vercoutter, J. *Mirgissa II.* Paris, 1975.

Vercoutter 1976a — Vercoutter, J. *Mirgissa III.* Paris, 1976.

Vercoutter 1976b — Vercoutter, J. "The Iconography of the Black in Ancient Egypt: From the Beginnings to the Twenty-fifth Dynasty." In: *The Image of the Black in Western Art,* vol. 1, pp. 33-88. Publication of the Menil Foundation, Inc. New York, 1976.

Vila 1967 — Vila, A. *Aksha II. Le cimetière méroïtique d'Aksha.* Paris, 1967.

Vila 1975 — Vila, A. *La Prospection archéologique de la Vallée du Nil, au Sud de la Cataracte de Dal (Nubie Soudanaise).* Fasc. 1, *General Introduction.* Fasc. 2, *Les Districts de Dal (rive gauche) et de Sarkamatto (rive droite).* Fasc. 3, *District de Ferka (Est et Ouest).* Fasc. 4, *District de Mograkka (Est et Ouest). District de Kosha (Est et Ouest).* Centre national de la recherche scientifique. Paris, 1975.

Volbach 1921 — Volbach, W. *Metallarbeiten des christlichen Kultus in der Spätantike und im frühen Mittelalter.* Mainz, Römisch-Germanisches Zentral-Museum. Kataloge, vol. 9. Mainz, 1921.

Vycichl 1958 — Vycichl, W. "Hindu Influence in Meroitic Art? On the Three-Headed Lion-God *Apezemak.*" *Kush* 6 (1958), pp. 174-76.

Waddington — Hanbury 1822 — Waddington, G., and Hanbury, B. *Journal of a Visit to Some Parts of Ethiopia.* London, 1822.

Waddington — Hanbury 1823 — Waddington, G., and Hanbury, B. *Reisen in verschiedene Gegenden Aethiopiens.* Weimar, 1823.

Wainwright 1928 — Wainwright, G. "The Aniconic Form of Amon in the New Kingdom." *Annales du Service des Antiquités de l'Égypte* 28 (1928), pp. 175-89.

Wainwright 1934 — Wainwright, G. "Some Aspects of Amūn." *JEA* 20 (1934), pp. 139-53.

Wallert 1967 — Wallert, I. *Der verzierte Löffel; seine Formgeschichte und Verwendung im Alten Ägypten.* Ägyptologische Abhandlungen, 16. Wiesbaden, 1967.

Ward 1905 — Ward, J. *Our Sudan: Its Pyramids and Progress.* London, 1905.

Weigall 1907 — Weigall, A. *A Report on the Antiquities of Lower Nubia (The First Cataract to the Sudan Frontier) and Their Condition in 1906-7.* Oxford, 1907.

Weitzmann 1970 — Weitzmann, K. "Some Remarks on the Sources of the Fresco Paintings of the Cathedral of Faras." In: Dinkler, E., ed., *Kunst und Geschichte Nubiens in christlicher Zeit,* pp. 325-46. Recklinghausen, 1970.

Wendorff 1968 — Wendorff, F., ed. *The Prehistory of Nubia.* 2 vols. Dallas, 1968.

Wenig 1964 — Wenig, S. "Untersuchungen zur Ikonographie der Darstellungen der meroitischen Königsfamilie und zu Fragen der Chronologie des Reiches von Meroe." Dissertation zur Erlangung des Doktorgrades genehmigt von der Philosophischen Fakultät der Humboldt-Universität zu Berlin, 1964.

Wenig 1967 — Wenig, S. "Bemerkungen zur Chronologie des Reiches von Meroe." *Mitteilungen des Instituts für Orientforschung* 13 (1967), pp. 1-44.

Wenig 1969a — Wenig, S. "Die meroitische Statuengruppe CG 684 in Ägyptischen Museum zu Kairo." *Meroitic Newsletter: Bulletin d'informations méroïtiques,* no. 3 (1969), pp. 13-17.

Wenig 1969b — Wenig, S. "Das Relief eines meroitischen Königs aus der ehem. Sammlung M. Rosenberg." *Meroitic Newsletter: Bulletin d'informations méroïtiques,* no. 3 (1969), pp. 18-24.

Wenig 1971 — Wenig, S. "Bericht uber archäologische Arbeiten an den Pyramidenkapellen des Nordfriedhofes von Begrawiya (Meroe)." *Berliner Beitrage zur Ägyptologie und Sudanarchäologie. Wissenschaftliche Zeitschrift der Humboldt-Universität zu Berlin. Gesellschafts- und Sprachwissenschaftliche Reihe* 20 (1971), pp. 267-73.

Wenig 1973a — Wenig, S. "Meroitische Kunst." Paper presented to Journées internationales d'études méroïtiques, Paris, 10-13 July 1973.

Wenig 1973b — Wenig, S. "Nochmals zur 1. and 2. meroitischen Nebendynastie von Napata." In: *Meroitica: Schriften zur altsudanesischen Geschichte und Archäologie,* vol. 1, pp. 147-60. Berlin/DDR, 1973.

Wenig 1974 — Wenig, S. "Arensnuphis und Sebiumeker; Bemerkungen zu zwei in Meroe verehrten Göttern." *ZÄS* 101 (1974), pp. 130-50.

Wenig 1975a — Wenig, S. "Die Kunst im Reich von Kusch zur Zeit der 25. Dynastie und der Herrscher von Napata." In: Vandersleyen, C., ed., *Das alte Ägypten,* pp. 400-412. Propyläen-Kunstgeschichte, 15. Berlin/West, 1975.

Wenig 1975b — Wenig, S. "Die Kunst im Reich von Meroe." In: Vandersleyen, C., ed., *Das alte Ägypten,* pp. 412-27. Propyläen-Kunstgeschichte, 15. Berlin/West, 1975.

Wenig 1976 Wenig, S. "Gebel Barkal." *Lexikon der Ägyptologie* 2 (1976), pp. 434-40.

Wenig 1977 Wenig, S. "Der meroitische Tempel von Amara." In: *Ägypten und Kusch* [Festschrift Hintze], pp. 459-75. Schriften zur Geschichte und Kultur des Alten Orients, 13. Berlin/DDR, 1977.

Werbrouck 1945 Werbrouck, M. "Archéologie de Nubie." *Bulletin des Musées Royaux d'Art et d'Histoire,* ser. 3, 17 (1945), pp. 1-9.

Wessel 1963 Wessel, K. *Koptische Kunst: Die Spätantike in Ägypten.* Recklinghausen, 1963.

Westendorf 1968 Westendorf, W. *Das Alte Ägypten.* Baden-Baden, 1968.

Wildung 1973 Wildung, D. "Der widdergestaltige Amun—Ikonographie einer Götterbildes." Paper presented to the International Congress of Orientalists, Paris, July 1973.

Wilson 1964 Wilson, J. *Signs and Wonders upon Pharaoh: A History of American Egyptology.* Chicago, 1964.

Winter 1968 Winter, E. *Untersuchungen zu den ägyptischen Tempel Reliefs der griechisch-römischen Zeit.* Österreichische Akademie der Wissenschaft, Philosophisch-historische Klasse. Denkschriften, 98. Vienna, 1968.

Winter 1973 Winter, E. "Arensnuphis sein Name und seine Herkunft." *Revue d'égyptologie* 25 (1973), pp. 235-50.

Wolf 1957 Wolf, W. *Die Kunst Aegyptens: Gestalt und Geschichte.* Stuttgart, 1957.

Woolley 1911 Woolley, C. *Karanòg, The Town.* Pennsylvania, University, University Museum, Egyptian Department. Eckley B. Coxe Junior Expedition to Nubia, vol. 5. Philadelphia, 1911.

Woolley — Randall-MacIver 1910 Woolley, C., and Randall-MacIver, D. *Karanòg, The Roman Nubian Cemetery.* Pennsylvania, University, University Museum, Egyptian Department. Eckley B. Coxe Junior Expedition to Nubia, vols. 3 and 4. Philadelphia, 1910.

Worcester 1973 Worcester, Massachusetts, Art Museum. *A Handbook to the Worcester Art Museum.* Worcester, 1973.

Yoyotte 1966 Yoyotte, J. "Arts des Nubiens antiques." *Revue du Louvre* 16 (1966), pp. 187-94.

Yoyotte 1968 Yoyotte, J. *Treasures of the Pharaohs: The Early Period, the New Kingdom, the Late Period.* Translated by R. Allen. Geneva, 1968.

Žabkar 1968 Žabkar, L. *A Study of the Ba Concept in Ancient Egyptian Texts.* Chicago, University, Oriental Institute. Studies in Ancient Oriental Civilization, 34. Chicago, 1968.

Žabkar 1974 Žabkar, L. "The Semna South Project." *Chicago, University, Oriental Institute. Report,* 1973/1974, pp. 41-45.

Žabkar 1975a Žabkar, L. *Apedemak, Lion God of Meroe: A Study in Egyptian-Meroitic Syncretism.* Warminster, 1975.

Žabkar 1975b Žabkar, L. "The Semna South Project." *Chicago, University, Oriental Institute. Report,* 1974/1975, pp. 29-32.

Žabkar ms. Žabkar, L. "The Oriental Institute Excavations at Semna South." *Kush* 16 (forthcoming).

Zeuner 1963 Zeuner, F. *A History of Domesticated Animals.* New York, 1963.

Zippert 1933-34 Zippert, E. "Nubien." *Archiv für Orientforschung* 9 (1933-34), pp. 153-54.

Zippert 1936-37 Zippert, E. "Nubien." *Archiv für Orientforschung* 11 (1936-37), pp. 182-84.

Zurich 1970 Zurich, Kunsthaus. *Faras: Christliche Fresken aus Nubien.* Exhibition catalogue. Zurich, 1970.

Zyhlarz 1928 Zyhlarz, E. *Grundzüge der nubischen Grammatik im christlichen Frühmittelalter (altnubisch); Grammatik, Texte, Kommentar und Glossar.* Abhandlungen für die Kunde des Morgenlandes, 18, no. 1. Leipzig, 1928.

Concordance I

Objects listed by Catalogue Number

Cat. No.	*Lender*	*Acc. No.*
1	Khartoum, Sudan National Museum	13729
2	Aswan, Aswan Museum	346
3	Chicago, Oriental Institute Museum	23845
4	Chicago, Oriental Institute Museum	24069
5	Brooklyn, The Brooklyn Museum	07.447.404
6	Cambridge, Fitzwilliam Museum	EGA. 4668.1943
7	Chicago, Oriental Institute Museum	21877
8	Chicago, Oriental Institute Museum	24259
9	Aswan, Aswan Museum	269
10	Chicago, Oriental Institute Museum	23772
11	Chicago, Oriental Institute Museum	23763
12	Los Angeles, University of California, Museum of Cultural History	400-1541
13	Cairo, Egyptian Museum	JE 65192
14	Leipzig, Karl-Marx-Universität, Ägyptisches Museum	4396
15	Khartoum, Sudan National Museum	62/12/66
16	Leipzig, Karl-Marx-Universität, Ägyptisches Museum	4403
17	Leipzig, Karl-Marx-Universität, Ägyptisches Museum	4395
18	Chicago, Oriental Institute Museum	23202
19	Leipzig, Karl-Marx-Universität, Ägyptisches Museum	4389
20	Leipzig, Karl-Marx-Universität, Ägyptisches Museum	4373
21	Leipzig, Karl-Marx-Universität, Ägyptisches Museum	2757
22	Leipzig, Karl-Marx-Universität, Ägyptisches Museum	4387
23	Leipzig, Karl-Marx-Universität, Ägyptisches Museum	4444
24	Leipzig, Karl-Marx-Universität, Ägyptisches Museum	4617
25	Leipzig, Karl-Marx-Universität, Ägyptisches Museum	4598
26	Leipzig, Karl-Marx-Universität, Ägyptisches Museum	4601
27	Chicago, Oriental Institute Museum	24264
28	Leipzig, Karl-Marx-Universität, Ägyptisches Museum	4232
29	Leipzig, Karl-Marx-Universität, Ägyptisches Museum	4231
30	London, British Museum	51218
31	Cairo, Egyptian Museum	JE 89989
32	Chicago, Oriental Institute Museum	23452
33	Leipzig, Karl-Marx-Universität, Ägyptisches Museum	4196
34	Leipzig, Karl-Marx-Universität, Ägyptisches Museum	4189
35	Leipzig, Karl-Marx-Universität, Ägyptisches Museum	4206
36	Leipzig, Karl-Marx-Universität, Ägyptisches Museum	4207
37	Aswan, Aswan Museum	587
38	Leipzig, Karl-Marx-Universität, Ägyptisches Museum	4212
39	Chicago, Oriental Institute Museum	23241
40	Leipzig, Karl-Marx-Universität, Ägyptisches Museum	4219
41	Leipzig, Karl-Marx-Universität, Ägyptisches Museum	4179-4180
42	Cairo, Egyptian Museum	JE 65145
43	Philadelphia, University Museum	E 10604 A
44	Boston, Museum of Fine Arts	20.1180
45	Boston, Museum of Fine Arts	13.4220c
46	Boston, Museum of Fine Arts	20.2027
47	Boston, Museum of Fine Arts	13.4219e
48	Boston, Museum of Fine Arts	13.4221e
49	Boston, Museum of Fine Arts	20.2028
50	Boston, Museum of Fine Arts	13.4211
51	Boston, Museum of Fine Arts	13.4222g
52	Liverpool, University	SAOS 1566
53	Leipzig, Karl-Marx-Universität, Ägyptisches Museum	3793
54	Leipzig, Karl-Marx-Universität, Ägyptisches Museum	3799
55	Leipzig, Karl-Marx-Universität, Ägyptisches Museum	3790
56	Leipzig, Karl-Marx-Universität, Ägyptisches Museum	3792

57	Leipzig, Karl-Marx-Universität, Ägyptisches Museum	3796
58	Khartoum, Sudan National Museum	1139
59	Leipzig, Karl-Marx-Universität, Ägyptisches Museum	3845
60	Khartoum, Sudan National Museum	1036
61	Boston, Museum of Fine Arts	S 14-2-1197
62	Boston, Museum of Fine Arts	13.4102
63	Khartoum, Sudan National Museum	1134
64	Boston, Museum of Fine Arts	S 14-3-285
65	Boston, Museum of Fine Arts	20.1714
66	Boston, Museum of Fine Arts	S 13-12-522
67	Boston, Museum of Fine Arts	20.2005
68	Khartoum, Sudan National Museum	1119
69	Boston, Museum of Fine Arts	S 14-2-1213
70	Berlin/DDR, Ägyptisches Museum	2103
71	Brooklyn, The Brooklyn Museum	70.1
72	Berlin/DDR, Ägyptisches Museum	2268
73	Khartoum, Sudan National Museum	1853
74	Boston, Museum of Fine Arts	21.3231
75	Athens, National Museum	632
76	Cairo, Egyptian Museum	CG 560
77	London, British Museum	1770
78	Brooklyn, The Brooklyn Museum	39.4
79	Brooklyn, The Brooklyn Museum	39.3
80	Brooklyn, The Brooklyn Museum	60.74
81	Brooklyn, The Brooklyn Museum	05.316
82	Brooklyn, The Brooklyn Museum (on loan from Christos G. Bastis Collection)	L75.6.6
83	Cairo, Egyptian Museum	JE 38018
84	Oxford, Ashmolean Museum	1922.157
85	Boston, Museum of Fine Arts	23.731
86	Khartoum, Sudan National Museum	1852
87	Brooklyn, The Brooklyn Museum	39.5
88	Berlin/DDR, Ägyptisches Museum	131.88
89	Khartoum, Sudan National Museum	1844
90	Oxford, Ashmolean Museum	1921.735
91	Boston, Museum of Fine Arts	21.2815
92	Boston, Museum of Fine Arts	21.3238
93	Boston, Museum of Fine Arts	21.321
94	Boston, Museum of Fine Arts	24.972
95	Boston, Museum of Fine Arts	24.928
96	Boston, Museum of Fine Arts	21.307
97	Brooklyn, The Brooklyn Museum	54.198
98	Boston, Museum of Fine Arts	23.333
99	Boston, Museum of Fine Arts	20.269
100	Khartoum, Sudan National Museum	690
101	Brooklyn, The Brooklyn Museum	49.29
102	Boston, Museum of Fine Arts	24.879
103	Boston, Museum of Fine Arts	24.616
104	Boston, Museum of Fine Arts	24.639
105	Boston, Museum of Fine Arts	24.670
106	Boston, Museum of Fine Arts	24.688
107	Boston, Museum of Fine Arts	24.781
108	Brooklyn, The Brooklyn Museum	75.166
109	Oxford, Ashmolean Museum	1914.462a
110	Oxford, Ashmolean Museum	1914.461
111	Boston, Museum of Fine Arts	20.341
112	Boston, Museum of Fine Arts	20.1070
113	Boston, Museum of Fine Arts	20.342
114	Boston, Museum of Fine Arts	21.339a-b
115	Boston, Museum of Fine Arts	21.338
116	Khartoum, Sudan National Museum	518
117	Khartoum, Sudan National Museum	1670
118	Boston, Museum of Fine Arts	23.870
119	Boston, Museum of Fine Arts	23.873
120	Berlin/DDR, Ägyptisches Museum	2253
121	Baltimore, Walters Art Gallery	22.258
122	Khartoum, Sudan National Museum	522
123	Khartoum, Sudan National Museum	62/10/129
124	Bolton, Bolton Museum and Art Gallery (on loan from Lady Lever Art Gallery)	A 245.1968
125	Worcester, Worcester Art Museum	1922.145
126	Philadelphia, University Museum	66.11.42
127	Cairo, Egyptian Museum	JE 40229
128	Philadelphia, University Museum	E 7079
129	Khartoum, Sudan National Museum	5261
130	Brooklyn, The Brooklyn Museum	76.8
131	Boston, Museum of Fine Arts	21.3234
132	Liverpool, University	SAOS 8524
133	London, British Museum	63585
134	London, British Museum	63597
135	Cairo, Egyptian Museum	CG 684
136	Khartoum, Sudan National Museum	517
137	Khartoum, Sudan National Museum	5457
138	Khartoum, Sudan National Museum	2715
139	London, British Museum	65222
140	Khartoum, Sudan National Museum	24397
141	Oxford, Ashmolean Museum	1912.1295
142	Khartoum, University, Department of Archaeology	1001
143	Philadelphia, University Museum	E 7662
144	Berlin/DDR, Ägyptisches Museum	25951
145	Berlin/DDR, Ägyptisches Museum	24300 [HU1]
146	Khartoum, Sudan National Museum	62/10/23
147	Berlin/DDR, Ägyptisches Museum	2247
148	Oxford, Ashmolean Museum	1932.830
149	London, British Museum	51740
150	Boston, Museum of Fine Arts	21.2633
151	Cairo, Egyptian Museum	JE 40194
152	Brooklyn, The Brooklyn Museum	75.26
153	Cairo, Egyptian Museum	JE 40232
154	Philadelphia, University Museum	E 7038
155	Philadelphia, University Museum	E 7037
156	Oxford, Ashmolean Museum	1912.456
157	Philadelphia, University Museum	E 5035
158	Khartoum, Sudan National Museum	759
159	Philadelphia, University Museum	E 5015
160	Khartoum, Sudan National Museum	13365
161	Munich, Staatliche Sammlung Ägyptischer Kunst	ÄS 1334
162	Berlin/DDR, Ägyptisches Museum	1755
163	Munich, Staatliche Sammlung Ägyptischer Kunst	Ant. 2495b
164	Munich, Staatliche Sammlung Ägyptischer Kunst	Ant. 2446b
165	Berlin/DDR, Ägyptisches Museum	1644
166	Berlin/DDR, Ägyptisches Museum	22872
167	Munich, Staatliche Sammlung Ägyptischer Kunst	Ant. 2446d
168	Munich, Staatliche Sammlung Ägyptischer Kunst	Ant. 2446c
169	Munich, Staatliche Sammlung Ägyptischer Kunst	Ant. 2495a
170	Munich, Staatliche Sammlung Ägyptischer Kunst	Ant. 2455
171	Berlin/DDR, Ägyptisches Museum	22870
172	Boston, Museum of Fine Arts	20.333
173	Berlin/DDR, Ägyptisches Museum	1759
174	Munich, Staatliche Sammlung Ägyptischer Kunst	Ant. 2497
175	Munich, Staatliche Sammlung Ägyptischer Kunst	Ant. 2499
176	London, British Museum	68502
177	Boston, Museum of Fine Arts	24.549
178	Liverpool, University	SAOS 8031
179	Khartoum, Sudan National Museum	762a
180	Liverpool, University	SAOS 8039
181	Berlin/DDR, Ägyptisches Museum	1723
182	Berlin/DDR, Ägyptisches Museum	1699
183	Berlin/DDR, Ägyptisches Museum	1711
184	Berlin/DDR, Ägyptisches Museum	1747
185	Berlin/DDR, Ägyptisches Museum	1696
186	Berlin/DDR, Ägyptisches Museum	1700
187	Berlin/DDR, Ägyptisches Museum	1720
188	Berlin/DDR, Ägyptisches Museum	1741
189	Berlin/DDR, Ägyptisches Museum	1671
190	Brussels, Musées Royaux d'Art et d'Histoire	E 3981
191	Khartoum, Sudan National Museum	18101
192	Khartoum, Sudan National Museum	23159
193	Oxford, Ashmolean Museum	1932.831
194	Liverpool, Merseyside County Museums	47.48.212
195	Liverpool, University	SAOS 8501
196	Cairo, Egyptian Museum	JE 41017
197	Philadelphia, University Museum	E 7145
198	Philadelphia, University Museum	E 7129
199	Philadelphia, University Museum	E 7512
200	Boston, Museum of Fine Arts	24.959
201	Oxford, Ashmolean Museum	1912.460
202	Boston, Museum of Fine Arts	42.125
203	Philadelphia, University Museum	E 7514
204	Philadelphia, University Museum	E 7570
205	Philadelphia, University Museum	E 7515a-b
206	Philadelphia, University Museum	E 7602a-b
207	Philadelphia, University Museum	E7525
208	Philadelphia, University Museum	E 7517
209	Cairo, Egyptian Museum	JE 40221
210	Khartoum, Sudan National Museum	728
211	Philadelphia, University Museum	E 8737
212	Philadelphia, University Museum	E 7422

213	Oxford, Ashmolean Museum	1932.808
214	Liverpool, Merseyside County Museums	49.47.847
215	Brussels, Musées Royaux d'Art et d'Histoire	E 3709
216	Khartoum, University, Department of Archaeology	101-102
217	Liverpool, Merseyside County Museums	49.47.819
218	Khartoum, Sudan National Museum	13965
219	Berlin/DDR, Ägyptisches Museum	29039 [HU11]
220	Liverpool, Merseyside County Museums	49.47.840
221	Brooklyn, The Brooklyn Museum	71.84
222	Philadelphia, University Museum	E 8162
223	Cairo, Egyptian Museum	JE 40086
224	Philadelphia, University Museum	E 8157
225	London, British Museum	51477
226	Oxford, Ashmolean Museum	1912.392
227	Brooklyn, The Brooklyn Museum	67.177
228	Philadelphia, University Museum	E 8168
229	Philadelphia, University Museum	E 8154
230	Philadelphia, University Museum	E 8183
231	Philadelphia, University Museum	E 8216
232	Oxford, Ashmolean Museum	1912.321
233	Philadelphia, University Museum	E 8451
234	Oxford, Ashmolean Museum	1912.322
235	Philadelphia, University Museum	E 8193
236	Oxford, Ashmolean Museum	1912.412
237	Oxford, Ashmolean Museum	1912.475
238	Philadelphia, University Museum	E 8275
239	Philadelphia, University Museum	E 8291
240	Philadelphia, University Museum	E 8310
241	Oxford, Ashmolean Museum	1912.410
242	Oxford, Ashmolean Museum	1912.449
243	Khartoum, University, Department of Archaeology	502
244	Philadelphia, University Museum	E 8313
245	Khartoum, Sudan National Museum	18886
246	Oxford, Ashmolean Museum	1912.397
247	Philadelphia, University Museum	E 8731
248	Oxford, Ashmolean Museum	1912.339
249	Boston, Museum of Fine Arts	23.1467
250	Boston, Museum of Fine Arts	23.1466
251	Boston, Museum of Fine Arts	23.1469
252	Boston, Museum of Fine Arts	13.4031
253	London, British Museum	51615
254	Cairo, Egyptian Museum	JE 89983
255	Edinburgh, Royal Scottish Museum	1912.315
256	Philadelphia, University Museum	E 8208
257	Washington, D.C., National Museum of Natural History, Smithsonian Institution	448,235
258	Brussels, Musées Royaux d'Art et d'Histoire	E. 3571
259	Philadelphia, University Museum	E 8704
260	Khartoum, Sudan National Museum	726
261	Philadelphia, University Museum	E 8735
262	Boston, Museum of Fine Arts	24.1003
263	Oxford, Ashmolean Museum	1912.366
264	Boston, Museum of Fine Arts	24.385
265	Philadelphia, University Museum	E 8967
266	Cairo, Egyptian Museum	JE 70455
267	Cairo, Egyptian Museum	JE 88885
268	Cairo, Egyptian Museum	JE 70357a-b
269	Cairo, Egyptian Museum	JE 70347
270	Cairo, Egyptian Museum	JE 70296
271	Cairo, Egyptian Museum	JE 70354
272	Cairo, Egyptian Museum	JE 70351
273	London, British Museum	64043
274	Cairo, Egyptian Museum	JE 70758
275	Cairo, Egyptian Museum	JE 70924
276	Cairo, Egyptian Museum	JE 70925
277	Oxford, Ashmolean Museum	1935.488
278	Cairo, Egyptian Museum	JE 71124
279	Cairo, Egyptian Museum	JE 71151
280	London, British Museum	66576
281	Cairo, Egyptian Museum	JE 89674
282	Cairo, Egyptian Museum	JE 70422
283	London, British Museum	67158
284	Brooklyn, The Brooklyn Museum	60.66.2
285	Cambridge, Fitzwilliam Museum	E.2.1962
286	Cairo, Egyptian Museum	JE 89935
287	Oxford, Ashmolean Museum	1912.897
288	Brussels, Musées Royaux d'Art et d'Histoire	E. 3106
289	Warsaw, Muzeum Narodowe	234081
290	Khartoum, Sudan National Museum	20719
291	London, British Library	OR 6805
292	Warsaw, Muzeum Narodowe	234031
293	Warsaw, Muzeum Narodowe	234033
294	Khartoum, Sudan National Museum	15309
295	Warsaw, Muzeum Narodowe	234566

Concordance II

Objects listed by Lender

Lender	*Acc. No.*	*Cat. No.*
Aswan, Aswan Museum	269	9
	346	2
	587	37
Athens, National Museum	632	75
Baltimore, Walters Art Gallery	22.258	121
Berlin/DDR, Ägyptisches Museum	1644	165
	1671	189
	1696	185
	1699	182
	1700	186
	1711	183
	1720	187
	1723	181
	1741	188
	1747	184
	1755	162
	1759	173
	2103	70
	2247	147
	2253	120
	2268	72
	13188	88
	22870	171
	22872	166
	24300 [HU 1]	145
	25951	144
	29039 [HU 11]	219
Bolton, Bolton Museum and Art Gallery (on loan from Lady Lever Art Gallery)	A 245.1968	124
Boston, Museum of Fine Arts	S 13-12-522	66
	S 14-2-1197	61
	S 14-2-1213	69
	S 14-3-285	64
	13.4031	252
	13.4102	62
	13.4211	50
	13.4219e	47
	13.4220c	45
	13.4221e	48
	13.4222g	51
	20.269	99
	20.333	172
	20.341	111
	20.342	113
	20.1070	112
	20.1180	44
	20.1714	65
	20.2005	67
	20.2027	46
	20.2028	49
	21.307	96
	21.321	93
	21.338	115
	21.339a-b	114
	21.2633	150
	21.2815	91
	21.3231	74
	21.3234	131
	21.3238	92
	23.333	98
	23.731	85
	23.870	118
	23.873	119
	23.1466	250
	23.1467	249
	23.1469	251
	24.385	264
	24.549	177
	24.616	103
	24.639	104
	24.670	105
	24.688	106
	24.781	107
	24.879	102
	24.928	95
	24.959	200
	24.972	94
	24.1003	262
	42.125	202

Brooklyn, The Brooklyn Museum	05.316	81
	07.447.404	5
	39.3	79
	39.4	78
	39.5	87
	49.29	101
	54.198	97
	60.74	80
	66.66.2	284
	67.177	227
	70.1	71
	71.84	221
	L75.6.6	82
	75.26	152
	75.166	108
	76.8	130
Brussels, Musées Royaux d'Art et d'Histoire	E. 3106	288
	E. 3571	258
	E. 3709	215
	E. 3981	190
Cairo, Egyptian Museum	CG 560	76
	CG 684	135
	JE 38018	83
	JE 40086	223
	JE 40194	151
	JE 40221	209
	JE 40229	127
	JE 40232	153
	JE 41017	196
	JE 65145	42
	JE 65192	13
	JE 70296	270
	JE 70347	269
	JE 70351	272
	JE 70354	271
	JE 70357a-b	268
	JE 70422	282
	JE 70455	266
	JE 70758	274
	JE 70924	275
	JE 70925	276
	JE 71124	278
	JE 71151	279
	JE 88885	267
	JE 89674	281
	JE 89935	286
	JE 89983	254
	JE 89989	31
Cambridge, Fitzwilliam Museum	E.2.1962	285
	EGA. 4668.1943	6
Chicago, Oriental Institute Museum	21877	7
	23202	18
	23241	39
	23452	32
	23763	11
	23772	10
	23845	3
	24069	4
	24259	8
	24264	27
Edinburgh, Royal Scottish Museum	1912.315	255
Khartoum, Sudan National Museum	517	136
	518	116
	522	122
	690	100
	726	260
	728	210
	759	158
	762a	179
	1036	60
	1119	68
	1134	63
	1139	58
	1670	117
	1844	89
	1852	86
	1853	73
	2715	138
	5261	129
	5457	137
	13365	160
	13729	1
	13965	218
	15309	294
	18101	191
	18886	245
	20719	290
	23159	192
	24397	140
	62/10/23	146
	62/10/129	123
	62/12/66	15
Khartoum, University, Department of Archaeology	101-102	216
	502	243
	1001	142
Leipzig, Karl-Marx-Universität, Ägyptisches Museum	2757	21
	3790	55
	3792	56
	3793	53
	3796	57
	3799	54
	3845	59
	4179-4180	41
	4189	34
	4196	33
	4206	35
	4207	36
	4212	38
	4219	40
	4231	29
	4232	28
	4373	20
	4387	22
	4389	19
	4395	17
	4396	14
	4403	16
	4444	23
	4598	25
	4601	26
	4617	24
Liverpool, Merseyside County Museums	47.48.212	194
	49.47.819	217
	49.47.840	220
	49.47.847	214
Liverpool, University	SAOS 1566	52
	SAOS 8031	178
	SAOS 8039	180
	SAOS 8501	195
	SAOS 8524	132
London, British Library	OR 6805	291
London, British Museum	1770	77
	51218	30
	51477	225
	51615	253
	51740	149
	63585	133
	63597	134
	64043	273
	65222	139
	66576	280
	67158	283
	68502	176
Los Angeles, University of California, Museum of Cultural History	400-1541	12
Munich, Staatliche Sammlung Ägyptischer Kunst	Ant. 2446b	164
	Ant. 2446c	168
	Ant. 2446d	167
	Ant. 2455	170
	Ant. 2495a	169
	Ant. 2495b	163
	Ant. 2497	174
	Ant. 2499	175
	ÄS 1334	161
New York, Christos G. Bastis Collection	none	82
Oxford, Ashmolean Museum	1912.321	232
	1912.322	234
	1912.339	248
	1912.366	263

Photo Credits

After Arkell 1949, Figs. 1, 2; Brooklyn CLES, Figs. 25, 27, 28, 29; Egypt Exploration Society, London, Fig. 48; after Garstang 1911, Fig. 35; after Griffith 1929, Fig. 33; U. and F. Hintze, Berlin/DDR, Figs. 5, 22, 38, 40, 42, 45, 46, 50, 51, 53, 54, 56, 57, 58, 59; after LD V, Fig. 44; Liverpool, SAOS, Fig. 71; after Macadam 1955, Fig. 23; Menil Foundation/Carrieri, Milano, Figs. 49, 67; Menil Foundation, Houston, Fig. 21; Menil Foundation/Hickey & Robertson, Houston, Cat. 72; after Michałowski 1967, Fig. 83; Museum of Fine Arts, Boston, Figs. 10, 11, 12, 13, 14, 17, 18, 20, 34; Náprstkovo Museum, Prague, Figs. 81, 82; after Nordström 1972, Figs. 4, 6, 7; Ny Carlsberg Glyptotek, Copenhagen, Figs. 26, 60, 61, 62, 65; Oriental Institute, University of Chicago, Fig. 43; Royal Ontario Museum, Toronto, Fig. 76; J.B. Sevette, Geneva, Fig. 63; P.L. Shinnie, Calgary, Fig. 55; P.L. Shinnie, Calgary, photo U. Hintze, Figs. 39, 72; Staatliche Sammlung Ägyptischer Kunst, Munich, Fig. 3; A. Vila, Paris, Fig. 69; Walters Art Gallery, Baltimore, Harry Connolly, cover.

Index

LIST OF FIGURES

VOLUME I

VOLUME II

Index